A CHARLTON STANDARD CATALOG

ROYAL DOULTON COLLECTABLES

FOURTH EDITION

By

Jean Dale

Louise Irvine

W.K. Cross

Publisher

TORONTO, ONTARIO ❖ PALM HARBOR, FLORIDA

Library and Archives Canada Cataloguing in Publication

Royal Doulton collectables ; a Charlton standard catalogue.

Annual.
4th ed.-
Continues: Charlton standard catalogue of Royal Doulton bunnykins.
ISSN 1714-9517
ISBN 0-88968-296-8 (4th edition)

1. Royal Doulton figurines--Catalogs. 2. Porcelain animals--Catalogs.
3. Children's china (Porcelain)-Catalogs.

NK4660.C515 738.8'2'029442 C2005-901630-2

EDITORIAL

Editor	Jean Dale
Graphic Technician	Davina Rowan
Cover Illustration	Clarissa the Clown

ACKNOWLEDGMENTS

The Charlton Press wishes to thank those who have assisted with the fourth edition of **Royal Doulton Collectables** (a Charlton Standard Catalogue).

We would like to thank Louise Irvine for her work on this edition. Louise is an independent writer and lecturer on Royal Doulton's history and products and is not in any way connected with the pricing of this guide.

Special Thanks

Our thanks go to the staff of Royal Doulton, who have helped with technical information and images, especially **Michael Poulson,** Category Manager, Royal Doulton (U.K.). **Simon Downs,** Marketing Assistant, Royal Doulton (U.K.); **Karen Hand,** International Collectors Club, (U.K.); **Marion Proctor**, Marketing Manager (Canada); **Tricia Clemens**, Public Relations Manager (Canada).

Contributors to the Fourth Edition

The publisher would also like to thank the following individuals and companies who graciously supplied photographs or information, or allowed us access to their collections for photographic purposes: **George Bagnall,** Precious Memories, Prince Edward Island; **Joan and Bob Barwick**, Ontario, Canada; **Maureen Decelles** Hudson, Quebec; **Rob Dolton,** U.K.; **David French**; **Mary MacNaughton** and **Ken Sharpe,** Ashton, Ontario; **Scott Reichenberg,** North Smithfield, Rhode Island; **Dan and Karen Roeder,** Chesapeake, Virginia; **Pat Sage,** Ontario, Canada; **Leah Selig,** "Rabbiting On", Merry Lands, NSW Australia.

A SPECIAL NOTE TO COLLECTORS

We welcome and appreciate any comments or suggestions in regard to **Royal Doulton Collectables**. If any errors or omissions come to your attention, please write to us, or if you would like to participate in pricing or supply previously unavailable data or information, please contact Jean Dale at (416) 488-1418, or e-mail us at **chpress@charltonpress.com**.

DISCLAIMER

Printed in Canada
in the Province of Manitoba

Editorial Office
P.O. Box 820, Station Willowdale B
North York, Ontario, Canada. M2K 2R1
Telephone: (416) 488-1418 Fax: (416) 488-4656
Telephone: (800) 442-6042 Fax: (800) 442-1542
E-mail chpress@charltonpress.com www.charltonpress.com

HOW TO USE THIS CATALOGUE

THE PURPOSE

As with other catalogues in Charlton's Royal Doulton reference and pricing library, this publication has been designed to serve two specific purposes. First, to furnish the Royal Doulton enthusiast with accurate listings containing vital information and illustrations to aid in the building of a rewarding collection. Secondly, this publication provides Royal Doulton collectors and dealers with current market prices for Royal Doulton collectables.

STYLES AND VERSIONS

Tableware

STYLES: If the same design name is used at various times by different designers, the earlier issue becomes **Style One**, and the next **Style Two**, and so on.

VERSIONS: The design may have one or more elements removed from the main design.

VARIATIONS: The design has all the elements intact but minor modifications have been made to allow the design to better fit the shape.

Figurines

STYLES: When two or more figures have the same name but different physical modelling characteristics, they are listed as **Style One**, **Style Two**, and so on.

VERSIONS: Versions are modifications in a major style element.

VARIATIONS: A change in colourway is a variation. For example, the five different colourways of the football uniform of Touchdown Bunnykins, DB96 through DB100.

THE LISTINGS

The Tableware Section has the Bunnykins designs listed in alphabetical order, beginning with the **ABC Theme** and ending with **Xmas Menu**. Within the design layout is a shape/price table incorporating, on the left side of the table, a vertical listing of the different shapes on which the design appears. To the right of the shape column is the price column indicating a level at which collectors may expect to see that design/shape trade.

The list of Bunnykins figures is simple by comparison. Royal Doulton numbered the Bunnykins figures in chronological order, as they were issued, starting with DB1 and carrying on to the present DB382.

In both the Storybook and Cartoon Characters Section and the Disney Characters Section the figures are alphabetically listed by series and then numerically within each series by the Royal Doulton number that appears on the base of the figurine.

PRICING

The system by which the Charlton Press gathers pricing information has changed greatly over the past five years. The internet has exerted a tremendous influence on pricing and will continue to do so. The one thing a collector must keep in mind is that prices trend down as well as up, they never go continuously in one direction. However, a price is still a commitment between a buyer and a seller, the two necessary ingredients for a transaction.

TABLE OF CONTENTS

HOW TO USE THIS CATALOGUE	iv
INTRODUCTION	vi
ROYAL DOULTON	
International Collectors Club	x
Royal Doulton Visitor Centre	x
Website and E-mail address	x
Doulton Chapters	x
SECTION ONE	
Bunnykins Tableware	3
Bunnykins Figurines	199
SECTION TWO	
Storybook and Cartoon Characters	337
SECTION THREE	
Disney Characters	403
SECTION FOUR	
Advertising Characters	475
INDICES	479
ADVERTISERS	494

INTRODUCTION

COLLECTING BUNNYKINS TABLEWARE

Generations of children around the world have been weaned with Bunnykins nursery ware as it has been in continuous production since 1934. Few could have imagined that their favourite baby plate would one day become collectable but that is the fate of many of the Bunnykins designs, particularly the early pieces featuring Barbara Vernon's signature.

Barbara Vernon Designs

Barbara Vernon was a young nun in an English convent school when she first imagined the exploits of the Bunnykins family to entertain the children in her class. Her father was the Manager of the Royal Doulton Pottery in Stoke-on-Trent and he recognised the potential of her rabbit drawings for a range of nursery ware. Sister Mary Barbara, as she was known in the convent, began to send her sketches to the factory where they were adapted for the lithographic printing process by one of the resident designers, Hubert Light. He also created the backstamp from the *Tug of War* scene LF1 and designed the chain of running rabbits which has appeared around the rim of the Bunnykins pieces since their launch in 1934.

A surviving catalogue of 1937 shows that the range grew quickly to include two sizes of baby plate, a child's dinner plate, Don beakers and mugs, cereal and porridge bowls, a Jaffa fruit saucer, a jam pot, a Casino teapot, cup, saucer, sugar bowl and jugs in various sizes. These shapes were all made in a deep ivory glazed earthenware and decorated with colourful transfer prints. Barbara Vernon's bunnies were usually dressed in sky blue and cherry red and the background was coloured in subtle shades of brown and green.

More shapes had been added by 1940, notably an oval baby plate, a hot water plate with cover and a candle holder. Bunnykins collectors usually like to find an example of each shape featuring a Barbara Vernon design and the jam pot and candle holder, which were withdrawn in 1952, are amongst the hardest to find in the earthenware range.

Some of the early Bunnykins designs were also available in a white bone china body. This finer body was only produced until the Second World War and, as not many bone china pieces survived the rough and tumble of nursery life, they are very rare today. One collector was fortunate enough to find an original boxed bone china breakfast set, complete with silver spoons, whilst another boasts a tea set in pristine condition.

The condition of Bunnykins nursery ware, whether it is bone china or earthenware, is very important for serious collectors who seek out pieces with the minimum of scratches. Sometimes it is very hard to find early baby plates which have not been scraped by enthusiastic eaters scooping up their porridge to enjoy the scene underneath. Collectors also like to find scenes incorporating Barbara Vernon's facsimile signature although sometimes this was cut off the transfer.

Many of Barbara Vernon's scenes had been withdrawn by 1952 and these are amongst the most desirable today. Collectors appreciate her simple designs and the charming subjects which evoke her era, for example one of her bunnies is being dosed with castor oil at *Medicine Time* SF1 and others dance the *Lambeth Walk* HW16. Her quiet sense of humour can also be enjoyed in scenes like *Frightening Spider* SF4 and *Pressing Trousers* HW14 which shows the bunny struggling to remove the creases with a garden roller! Sadly, Barbara Vernon only produced Bunnykins drawings for a few years because of her commitments at the convent and so Walter Hayward, one of Royal Doultons Art Directors, took over the range after the Second World War.

Walter Hayward Designs

Initially Walter Hayward adapted the remaining Barbara Vernon drawings for production but he soon began to create his own scenes although her facsimile signature continued to appear on the ware until the mid 1950s. However, Walter Hayward's work can usually be identified by the presence of some lively little mice that became his trademark. Generally his scenes are much busier than their predecessors and some reflect new topical themes such as the advent of television and space travel. Over the years, he was encouraged to add more and more bunnies, particularly by Doulton's agent in Australia which was one of the strongest markets for Bunnykins. Some of his most ambitious designs, such as *Juggling* LF127 and *Hoopla* LF129, were only available for three years and so these are two of the hardest Hayward designs to find today.

The Bunnykins shapes remained much the same throughout the 1950s and 60s although some larger sizes of Casino teapots and jugs were added in 1952. They were all withdrawn in the late 1960s together with a wide range of scenes when the original earthenware body was replaced with new ivory bone china. By the late 1970s, new shapes had been developed for the china body including the Hug-a-mug which replaced the original Don mug and a range of egg-shaped boxes. Unfortunately, the egg boxes were not made for long and they are now very collectable. Savings books and money balls followed in the early 1980s and these were used occasionally to commemorate special events, such as royal births and weddings.

In the early 1980s, Walter Hayward was commissioned to design a range of scenes celebrating birthdays, christenings and Christmas. He also helped the Bunnykins family celebrate their own birthday with special commemorative pieces to mark their Golden Jubilee in 1984. In addition, all the nursery ware made during 1984 had the inscription Golden Jubilee Celebration added to the backstamp. Bunnykins birthday parties were held all over the world during 1984 and the resulting publicity attracted many new enthusiasts.

An anniversary weekend in Stoke-on-Trent was the catalyst for the largest Bunnykins collection in the U.K. which boasts examples of every scene and shape from 1934 to the present day. The first Bunnykins reference book was published at the end of 1984 and for the first time collectors could see the full extent of the range. Some scenes could only be illustrated from the pattern books and collectors all over the world began hunting for rarities like *Air Mail Delivery* LFa, *Carving the Chicken* LFc and *Dodgems* LF4.

No longer was Bunnykins intended exclusively for youngsters, Walter Hayward designed a set of Bunnykins for Grown Ups featuring bunnies with brief-cases dashing to work. These adult designs only remained in production from 1986 to 1988 so examples are very hard to find today. Walter Hayward's last Bunnykins design following his retirement was the plate to commemorate Australia's Bicentenary in 1988. Meanwhile, another artist was getting to know the Bunnykins family for a series of story books.

Colin Twinn Designs

In 1987, Colin Twinn was commissioned to produce a collection of Bunnykins books for the publishers, Frederick Warne, and many of his drawings were adapted for use on nursery ware. As a successful illustrator of children's books, Twinn had considerable experience with anthropomorphic characters, particularly rabbits, and he created a new look for the Bunnykins family. Pastel colours predominate in his detailed scenes and his bunnies seem softer and fluffier than the originals. Whilst this approach worked well in the little picture books, the new Bunnykins nursery ware designs did not have sufficient impact on the china shop shelves. Established collectors felt that the Bunnykins characters had lost their identity and it would appear that general gift buyers were not enthused either as production of Colin Twinn designs had ceased by the early 1990s.

Many of Colin Twinn's designs appeared on the new shapes which were developed in the late 1980s. An Albion style tea service was introduced in 1987 together with a Stratford tea cup and saucer which replaced the Casino shape. The traditional Don beaker was replaced by a straight sided Malvern beaker and a 10½ inch dinner plate was added to the range. Decorative accessories, such as a lamp and two picture plaques, were also available for a few years and these are now sought after by collectors.

Gradually, as Colin Twinn's designs began to disappear from the shops, new stocks of Barbara Vernon and Walter Hayward designs appeared. Around 50 patterns for hollow ware and flat ware had never been withdrawn and these were modified in line with new requirements for colour printing. A tuft of green grass on the left of the backstamp distinguishes the more recent Vernon/Hayward wares from earlier examples. A classic Barbara Vernon scene *Dancing in the Moonlight* was re-drawn for the 60th Anniversary of the Bunnykins range in 1994 and a set of commemorative ware was made for that year only. Royal Doulton's company in Australia commissioned their own exclusive anniversary scene featuring an Aussie picnic complete with kangaroos and koalas and this was one of the last designs by Colin Twinn as a new artist had been found to continue the Bunnykins tradition, Frank Endersby.

Frank Endersby Designs

Frank Endersby is a freelance illustrator who works from his own studio in the idyllic Cotswolds region. During his career, he has worked in a busy graphic design studio and also with a children's book publisher so he has a wide experience of all aspects of design and illustration. He quickly assimilated the essential qualities of the original Bunnykins style and his scenes feature the strong outlines used for the original characters as well as their bright blue and red clothes. To date he has worked on 20 new sets of Bunnykins designs and each set incorporates three scenes, the larger for decorating plates and two smaller ones to use on the front and reverse of cups and other hollow ware. These scenes began to appear in the shops in 1995 but it was a couple of years before dedicated collectors had located all his designs.

COLLECTING BUNNYKINS FIGURINES

Bunnykins figures made their debut in 1939 but the war soon halted production and the original six characters are extremely rare today. It is believed that they were modelled by Charles Noke, the Art Director who developed the HN range of Royal Doulton figures, as they resemble some of his early character animals. These large scale figures, which range in size from 3 to 7 inches, have little in common with Barbara Vernon's design which might explain why they were never revived after the war.

As well as these characters figures, Noke also introduced a Bunny shaped breakfast set, featuring a teapot, cream jug, sugar bowl, sugar sifter and egg cup, but this suffered a similar fate in the war years. The idea of Bunny shaped ware to accompany the successful nursery ware was not revived until 1967 when a Bunny money bank was added to the range and this remained in production until 1981.

The DB Range

When Royal Doulton took over the Beswick factory in 1969, they acquired the modelling skills of Albert Hallam who worked on the Beatrix Potter range figures. These little character animals were amongst Beswick's most successful product and it was decided to create a similar collection of Bunnykins figures. The first nine figures were launched in 1972 with DB pattern numbers and they averaged 4 inches in height. All were inspired by Walter Hayward's nursery ware patterns, for example *The Artist* DB13 is derived from *The Portrait Painter* SF20. This approach continued until 1974 when there was a total of 15 characters in the range but a new look developed in the 1980s.

Harry Sales Designs

Harry Sales, the Design Manager of the Beswick factory, took over responsibility for the Bunnykins range in 1980. He believed that the rabbit character should reflect the interests of contemporary children and his first figure of a guitar-playing rock star *Mr. Bunnybeat Strumming* DB16 was followed by a space traveller *Astro Bunnykins Rocket Man* DB20. After seeing his colleagues' response to these entertaining designs, it occurred to Harry that Bunnykins figures could also have an adult audience and he began to work on a collection of sporting subjects at the time of the Los Angeles Olympics in 1984. Adults began to purchase these figures as whimsical gifts, sharing Harry's sense of humour in subjects like *Freefall Bunnykins* DB41 whose pained expression suggested a not so perfect landing.

This new direction coincided with the Bunnykins Golden Jubilee when nursery ware first began to be taken seriously by collectors. Before long, the figures were also included in the hunt and early discontinued models, such as *Mr. Bunnykins Autumn Days* DB5 and *Daisy Bunnykins Spring Time* DB7 were sought at collectors fairs and markets. In 1987, the Royal Doulton International Collectors Club commissioned a figure exclusively for its members and *Collector Bunnykins* DB54 is now one of the most expensive figures on the secondary market.

Several special commissions were produced in the late 1980s and these now command premium prices. National subjects such as *Australian Bunnykins* DB58 were made to celebrate that country's bicentenary and new colourways of existing models were produced for sale at special events in the USA, notably *Mr. And Mrs. Bunnykins at the Easter Parade* DB51 and 52.

Graham Tongue Designs

When Harry Sales left Royal Doulton in 1986 to pursue a freelance career, Graham Tongue became the Beswick Studio Manager and he has been responsible for a number of Bunnykins figures, either as designer or modeller. His most popular figure is *Bedtime Bunnykins* DB55 which was made in four different colourways for special occasions. He also produced some figures inspired by Colin Twinn's nursery ware illustrations, for example *Lollipopman Bunnykins* DB65, but these were less successful and were withdrawn after a few years. For a few years following his retirement in 1995, Graham continued to model Bunnykins figures at his own studio and he created *Ballerina Bunnykins* DB176 and *Cavalier Bunnykins* DB179, a limited edition design.

Limited Edition Designs

The first limited edition Bunnykins figures were commissioned in 1990 for sale at a Doulton collectors fair in London. The *Oompah Band* was renamed the *Royal Doulton Collectors Band* for this occasion and the new blue colourway was so successful that other special editions swiftly followed. Denise Andrews, a freelance illustrator from Suffolk, was invited to produce special designs which were modelled by the team of resident artists at the Beswick studio. Her footballing and cricketing characters augmented the earlier sporting range and her colourful *Clown* and *Jester Bunnykins* have entertained collectors all over the world. Over the years, limited edition sizes have grown from 250 to 3,500 but many new Bunnykins figures are over-subscribed as soon as they are launched. Collectors were bewitched by *Trick or Treat Bunnykins* DB162, which was issued in 1995 and was soon changing hands for many times its issue price. In 1996, Royal Doulton introduced their first Bunnykins Figure of the Year and collectors responded enthusiastically to this new initiative.

Resin Bunnykins Figurines

In 1995, the Bunnykins characters became movie stars when an animated feature film was screened in North America and the UK. *Happy Birthday Bunnykins* was later distributed in video form and inspired a new collection of Bunnykins figures in a resin body. Resin is the name given to a cold cast sculptural material which retains intricate modelling detail more effectively than conventional fired clay bodies. The resin Bunnykins figures are smaller in scale than their ceramic cousins and are decorated primarily in pastel colours. During 1996 and 1997, twenty models were issued in the resin range, including two ambitious musical boxes and two photograph frames, but they did not appeal to collectors or gift buyers and were all withdrawn at the end of 1997. Fortunately the traditional ceramic figures continue to go from strength to strength.

The Success of the DB Range

After 40 years in production, the DB figures are amongst the most collectable Royal Doulton products and Bunnykins fans are multiplying faster than rabbits. With this in mind, it is a good idea to buy the new Bunnykins figures as soon as they are issued. Royal Doulton have now allocated 382 DB numbers and, although a few intervening numbers have not been issued, committed collectors now have quite a challenge to find them all. Figures are now withdrawn regularly from the range, adding to the excitement of the chase so, in the words of the song, if you want to keep up you'll have to ..run rabbit…run rabbit…run..run..run!

In 2004/2005 the production of Bunnykin figures was moved from Stoke to the far east, while causing concern with the "Nile Street" followers the move resulted in no loss of quality and a larger benefit of a reduced price for the collector.

COLLECTING BRAMBLY HEDGE FIGURES

Since the introduction in 1983, the Brambly Hedge mice have overrun households in many parts of the world. They are scurrying about the shelves as Royal Doulton figures and even climbing up the walls on decorative plates. Far from being undesirable, these particular mice are considered indispensable members of the family. Children frequently receive them as gifts from doting grandparents, but adults have also been seduced by the cosy, timeless mouse world which Jill Barklem has created. The mood of rustic nostalgia has all been painstakingly researched. The interiors of the field mice homes are the sort in common in English farmhouses at the end of the 19th century, and the food served is genuine county fare, based on old recipes and tested in Jill Barklem's kitchen. The Brambly Hedge residents were all expertly drawn with the aid of her two house models, a keen understanding of zoology and a knowledge of historical costume.

The same attention to detail went into the Royal Doulton figures designed by Harry Sales. As he explains, "One important feature in the concept was that I chose poses which, when the figures are together, appear to be reacting to one another. I can imagine the fun children and the young at heart will have arranging the figures in conversational situations." Essentially this sums up the collectability of the Brambly Hedge mice, and as there are only 25 figures in the first series, they can all be displayed effectively together on one shelf. There are, however, a couple of unusual modelling variations to look out for as "Mr. Toadflax's" tail was altered shortly after its introduction, plus some colour variations. Royal Doulton retired the first Brambly Hedge collection in 1997, but a new collection of figures was introduced in 2000 to celebrate the 20th anniversary of Brambly Hedge.

COLLECTING SNOWMAN FIGURES

Initially, the seasonal appeal of the Snowman tended to limit his collectability, as most purchases were made around Christmas time, and he was more popular in areas which regularly experience snow. Having said this, for some fans the wintery connotations were overshadowed by the inherent quality and humour of the models and there are now keen collectors in sunny Florida as well as in Australia, where beach barbecues are typical Christmas celebrations.

Between 1985 and 1990, young children regularly received the new Snowman models in their Christmas stockings, and the characters have been widely used as holiday decorations. Like the Brambly Hedge models, they were designed to interact, and the little figure of James, gazing up in wonder, can be positioned with various Snowman characters, whilst the band works very well as a separate display grouping. There are 19 figures and two musical boxes to collect in the first series, and as the range was withdrawn in 1994, they can now be quite difficult to locate. In fact, prices have been snowballing, particularly for the figures that were not in production for long, notably "The Snowman Skiing." The antics of the Snowman were revived in 1999 for a limited edition collection commissioned by Lawleys By Post.

COLLECTING CARTOON CHARACTERS

Cartoon characters, whether they be from animated films or comic book strips, are becoming a popular field for collectors. A major reference book on the subject, together with introductions such as the Hanna Barbera and Disney collections have already generated even more interest. Now is the time to start collecting, if you have not already done so.

Mickey Mouse is the best known cartoon character in the world. Within a year of his 1928 screen debut in "Steamboat Willie," his image was being used to endorse children's products, and by the 1950s there were more than 3,000 different Mickey Mouse items, including plates, dolls, watches and clothes. With all this merchandising activity, it is not surprising that Royal Doulton sought a license for portraying Mickey and his friends in ceramic.

The 1960s saw the rise of a new Disney star, Winnie the Pooh, who became a very popular merchandising character after his cartoon debut in 1966. "The Bear of Little Brain" originated in bedtime stories about nursery toys told by A. A. Milne to his son Christopher Robin in the 1920s, and he was visualised in the resulting books by the illustrator E. H. Shepard. To celebrate the 70th anniversary of the first "Winnie the Pooh" book, Royal Doulton launched a series of figures in 1996 and these have been a great success. Royal Doulton continue to work closely with the Walt Disney company today and they have launched two exciting figurine collections featuring Disney "Princesses" and "Villains" exclusively for sale in the Disney stores. The other new Disney collections have been distributed through specialist china shops, notably the "101 Dalmatians" series, which was inspired by the live action film, and the series of "Snow White and the Seven Dwarfs," which was prompted by the 60th anniversary of the film. A new Disney series featuring Mickey Mouse and his gang, was launched during 1998.

The massive marketing campaigns for Disney characters have made them household names all over the world. British cartoon characters, by comparison, are less well known internationally. The "Daily Express" newspaper was slow to capitalise on the success of "Rupert the Bear," who has been the star of their children's comic strip since 1920. Originated by Mary Tourtel, the Rupert stories were enlivened by Alfred Bestall who took over the daily drawings in 1935. Rupert enjoys the most extraordinary adventures with his friends Bill the Badger, Algy Pug and

Pong-Ping, always returning safely to his comfortable family home in Nutwood. Rupert Bear annuals sold in millions from the mid 1930s, and his exploits were adapted for TV in the 1970s, but his following is essentially British. The Royal Doulton Rupert Bear collection, launched in 1998, proved very popular with Lawleys By Post customers.

Norman Thelwell was a humorous illustrator for "Punch" magazine, who made his reputation with comical observations of young riders and their mounts. "Angels on Horseback," published in 1957, was the first compilation of his successful cartoons, and many other popular books followed. In 2001 Amanda Hughes-Lubeck created six humorous figures depicting the young riders and their ponies. In 2003 a further six models joined the series, these were modelled by Shane Ridge, Martyn Alcock and Warren Platt.

RESIN FIGURES

Several collectables manufacturers began experimenting with new sculptural materials in the 1980s and developed different types of resin bodies that allow more intricately modelled detail than conventional ceramic processes. Royal Doulton launched its new "bonded ceramic body" in 1984.

Production was short-lived, despite the minute detailing of the animals' fur and the tiny pebbles and grasses in their habitat, which would have been impossible to achieve in traditional earthenware. Royal Doulton ceased production of resin at the end of 1985, but designs have been commissioned from resin specialists, notably the "Paddington Bear" and "St. Tiggywinkles series."

ROYAL DOULTON YEAR CYPHERS

Beginning in 1998 a cypher was added to the base of each figurine. The cypher for 1998 was an umbrella, for 1999 the Top Hat as worn by Sir Henry Doulton, for 2000 a fob watch, for 2001 a waistcoat, for 2002 a boot, for 2003 a pair of gloves, for 2004 a Bottle Oven and for 2005 a Henry Doulton Cameo. These cyphers apply to production at Nile Street and do not appear to have been carried forward to figures produced in the Far East.

1998 Umbrella

1999 Top Hat

2000 Fob Watch

2001 Waistcoat

2002 Boot

2003 Gloves

2004 Bottle Oven

2005 Henry Doulton

ROYAL DOULTON

INTERNATIONAL COLLECTORS CLUB

Founded in 1980, the Royal Doulton International Collectors Club provides an information service on all aspects of the company's products, past and present. A club magazine, "Gallery," is published four times a year with information on new products and current events that will keep the collector up-to-date on the happenings in the world of Royal Doulton. Upon joining the club, each new member will receive a free gift and invitations to special events and exclusive offers throughout the year.

To join the Royal Doulton Collectors Club, please contact the club directly by writing to the address opposite or calling the appropriate number.

International Collectors Club
Sir Henry Doulton House
Forge Lane, Etruria
Stoke-on-Trent, Staffordshire
ST1 5NN, England
Telephone:
U.K.: 8702 412696
Overseas: +44 1782 404045
U.K. Fax: +44 (0) 1782 404000
On-line at www.doulton-direct.co.uk
E-mail: icc@royal-doulton.com

VISITOR CENTRE

Opened in the Summer of 1996, the Royal Doulton Visitor Centre houses the largest collection of Royal Doulton figurines in the world. Demonstration areas offer the collector a first hand insight on how figurines are assembled and decorated. Also at the Visitor Centre is a restaurant and a retail shop offering both best quality ware and slight seconds. Factory tours may be booked, Monday to Friday.

Royal Doulton Visitor Centre
Nile Street, Burslem
Stoke-on-Trent, ST6 2AJ, England
Visitor Centre: Tel.: +44 (0) 1782 292434
Fax: +44 (0) 1782 292424
Factory Store: Tel.: +44 (0) 1782 292451

WEBSITE AND E-MAIL ADDRESS

Web Sites:

www.royaldoulton.com

E-mail:

Visitor Centre: visitor@royaldoulton.com
Consumer Enquiries: enquiries@royaldoulton.com
Museum Curator: heritage@royaldoulton.com
Doulton-Direct: direct@royaldoulton.cm

DOULTON CHAPTERS

Detroit Chapter
Ronald Griffin, President
629 Lynne Avenue
Ypsilanti, MI 48198-3829

Edmonton Chapter
Mildred's Collectibles
6813 104 Street, Edmonton, AB

New England Chapter
Lee Piper, President
Meridith Nelson, Vice President
Michael Lynch, Secretary
Scott Reichenberg, Treasurer
E-mail doingantiq@aol.com

Northern California Chapter
Edward L. Khachadourian, President
P.O. Box 214, Moraga, Ca.
94556-0214
Tel.: (925) 376-2221
Fax: (925) 376-3581
E-mail: khack@pacbell.net

Northwest, Bob Haynes, Chapter
Alan Matthew, President
15202 93rd Place N.E., Bothell
WA., 98011 Tel.: (425) 488-9604

Rochester Chapter
Judith L. Trost, President
103 Garfield Street, Rochester
NY, 14611 Tel.: (716) 436-3321

Ohio Chapter
Reg Morris, President
5556 Whitehaven Avenue
North Olmstead, OH, 44070
Tel.: (216) 779-5554

Western Pennsylvania Chapter
John Re, President
9589 Parkedge Drive,
Allison Park, PA 15101
Tel.: (412) 366-0201

SECTION ONE

BUNNYKINS

Pillar Box; *Letterbox*, SF13, front; *Holding Hat and Coat,* EC4, back
From the Royal Doulton Archives.

Bunnybank, First Version D6615A; Bunnybank, Second Version, First Variation D6615B

BUNNYKINS TABLEWARE

BUNNYKINS TABLEWARE
Issues of 1934 to 2005 13
BUNNYKINS BREAKFAST SET
Issues of 1939 - 1945 179
BUNNYKINS TEAPOTS
Issues of 1994 - 1998 181
BUNNYKINS TEA SETS
Issues of 1998 - 2003 182
BUNNYKINS TOBY JUGS
Issues of 1999 - 2003 184

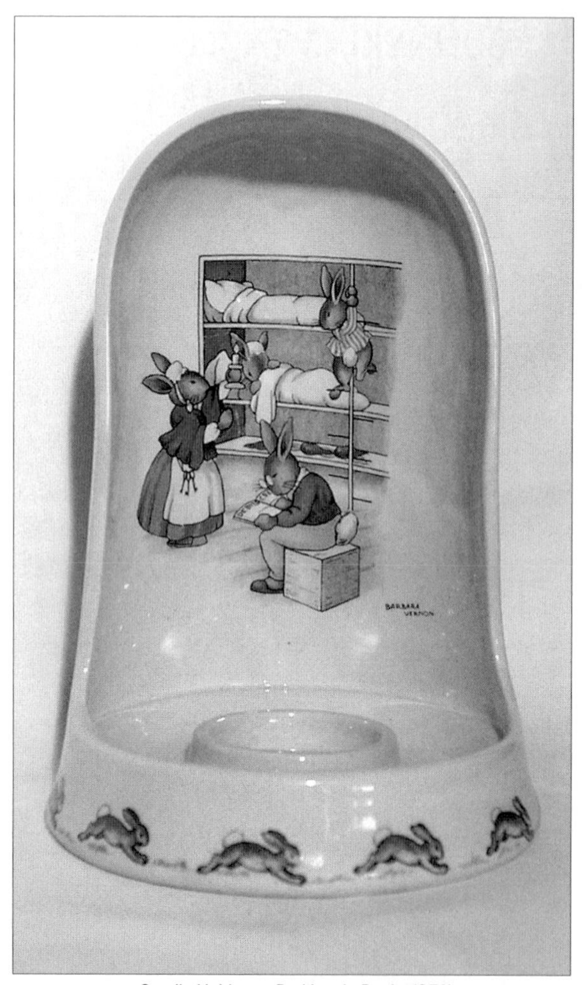

Candle Holder — *Bedtime in Bunks* (SF3)

BUNNYKINS TABLEWARE BACKSTAMPS

BKT-1. 1934 - 1937

1a

1b

1a. The crown and lion, MADE IN ENGLAND upon the ROYAL DOULTON logo, with or without date code.
1b. As 1a, but with "BUNNYKINS" added.

BKT-2. 1937 - c.1940

2a

2b

2a. The "Tug of War" group, (three bunnies from Barbara Vernon;s "Tug of War" scene) supports a crown and lion upon the Royal Doulton logo. "Made in England" is printed in green, the lion is uncoloured. "Bunnykins" below
2b. As 2a, but with date code (1927 + number = date of manufacture).

BKT-3. 1937 - 1953

3a

3c

3a. As 2a, but the lion is now coloured brown and "MADE In ENGLAND" is printed in brown also.

3b. As 3a, but with additional "A" mark for kiln identification. The "A" is printed in green

3c. As 3b, but an extra, crown, lion, Doulton logo is added, with or without date code., the extra logo is green.

3d. As 3c but with BONE CHINA, in green added below England on the lion, crown and Doulton logo stamp (not illustrated).

BKT-4. 1940s

4

4. As 3a, but a completely monochrome logo.

BKT-5. 1954 - 1958

5

5. As 3a, but "MADE IN ENGLAND" is printed in black and under "BUNNYKINS" the registration symbol ® is added; all is encircled with registration and trade mark numbers.

BKT-6a. 1959 - 1975 Earthenware
BKT-6b. 1968 - 1975 Fine Bone China

6a

6b

6a. As 5a, but the cirle of registration and trade mark numbers is removed and replaced by "REGD TRADE MARK" below the registration symbol ®.

6b. As 6a, but now with " ENGLISH FINE BONE CHINA" added between the Tug of War group and "BUNNYKINS".

BKT-7. 1976 - 1984

7a

7b

7a As 6a, but the " BUNNYKINS" and the registration symbol ® are now on one line with © ROYAL DOULTON / TABLEWARE LTD 1936, on two lines below.

7b As 7a but now with "ENGLISH FINE BONE CHINA" added between the Tug of War group and "BUNNYKINS" ®

BKT-8. 1976 - 1984

8a

8b

8a. As 7a, but with 19 – 84 on either side of the "Tug of War logo, below is "GOLDEN JUBLIEE CELEBRATION"

8b As 8a but with "ENGLISH FINE BONE CHINA" added between the "Tug of War" group and "BUNNYKINS" ®

BKT-9. 1985 - 1987

9a

9b

9a. As 7a, but with (U.K.) added to the single copyright line © 1936 ROYAL DOULTON.

9b As 9a but with "ENGLISH FINE BONE CHINA" added between the Tug of War group and "BUNNYKINS"

BKT-10. 1988 - c.1993

10a

10b

10a. As 7a but with © 1936 ROYAL DOULTON (U.K.) replaced by © 1988 ROYAL DOULTON.

10b. As 10a but with "ENGLISH FINE BONE CHINA" added between the "Tug of War" group and "BUNNYKINS" ®

BKT-11. c.1993 - 2002

11a

11b

11a. As 7a, but © 1988 is replaced by the original date © 1936.

11b As 11a but with "ENGLISH FINE BONE CHINA" added between the "Tug of War" group and "BUNNYKINS" ®

BKT-SPECIAL

Over the years special backstamps were created incorporating the Tug of War logo, and the various text changes with other special design elements such as the logo for the Australian Bicentenary or a wreath of holly leaves for the Christmas plate. We are classifying this group of backstamps under one heading "Special".

SHAPE GUIDE

This guide includes the standard Bunnykins shapes, their sizes and production dates. Originally Bunnykins was produced in either a deep ivory earthenware or a fine white bone china. The white china body was discontinued during the Second World War so examples are very hard to find today. A list of white china shapes from an early catalogue is included on page 12.

In 1968, an ivory bone china body replaced the original earthenware and many early shapes were withdrawn. Those that remained were remodelled for the new body. Today, the majority of Bunnykins nurseryware is made in ivory bone china, the exceptions being the money ball and savings book which are made in a earthenware body.

Some shapes were remodelled specifically for the Bunnykins range, for example the candle holder. Others were adapted from existing tableware ranges. The Casino tea wares, for instance, were originally designed for a striking art deco pattern of that name and the Jaffa fruit saucer takes its name from a fruit set which was produced with various patterns in 1930s.

The early Casino teapots and jugs were sold in several different sizes that are described as 24s, 30s, 36s and 42s and usually this number is incised on the base. This method of sizing was an industry standard and referred to the number of pieces which could be fitted on to a potter's board as he took them from the wheel. Thus the largest size is 24 as only that number of pieces could be accommodated on the potters board compared to 42 smaller pieces. The capacity in pints is also given for reference. Collectors will find some slight differences in capacity and sizes because of potting variations, such as clay thickness and kiln shrinkage. There were also slight modifications to handles and spouts in the early years.

The baby plates have also been altered over the years and the shape records indicate that the oval design was remodelled in 1947 and the round ones were reduced in weight by 5 ounces, also in 1947. Collectors will notice some variations in the profile and depth of baby plates.

From time to time, shapes have been developed for the Bunnykins range and then not produced. The model books record that a framed stand for Bunnykins subjects was modelled in 1940 but not approved. Stands featuring *Going Shopping* SF10 and *Dancing in the Moonlight* LFb have turned up in recent years. Other unusual shapes that have come to light include a vegetable tureen, a sauce boat, an oval plate and a small vase. In the early 1980s, a money box in the form of a post box was modelled but it did not go into production at that time and two examples were recorded, one in the Royal Doulton archives and another in a private collection. In 2001, a limited edition of this post box shape was produced for the Bunnykins Extravaganza Fair.

As with the original earthenware range, the Bunnykins fine white china shapes were also used for other patterns, for instance the Rex mug can be found with several different nurseryware designs. As yet, not all the fine white china shapes have appeared in the market-place so information is limited. It is believed that the majority of them were exported to the USA and Canada during the Second World War as this is where examples tend to be found.

"Space Ship" Music Box
Tune: *Fly Me To the Moon*
Possible prototype.

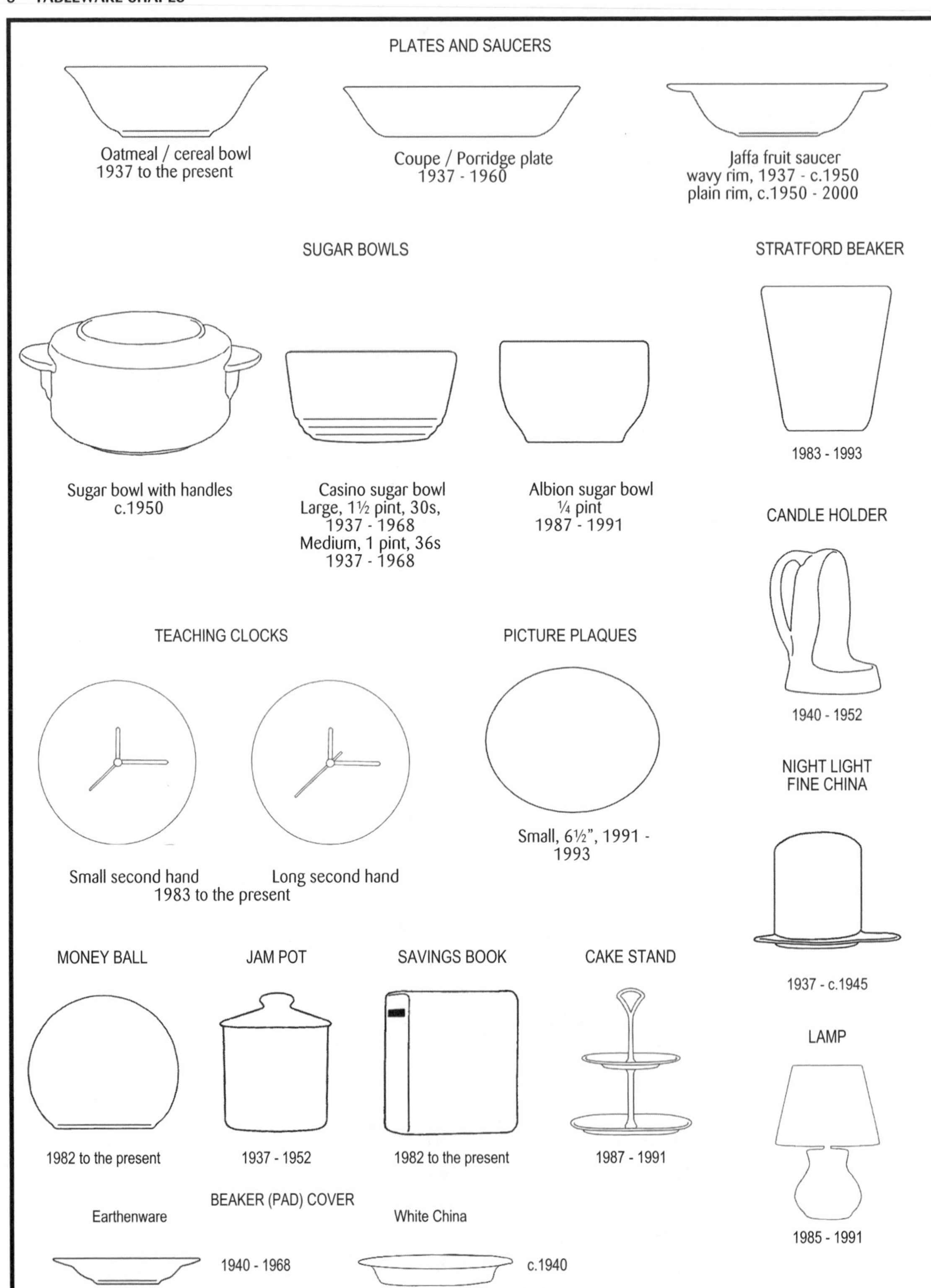
PLATES AND SAUCERS
Oatmeal / cereal bowl
1937 to the present
Coupe / Porridge plate
1937 - 1960
Jaffa fruit saucer
wavy rim, 1937 - c.1950
plain rim, c.1950 - 2000
SUGAR BOWLS
Sugar bowl with handles
c.1950
Casino sugar bowl
Large, 1½ pint, 30s,
1937 - 1968
Medium, 1 pint, 36s
1937 - 1968
Albion sugar bowl
¼ pint
1987 - 1991
STRATFORD BEAKER
1983 - 1993
CANDLE HOLDER
1940 - 1952
TEACHING CLOCKS
Small second hand
Long second hand
1983 to the present
PICTURE PLAQUES
Small, 6½", 1991 - 1993
NIGHT LIGHT
FINE CHINA
1937 - c.1945
MONEY BALL
1982 to the present
JAM POT
1937 - 1952
SAVINGS BOOK
1982 to the present
CAKE STAND
1987 - 1991
LAMP
1985 - 1991
BEAKER (PAD) COVER
Earthenware
1940 - 1968
White China
c.1940

RIM PLATES
COUPE PLATE
6 7/8", c.1956 - c1971
TEA CUPS AND SAUCERS
Casino 1937 - 1989
modified 1968
Plates in eight sizes
5", 1937 - c.1959
6", 1937 - c.1959
6½", 1937 to the present
7", 1937 - c.1959
7½", 1959 - 1968
8", 1968 to the present
8½", 1937 - 1969
10½", 1987 - 2000
Bread and butter plate
1940 - 1968
Stratford 1987 - 1997
TYPES of JUGS
DON BEAKERS
Casino jug in four sizes
¾ pint, 42s, 1937 - 1968
1 pint, 36s, 1937 - 1968
1½ pint, 30s, 1937 - 1968
2 pint, 24s, 1937 - 1968
Albion jug in three sizes
¼ pint, 1987 - 1991
½ pint, 1988 - 1991
1 pint, 1988 - 1991
Don beaker, 1937 - 1989
Don beaker with handle, 1940 - 1989
Early Don beakers have a running rabbits
border inside the rim, later outside
Standard sizes are listed above, however, other sizes do
exist which are variations on the standards.
EGG SAUCER, CUPS, AND BOXES
Egg saucer
one size, 1991 - 1996
Egg cup, three styles
Footless, 1937 - 1968
Footed, 1940 - 1968
Semi-footed, 1968 to the present
Egg boxes in three sizes
Large, 4¾", 1979 - 1981
Medium, 3¾", 1979 - 1981
Small, 3", 1979 - 1981

BABY PLATES

Oval baby plate, two sizes
Small 8¼", 1940 - 1952
Large 8½", 1940 - 1968

Round baby plate, small 6"
1937 to the present
modified in 1978 and 1988

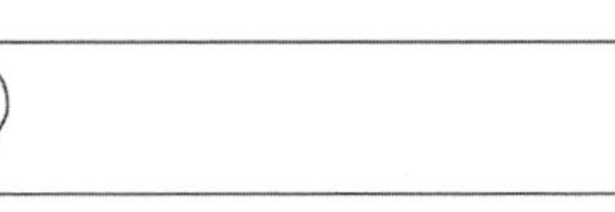

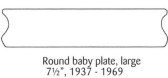

Round baby plate, large
7½", 1937 - 1969

Slightly different shapes and depths are found in baby plates

HOT WATER PLATES

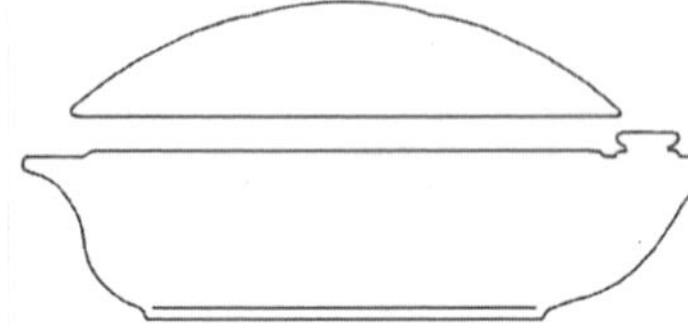

Hot Water Plate with Cover
One stopper, 1940 - 1959; Two stopper, 1959 - 1969

TEAPOTS

Albion teapot
1 pint size
1987 - 1991

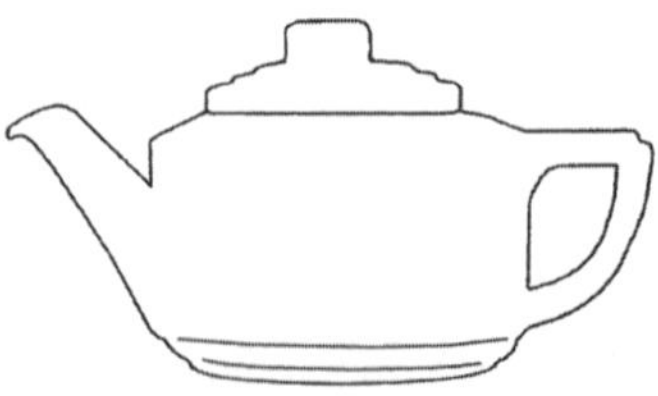

Casino teapot
1 pint size, 36s, 1937 - 1968
Base: 3 ½" diameter
1½ pint size, 30s, 1937 -1968
Base: 4" diameter
2 pint size, 24s, 1952 - 1968
Base: 4 ½" diameter

Collectors will find teapots that differ slightly in capacity from the standard sizes

DON MUGS

One handle, 1937 - 1983
modified in 1968

Two handles, 1940 - 1983

HUG-A-MUGS

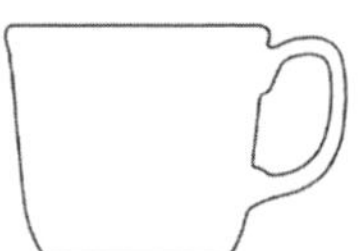

One handle, 1979 to the present

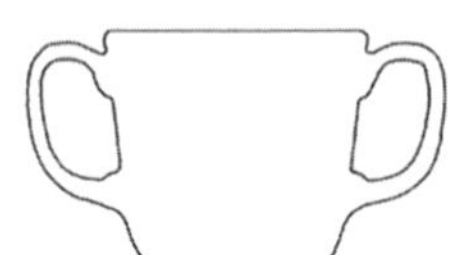

Two handles, 1979 to the present

MALVERN BEAKER

1989 - 1997

LARGE CUP / MUG

1937 - c.1945

THE COLLECTOR'S CHECKLIST OF SHAPES

The following provides the collector with a starting point to developing a checklist of designs vs. shapes. As the Barbara Vernon facsimile signature plays an important role in Bunnykins tableware we have also included that information in the listing. For continuity in the listing, we have noted where a signature was not included in the design.

On checking your collection you may find we have not included a particular design/shape with or without a signature. Why not bring this information to our attention? Please contact:

The Charlton Press at (416) 488-1418 or (800) 442-6042, you can fax us at (416) 488-4656 or (800) 442-1542, or you may e-mail us at chpress@charltonpress.com.

ALBION; 1987 - 1991
- **Cream jug**
  - ¼ pint, 1987 - 1991
    - without signature
- **Jug**
  - ¼ pint, 1987 - 1991
    - without signature
  - ½ pint, 1988 - 1991
    - without signature
  - 1 pint, 1988 - 1991
    - without signature
- **Sugar Bowl**
  - ¼ pint, 1987 - 1991
    - without signature
- **Teapot**
  - 1 pint, 1987 - 1991
    - without signature

BABY PLATES; 1937 to date
- **Small**
  - oval, 8 ¼", 1940 - 1952
    - with signature
    - without signature
  - round, 6", first issue, 1937 - 1978
    - with signature
    - without signature
  - round, 6", second issue, 1978-1988
  - without signature
  - round, 6", third issue, 1988 to date
    - without signature
- **Large**
  - oval, 8 ½", 1940 - 1968
    - with signature
    - without signature
  - round, 7 ½", 1937 - 1969
    - with signature
    - without signature

BEAKER PAD; 1940 - 1968
- with signature
- without signature

BREAD AND BUTTER PLATE; 1940 - 1968
- with signature
- without signature

CAKE PLATE, Footed, 11"

CAKE STAND; 1987 - 1991
- without signature

CANDLE HOLDER; 1940 - 1952
- with signature
- without signature

CASINO; 1937 - 1968
- **Jug**
  - 42s, ¾ pint, 1937 - 1968
    - with signature
    - without signature
  - 36s, 1 pint, 1937 - 1968
    - with signature
    - without signature
  - 30s, 1 ½ pint, 1937 - 1968
    - with signature
    - without signature
  - 24s, 2 pint, 1937 - 1968
    - with signature
    - without signature
- **Saucer**
  - 1937 - 1989
    - with signature
    - without signature
- **Sugar**
  - 36s, 1 pint, 1937 - 1968
    - with signature
    - without signature
  - 30s, 1 ½ pint, 1937 - 1968
    - with signature
    - without signature
- **Teacup**
  - First issue, 1937 - 1968
    - with signature
    - without signature
  - Second issue, 1968 - 1989
    - without signature
- **Teapot**
  - 36s, 1 pint, 1937 - 1968
    - with signature
    - without signature
  - 30s, 1 ½ pint, 1937 - 1968
    - with signature
    - without signature
  - 24s, 2 pint, 1952 - 1968
    - with signature
    - without signature

CEREAL / OATMEAL BOWL; 1937 to date
- with signature
- without signature

CEREAL / PORRIDGE PLATE; 1937 - 1960
- with signature
- without signature

CLOCK; 1983 to date
- without signature

COUPE; 1959 - 1971
- without signature

CUP / MUG LARGE; 1937 - c.1945
- with signature

DIVIDER DISH; 1993 - 1997
- 8 ¾", 1993 - 1997
  - without signature

DON; 1937-1989
- **Beaker**, 1937 - 1989
  - with signature
  - without signature
- **Beaker, one handle**, 1940 - 1989
  - with signature
  - without signature
- **Mug, one handle**
  - First issue, 1937 - 1968
    - with signature
    - without signature
  - Second issue, 1968 - 1983
    - without signature
- **Mug, two handles**, 1940 - 1983
  - with signature
  - without signature

EGG BOX; 1979 - 1981
- **Small**, 3", 1979 - 1981
  - without signature
- **Medium**, 3 ¾", 1979 - 1981
  - without signature
- **Large**, 4 ¾", 1979 - 1981
  - without signature

EGG CUP TRAY; c.1937

EGG CUPS; 1937 to date
- **Style One,** footless, 1937 - 1968
  - with signature
  - without signature
- **Style Two,** footed, 1940 - 1968
  - with signature
  - without signature
- **Style Three,** footless modified, 1968 to date
  - without signature

EGG SAUCER; 1991 - 1996
- without signature

HOT WATER PLATE WITH COVER; 1940 - 1969
- **Plate**
  - First issue, one stopper, 1940 - 1959
    - with signature
    - without signature
  - Second issue, two stoppers, 1959 - 1969
    - without signature
- **Cover**, 1940 - 1969
  - with signature
  - without signature

HUG-A-MUG; 1979 to date
- **One handle**, 1979 to date
  - without signature
- **Two handles**, 1979 to date
  - without signature

JAFFA FRUIT SAUCER; 1937 - 2000
- **Wavy rim**, 1937 - c.1950
  - with signature
  - without signature
- **Plain rim**, c.1950 - 2000
  - with signature
  - without signature

JAM POT; 1937 - 1952
- with signature
- without signature

LAMP; 1985 - 1991
- without signature

MALVERN BEAKER; 1989 - 1997
- without signature

MONEY BALL; 1982 to date
- without signature

NIGHT LIGHT; 1937 - c.1945
- with signature

PICTURE PLAQUE; 1991 - 1993
- **Small**, 6 ½", 1991 - 1993
  - without signature
- **Large**, 7 ¼", 1991 - 1993
  - without signature

PLATES; 1937 to date
- 5", 1937 - c.1959
  - with signature
  - without signature
- 6", 1937 - c.1959
  - with signature
  - without signature
- 6 ½", 1937 to date
  - with signature
  - without signature
- 7", 1937 - c.1959
  - with signature
  - without signature
- 7 ½", 1937 - 1968
  - with signature
  - without signature

PLATES (cont.)
- 8", 1968 to date
  - without signature
- 8 ½", 1937 - 1969
  - with signature
  - without signature
- 10 ½", 1987 - 2000
  - without signature

SAVINGS BOOK; 1982 to date
- without signature

STRATFORD; 1983 - 1997
- **Beaker**, 1983 - 1993
  - without signature
- **Saucer**, 1987 - 1997
  - without signature
- **Teacup**, 1987 - 1997
  - without signature

SUGAR BOWL WITH HANDLES; c.1950
- with signature
- without signature

FINE WHITE CHINA

The following is a list of shapes that were included in a price list of 1937.

- **Beaker**
  - Large
    - Height, 3 7/8"
    - Base diameter, 2 3/8"
  - Small
    - Height, 3 9/16"
    - Base diameter, 1 7/8"
- **Beaker with one handle**
- **Beaker pad**
- **Bread and butter plate**
- **Carlton Jug**
  - 24s (1 ¼ pint)
  - 30s (1 pint)
  - 36s (¾ pint)
  - 42s (½ pint)
- **Cecil bowl UBC**
- **Egg cup**
- **Night light**
- **Oatmeal saucer**
- **Phillips bowl**
  - 30s
  - 36s
  - 48s
- **Plate**
  - 4 inches
  - 5 inches
  - 6 inches
  - 7 inches
- **Porridge plate**
- **Prince**
  - Cream jug
    - 30s (½ pint)
  - Sugar bowl
  - Teapot
    - 30s (1 ½ pint)
    - 42s (1 pint)
- **Rex Mug**
  - Large
    - Height, 3 ¼"
    - Base diameter, 3 3/8"
  - Small
    - Height, 3"
    - Base diameter, 3"
- **Teacup and saucer**

Note: Small beaker measurements are approximate.

BUNNYKINS TABLEWARE

Issues of 1934 to the present

ABC THEME — Colin Twinn

ABCDEF SCENE

Design No.: CT94 ABCDEF Scene
Designer: Colin Twinn
Issued: 1994 - 1999

Shape	U.S. $	Can. $	U.K. £	Aust. $
Baby plate, round, small	20.00	25.00	12.00	30.00
Oatmeal / Cereal bowl	15.00	20.00	10.00	25.00
Plate, 8"	15.00	20.00	10.00	25.00

ABCDEF Scene (CT94)

ABC Scene (CT95)

ABC SCENE / A SCENE

Design No.: Front — CT95 ABC Scene
Reverse — CT96 A Scene
Designer: Colin Twinn
Issued: 1994 - 1999

Shape	U.S. $	Can. $	U.K. £	Aust. $
Hug-a-mug, one handle	10.00	12.00	6.00	15.00
Money ball	10.00	12.00	6.00	15.00

A Scene (CT96)

Aerobics

AEROBICS / JOGGING

A boxed Bunnykins for Grown Ups set containing a cereal bowl and hug-a-mug with one handle with the *Aerobics/Jogging* design, a 6" plate with the *Aeroplane* design, an 8" plate with the *Breakfast Time* design and a cereal bowl with *Tennis* design was distributed mainly in the U.S.A.

Design: Front — Aerobics
Reverse — Jogging
Designer: Walter Hayward
Issued: 1986 - 1988
Series: Bunnykins for Grown Ups

Shape	U.S. $	Can. $	U.K. £	Aust. $
Cereal / oatmeal bowl	60.00	70.00	35.00	75.00
Hug-a-mug, one handle	40.00	50.00	25.00	55.00
Complete set (M.I.B)	180.00	220.00	110.00	240.00

Note: See also *Aeroplane* below, *Breakfast Time* page 32 and *Tennis* page 160.

Jogging

AEROPLANE

A boxed Bunnykins for Grown Ups set containing a cereal bowl and hug-a-mug with one handle with the *Aerobics/Jogging* design, a 6" plate with the *Aeroplane* design, an 8" plate with the *Breakfast Time* design and a cereal bowl with *Tennis* design was distributed mainly in the U.S.A.

Design: Aeroplane
Designer: Walter Hayward
Issued: 1986 - 1988
Series: Bunnykins for Grown Ups

Shape	U.S. $	Can. $	U.K. £	Aust. $
Plate, 6"	40.00	50.00	25.00	55.00
Complete Set (M.I.B)	180.00	220.00	110.00	240.00

Aeroplane

Note: See Also *Aerobics* above, *Breakfast Time* page 32 and *Tennis* page 160.

AFTERNOON TEA / SERVING TEA

Design No.: Front — HW116 Afternoon Tea
Reverse — HW116R Serving Tea
Designer: Walter Hayward
Issued: 1959 - by 1998
Combined with: *Bugler with Toy Donkey*, HW26R
Dress Making, HW26
Hikers, EC124
Ice Cream on the Beach, HW136R
Playing with Dolls and Prams, HW115
Sheltering Under an Umbrella, EC3
Sledging, Style One, HW141
Trying on Hats, HW28R

Shape	U.S. $	Can. $	U.K. £	Aust. $
Albion cream jug	35.00	45.00	20.00	50.00
Albion jug, ½ pint	85.00	100.00	50.00	110.00
Albion jug, 1 pint	100.00	125.00	60.00	135.00
Albion sugar bowl	30.00	35.00	17.50	40.00
Albion teapot	50.00	60.00	30.00	65.00
Casino jug, 36s	125.00	150.00	75.00	160.00
Casino jug, 42s	100.00	125.00	60.00	135.00
Casino saucer	8.00	10.00	5.00	12.00
Casino sugar bowl, 30s	125.00	150.00	75.00	160.00
Casino sugar bowl, 36s	100.00	125.00	60.00	135.00
Casino teacup	8.00	10.00	5.00	12.00
Casino teapot, 30s	150.00	200.00	90.00	225.00
Divider dish	50.00	60.00	30.00	65.00
Don beaker	25.00	30.00	15.00	35.00
Don beaker, one handle	25.00	30.00	15.00	35.00
Don mug, one handle	10.00	12.00	6.00	15.00
Don mug, two handles	10.00	12.00	6.00	15.00
Egg box				
small	175.00	200.00	100.00	225.00
medium	200.00	250.00	115.00	275.00
large	225.00	275.00	125.00	300.00
Hug-a-mug, one handle	10.00	12.00	6.00	15.00
Hug-a-mug, two handles	10.00	12.00	6.00	15.00
Jaffa fruit saucer (plain)	15.00	20.00	10.00	25.00
Lamp	50.00	60.00	30.00	65.00
Lid of hot water plate	50.00	60.00	30.00	65.00
Malvern beaker	15.00	20.00	10.00	25.00
Money ball	10.00	12.00	6.00	15.00
Picture plaque, small	20.00	25.00	12.00	30.00
Plate, 6 ½"	15.00	20.00	10.00	25.00
Savings book	15.00	20.00	10.00	25.00
Stratford teacup	10.00	12.00	6.00	15.00

Afternoon Tea (HW116)

Serving Tea (HW116R)

Note: Retirement dates are all approximate. When a design is retired all remaining stocks of the retired litho prints are used until exhausted.

Airmail Delivery (LFa)

AIRMAIL DELIVERY

Design No. LFa
Designer: Barbara Vernon
Issued: By 1937 - by 1952

Shape	U.S. $	Can. $	U.K. £	Aust. $
Baby plate, round, small	300.00	375.00	175.00	400.00
Baby plate, round, large	400.00	475.00	225.00	500.00
Bread and butter plate	400.00	475.00	225.00	500.00
Casino Jug, 24s	550.00	650.00	315.00	675.00
Hot water plate	375.00	450.00	215.00	475.00
Plate, 7 ½"	400.00	475.00	225.00	500.00
Plate, 8 ½"	300.00	350.00	175.00	375.00
Porridge plate	350.00	425.00	200.00	450.00

Note: This design should appear with the Barbara Vernon facsimile signature.

Casino Jugs — Three sizes shown

Family at Breakfast (HW12) *Frightening Spider* (SF4) *Going Shopping* (SF10)

Four standard sizes of Casino jugs exist; ¾, 1, 1½ and 2 pint capacity. Only these sizes are listed in the shape book. However in between sizes are found in 1¼, 1¾ and 2¼ pint capacity which may have been standard sizes modified for numerous reasons.

¾ Pint	1 Pint	1 ½ Pint	2 Pint
42s - Height 4¼"	36s - Height 4 ¾"	30s - Height 5"	24s - Height 5 ½"

APPLE PICKING

Design No.: SF25
Designer: Walter Hayward
Issued: 1954 - by 1998
Combined with: *Lunch Break*, HW29R
Windy Day, HW27

Shape	U.S. $	Can. $	U.K. £	Aust. $
Baby plate, round, small				
with signature	30.00	35.00	17.50	40.00
without signature	20.00	25.00	12.50	30.00
Cake stand	150.00	180.00	90.00	190.00
Casino jug, 30s				
with signature	200.00	250.00	115.00	275.00
without signature	150.00	180.00	90.00	190.00
Casino jug, 36s				
with signature	150.00	180.00	90.00	190.00
without signature	125.00	150.00	75.00	160.00
Casino saucer				
with signature	15.00	20.00	10.00	25.00
without signature	8.00	10.00	5.00	12.00
Casino sugar, 30s				
with signature	150.00	180.00	90.00	190.00
without signature	125.00	150.00	75.00	160.00
Cereal / oatmeal bowl				
with signature	25.00	30.00	15.00	35.00
without signature	15.00	20.00	12.00	25.00
Hot water plate				
with signature	100.00	125.00	60.00	135.00
without signature	75.00	90.00	45.00	95.00
Jaffa fruit saucer (plain)	20.00	25.00	12.50	30.00
Picture plaque, large	20.00	25.00	12.50	30.00
Plate, 6 ½"				
with signature	25.00	30.00	15.00	35.00
without signature	15.00	20.00	10.00	25.00
Plate, 7 ½"				
with signature	30.00	35.00	17.50	40.00
without signature	15.00	20.00	10.00	25.00
Plate, 8"				
with signature	30.00	35.00	17.50	40.00
without signature	15.00	20.00	10.00	25.00

Note: An 8" plate was issued for the 'U.S. Special Events Tour. 1990,' see page 191.

Apple Picking (SF25)

'Special Events Tour 1990'

Art Class (LF107)

ART CLASS

Design No.: LF107
Designer: Walter Hayward
Issued: 1959 - 1970

Shape	U.S. $	Can. $	U.K. £	Aust. $
Baby plate, oval, large	300.00	375.00	175.00	400.00
Baby plate, oval, small	300.00	375.00	175.00	400.00
Baby plate, round, large	200.00	250.00	125.00	275.00
Plate, 6 ½"	75.00	90.00	45.00	100.00
Plate, 8 ½"	100.00	125.00	60.00	135.00
Porridge plate	100.00	125.00	60.00	135.00

Artist (HW1)

ARTIST

Design No.: HW1
Designer: Barbara Vernon
Issued: By 1937 - by 1952
Combined with: *Dunce*, HW1R
Fishing in the Goldfish Bowl, HW3R
Greetings, HW7
Netting a Cricket, HW6
Playing with Cup and Spoon, EC6
Pulling on Trousers, HW2

Shape	U.S. $	Can. $	U.K. £	Aust. $
Baby plate, round, small				
with signature	50.00	60.00	30.00	65.00
without signature	30.00	35.00	17.50	40.00
Casino jug, 42s				
with signature	300.00	350.00	175.00	375.00
without signature	250.00	300.00	150.00	325.00
Casino saucer				
with signature	100.00	125.00	60.00	135.00
without signature	75.00	90.00	45.00	95.00
Casino sugar bowl, 30s				
with signature	250.00	300.00	150.00	325.00
without signature	175.00	200.00	100.00	225.00
Casino teacup				
with signature	100.00	125.00	60.00	135.00
without signature	75.00	90.00	45.00	95.00
Don beaker				
with signature	65.00	80.00	40.00	85.00
without signature	35.00	45.00	20.00	50.00
Don beaker, one handle				
with signature	65.00	80.00	40.00	85.00
without signature	35.00	45.00	20.00	50.00
Don mug, one handle				
with signature	50.00	60.00	30.00	65.00
without signature	15.00	20.00	10.00	25.00
Don mug, two handles				
with signature	50.00	60.00	30.00	65.00
without signature	15.00	20.00	10.00	25.00
Jam pot	1,500.00	1,800.00	850.00	1,900.00
Jaffa fruit saucer				
plain rim	50.00	60.00	30.00	65.00
wavy rim	75.00	90.00	45.00	95.00
Plate, 6 ½"				
with signature	30.00	35.00	17.50	40.00
without signature	20.00	25.00	12.00	30.00
FINE WHITE CHINA				
Beaker, large		Very Rare		
Beaker, one handle	525.00	625.00	300.00	675.00
Plate, 5"	1,100.00	1,300.00	650.00	1,400.00
Plate, 6"	1,100.00	1,300.00	650.00	1,400.00
Plate, 7"	1,100.00	1,300.00	650.00	1,400.00
Saucer	525.00	625.00	300.00	675.00
Teacup	525.00	625.00	300.00	675.00

Note: White china prices are indications only due to the scarcity of the items. Prices will fluctuate.

ASLEEP IN THE OPEN AIR

Design No.: HW10
Designer: Barbara Vernon
Issued: By 1937 - by 1967
Combined with: *Bathtime*, Style One, SF18
Convalescing, SF5
Gardening, Style One, HW9
Leapfrog, HW12R
Washing in the Open Air, HW10R
Wheelbarrow Race, Style One, HW22

Asleep in the Open Air (HW10)

Shape	U.S. $	Can. $	U.K. £	Aust. $
Casino jug, 30s				
with signature	375.00	450.00	210.00	475.00
without signature	300.00	350.00	175.00	375.00
Casino jug, 36s				
with signature	300.00	350.00	175.00	375.00
without signature	275.00	325.00	160.00	350.00
Casino jug, 42s				
with signature	275.00	325.00	160.00	350.00
without signature	200.00	250.00	115.00	275.00
Casino saucer				
with signature	75.00	90.00	45.00	95.00
without signature	50.00	60.00	30.00	65.00
Casino sugar bowl, 30s				
with signature	200.00	250.00	115.00	275.00
without signature	175.00	200.00	100.00	225.00
Casino sugar bowl 36s				
with signature	150.00	180.00	90.00	190.00
without signature	125.00	150.00	75.00	160.00
Casino teacup				
with signature	100.00	125.00	60.00	135.00
without signature	75.00	90.00	45.00	95.00
Casino teapot, 24s				
with signature	375.00	450.00	210.00	475.00
without signature	300.00	350.00	175.00	375.00

Shape	U.S. $	Can. $	U.K. £	Aust. $
Casino teapot, 30s				
with signature	300.00	350.00	175.00	375.00
without signature	225.00	275.00	125.00	300.00
Casino teapot, 36s				
with signature	275.00	325.00	160.00	350.00
without signature	200.00	250.00	115.00	275.00
Don beaker				
with signature	150.00	180.00	90.00	190.00
without signature	100.00	125.00	60.00	135.00
Don beaker, one handle				
with signature	150.00	180.00	90.00	190.00
without signature	100.00	125.00	60.00	135.00
Don mug, one handle				
with silver rim	400.00	475.00	225.00	500.00
with signature	75.00	90.00	45.00	95.00
without signature	35.00	45.00	20.00	50.00
Don mug, two handles				
with signature	75.00	90.00	45.00	95.00
without signature	35.00	45.00	20.00	50.00
Jaffa fruit saucer				
plain rim	35.00	45.00	20.00	50.00
wavy rim	65.00	80.00	40.00	85.00
Plate, 6 ½"				
with signature	60.00	70.00	35.00	75.00
without signature	35.00	45.00	20.00	50.00

AUSTRALIANA BUNNYKINS – Colin Twinn

PICNIC WITH KANGAROO AND KOALA
First Variation, Large Size

The 1994 plates have a leaf border with the inscription Bunnykins 60th Anniversary 1994.

Design No.:	Front — CT84 Picnic with Kangaroo and Koala Reverse — CT85 Commemorative Leaf Border
Designer:	Colin Twinn
Issued:	1994 - 1994
Backstamp:	'Bunnykins 60th Anniversary Australiana Bunnykins. Produced exclusively for Royal Doulton Australia.'

Shape	U.S. $	Can. $	U.K. £	Aust. $
Plate, 8"	25.00	30.00	15.00	35.00

Picnic with Kangaroo and Koala, First Variation (CT84)

PICNIC WITH KANGAROO AND KOALA
Second Variation, Small Size

Design No.:	CT86 Picnic with Kangaroo and Koala
Designer:	Colin Twinn
Issued:	1994 - 1994
Backstamp:	'Australiana Bunnykins. Produced exclusively for Royal Doulton Australia.'

Shape	U.S. $	Can. $	U.K. £	Aust. $
Baby plate, round, small	25.00	30.00	15.00	35.00
Cereal / oatmeal bowl	15.00	20.00	10.00	25.00

Picnic with Kangaroo and Koala, Second Variation (CT86)

Backstamp (CT86)

PICNIC SCENE / BUNNY WITH CAKE PLATE

The backstamp on this teacup and saucer does not refer to the 60th Anniversary celebrations.

Design No.: Front — CT87 Picnic Scene
Reverse — CT88 Bunny with Cake Plate
Designer: Colin Twinn
Issued: 1994 - 1994

Shape	U.S. $	Can. $	U.K. £	Aust. $
Stratford teacup	40.00	50.00	25.00	55.00

Front — Picnic Scene (CT87)

Front — Picinic Scene with Hamper (CT89)

Reverse — Bunny with Cake Plate (CT88)

Reverse — Father Asleep (CT90)

PICNIC SCENE WITH HAMPER / FATHER ASLEEP

Design No.: Front — CT89 Picnic Scene with Hamper
Reverse — CT90 Father Asleep
Designer: Colin Twinn
Issued: 1994 - 1994
Backstamp: 'Australiana Bunnykins. Produced exclusively for Royal Doulton Australia.'

Shape	U.S. $	Can. $	U.K. £	Aust. $
Hug-a-mug, one handle	25.00	30.00	15.00	35.00
Money ball	15.00	20.00	10.00	25.00

Baking (SF19)

BAKING

Design No.: SF19
Designer: Walter Hayward after Barbara Vernon
Issued: By 1952 - by 1998
Combined with: *Convalescing*, SF5
Cricketer, HW22R
Soldiers Marching to Music, HW16
Wheelbarrow Race, HW22

Shape	U.S. $	Can. $	U.K. £	Aust. $
Baby plate, round, large				
with signature	75.00	90.00	45.00	95.00
without signature	50.00	60.00	30.00	65.00
Baby plate, round, small				
with signature	30.00	35.00	17.50	40.00
without signature	20.00	25.00	12.50	30.00
Casino jug, 24s				
with signature	325.00	400.00	185.00	425.00
without signature	175.00	200.00	100.00	225.00
Casino jug, 30s				
with signature	250.00	300.00	150.00	325.00
without signature	150.00	180.00	90.00	190.00
Casino saucer				
with signature	15.00	20.00	10.00	25.00
without signature	8.00	10.00	5.00	12.00
Casino teapot, 24s				
with signature	275.00	325.00	160.00	350.00
without signature	175.00	200.00	100.00	225.00
Casino teapot, 30s				
with signature	225.00	275.00	125.00	300.00
without signature	150.00	180.00	90.00	190.00
Cereal / oatmeal bowl				
with signature	25.00	30.00	15.00	35.00
without signature	15.00	20.00	10.00	25.00
Hot water plate				
with signature	100.00	125.00	60.00	135.00
without signature	75.00	90.00	45.00	95.00
Jaffa fruit saucer				
plain rim	15.00	20.00	10.00	25.00
wavy rim	35.00	45.00	20.00	50.00
Picture plaque, large	20.00	25.00	12.50	30.00
Plate, 6 ½"				
with signature	25.00	30.00	15.00	35.00
without signature	15.00	20.00	10.00	25.00
Plate, 8"	15.00	20.00	10.00	25.00
Plate, 8 ½"				
with signature	30.00	35.00	17.50	40.00
without signature	15.00	20.00	10.00	25.00

BAKING THEME – Frank Endersby

BAKING CAKES WITH MOTHER

Design No.: 7 Baking Cakes with Mother
Designer: Frank Endersby
Issued: 1995 to the present

Shape	U.S. $	Can. $	U.K. £	Aust. $
Baby plate, round, small	25.00	30.00	15.00	35.00
Cereal / oatmeal bowl	15.00	20.00	10.00	25.00
Jaffa fruit saucer	15.00	20.00	10.00	25.00
Plate, 6 ½"	15.00	20.00	10.00	25.00
Plate, 8"	15.00	20.00	10.00	25.00

Baking Cakes with Mother (7)

Taking Cake from Oven (8)

TAKING CAKE FROM OVEN / DECORATING THE CAKE

Design No.: Front — 8 Taking Cake from Oven
Reverse — 9 Decorating the Cake
Designer: Frank Endersby
Issued: 1995 to the present
Combined with: **Carrying Letter*, (30)

Shape	U.S. $	Can. $	U.K. £	Aust. $
Hug-a-mug, one handle	17.50	20.00	10.00	25.00
Hug-a-mug, two handles	17.50	20.00	10.00	25.00
Divider dish	50.00	60.00	30.00	65.00
Money ball	25.00	30.00	15.00	35.00
Stratford teacup	17.50	20.00	10.00	25.00

* Indicates scene on divider dish.

Decorating the Cake (9)

Bath Night (LF7)

BATH NIGHT

Design No.: LF7
Designer: Barbara Vernon
Issued: By 1940 - by 1952
Combined with: *Postman Delivering Letters*, HW19

Shape	U.S. $	Can. $	U.K. £	Aust. $
Baby plate, oval, small				
with signature	350.00	425.00	200.00	450.00
without signature	300.00	375.00	175.00	400.00
Baby plate, round, large				
with silver rim	300.00	375.00	175.00	400.00
with signature	250.00	300.00	150.00	325.00
without signature	200.00	250.00	125.00	275.00
Bread and butter plate				
with signature	300.00	350.00	175.00	375.00
without signature	275.00	325.00	160.00	350.00
Casino jug, 24s	275.00	325.00	160.00	350.00
Cereal / oatmeal bowl				
with signature	100.00	125.00	60.00	135.00
without signature	90.00	110.00	50.00	120.00
Plate, 8 ½"				
with signature	100.00	125.00	60.00	135.00
without signature	75.00	100.00	45.00	110.00
Porridge plate				
with signature	125.00	150.00	75.00	160.00
without signature	100.00	125.00	60.00	135.00

Note: Condition is important. Prices listed are based on nurseryware in mint condition. Items in less than mint condition will command lower prices.

BATHTIME, Style One

Design No.: SF18
Designer: Walter Hayward after Barbara Vernon
Issued: By 1952 - 1994
Combined with: *Asleep in the Open Air*, HW10

Shape	U.S. $	Can. $	U.K. £	Aust. $
Baby plate, round, small				
with signature	30.00	35.00	17.50	40.00
without signature	20.00	25.00	12.50	30.00
Cake stand	150.00	180.00	90.00	190.00
Casino jug, 30s				
with signature	250.00	300.00	150.00	325.00
without signature	150.00	180.00	90.00	190.00
Casino saucer				
with signature	15.00	20.00	10.00	25.00
without signature	8.00	10.00	5.00	12.00
Cereal / oatmeal bowl				
with signature	25.00	30.00	15.00	35.00
without signature	15.00	20.00	10.00	25.00
Hot water plate				
with signature	100.00	125.00	60.00	135.00
without signature	75.00	90.00	45.00	95.00
Jaffa fruit saucer				
plain rim				
with signature	25.00	30.00	15.00	35.00
without signature	15.00	20.00	10.00	25.00
wavy rim	35.00	45.00	20.00	50.00
Picture plaque, large	20.00	25.00	12.50	30.00
Plate, 6 ½"				
with signature	25.00	30.00	15.00	35.00
without signature	15.00	20.00	10.00	25.00
Plate, 7 ½"				
with signature	30.00	35.00	17.50	40.00
without signature	15.00	20.00	10.00	25.00
Plate, 8 ½"				
with signature	30.00	35.00	17.50	40.00
without signature	15.00	20.00	10.00	25.00

Bathtime, Style One (SF18)

BATHTIME THEME – Colin Twinn

Bathtime, Style Two, First Variation (CT21)

BATHTIME
Style Two, First Variation

Design No.:	CT21 Bathtime
Designer:	Colin Twinn
Issued:	1991 - 1993

Shape	U.S. $	Can. $	U.K. £	Aust. $
Albion jug, 1 pint	100.00	125.00	60.00	135.00
Albion teapot	50.00	60.00	30.00	65.00
Baby plate, round, small	10.00	12.50	6.00	15.00
Cereal / oatmeal bowl	15.00	20.00	10.00	25.00
Picture plaque, large	20.00	25.00	12.50	30.00
Plate, 8"	15.00	20.00	10.00	25.00

BATHTIME SCENE
Style Two, Second Variation / BUNNIES IN THE BATH, First Version

Design No.:	Front — CT24 Bathtime Scene Reverse — CT25 Bunnies in the Bath, First Version
Designer:	Colin Twinn
Issued:	1991 - 1993
Combined with:	*Bunnies in Bath*, Second Version, CT34 *Bunny on Trike*, CT23 *School Gates*, Second Variation, CT22

Shape	U.S. $	Can. $	U.K. £	Aust. $
Albion cream jug	35.00	45.00	20.00	50.00
Albion jug, ½ pint	85.00	100.00	50.00	110.00
Albion jug, 1 pint	100.00	125.00	60.00	135.00
Albion teapot	50.00	60.00	30.00	65.00
Hug-a-mug, one handle	10.00	12.50	6.00	15.00
Hug-a-mug, two handles	10.00	12.50	6.00	15.00
Lamp	50.00	60.00	30.00	65.00
Malvern beaker	15.00	20.00	10.00	25.00
Money ball	10.00	12.50	6.00	15.00
Stratford straight beaker	15.00	20.00	10.00	25.00
Stratford teacup	8.00	10.00	5.00	12.00

Bathtime Scene, Style Two, Second Variation (CT24)

Bunnies in the Bath, First Version (CT25)

Note: *Bunnies in the Bath* (CT34) is combined with *Bathtime Scene* (CT24) on a Stratford straight beaker.

BUNNIES IN THE BATH
Second Version

Design No.: CT34
Designer: Colin Twinn
Issued: 1991 - 1993
Combined with: *Bathtime Scene*, Style Two, Second Variation, (CT24)
Bunny with Mirror, CT35
Pushing the Wheelbarrow, CT3

Shape	U.S. $	Can. $	U.K. £	Aust. $
Albion sugar bowl	30.00	35.00	17.50	40.00
Albion teapot	50.00	60.00	30.00	65.00
Egg cup				
Style Three	10.00	12.50	6.00	15.00
Savings book	15.00	20.00	10.00	25.00
Stratford straight beaker	15.00	20.00	10.00	25.00

Bunnies in the Bath, Second Version (CT34)

Rex Mug (small), *Family at Breakfast* (HW12)

BATHTIME THEME – Frank Endersby

Bathtime, Style Three (22)

BATHTIME
Style Three

Design No.: 22 Bathtime
Designer: Frank Endersby
Issued: 1995 to the present

Shape	U.S. $	Can. $	U.K. £	Aust. $
Baby plate, round, small	25.00	30.00	15.00	35.00
Plate, 6½"	15.00	20.00	10.00	25.00
Plate, 8"	15.00	20.00	10.00	25.00

Blowing and Bursting Bubbles (23)

BLOWING AND BURSTING BUBBLES / BLOWING BUBBLES AND SAILING BOATS

Design No.: Front — 23 Blowing and Bursting Bubbles
Reverse — 24 Blowing Bubbles and Sailing Boats
Designer: Frank Endersby
Issued: 1996 to the present

Shape	U.S. $	Can. $	U.K. £	Aust. $
Hug-a-mug, one handle	15.00	20.00	10.00	25.00
Hug-a-mug, two handles	15.00	20.00	10.00	25.00
Stratford teacup	8.00	10.00	5.00	12.00

Blowing Bubbles and Sailing Boats (24)

BEDTIME IN BUNKS, Style One

Bedtime in Bunks, Style One (SF3)

Design No.:	SF3
Designer:	Barbara Vernon
Issued:	By 1937 - by 1952
Combined with:	*Family at Breakfast,* HW12
	Feeding the Baby, HW13
	Proposal, HW11
	Pulling on Trousers, HW2

Shape	U.S. $	Can. $	U.K. £	Aust. $
Candle holder	1,500.00	1,800.00	850.00	1,900.00
Casino jug, 42s	275.00	325.00	160.00	350.00
Hot water plate	200.00	250.00	115.00	275.00
Plate, 7"	90.00	110.00	50.00	120.00
Plate, 7 ½"	100.00	125.00	60.00	135.00
Plate, 8 ½"	100.00	125.00	60.00	135.00

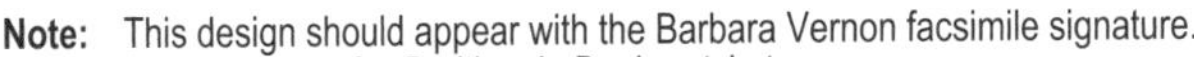

Note: This design should appear with the Barbara Vernon facsimile signature. See next page for *Bedtime In Bunks*, style two.

BEDTIME STORY

Bedtime Story (SF130)

Design No.:	SF130
Designer:	Walter Hayward
Issued:	1967 - 1994

Shape	U.S. $	Can. $	U.K. £	Aust. $
Baby plate round, small	20.00	25.00	12.50	30.00
Cake stand	150.00	180.00	90.00	190.00
Casino saucer	8.00	10.00	5.00	12.00
Casino teapot, 24s	175.00	200.00	100.00	300.00
Cereal / oatmeal bowl	15.00	20.00	10.00	25.00
Coupe dish, 6 ¾"			Rare	
Hot water plate	75.00	90.00	45.00	95.00
Jaffa fruit saucer (plain)	15.00	20.00	10.00	25.00
Picture plaque, large	20.00	25.00	12.50	30.00
Plate, 6"	15.00	20.00	10.00	25.00
Plate, 6 ½"	15.00	20.00	10.00	25.00
Plate, 8"	15.00	20.00	10.00	25.00

BEDTIME THEME – Frank Endersby

Bedtime in Bunks, Style Two (13)

BEDTIME IN BUNKS, Style Two

Design No.: 13 Bedtime in Bunks
Designer: Frank Endersby
Issued: 1995 to the present

Shape	U.S. $	Can. $	U.K. £	Aust. $
Baby plate, round, small	25.00	30.00	15.00	35.00
Cereal / oatmeal bowl	15.00	20.00	10.00	25.00
Plate, 6 ½"	15.00	20.00	10.00	25.00
Plate, 8"	15.00	20.00	10.00	25.00

Pillow Fight, Style Two (14)

PILLOW FIGHT, Style Two / PLAYING AND READING

Design No.: Front — 14 Pillow Fight
Reverse — 15 Playing and Reading
Designer: Frank Endersby
Issued: 1995 to the present
Combined with: **Playing with Ball*, (42)

Shape	U.S. $	Can. $	U.K. £	Aust. $
Hug-a-mug, one handle	20.00	25.00	12.00	30.00
Hug-a-mug, two handles	20.00	25.00	12.00	30.00
Divider dish	50.00	60.00	30.00	65.00
Stratford teacup	8.00	10.00	5.00	12.00

* Indicates scene on divider dish.

Playing and Reading (15)

BEDTIME WITH DOLLIES

Design No.: EC125
Designer: Walter Hayward
Issued: 1959 - 1992
Combined with: *Cricketer*, HW22R
Drummer, EC2
Drummer and Bugler, EC126
Hat Shop, HW28
Hikers, EC124
Holding Hat and Coat, EC4
Playing with Cup and Spoon, EC6
Playing with Doll and Pram, EC123
Raising Hat, Style Two, EC7
Reading, EC122
Sheltering Under an Umbrella, EC3
Trumpeter, EC5
Trying on Knitting, HW119R
Unravelling the Knitting, HW119
Wheelbarrow Race, Style One, HW22

Shape	U.S. $	Can. $	U.K. £	Aust. $
Albion sugar bowl	30.00	35.00	17.50	40.00
Beaker cover	65.00	80.00	40.00	85.00
Casino sugar bowl, 36s	100.00	125.00	60.00	135.00
Egg cup				
Style One	30.00	35.00	17.50	40.00
Style Two	40.00	50.00	25.00	55.00
Style Three	10.00	12.50	6.00	15.00
Lid of hot water plate	50.00	60.00	30.00	65.00
Money Ball	10.00	12.50	6.00	15.00

Bedtime with Dollies (EC125)

Beware of the Bull (LF108)

BEWARE OF THE BULL

Design No.: LF108
Designer: Walter Hayward
Issued: 1959 - 1970

Shape	U.S. $	Can. $	U.K. £	Aust. $
Baby plate, oval, large	150.00	180.00	90.00	190.00
Baby plate, oval, small	150.00	180.00	90.00	190.00
Baby plate, round, large	75.00	90.00	45.00	95.00
Plate, 8"	25.00	30.00	15.00	35.00
Plate, 8 ½"	25.00	30.00	15.00	35.00
Porridge plate	85.00	100.00	50.00	110.00

Bonfire (LF128)

BONFIRE

Design No.: LF128
Designer: Walter Hayward
Issued: 1967 - 1970

Shape	U.S. $	Can. $	U.K. £	Aust. $
Baby plate, round, large	350.00	425.00	200.00	450.00
Plate, 7 ½"	450.00	550.00	260.00	575.00
Plate, 8"	250.00	300.00	150.00	325.00
Plate, 8 ½"	275.00	325.00	160.00	350.00
Porridge Plate	250.00	300.00	150.00	325.00

BREAKFAST TIME

A boxed Bunnykins for Grown Ups set containing a cereal bowl and hug-a-mug with one handle with the *Aerobics/Jogging* design, a 6" plate with the *Aeroplane* design, an 8" plate with the *Breakfast Time* design a cereal bowl in the *Tennis* design was distributed mainly in the U.S.A.

Design No.: Breakfast Time
Designer: Walter Hayward
Issued: 1986 - 1988
Series: Bunnykins for Grown Ups

Shape	U.S. $	Can. $	U.K. £	Aust. $
Plate, 8"	40.00	50.00	25.00	55.00
Complete set (M.I.B.)	180.00	220.00	110.00	240.00

Breakfast Time

Note: See also *Aerobics/Jogging* and *Aeroplane* page 14 and *Tennis* page 160.

BUILDING SAND CASTLES / SAILING BOATS

Design No.: Front — HW138 Building Sand Castles
Reverse — HW138R Sailing Boats
Designer: Walter Hayward
Issued: 1967 - by 1998
Combined with: *Ice Cream on Beach,* HW136R
Playing with Doll and Pram, EC123
Raising Hat, Style Two, EC7
Roller Skating Arm in Arm, HW137R
Roller Skating Race, HW137

Shape	U.S. $	Can. $	U.K. £	Aust. $
Albion cream jug	35.00	45.00	20.00	50.00
Albion jug, ½ pint	85.00	100.00	50.00	110.00
Albion teapot	50.00	60.00	30.00	65.00
Casino teacup	8.00	10.00	5.00	12.00
Don beaker	25.00	30.00	15.00	35.00
Don beaker, one handle	25.00	30.00	15.00	35.00
Don mug, one handles	10.00	12.00	6.00	15.00
Don mug, two handles	10.00	12.00	6.00	15.00
Hug-a-mug, one handle	10.00	12.00	6.00	15.00
Hug-a-mug, two handles	10.00	12.00	6.00	15.00
Lamp	50.00	60.00	30.00	65.00
Lid of hot water plate	50.00	60.00	30.00	65.00
Malvern beaker	15.00	20.00	10.00	25.00
Money ball	10.00	12.00	6.00	15.00
Picture plaque, small	20.00	25.00	12.50	30.00
Stratford straight beaker	15.00	20.00	10.00	25.00
Stratford teacup	8.00	10.00	5.00	12.00
Savings book	15.00	20.00	10.00	25.00

Building Sand Castles (HW138)

Sailing Boats (HW138R)

Bunnykins Build a Snowman (PN198)

BUNNYKINS BUILD A SNOWMAN

Design No.: PN198
Designer: Frank Endersby
Issued: 1998 - 1998
Series: ICC Plate of the Year, Number 2

Shape	U.S. $	Can. $	U.K. £	Aust. $
Plate, 8"	25.00	30.00	15.00	35.00

Divider Dish decorated with Frank Endersby scenes; *Building a Snowman* (59), *Sleding*, Style Two (60) and *Resting in Wheelbarrow (57)*

BUNNYKINS CELEBRATES YOUR CHRISTENING – Walter Hayward

BUNNYKINS CELEBRATE YOUR CHRISTENING
Style One, First Version

Design No.: SF139 Bunnykins celebrate your Christening
Designer: Walter Hayward
Issued: 1984 - 1989

Shape	U.S. $	Can. $	U.K. £	Aust. $
Money ball	15.00	20.00	10.00	25.00
Plate, 8"	15.00	20.00	10.00	25.00

Bunnykins Celebrate Your Christening
First Version (SF139)

Bunnykins Celebrate Your Christening
Second Version (HW142)

Style One, Second Version

Design No.: Front — HW142 Bunnykins celebrate your Christening
Reverse — HW142R Christening inscription
Designer: Walter Hayward
Issued: 1984 - 1990

Shape	U.S. $	Can. $	U.K. £	Aust. $
Hug-a-mug, one handle	10.00	12.00	6.00	15.00
Hug-a-mug, two handles	10.00	12.00	6.00	15.00
Money ball	10.00	12.00	6.00	15.00
Savings book	15.00	20.00	10.00	25.00

Christening Inscription (HW142R)

BUNNYKINS CELEBRATES YOUR CHRISTENING – Colin Twinn

Bunnykins Celebrate Your Christening
First Variation (CT38)

BUNNYKINS CELEBRATE YOUR CHRISTENING
Style Two, First Variation, Large Size

Design No.: Front — CT38 Bunnykins Celebrate your Christening
Reverse no. one — without rhyme
Reverse no. two — CT65 with rhyme
Designer: Colin Twinn
Issued: 1990 - 1993
Rhyme: "Today, as your family welcomes you,
To bless who you are and all you will do,
The Bunnykins join in your bright celebration.
And bring you a message of jubilation
For, on this your day, we all wish for you
A lifetime of love and much happiness too."

Shape	U.S. $	Can. $	U.K. £	Aust. $
Plate, 8"	15.00	20.00	10.00	25.00

Christening Rhyme (CT65)

Bunnykins Celebrate Your Christening
Second Variation (CT41)

Style Two, Second Variation, Small Size

Design No.: Front — CT41 Bunnykins celebrate your Christening
Reverse — CT42 Christening inscription
Designer: Colin Twinn
Issued: 1991 - 1993

Shape	U.S. $	Can. $	U.K. £	Aust. $
Hug-a-mug, one handle	10.00	12.00	6.00	15.00
Hug-a-mug, two handles	10.00	12.00	6.00	15.00
Money ball	10.00	12.00	6.00	15.00

Christening Inscription (CT42)

BABY IN CRIB WITH FATHER LOOKING ON
Style Three, First Variation

Design No.: Front — CT76 Baby in Crib with Father Looking On
Reverse — CT77 Rhyme
Designer: Colin Twinn
Issued: 1993 to the present
Rhyme: "Today, as your family welcomes you,
To bless who you are and all you will do,
The Bunnykins join in your bright celebration.
And bring you a message of jubilation
For, on this your day, we all wish for you
A lifetime of love and much happiness too."

Shape	U.S. $	Can. $	U.K. £	Aust. $
Plate, 8"	20.00	25.00	12.00	30.00

Bunnykins celebrate your Christening

Baby in Crib with Father Looking On (CT76)

Baby in Crib (CT78)

BABY IN CRIB
Style Three, Second Variation

Design No.: Front — CT78 Baby in Crib
Reverse — CT79 Christening inscription
Designer: Colin Twinn
Issued: 1993 to the present

Shape	U.S. $	Can. $	U.K. £	Aust. $
Hug-a-mug, one handle	15.00	20.00	10.00	25.00
Hug-a-mug, two handles	15.00	20.00	10.00	25.00
Money ball	25.00	30.00	15.00	35.00

Bunnykins celebrate
your Christening

Christening Inscription (CT79)

BUNNYKINS COLLECTORS CLUB, AUSTRALIA

Member of Bunnykins Club/Television Time (SF112)

MEMBER OF BUNNYKINS CLUB BUNNYKINS BUNNIES ARE CHILDREN LIKE YOU

These plates, with the Member of Bunnykins Club inscription, were made exclusively for the Bunnykins club members in Australia. Other designs with this inscription may exist.

Design No.: SF18 — *Bathtime*, Style One
SF112 — *Television Time*
SF113 — *Camp Site*
SF130 — *Bedtime Story*
SF131 — *Home Decorating*
SF132 — *Space Rocket Launch*
SF133 — *Flying Kites*
SF134 — *Toppling the Fruit Cart*
SF135 — *Family in the Garden*

Issued: 1979 - 1985

Shape	Design	U.S. $	Can. $	U.K. £	Aust. $
Plate, 6 ½"	Various	200.00	250.00	125.00	275.00

BUNNYKINS HELP SANTA

Design No.: PN175
Designer: Frank Endersby
Issued: 1997 - 1997
Series: ICC Plate of the Year, Number 1
Backstamp: ICC plus Bunnykins and Frank Endersby facsimile signature

Shape	U.S. $	Can. $	U.K. £	Aust. $
Plate, 8"	25.00	30.00	15.00	35.00

Bunnykins Help Santa (PN175)

BUNNYKINS TEACHING CLOCKS
Walter Hayward, Colin Twinn, Frank Endersby

BUNNYKINS TEACHING CLOCK
Classroom Scene, Style One

Design No.:	Front — SF138 Classroom Scene
	Reverse — Inscription
Designer:	Walter Hayward
Issued:	1983 to the present
Rhyme:	"Learning can be hours of fun For Bunnykins and everyone To tell the time we learn today As we see the clock tick minutes away."

Shape	U.S. $	Can. $	U.K. £	Aust. $
Teaching clock	60.00	70.00	35.00	75.00

Bunnykins Teaching Clock
Classroom Scene, Style One (SF138)

Note: Two second hand varieties exist; long and short.

BUNNYKINS TEACHING CLOCK,
Classroom Scene, Style Two, First Version

Design No.:	Front — CT36 Classroom Scene
Designer:	Colin Twinn
Issued:	1991 - 1993
Rhyme:	"Learning can be hours of fun For Bunnykins and everyone To tell the time we learn today As we see the clock tick minutes away."

Shape	U.S. $	Can. $	U.K. £	Aust. $
Teaching clock	30.00	45.00	20.00	50.00

Bunnykins Teaching Clock
Classroom Scene, Style Two (CT36)

Note: 1. This clock has a short second hand.
2. For information on others shapes with this design see page 46.

Bunnykins Teaching Clock
Four Individual Scenes

BUNNYKINS TEACHING CLOCK
Four Individual Scenes

Design No.: None — Four individual scenes
Designer: Frank Endersby
Issued: 1996 to the present

Shape	U.S. $	Can. $	U.K. £	Aust. $
Teaching clock	60.00	70.00	30.00	75.00

Note: This clock has a short second hand.

CAMP SITE

Design No.: SF113
Designer: Walter Hayward
Issued: 1959 - by 1998

Shape	U.S. $	Can. $	U.K. £	Aust. $
Baby plate, round, small	20.00	25.00	12.50	30.00
Cake stand	150.00	180.00	90.00	190.00
Casino saucer	8.00	10.00	5.00	12.00
Cereal / oatmeal bowl	15.00	20.00	10.00	25.00
Jaffa fruit saucer (plain)	15.00	20.00	10.00	25.00
Hot water plate	75.00	90.00	45.00	95.00
Picture plaque, large	20.00	25.00	12.50	30.00
Plate, 6 ½"	15.00	20.00	10.00	25.00
Plate, 7 ½"	15.00	20.00	10.00	25.00
Plate, 8"	15.00	20.00	10.00	25.00

Camp Site (SF113)

CAMPING THEME – Frank Endersby

CAMPING

Design No.: 34 Camping
Designer: Frank Endersby
Issued: 1996 to the present

Shape	U.S. $	Can. $	U.K. £	Aust. $
Baby plate, round, small	25.00	30.00	15.00	35.00
Cereal / oatmeal bowl	15.00	20.00	10.00	25.00
Plate, 6 ½"	15.00	20.00	10.00	25.00
Plate, 8"	15.00	20.00	10.00	25.00

Camping (34)

Campfire (35)

CAMPFIRE / ASLEEP IN A SLEEPING BAG

Design No.: Front — 35 Campfire
Reverse — 36 Asleep in a Sleeping Bag
Designer: Frank Endersby
Issued: 1996 to the present

Shape	U.S. $	Can. $	U.K. £	Aust. $
Hug-a-mug, one handle	15.00	20.00	10.00	25.00
Hug-a-mug, two handles	15.00	20.00	10.00	25.00
Stratford teacup	8.00	10.00	5.00	12.00

Asleep in a Sleeping Bag (36)

CAROL SINGER BUNNYKINS CHRISTMAS TREE ORNAMENT

Design No.:	Front – CT70
	Reverse – CT71
Designer:	Colin Twinn
Issued:	1992 - 1992
Series:	Christmas Tree Ornaments

Shape	U.S. $	Can. $	U.K. £	Aust. $
Christmas tree ornament	25.00	30.00	15.00	35.00

Note: For other Christmas ornaments in this series see page 44, 80, 143 and 165.

Carol Singer Bunnykins (CT70)

Christmas 1992 (CT71)

CARVING THE CHICKEN

Design No.:	LFc
Designer:	Barbara Vernon
Issued:	By 1937 - by 1952
Combined with:	*Medicine Time,* CF1

Shape	U.S. $	Can. $	U.K. £	Aust. $
Baby plate, oval, small	400.00	475.00	225.00	500.00
Bread and butter plate	500.00	600.00	285.00	625.00
Casino teapot, 30s	450.00	550.00	260.00	575.00
Casino teapot, 36s	350.00	425.00	200.00	450.00
Plate, 7 ½"	225.00	275.00	125.00	300.00
Plate, 8 ½"	225.00	275.00	125.00	300.00
Porridge plate	400.00	475.00	225.00	500.00

Note: This design should appear with the Barbara Vernon facsimile signature.

Carving the Chicken (LFc)

CHICKEN PULLING A CART

Design No.: SF8
Designer: Barbara Vernon
Issued: By 1940 - by 1952
Combined with: *Cycling*, HW15R
Family at Breakfast, HW12
Family Going out on Washing Day, HW8
Family with Pram, HW15
Fixing Braces, HW3
Gardener with Wheelbarrow, HW9R
Going Shopping, SF10
Leapfrog, HW12R
Pillow Fight, Style One, SF7
Pulling on Trousers, HW2
Swinging, HW20
Washing Day, HW8R

Chicken Pulling A Cart (SF8)

Shape	U.S. $	Can. $	U.K. £	Aust. $
Baby plate, round, small				
with signature	50.00	60.00	30.00	65.00
without signature	30.00	35.00	17.50	40.00
Casino jug, 24s				
with signature	400.00	475.00	225.00	500.00
without signature	350.00	425.00	200.00	450.00
Casino jug, 30s	300.00	350.00	175.00	375.00
Casino jug, 36s				
with signature	300.00	350.00	175.00	375.00
without signature	250.00	300.00	150.00	325.00
Casino jug, 42s				
with signature	250.00	300.00	150.00	325.00
without signature	200.00	250.00	115.00	275.00
Casino saucer				
with signature	75.00	90.00	45.00	95.00
without signature	50.00	60.00	30.00	65.00
Casino sugar bowl, 30s				
with signature	175.00	200.00	100.00	225.00
without signature	125.00	150.00	75.00	175.00
Casino teapot, 24s				
with signature	375.00	450.00	210.00	475.00
without signature	300.00	350.00	175.00	375.00
Casino teapot, 30s				
with signature	325.00	400.00	185.00	425.00
without signature	250.00	300.00	150.00	325.00

Shape	U.S. $	Can. $	U.K. £	Aust. $
Cereal / oatmeal bowl				
with signature	35.00	45.00	20.00	50.00
without signature	25.00	30.00	15.00	35.00
Don beaker				
with signature	65.00	80.00	40.00	85.00
without signature	35.00	45.00	20.00	50.00
Don Beaker, one handle				
with signature	65.00	80.00	40.00	85.00
without signature	35.00	45.00	20.00	50.00
Jaffa fruit saucer				
plain rim	50.00	60.00	30.00	65.00
wavy rim	75.00	90.00	45.00	95.00
Hot water plate				
with signature	125.00	150.00	75.00	160.00
without signature	100.00	125.00	60.00	135.00
Plate, 6 ½"				
with signature	30.00	35.00	17.50	40.00
without signature	20.00	25.00	12.00	30.00
Plate, 7 ½"				
with signature	65.00	80.00	40.00	85.00
without signature	25.00	30.00	15.00	35.00
Plate, 8 ½"				
with signature	75.00	90.00	45.00	95.00
without signature	25.00	30.00	15.00	35.00
FINE WHITE CHINA				
Saucer	300.00	350.00	175.00	375.00
Teacup	300.00	350.00	175.00	375.00

Note: This scene was re-issued on an 8" plate in 1984 with the Bunnykins Golden Jubilee backstamp see page 188.

Christmas Morn

Christmas Morn backstamp

Christmas Party (LF9)

CHRISTMAS MORN
CHRISTMAS TREE ORNAMENT

This Christmas tree ornament has a rabbit-shaped rim. It was commissioned by Royal Doulton U.S.A. and made in the U.S.A.

Design No.: None
Designer: Frank Endersby
Issued: 1996 - 1996
Backstamp: "Christmas Morn" Christmas 1996 Royal Doulton "Bunnykins" ® © 1996 Royal Doulton made in U.S.A.
Series: Christmas Tree Ornaments

Shape	U.S. $	Can. $	U.K. £	Aust. $
Christmas tree ornament	25.00	30.00	15.00	35.00

Note: For other Christmas ornaments in this series see pages 42, 80, 143 and 165.

CHRISTMAS PARTY

Design No.: LF9
Designer: Barbara Vernon
Issued: By 1940 - 1967

Shape	U.S. $	Can. $	U.K. £	Aust. $
Baby plate, oval, large				
with signature	350.00	425.00	200.00	450.00
without signature	300.00	350.00	175.00	375.00
Baby plate, round, large				
with silver rim	450.00	550.00	260.00	575.00
with signature	250.00	300.00	150.00	325.00
without signature	200.00	250.00	115.00	275.00
Bread and butter plate				
with signature	300.00	350.00	175.00	375.00
without signature	275.00	325.00	160.00	350.00
Plate, 8 ½"				
with signature	100.00	125.00	60.00	135.00
without signature	75.00	90.00	45.00	95.00
Porridge plate				
with signature	125.00	150.00	75.00	160.00
without signature	100.00	125.00	60.00	135.00

CHRISTMAS TREE

Design No.: LF16
Designer: Walter Hayward
Issued: 1954 - 1967

Shape	U.S. $	Can. $	U.K. £	Aust. $
Baby plate, oval, large				
with signature	200.00	250.00	115.00	275.00
without signature	150.00	180.00	90.00	190.00
Baby plate, round, large				
with signature	100.00	125.00	60.00	135.00
without signature	75.00	90.00	45.00	95.00
Bread and butter plate				
with signature	250.00	300.00	150.00	325.00
without signature	200.00	250.00	115.00	275.00
Plate, 7"				
with signature	100.00	125.00	60.00	135.00
without signature	75.00	90.00	45.00	95.00
Plate, 8 ½"				
with signature	150.00	180.00	90.00	190.00
without signature	100.00	125.00	60.00	135.00
Porridge plate				
with signature	110.00	135.00	65.00	145.00
without signature	85.00	100.00	50.00	110.00

Christmas Tree (LF16)

Christmas Morn Christmas ornament, 1996

For illustration of
this design see
Bunnykins Teaching Clock
page 39.

CLASSROOM SCENE
Style Two, First Version

Design No.: CT36 Classroom Scene
Designer: Colin Twinn
Issued: 1991 - 1993
Combined with: *Bunny with Mirror,* CT35

Shape	U.S. $	Can. $	U.K. £	Aust. $
Albion jug, 1 pint	100.00	125.00	60.00	135.00
Plate, 6"	15.00	20.00	10.00	25.00
Plate, 8"	15.00	20.00	10.00	25.00

Note: For information on the Bunnykins Teaching Clock with this design see page 39.

CLASSROOM SCENE
Style Two, Second Version

Design No.: CT16 Classroom
Designer: Colin Twinn
Issued: 1990 - 1993
Combined with: *Bunny on Trike,* CT23
Bunny with Mirror, CT35
Picking Daisies, CT4

Shape	U.S. $	Can. $	U.K. £	Aust. $
Albion cream jug	35.00	45.00	20.00	50.00
Albion jug, ½ pint	85.00	100.00	50.00	110.00
Albion jug, 1 pint	100.00	125.00	60.00	135.00
Albion teapot	50.00	60.00	30.00	65.00
Baby plate, round small	20.00	25.00	12.50	30.00
Cake stand	150.00	180.00	90.00	190.00
Cereal / oatmeal bowl	15.00	20.00	10.00	25.00
Jaffa fruit saucer (plain)	15.00	20.00	10.00	25.00
Stratford straight beaker	15.00	20.00	10.00	25.00

Classroom Scene, Style Two (CT16)

CONDUCTING THE ORCHESTRA

Design No.: LF5
Designer: Barbara Vernon
Issued: By 1940 - by 1952
Combined with: *Frightening Spider*, SF4

Shape	U.S. $	Can. $	U.K. £	Aust. $
Baby plate, oval, large				
with signature	200.00	250.00	115.00	275.00
without signature	150.00	180.00	90.00	190.00
Baby plate, round, large				
with silver rim			Rare	
with signature	100.00	125.00	60.00	135.00
without signature	75.00	90.00	45.00	95.00
Bread and butter plate				
with signature	250.00	300.00	150.00	325.00
without signature	200.00	250.00	115.00	275.00
Casino jug, 24s				
with signature	400.00	475.00	225.00	500.00
without signature	350.00	425.00	200.00	450.00
Hot water plate				
with signature	125.00	150.00	75.00	160.00
without signature	100.00	125.00	60.00	135.00
Plate, 8 ½"				
with signature	75.00	90.00	45.00	95.00
without signature	25.00	30.00	15.00	35.00
Porridge plate				
with signature	110.00	135.00	65.00	145.00
without signature	85.00	100.00	50.00	110.00

Conducting the Orchestra (LF5)

CONVALESCING

Design No.: SF5
Designer: Barbara Vernon
Issued: By 1940 - by 1952
Combined with: *Asleep in the Open Air*, HW10
Baking, SF19
Leapfrog, HW12R
Soldiers Marching to the Music, HW18
Washing in the Open Air, HW10R

Convalescing (SF5)

Shape	U.S. $	Can. $	U.K. £	Aust. $
Baby plate, round, small	50.00	60.00	30.00	65.00
Bread and butter plate	250.00	300.00	150.00	325.00
Casino jug, 42s	250.00	300.00	150.00	325.00
Casino saucer	75.00	90.00	45.00	95.00
Casino teapot, 24s	375.00	450.00	210.00	475.00
Cereal / oatmeal bowl	35.00	45.00	20.00	50.00
Jaffa fruit saucer				
plain rim	50.00	60.00	30.00	65.00
wavy rim	75.00	90.00	45.00	95.00
Hot water plate	125.00	150.00	75.00	160.00
Plate, 6 ½"	30.00	35.00	17.50	40.00
Plate, 7 ½"	65.00	80.00	40.00	85.00

Note: This design should appear with the Barbara Vernon facsimile signature.

Cowboys and Indians (HW140)

Cowboy on Rocking Horse (HW140R)

COWBOYS AND INDIANS / COWBOY ON ROCKING HORSE

Design No.: Front — HW140 Cowboys and Indians
Reverse — HW140R Cowboy on Rocking Horse
Designer: Walter Hayward
Issued: 1967 - by 1998
Combined with: *Hobby Horse*, Style Two, EC121
**Ice Cream on the Beach*, HW136R
**Peashooter*, HW118R
**Punch and Judy Show*, HW136
**Roller Skating Arm in Arm*, HW137R
**Trying on Hats*, HW28R

Shape	U.S. $	Can. $	U.K. £	Aust. $
Albion cream jug	35.00	45.00	20.00	50.00
Albion teapot	50.00	60.00	30.00	65.00
Casino teacup	8.00	10.00	5.00	12.00
Divider dish	50.00	60.00	30.00	65.00
Don beaker	25.00	30.00	15.00	35.00
Don beaker, one handle	25.00	30.00	15.00	35.00
Don mug, one handle	10.00	12.00	6.00	15.00
Don mug, two handles	10.00	12.00	6.00	15.00
Egg box				
small	175.00	200.00	100.00	225.00
medium	200.00	250.00	115.00	275.00
large	225.00	275.00	125.00	300.00
Hug-a-mug, one handle	10.00	12.00	6.00	15.00
Hug-a-mug, two handles	10.00	12.00	6.00	15.00
Lamp	50.00	60.00	30.00	65.00
Lid of hot water plate	50.00	60.00	30.00	65.00
Malvern beaker	15.00	20.00	10.00	25.00
Money ball	10.00	12.00	6.00	15.00
Picture plaque, small	20.00	25.00	12.00	30.00
Savings book	15.00	20.00	10.00	25.00
Stratford teacup	8.00	10.00	5.00	12.00

* Indicates scene on divider dish.

CRICKET GAME

Design No.: LF12
Designer: Walter Hayward after Barbara Vernon
Issued: 1952 - 1967

Shape	U.S. $	Can. $	U.K. £	Aust. $
Baby plate, oval, large				
with signature	150.00	180.00	90.00	190.00
without signature	100.00	125.00	60.00	135.00
Baby plate, oval, small				
with signature	150.00	180.00	90.00	190.00
without signature	100.00	125.00	60.00	135.00
Baby plate, round large				
with signature	75.00	90.00	45.00	95.00
without signature	50.00	60.00	30.00	65.00
Bread and butter plate				
with signature	250.00	300.00	150.00	325.00
without signature	200.00	250.00	115.00	275.00
Plate, 8 ½"				
with signature	30.00	35.00	17.50	40.00
without signature	15.00	20.00	12.00	25.00
Porridge plate				
with signature	110.00	135.00	65.00	145.00
without signature	85.00	100.00	50.00	110.00

Cricket Game (LF12)

CUDDLING UNDER A MUSHROOM

Design No.: HW4
Designer: Barbara Vernon
Issued: By 1937 - by 1952
Combined with: *Dunce*, HW1R
Footballer, HW13R
Golfer, HW4R
Netting a Cricket, HW6

Shape	U.S. $	Can. $	U.K. £	Aust. $
Casino sugar bowl, 30s				
with signature	200.00	250.00	115.00	275.00
without signature	125.00	150.00	75.00	160.00
Casino sugar bowl, 36s				
with signature	175.00	200.00	100.00	225.00
without signature	100.00	125.00	60.00	135.00
Casino teacup				
with signature	75.00	90.00	45.00	95.00
without signature	50.00	60.00	30.00	65.00
Don beaker				
with signature	150.00	180.00	90.00	190.00
without signature	100.00	125.00	60.00	135.00
Don beaker, one handle				
with signature	150.00	180.00	90.00	190.00
without signature	100.00	125.00	60.00	135.00
Don mug, one handle				
with signature	75.00	90.00	45.00	95.00
without signature	35.00	45.00	20.00	50.00
Don mug, two handles				
with signature	75.00	90.00	45.00	95.00
without signature	35.00	45.00	20.00	50.00
Lid of hot water plate				
with signature	175.00	200.00	100.00	225.00
without signature	125.00	150.00	75.00	160.00
FINE WHITE CHINA				
Saucer	300.00	350.00	175.00	375.00
Teacup	300.00	350.00	175.00	375.00

Cuddling under a Mushroom (HW4)

Cycling (HW15R)

CYCLING

Design No.:	HW15R
Designer:	Barbara Vernon
Issued:	By 1937 - by 1967
Combined with:	*Embracing at a Window*, HW5
	Family at Breakfast, HW12
	Family Going Out on Washing Day, HW8
	Family with Pram, Style One, HW15
	Feeding the Baby, HW13
	Fixing Braces, HW3
	Golfer, HW4R
	Lambeth Walk, First and Second Version, HW16
	Kissing Under Mistletoe, HW11R
	Pressing Trousers, HW14
	Proposal, HW11
	Reading the Times, HW2R
	Trumpeter, EC5

Shape	U.S. $	Can. $	U.K. £	Aust. $
Beaker cover				
with signature	200.00	250.00	115.00	275.00
without signature	150.00	180.00	90.00	190.00
Casino jug, 42s				
with signature	275.00	325.00	160.00	350.00
without signature	200.00	250.00	115.00	275.00
Casino sugar bowl, 30s				
with signature	200.00	250.00	115.00	275.00
without signature	175.00	200.00	100.00	225.00
Casino sugar bowl, 36s				
with signature	150.00	180.00	90.00	190.00
without signature	125.00	150.00	75.00	160.00
Casino teacup				
with signature	75.00	90.00	45.00	95.00
without signature	50.00	60.00	30.00	65.00
Casino teapot, 30s				
with signature	300.00	350.00	175.00	375.00
without signature	225.00	275.00	125.00	300.00
Cup / mug, large				
with signature	500.00	600.00	285.00	625.00
without signature	450.00	550.00	260.00	575.00
Don beaker, one handle				
with signature	150.00	180.00	90.00	190.00
without signature	100.00	125.00	60.00	135.00
Don mug, one handle				
with signature	75.00	90.00	45.00	95.00
without signature	35.00	45.00	20.00	50.00
Don mug, two handles				
with signature	75.00	90.00	45.00	95.00
without signature	35.00	45.00	20.00	50.00
Jam pot	1,500.00	1,800.00	850.00	1,900.00
Lid of hot water plate				
with signature	175.00	200.00	100.00	225.00
without signature	125.00	150.00	75.00	160.00
FINE WHITE CHINA				
Rex mug, small	750.00	900.00	425.00	950.00
Teacup	500.00	600.00	300.00	625.00

Note: Rex mugs are found combining *Cycling* (HW15R) with any of the following: *Family at Breakfast*, (HW12), *Pressing Trousers* (HW14), or *Proposal* (HW11).

CYCLING THEME – Frank Endersby

CYCLE RIDE

Design No.: 46 Cycle Ride
Designer: Frank Endersby
Issued: 1995 - 2003

Shape	U.S. $	Can. $	U.K. £	Aust. $
Baby plate, round, small	20.00	25.00	12.50	30.00
Jaffa fruit saucer	15.00	20.00	10.00	25.00
Plate, 6 ½"	15.00	20.00	10.00	25.00
Plate, 8"	15.00	20.00	10.00	25.00

Cycle Ride (46)

Resting (47)

RESTING / CLEANING BIKE

Design No.: Front – 47 Resting, Style Three
Reverse – 48 Cleaning Bike
Designer: Frank Endersby
Issued: 1995 - 2003

Shape	U.S. $	Can. $	U.K. £	Aust. $
Hug-a-mug, one handle	10.00	12.00	6.00	15.00
Hug-a-mug, two handles	10.00	12.00	6.00	15.00

Cleaning Bike (48)

DAISY CHAINS / SMELLING FLOWERS

Daisy Chains (HW25)

Smelling Flowers (HW25R)

Design No.: Front — HW25 Daisy Chains
Reverse — HW25R Smelling Flowers
Designer: Walter Hayward
Issued: 1954 - by 1998

Combined with: *Hikers*, EC124
Holding Hat and Coat, EC4
Ice Cream Vendor, HW23
Playing with Cup and Spoon, EC6
Toast for Tea Today, SF23

Shape	U.S. $	Can. $	U.K. £	Aust. $
Albion cream jug	35.00	45.00	20.00	50.00
Albion jug, ½ pint	85.00	100.00	50.00	110.00
Albion jug, 1 pint	100.00	125.00	60.00	135.00
Albion teapot	50.00	60.00	30.00	65.00
Casino jug, 24s				
with signature	350.00	425.00	200.00	450.00
without signature	300.00	350.00	175.00	375.00
Casino jug, 36s				
with signature	300.00	350.00	175.00	375.00
without signature	250.00	300.00	150.00	325.00
Casino jug, 42s				
with signature	150.00	180.00	90.00	190.00
without signature	100.00	125.00	60.00	135.00
Casino saucer				
with signature	15.00	20.00	12.00	25.00
without signature	8.00	10.00	5.00	12.00
Casino teacup				
with signature	15.00	20.00	12.00	25.00
without signature	8.00	10.00	5.00	12.00
Casino teapot, 30s				
with signature	200.00	250.00	115.00	275.00
without signature	150.00	180.00	90.00	190.00
Casino teapot, 36s				
with signature	200.00	250.00	115.00	275.00
without signature	150.00	180.00	90.00	190.00
Don beaker				
with signature	50.00	60.00	30.00	65.00
without signature	25.00	30.00	15.00	35.00
Don beaker, one handle				
with signature	50.00	60.00	30.00	65.00
without signature	25.00	30.00	15.00	35.00

Shape	U.S. $	Can. $	U.K. £	Aust. $
Don mug, one handle				
with signature	40.00	50.00	25.00	55.00
without signature	10.00	12.00	6.00	15.00
Don mug, two handles				
with signature	40.00	50.00	25.00	55.00
without signature	10.00	12.00	6.00	15.00
Egg box				
small	175.00	200.00	100.00	225.00
medium	200.00	250.00	115.00	275.00
large	225.00	275.00	125.00	300.00
Hug-a-mug, one handle	10.00	12.00	6.00	15.00
Hug-a-mug, two handles	10.00	12.00	6.00	15.00
Jaffa fruit saucer (plain)	15.00	20.00	10.00	25.00
Lamp	50.00	60.00	30.00	65.00
Lid of hot water plate				
with signature	75.00	90.00	45.00	95.00
without signature	50.00	60.00	30.00	65.00
Malvern beaker	15.00	20.00	10.00	25.00
Money ball	10.00	12.00	6.00	15.00
Picture plaque, small	20.00	25.00	12.00	30.00
Picture plaque, large	20.00	25.00	12.00	30.00
Plate, 6 ½"				
with signature	25.00	30.00	15.00	35.00
without signature	15.00	20.00	10.00	25.00
Savings book	15.00	20.00	12.00	25.00
Stratford straight beaker	15.00	20.00	12.00	25.00
Stratford teacup	8.00	10.00	5.00	12.00

Note: **1.** A Hug-a-mug (two handles) was issued for the U.S. Special Event Tour in 1993, see page 192.
2. A Casino jug combines *Daisy Chains*, (HW25) with *Ice Cream Vendor*, (HW23).

DANCING IN THE MOONLIGHT
First Version

Design No.: LFb
Designer: Barbara Vernon
Issued: 1937 - by 1952

Shape	U.S. $	Can. $	U.K. £	Aust. $
Baby plate, round, large				
with signature	450.00	550.00	260.00	575.00
without signature	400.00	475.00	225.00	500.00
Bread and butter plate				
with signature	550.00	650.00	315.00	675.00
without signature	450.00	550.00	260.00	575.00
Plate, 8 ½"				
with signature	225.00	275.00	125.00	300.00
without signature	175.00	200.00	100.00	225.00
Porridge plate				
with signature	300.00	350.00	175.00	375.00
without signature	250.00	300.00	150.00	325.00

Dancing in the Moonlight, First Version (LFb)

DANCING IN THE MOONLIGHT
Second Version, Second Variation, Small Size

Design No.: CT92
Designer: Justin Clarke based on a design by Barbara Vernon
Issued: Circa 1994
Combined with: *Bunny with Cake Plate*, (CT88)

Shape	U.S. $	Can. $	U.K. £	Aust. $
Cereal / oatmeal bowl	15.00	20.00	10.00	25.00
Don beaker, one handle	10.00	12.00	6.00	15.00
Don mug, one handle	10.00	12.00	6.00	15.00
Malvern beaker	10.00	12.00	6.00	15.00

Note: See also Bunnykins 60th Anniversary page 190.

Dancing Round the Barrel Organ (HW139)

Skipping Game (HW139R)

DANCING ROUND THE BARREL ORGAN / SKIPPING GAME

Design No.:	Front — HW139 Dancing Round the Barrel Organ Reverse — HW139R Skipping Game
Designer:	Walter Hayward
Issued:	1967 - by 1998
Combined with:	**Hiker Resting with Ice Cream*, HW23R **Ice Cream Vendor*, HW23 **Peashooter*, HW118R **Sailing Boats*, HW138R

Shape	U.S. $	Can. $	U.K. £	Aust. $
Albion cream jug	35.00	45.00	20.00	50.00
Albion jug, ½ pint	85.00	100.00	50.00	110.00
Albion jug, 1 pint	100.00	125.00	60.00	135.00
Albion teapot	50.00	65.00	30.00	70.00
Casino jug, 36s	125.00	150.00	75.00	160.00
Casino saucer	8.00	10.00	5.00	12.00
Casino teacup	8.00	10.00	5.00	12.00
Divider dish	50.00	60.00	30.00	65.00
Don beaker	25.00	30.00	15.00	35.00
Don beaker, one handle	25.00	30.00	15.00	35.00
Don mug, one handle	10.00	12.00	6.00	15.00
Don mug, two handles	10.00	12.00	6.00	15.00
Egg box				
small	175.00	200.00	100.00	225.00
medium	200.00	250.00	115.00	275.00
large	225.00	275.00	125.00	300.00
Hug-a-mug, one handle	10.00	12.00	6.00	15.00
Hug-a-mug, two handles	10.00	12.00	6.00	15.00
Jaffa fruit saucer (plain)	15.00	20.00	12.00	25.00
Lamp	50.00	60.00	30.00	65.00
Malvern beaker	15.00	20.00	10.00	25.00
Money ball	10.00	12.00	6.00	15.00
Picture plaque, small	20.00	25.00	12.50	30.00
Plate, 6 ½"	15.00	20.00	10.00	25.00
Savings book	15.00	20.00	10.00	25.00
Stratford straight beaker	15.00	20.00	10.00	25.00
Stratford teacup	8.00	10.00	5.00	12.00

* Indicates scene on divider dish.

Note: A savings book was issued for the U.S. Special Events Tour 1994. The front features *Skipping Game* (HW139R) and the reverse is inscribed 'To' and 'From' for the customer to complete and '*US Special Events Tour 1994*,' see page 192.

DINNER THEME – Frank Endersby

PREPARING DINNER

Design No.: 43 — Preparing Dinner
Designer: Frank Endersby
Issued: 1995 - 2003

Shape	U.S. $	Can. $	U.K. £	Aust. $
Baby plate, round, small	20.00	25.00	12.50	30.00
Jaffa fruit saucer	15.00	20.00	10.00	25.00
Plate, 6 ½"	15.00	20.00	10.00	25.00
Plate, 8"	15.00	20.00	10.00	25.00

Preparing Dinner (43)

Serving Dinner (44)

SERVING DINNER / CARRYING PLATES

Design No.: Front — 44 Serving Dinner
Reverse — 45 Carrying Plates
Designer: Frank Endersby
Issued: 1995 - 2003
Combined with: **Sitting on Suitcase*, (51)

Shape	U.S. $	Can. $	U.K. £	Aust. $
Hug-a-mug, one handle	10.00	12.00	6.00	15.00
Hug-a-mug, two handles	10.00	12.00	6.00	15.00
Divider dish	50.00	60.00	30.00	65.00
Stratford teacup	8.00	10.00	5.00	12.00

* Indicates scenes on divider dish.

Carrying Plates (45)

Disturbing Sleeping Father (HW118)

Pea Shooter (HW118R)

DISTURBING SLEEPING FATHER / PEA SHOOTER

Design No.:	Front — HW118 Disturbing Sleeping Father Reverse — HW118R Pea Shooter
Designer:	Walter Hayward
Issued:	1959 - by 1998
Combined with:	*Dancing with Doll*, HW115R **Nipped by a Crab,* HW21R **Sledging*, Style One, HW141 **Snowball Fight*, HW141R *Wheelbarrow Race,* Style One, (HW22)

Shape	U.S. $	Can. $	U.K. £	Aust. $
Albion cream jug	35.00	45.00	20.00	50.00
Albion jug, ½ pint	85.00	100.00	50.00	110.00
Albion jug, 1 pint	100.00	125.00	60.00	135.00
Albion teapot	50.00	60.00	30.00	65.00
Casino jug, 36s	125.00	150.00	75.00	160.00
Casino jug, 42s	100.00	125.00	60.00	135.00
Casino saucer	8.00	10.00	5.00	12.00
Casino teacup	8.00	10.00	5.00	12.00
Divider dish	50.00	60.00	30.00	65.00
Don beaker	25.00	30.00	15.00	35.00
Don beaker, one handle	25.00	30.00	15.00	35.00
Don mug, one handle	10.00	12.00	6.00	15.00
Don mug, two handles	10.00	12.00	6.00	15.00
Egg box				
small	175.00	200.00	100.00	225.00
medium	200.00	250.00	115.00	275.00
large	225.00	275.00	125.00	300.00
Hug-a-mug, one handle	10.00	12.00	6.00	15.00
Hug-a-mug, two handles	10.00	12.00	6.00	15.00
Jaffa fruit saucer (plain)	15.00	20.00	10.00	25.00
Lamp	50.00	60.00	30.00	65.00
Lid of hot water plate	50.00	60.00	30.00	65.00
Malvern beaker	15.00	20.00	10.00	25.00
Money ball	10.00	12.00	6.00	15.00
Picture plaque, small	20.00	25.00	12.50	30.00
Plate, 6 ½"	15.00	20.00	10.00	25.00
Stratford straight beaker	15.00	20.00	10.00	25.00
Stratford teacup	8.00	10.00	5.00	12.00

* Indicates scene on divider dish.

Note: An Albion teapot combines *Pea Shooter* (HW118R) with *Wheelbarrow Race*, Style One (HW22).

DODGEM CARS

Design No.: LF4
Designer: Barbara Vernon
Issued: By 1940 - by 1952

Shape	U.S. $	Can. $	U.K. £	Aust. $
Baby plate, oval, large				
with signature	350.00	425.00	200.00	450.00
without signature	300.00	350.00	175.00	375.00
Baby plate, round large				
with signature	250.00	300.00	150.00	325.00
without signature	200.00	250.00	115.00	275.00
Bread and butter plate				
with signature	450.00	550.00	260.00	575.00
without signature	300.00	350.00	175.00	375.00
Cereal / oatmeal bowl				
with signature	100.00	125.00	60.00	135.00
without signature	90.00	110.00	50.00	120.00
Plate 8 ½"				
with signature	100.00	125.00	60.00	135.00
without signature	75.00	90.00	45.00	95.00
Porridge plate				
with signature	125.00	150.00	75.00	160.00
without signature	100.00	125.00	60.00	135.00

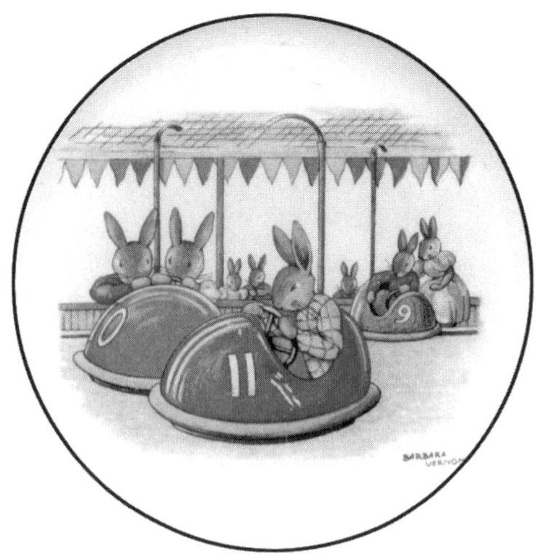

Dodgem Cars (LF4)

DOG CARRIAGE

Design No.: LFe
Designer: Barbara Vernon
Issued: By 1937 - by 1952
Combined with: *Carving the Chicken*, LFc

Shape	U.S. $	Can. $	U.K. £	Aust. $
Baby plate, oval, large				
with signature	500.00	600.00	285.00	625.00
without signature	450.00	550.00	260.00	575.00
Baby plate, round large				
with signature	400.00	475.00	225.00	500.00
without signature	350.00	425.00	200.00	450.00
Bread / butter plate, handles				
with signature	500.00	600.00	285.00	625.00
without signature	400.00	475.00	225.00	500.00
Casino teapot, 24s				
with signature	650.00	775.00	375.00	800.00
without signature	600.00	725.00	340.00	750.00
Cereal / oatmeal bowl				
with signature	300.00	350.00	175.00	375.00
without signature	250.00	300.00	150.00	325.00
Plate, 7 ½"				
with signature	375.00	450.00	210.00	475.00
without signature	325.00	400.00	185.00	425.00
Plate, 8 ½"				
with signature	225.00	275.00	125.00	300.00
without signature	175.00	200.00	100.00	225.00
Porridge plate				
with signature	400.00	475.00	225.00	500.00
without signature	350.00	425.00	200.00	450.00

Dog Carriage (LFe)

THE DOLL'S HOUSE / PLAYING WITH DOLL AND TEDDY

The Doll's House (HW120)

Playing with Doll and Teddy (HW120R)

Design No.:	Front — HW120 The Doll's House Reverse — HW120R Playing with Doll and Teddy
Designer:	Walter Hayward
Issued:	1959 - by 1998
Combined with:	**Dancing with Doll,* HW115R *Drummer and Bugler,* EC126 *Hikers,* EC124 **Nipped by a Crab,* HW21R *Reading,* EC122 **Serving Tea,* HW116R

Shape	U.S. $	Can. $	U.K. £	Aust. $
Albion cream jug	35.00	45.00	20.00	50.00
Albion jug, ½ pint	85.00	100.00	50.00	110.00
Albion teapot	50.00	60.00	30.00	65.00
Cake stand	150.00	180.00	90.00	190.00
Casino jug, 42s	100.00	125.00	60.00	135.00
Casino saucer	8.00	10.00	5.00	12.00
Casino teacup	8.00	10.00	5.00	12.00
Divider dish	50.00	60.00	30.00	65.00
Don beaker	25.00	30.00	15.00	35.00
Don beaker, one handle	25.00	30.00	15.00	35.00
Don mug, one handle	10.00	12.00	6.00	15.00
Don mug, two handles	10.00	12.00	6.00	15.00
Egg box				
small	175.00	200.00	100.00	225.00
medium	200.00	250.00	115.00	275.00
large	225.00	275.00	125.00	300.00
Hug-a-mug, one handle	10.00	12.00	6.00	15.00
Hug-a-mug, two handles	10.00	12.00	6.00	15.00
Jaffa fruit saucer (plain)	15.00	20.00	10.00	25.00
Lamp	50.00	60.00	30.00	65.00
Lid of hot water plate	50.00	60.00	30.00	65.00
Malvern beaker	15.00	20.00	10.00	25.00
Money ball	10.00	12.00	6.00	15.00
Picture plaque, small	20.00	25.00	12.50	30.00
Plate, 6 ½"	15.00	20.00	10.00	25.00
Savings book	15.00	20.00	10.00	25.00
Stratford straight beaker	15.00	20.00	10.00	25.00
Stratford teacup	8.00	10.00	5.00	12.00

* Indicates scene on divider dish.

DRESS MAKING / BUGLER WITH TOY DONKEY

Dress Making (HW26)

Bugler with Toy Donkey (HW26R)

Design No.: Front — HW26 Dress Making
Reverse — HW26R Bugler with Toy Donkey
Designer: Walter Hayward
Issued: 1954 - by 1998
Combined with: *Mr. Piggly's Store*, SF14
Proposal, HW11
Roller Skating Arm in Arm, HW137R
Serving Tea, HW116R
Sleeping in a Rocking Chair, EC1
Snowball Fight, HW141R
Toast for Tea Today, SF23
Windy Day, HW27

Shape	U.S. $	Can. $	U.K. £	Aust. $
Albion cream jug	35.00	45.00	20.00	50.00
Albion jug, ½ pint	85.00	100.00	50.00	110.00
Albion jug, 1 pint	100.00	125.00	60.00	135.00
Albion teapot	50.00	60.00	30.00	65.00
Casino jug, 30s				
with signature	200.00	250.00	115.00	275.00
without signature	150.00	180.00	90.00	190.00
Casino jug, 36s				
with signature	150.00	180.00	90.00	190.00
without signature	125.00	150.00	75.00	160.00
Casino jug, 42s				
with signature	125.00	150.00	75.00	160.00
without signature	100.00	125.00	60.00	135.00
Casino saucer				
with signature	15.00	20.00	10.00	25.00
without signature	8.00	10.00	5.00	12.00
Casino teacup				
with signature	15.00	20.00	10.00	25.00
without signature	8.00	10.00	5.00	12.00
Casino teapot, 24s				
with signature	225.00	275.00	125.00	300.00
without signature	175.00	200.00	100.00	225.00
Casino teapot, 30s				
with signature	200.00	250.00	115.00	275.00
without signature	150.00	180.00	90.00	190.00
Casino teapot, 36s				
with signature	275.00	325.00	160.00	350.00
without signature	225.00	275.00	125.00	300.00
Divider dish	50.00	60.00	30.00	65.00
Don beaker				
with signature	50.00	60.00	30.00	65.00
without signature	25.00	30.00	15.00	35.00

Shape	U.S. $	Can. $	U.K. £	Aust. $
Don beaker, one handle				
with signature	50.00	60.00	30.00	65.00
without signature	25.00	30.00	15.00	35.00
Don mug, one handle				
with signature	40.00	50.00	25.00	55.00
without signature	10.00	12.00	6.00	15.00
Don mug, two handles				
with signature	40.00	50.00	25.00	55.00
without signature	10.00	12.00	6.00	15.00
Egg box				
small	175.00	200.00	100.00	225.00
medium	200.00	250.00	115.00	275.00
large	225.00	275.00	125.00	300.00
Hug-a-mug, one handle	10.00	12.00	6.00	15.00
Hug-a-mug, two handles	10.00	12.00	6.00	15.00
Jaffa fruit saucer (plain)				
with signature	25.00	30.00	15.00	35.00
without signature	15.00	20.00	10.00	25.00
Lamp	50.00	60.00	30.00	65.00
Lid of hot water plate				
with signature	75.00	90.00	45.00	95.00
without signature	50.00	60.00	30.00	65.00
Malvern beaker	15.00	20.00	10.00	25.00
Money ball	10.00	12.00	6.00	15.00
Picture plaque, small	20.00	25.00	12.50	30.00
Savings book	15.00	20.00	10.00	25.00
Stratford straight beaker	15.00	20.00	10.00	25.00
Stratford teacup	8.00	10.00	5.00	12.00

Dressing Up, First Version (SF22)

DRESSING UP
First Version

Design No.:	SF22
Designer:	Walter Hayward
Issued:	1954 - by 1998
Combined with:	*Toast for Tea Today*, SF23

Shape	U.S. $	Can. $	U.K. £	Aust. $
Albion jug, 1 pint	100.00	125.00	60.00	135.00
Baby plate, round, small				
with signature	30.00	35.00	17.50	40.00
without signature	20.00	25.00	12.50	30.00
Cake stand	150.00	180.00	90.00	190.00
Casino jug, 30s				
with signature	200.00	250.00	115.00	275.00
without signature	150.00	180.00	90.00	190.00
Casino saucer				
with signature	15.00	20.00	10.00	25.00
without signature	8.00	10.00	5.00	12.00
Casino teapot, 30s				
with signature	175.00	200.00	100.00	225.00
without signature	125.00	150.00	75.00	160.00
Cereal / oatmeal bowl				
with signature	25.00	30.00	15.00	35.00
without signature	15.00	20.00	10.00	25.00
Jaffa fruit saucer (plain)	15.00	20.00	10.00	25.00
Hot water plate				
with signature	100.00	125.00	60.00	135.00
without signature	75.00	90.00	45.00	100.00
Picture plaque, large	20.00	25.00	12.50	30.00
Plate, 6 ½"				
with signature	25.00	30.00	15.00	35.00
without signature	15.00	20.00	10.00	25.00
Plate, 8"	15.00	20.00	10.00	25.00

DRESSING UP
Second Version

This design incorporates scenes from SF22 and EC4.

Design No.:	None
Designer:	Monica Ford based on designs by Walter Hayward
Issued:	1987 - 1993

Shape	U.S. $	Can. $	U.K. £	Aust. $
Cake plate, footed, 11"	175.00	225.00	100.00	250.00
Plate, 10 ½"	35.00	45.00	20.00	50.00

Dressing Up, Second Version

DRUMMER

Design No.: EC2
Designer: Barbara Vernon
Issued: 1937 to the present
Combined with:

Bedtime with Dollies, EC125
Cricketer, HW22R
Drummer and Bugler, EC126
Hikers, EC124
Hobby Horse, Style Two, EC121
Holding Hat and Coat, EC4
Playing with Cup and Spoon, EC6
Playing with Doll and Pram, EC123
Raising Hat, Style Two, EC7
Reading, EC122
Sheltering Under an Umbrella, EC3
Sleeping in a Rocking Chair, EC1
Trumpeter, EC5
Wheelbarrow Race, Style One, HW22
Windy Day, HW27

Shape	U.S. $	Can. $	U.K. £	Aust. $
Albion sugar bowl	30.00	35.00	17.50	40.00
Beaker cover				
with signature	75.00	90.00	45.00	95.00
without signature	65.00	80.00	40.00	85.00
Casino sugar bowl				
with signature	125.00	150.00	75.00	160.00
without signature	100.00	125.00	60.00	135.00
Egg cup				
Style One	30.00	35.00	17.50	40.00
Style Two	40.00	50.00	25.00	55.00
Style Three	10.00	12.50	6.00	15.00
Money Ball	25.00	30.00	15.00	35.00

Drummer (EC2)

DRUMMER AND BUGLER

Design No.: EC126
Designer: Walter Hayward
Issued: 1959 to the present
Combined with:
Bedtime with Dollies, EC125
The Doll's House, HW120
Drummer, EC2
Hat Shop, HW28
Hikers, EC124
Hobby Horse, Style Two, EC121
Holding Hat and Coat, EC4
Playing with Cup and Spoon, EC6
Playing with Doll and Pram, EC123
Raising Hat, Style Two, EC7
Reading, EC122
Sleeping in a Rocking Chair, EC1
Trumpeter, EC5
Trying on Hats, HW28R

Drummer and Bugler (EC126)

Shape	U.S. $	Can. $	U.K. £	Aust. $
Albion sugar bowl	30.00	35.00	17.50	40.00
Beaker cover	65.00	80.00	40.00	85.00
Egg cup				
Style One	30.00	35.00	17.50	40.00
Style Two	40.00	50.00	25.00	55.00
Style Three	10.00	12.00	6.00	15.00
Lid of hot water plate	50.00	60.00	30.00	65.00
Money Ball	25.00	30.00	15.00	35.00

The Duet (LF13)

DUET, THE

Design No.: LF13
Designer: Walter Hayward after Barbara Vernon
Issued: By 1952 - 1970

Shape	U.S. $	Can. $	U.K. £	Aust. $
Baby plate, oval, large				
with signature	250.00	300.00	150.00	325.00
without signature	200.00	250.00	115.00	275.00
Baby plate, round large				
with signature	150.00	180.00	90.00	190.00
without signature	100.00	125.00	60.00	135.00
Bread and butter plate				
with signature	250.00	300.00	150.00	325.00
without signature	200.00	250.00	115.00	275.00
Cereal / oatmeal bowl				
with signature	35.00	45.00	20.00	50.00
without signature	25.00	30.00	15.00	35.00
Hot water plate				
with signature	125.00	150.00	75.00	160.00
without signature	100.00	125.00	60.00	135.00
Plate, 8"	25.00	30.00	15.00	35.00
Plate, 8 ½"				
with signature	75.00	90.00	45.00	95.00
without signature	25.00	30.00	15.00	40.00
Porridge plate				
with signature	110.00	135.00	65.00	145.00
without signature	85.00	100.00	50.00	110.00

Key fobs commemorating the 2000 Australian Tour
Trumpeter (EC5), Drummer (EC2), *Drummer and Bugler (EC126)*

DUNCE

Design No.: HW1R
Designer: Barbara Vernon
Issued: By 1937 - by 1952
Combined with: *Artist*, HW1
Cuddling Under a Mushroom, HW4
Embracing at a Window, HW5
Greetings, HW7
Netting a Cricket, HW6
Playing with Cup and Spoon, EC6
Pressing Trousers, HW14
Proposal, HW11

Dunce (HW1R)

Shape	U.S. $	Can. $	U.K. £	Aust. $
Casino jug, 42s				
with signature	275.00	325.00	160.00	350.00
without signature	200.00	250.00	115.00	275.00
Casino sugar bowl, 30s				
with signature	200.00	250.00	115.00	275.00
without signature	125.00	150.00	75.00	160.00
Casino sugar bowl, 36s				
with signature	150.00	180.00	90.00	190.00
without signature	125.00	150.00	75.00	160.00
Casino teacup				
with signature	75.00	90.00	45.00	95.00
without signature	30.00	35.00	17.50	40.00
Casino teapot, 36s				
with signature	275.00	325.00	160.00	350.00
without signature	200.00	250.00	115.00	275.00
Cup / mug, large				
with signature	200.00	250.00	115.00	275.00
without signature	150.00	180.00	90.00	190.00
Don beaker				
with signature	150.00	180.00	90.00	190.00
without signature	100.00	125.00	60.00	135.00
Don beaker, one handle				
with signature	150.00	180.00	90.00	190.00
without signature	100.00	125.00	60.00	135.00
Don mug, one handle				
with signature	75.00	90.00	45.00	95.00
without signature	35.00	45.00	20.00	50.00
Don mug, two handles				
with signature	75.00	90.00	45.00	95.00
without signature	35.00	45.00	20.00	50.00
Jam pot	1,500.00	1,800.00	850.00	1,900.00
Lid of hot water plate				
with signature	175.00	200.00	100.00	225.00
without signature	125.00	150.00	75.00	160.00
FINE WHITE CHINA				
Beaker, one handle	300.00	350.00	175.00	375.00
Rex mug, small	750.00	900.00	425.00	950.00

Note: *Dunce* (HW1R) is combined with *Proposal* (HW11) on the Rex mug.

EMBRACING AT A WINDOW

Embracing at a Window (HW5)

Design No.: HW5
Designer: Barbara Vernon
Issued: By 1937 - by 1952
Combined with: *Cycling*, HW15R
Dunce, HW1R
Fixing Braces, HW3
Leapfrog, HW12R
Top Hat, HW14R

Shape	U.S. $	Can. $	U.K. £	Aust. $
Casino jug, 36s	500.00	600.00	285.00	625.00
Casino jug, 42s	400.00	475.00	225.00	500.00
Casino saucer	150.00	180.00	90.00	190.00
Casino teacup	250.00	300.00	150.00	325.00
Casino teapot, 30s	600.00	725.00	350.00	750.00
Don beaker	300.00	350.00	175.00	375.00
Don beaker, one handle	250.00	300.00	150.00	325.00
Don mug, one handle	250.00	300.00	150.00	325.00
Don mug, two handles	150.00	180.00	90.00	190.00
Jaffa fruit saucer	250.00	300.00	150.00	325.00
Jam pot	1,250.00	1,500.00	700.00	1,600.00
Plate, 6 ½"	125.00	150.00	75.00	160.00

Note: This design should appear with the Barbara Vernon facsimile signature.

Jam Pot combining *Proposal* (HW11), and *Netting a Cricket* (HW6)

ENGINE PULLING A CARRIAGE / TO THE STATION

Engine Pulling a Carriage (HW17)

To the Station (HW17R)

Design No.: Front — HW17 Engine Pulling a Carriage
Reverse — HW17R To the Station
Designer: Walter Hayward after Barbara Vernon
Issued: By 1952 - by 1998
Combined with: *Family with Pram,* Style One, HW15
Going Shopping, SF10
Ice Cream on the Beach, HW136R
Ice Cream Vendor, HW23
Letterbox, SF13
Raising Hat, Style Two, EC7
See-saw, Style One, SF14
Sleeping in a Rocking Chair, EC1
Snowball Fight, HW141R

Shape	U.S. $	Can. $	U.K. £	Aust. $
Albion cream jug	35.00	45.00	20.00	50.00
Albion jug, ½ pint	85.00	100.00	50.00	110.00
Albion teapot	50.00	60.00	30.00	65.00
Casino jug, 30s				
with signature	200.00	250.00	115.00	275.00
without signature	150.00	180.00	90.00	190.00
Casino jug, 36s				
with signature	175.00	200.00	100.00	225.00
without signature	125.00	150.00	75.00	160.00
Casino jug, 42s				
with signature	150.00	180.00	90.00	190.00
without signature	100.00	125.00	60.00	135.00
Casino saucer				
with signature	20.00	25.00	12.00	30.00
without signature	8.00	10.00	5.00	12.00
Casino sugar bowl, 36s				
with signature	125.00	150.00	75.00	160.00
without signature	100.00	125.00	60.00	135.00
Casino teacup				
with signature	20.00	25.00	12.00	30.00
without signature	8.00	10.00	5.00	12.00
Casino teapot, 24s				
with signature	275.00	325.00	160.00	350.00
without signature	175.00	200.00	100.00	225.00
Casino teapot, 30s				
with signature	250.00	300.00	150.00	325.00
without signature	150.00	180.00	90.00	190.00
Casino teapot, 36s				
with signature	200.00	250.00	115.00	275.00
without signature	125.00	150.00	75.00	160.00
Don beaker				
with signature	50.00	60.00	30.00	65.00
without signature	25.00	30.00	15.00	35.00
Don beaker, one handle				
with signature	50.00	60.00	30.00	65.00

Shape	U.S. $	Can. $	U.K. £	Aust. $
Don beaker, one handle				
without signature	25.00	30.00	15.00	35.00
Don mug, one handle				
with signature	40.00	50.00	25.00	55.00
without signature	10.00	12.50	6.00	15.00
Don mug, two handles				
with signature	40.00	50.00	25.00	55.00
without signature	10.00	12.50	6.00	15.00
Egg box				
small	175.00	200.00	100.00	225.00
medium	200.00	250.00	115.00	275.00
large	225.00	275.00	125.00	300.00
Hot water plate				
with signature	175.00	200.00	100.00	225.00
without signature	125.00	150.00	75.00	160.00
Hug-a-mug, one handle	15.00	20.00	8.00	25.00
Hug-a-mug, two handles	15.00	20.00	8.00	25.00
Jaffa fruit saucer (plain)	15.00	20.00	10.00	25.00
Lamp	50.00	60.00	30.00	65.00
Lid of hot water plate				
with signature	75.00	90.00	45.00	95.00
without signature	50.00	60.00	30.00	65.00
Malvern beaker	15.00	20.00	10.00	25.00
Money ball	10.00	12.50	6.00	15.00
Picture plaque, small	20.00	25.00	12.00	30.00
Plate, 6 ½"				
with signature	25.00	30.00	15.00	35.00
without signature	15.00	20.00	10.00	25.00
Plate, 7 ½"				
with signature	30.00	35.00	17.50	40.00
without signature	10.00	12.50	6.00	15.00
Savings book	15.00	20.00	10.00	25.50
Stratford straight beaker	15.00	20.00	10.00	25.00
Stratford teacup	8.00	10.00	5.00	12.00

FAIRGROUND THEME – Frank Endersby

Swinging Boats (31)

SWINGING BOATS

Design No.: 31 Swinging Boats
Designer: Frank Endersby
Issued: 1995 to the present

Shape	U.S. $	Can. $	U.K. £	Aust. $
Baby plate, round, small	25.00	30.00	15.00	35.00
Cereal / oatmeal bowl	15.00	20.00	10.00	25.00
Plate, 6 ½"	10.00	12.50	6.00	15.00
Plate, 8"	15.00	20.00	10.00	25.00

Coconut Shy (32)

COCONUT SHY / PLAYING WITH BALLOONS

Design No.: Front — 32 Coconut Shy
Reverse — 33 Playing with Balloons
Designer: Frank Endersby
Issued: 1995 to the present
Combined with: **Butterfly Net*, (6)

Shape	U.S. $	Can. $	U.K. £	Aust. $
Hug-a-mug, one handle	20.00	25.00	12.00	30.00
Hug-a-mug, two handles	20.00	25.00	12.00	30.00
Divider dish	50.00	60.00	30.00	65.00
Malvern beaker	15.00	20.00	10.00	25.00
Money ball	25.00	30.00	15.00	35.00
Stratford teacup	8.00	10.00	5.00	12.00

* Indicates scene on divider dish.

Playing with Balloons (33)

FAMILY AT BREAKFAST

Design No.: HW12
Designer: Barbara Vernon
Issued: By 1937 - by 1952
Combined with: *Bedtime in Bunks*, SF3
Chicken Pulling a Cart, SF8
Cycling, HW15R
Feeding the Baby, HW13
Fixing Braces, HW3
Footballer, HW13R
Golfer, HW4R
Kissing Under the Mistletoe, HW11R
Lambeth Walk, HW16
Leapfrog, HW12R
Orange Vendor, SF12
Proposal, HW11
Pulling On Trousers, HW2
Raising Hat, Style One, HW16R
Smoking in the Doorway, SF2
Top Hat, HW14R
Trumpeter, EC5
Washing Day, HW8R
Wedding, LFd

Family at Breakfast (HW12)

Shape	U.S. $	Can. $	U.K. £	Aust. $
Baby plate, round, small				
with signature	50.00	60.00	30.00	65.00
without signature	30.00	35.00	17.50	40.00
Candle holder	2,000.00	2,500.00	1,100.00	2,750.00
Casino jug, 36s				
with signature	300.00	350.00	175.00	375.00
without signature	250.00	300.00	150.00	325.00
Casino jug, 42s				
with signature	250.00	300.00	150.00	325.00
without signature	200.00	250.00	115.00	275.00
Casino saucer				
with signature	75.00	90.00	45.00	95.00
without signature	50.00	60.00	30.00	65.00
Casino sugar bowl, 30s				
with signature	200.00	250.00	115.00	275.00
without signature	150.00	180.00	90.00	190.00
Casino sugar bowl, 36s				
with signature	175.00	200.00	100.00	225.00
without signature	125.00	150.00	75.00	160.00
Casino teacup				
with signature	75.00	90.00	45.00	95.00
without signature	50.00	60.00	30.00	65.00
Casino teapot, 30s				
with signature	325.00	400.00	185.00	425.00
without signature	250.00	300.00	150.00	325.00
Casino teapot, 36s				
with signature	250.00	300.00	150.00	325.00
without signature	225.00	275.00	125.00	300.00
Cereal / oatmeal bowl				
with signature	35.00	45.00	20.00	50.00
without signature	25.00	30.00	15.00	35.00
Cup / mug, large	250.00	300.00	150.00	325.00
Don beaker				
with signature	65.00	80.00	40.00	85.00
without signature	35.00	45.00	20.00	50.00

Shape	U.S. $	Can. $	U.K. £	Aust. $
Don beaker, one handle				
with signature	65.00	80.00	40.00	85.00
without signature	35.00	45.00	20.00	50.00
Don mug, one handle				
with signature	50.00	60.00	30.00	65.00
without signature	15.00	20.00	10.00	25.00
Don mug, two handles				
with signature	50.00	60.00	30.00	65.00
without signature	15.00	20.00	10.00	25.00
Hot water plate				
with signature	125.00	150.00	75.00	160.00
without signature	100.00	125.00	60.00	130.00
Jaffa fruit saucer (wavy)				
with signature	75.00	90.00	45.00	95.00
without signature	50.00	60.00	30.00	65.00
Jam pot	1,500.00	1,800.00	850.00	1,900.00
Lid of hot water plate				
with signature	100.00	125.00	60.00	135.00
without signature	75.00	90.00	45.00	95.00
Plate, 6 ½"				
with signature	30.00	35.00	17.50	40.00
without signature	20.00	25.00	12.50	30.00
Plate, 7 ½"				
with signature	65.00	80.00	40.00	85.00
without signature	25.00	30.00	15.00	35.00
FINE WHITE CHINA				
Beaker, one handle	300.00	350.00	175.00	375.00
Rex mug, small	750.00	900.00	425.00	950.00
Saucer	300.00	350.00	175.00	375.00
Teacup	300.00	350.00	175.00	375.00

Note: *Family at Breakfast* (HW12) is combined with *Gardener with Wheelbarrow* (HW9R) on the fine white china beaker, and with *Cycling* (HW15R) or *Golfer* (HW12R) on the Rex mug.

Family Cycling (LF11)

FAMILY CYCLING

Design No.: LF11
Designer: Walter Hayward
Issued: By 1952 - 1970

Shape	U.S. $	Can. $	U.K. £	Aust. $
Baby plate, oval, large				
with signature	200.00	250.00	115.00	275.00
without signature	150.00	180.00	90.00	190.00
Baby plate, round large				
with signature	100.00	125.00	60.00	135.00
without signature	75.00	90.00	45.00	95.00
Bread and butter plate				
with signature	250.00	300.00	150.00	325.00
without signature	200.00	250.00	115.00	275.00
Cereal / oatmeal bowl				
with signature	35.00	45.00	20.00	50.00
without signature	25.00	30.00	15.00	35.00
Hot water plate				
with signature	125.00	150.00	75.00	160.00
without signature	100.00	125.00	60.00	135.00
Plate, 8 ½"				
with signature	75.00	90.00	45.00	95.00
without signature	25.00	30.00	15.00	35.00
Porridge plate				
with signature	250.00	300.00	150.00	325.00
without signature	200.00	250.00	115.00	275.00

Note: Retirement dates are all approximate. When a design is retired all remaining stocks of the retired litho prints are used until exhausted.

FAMILY GOING OUT ON WASHING DAY

Design No.: HW8
Designer: Barbara Vernon
Issued: By 1937 - by 1967
Combined with: *Chicken Pulling a Cart*, SF8
Cycling, HW15R
Leapfrog, HW12R
Netting a Cricket, HW6
Orange Vendor, SF12
Sheltering Under Umbrella, EC3
Trumpeter, EC5
Washing Day, HW8R

Shape	U.S. $	Can. $	U.K. £	Aust. $
Casino jug, 24s				
with signature	475.00	575.00	270.00	600.00
without signature	400.00	475.00	225.00	500.00
Casino jug, 30s				
with signature	250.00	300.00	150.00	325.00
without signature	150.00	180.00	90.00	190.00
Casino jug, 36s				
with signature	275.00	325.00	160.00	350.00
without signature	225.00	275.00	125.00	300.00
Casino saucer				
with signature	75.00	90.00	45.00	95.00
without signature	50.00	60.00	30.00	65.00
Casino sugar bowl, 36s				
with signature	150.00	180.00	90.00	190.00
without signature	125.00	150.00	75.00	160.00
Casino teacup				
with signature	75.00	90.00	45.00	95.00
without signature	50.00	60.00	30.00	65.00
Casino teapot, 30s				
with signature	300.00	350.00	175.00	375.00
without signature	225.00	375.00	125.00	300.00
Don beaker				
with signature	150.00	180.00	90.00	190.00
without signature	100.00	125.00	60.00	135.00
Don beaker, one handle				
with signature	150.00	180.00	90.00	190.00
without signature	100.00	125.00	60.00	135.00
Don mug, one handle				
with signature	75.00	90.00	45.00	95.00
without signature	35.00	45.00	20.00	50.00
Don mug, two handles				
with signature	75.00	90.00	45.00	95.00
without signature	35.00	45.00	20.00	50.00
Jaffa fruit saucer				
plain rim				
with signature	95.00	115.00	55.00	125.00
without signature	65.00	80.00	40.00	85.00
wavy rim				
with signature	125.00	150.00	75.00	160.00
without signature	85.00	100.00	50.00	110.00
Plate, 6 ½"				
with signature	90.00	110.00	50.00	120.00
without signature	60.00	70.00	35.00	75.00

Family Going out on Washing Day (HW8)

Family in the Garden (SF135)

FAMILY IN THE GARDEN

Design No.: SF135
Designer: Walter Hayward
Issued: 1967 - by 1998
Combined with: *Dressing,* HW26

Shape	U.S. $	Can. $	U.K. £	Aust. $
Albion jug, 1 pint	100.00	125.00	60.00	135.00
Baby plate, round, large	50.00	60.00	30.00	65.00
Baby plate, round, small	20.00	25.00	12.00	30.00
Cake stand	150.00	180.00	90.00	190.00
Cereal / oatmeal bowl	15.00	20.00	10.00	25.00
Hot water plate	75.00	90.00	45.00	95.00
Jaffa fruit saucer (plain)	15.00	20.00	10.00	25.00
Picture plaque, large	20.00	25.00	12.00	30.00
Plate, 6 ½"	15.00	20.00	10.00	25.00
Plate, 8"	15.00	20.00	10.00	25.00

FAMILY PHOTOGRAPH

Design No.: LF15
Designer: Walter Hayward
Issued: By 1954 - 1970

Shape	U.S. $	Can. $	U.K. £	Aust. $
Baby plate, oval, large				
with signature	200.00	250.00	115.00	275.00
without signature	150.00	180.00	90.00	190.00
Baby plate, round large				
with signature	100.00	125.00	60.00	135.00
without signature	75.00	90.00	45.00	95.00
Bread and butter plate				
with signature	300.00	350.00	175.00	375.00
without signature	150.00	180.00	90.00	190.00
Cereal / oatmeal bowl				
with signature	35.00	45.00	20.00	50.00
without signature	25.00	30.00	15.00	35.00
Plate, 8"	25.00	30.00	15.00	35.00
Plate, 8 ½"				
with signature	75.00	90.00	45.00	95.00
without signature	25.00	30.00	15.00	35.00
Porridge plate				
with signature	110.00	135.00	65.00	145.00
without signature	85.00	100.00	50.00	110.00

Family Photograph (LF15)

FAMILY WITH PRAM
Style One

Design No.: HW15
Designer: Barbara Vernon
Issued: By 1937 - by 1952
Combined with: *Chicken Pulling a Cart,* SF8
Cycling, HW15R
Engine Pulling a Carriage, HW17
Footballer, HW13R
Leapfrog, HW12R
Proposal, HW11
Pulling on Trousers, HW2
Raising Hat, Style One, HW16R
Raising Hat, Style Two, EC7
Rowboat, HW21
Washing in the Open Air, HW10R

Family with Pram, Style One (HW15)

Shape	U.S. $	Can. $	U.K. £	Aust. $
Baby plate, oval, large	200.00	250.00	115.00	275.00
Baby plate, round, large	100.00	125.00	60.00	135.00
Casino jug, 30s	300.00	350.00	175.00	375.00
Casino saucer	75.00	90.00	45.00	95.00
Casino sugar bowl, 30s	200.00	250.00	115.00	275.00
Casino teacup	75.00	90.00	45.00	95.00
Casino teapot, 24s	375.00	450.00	210.00	475.00
Casino teapot, 30s	325.00	400.00	185.00	425.00
Don beaker	65.00	80.00	40.00	85.00
Don beaker, one handle	65.00	80.00	40.00	85.00
Don mug, one handle	50.00	60.00	30.00	65.00
Don mug, two handles	50.00	60.00	30.00	65.00
Jaffa fruit saucer	50.00	60.00	30.00	60.00
Jam pot	1,500.00	1,800.00	850.00	1,900.00
Lid of hot water plate	100.00	125.00	60.00	135.00
Plate, 6 ½"	30.00	35.00	17.50	40.00
Plate, 7 ½"	20.00	25.00	12.50	30.00

Note: 1. This design should appear with the Barbara Vernon facsimile signature.
2. This design is found on in-between sizes of Casino jugs.

Family with Pram (HW15) / Raising Hat (HW16R)

FAMILY WITH PRAM / RAISING HAT

The unusual combination of *Family with Pram,* Style One (HW15) and *Raising Hat,* Style One (HW16R), has been found on large round and oval baby plates, a casino sugar bowl, a casino teapot and a 7½" plate., plus a 7" plate in fine white china.

Design No.: HW15 / HW16R
Designer: Barbara Vernon
Issued: By 1937 - by 1952

Shape	U.S. $	Can. $	U.K. £	Aust. $
Baby plate, oval, large			Rare	
Baby plate, round, large	400.00	475.00	225.00	500.00
Casino sugar bowl			Rare	
Casino teapot, 30s	550.00	650.00	315.00	675.00
Plate, 7 ½"	250.00	300.00	150.00	325.00
FINE WHITE CHINA				
Plate, 7"			Rare	

Family with Pram, Style Two (CT14)

Standing by Pram (CT6)

FAMILY WITH PRAM
Style Two

Design No.:	Front — CT14 Family with Pram Reverse — CT6 Standing by Pram
Designer:	Colin Twinn
Issued:	1989 - 1993
Combined with:	*Bunny on Rocking Horse*, CT29 *Father Bunnykins with Fishing Rod*, CT27 *Home from Fishing*, CT26 *Nursery*, First Version, CT19 *Picking Daisies*, CT4

Shape	U.S. $	Can. $	U.K. £	Aust. $
Albion cream jug	35.00	45.00	20.00	50.00
Albion jug, ½ pint	85.00	100.00	50.00	110.00
Albion jug, 1 pint	100.00	125.00	60.00	135.00
Cake stand	150.00	180.00	90.00	190.00
Divider dish	75.00	90.00	45.00	95.00
Hug-a-mug, one handle	10.00	12.00	6.00	15.00
Hug-a-mug, two handles	10.00	12.00	6.00	15.00
Lamp	50.00	60.00	30.00	65.00
Malvern beaker	15.00	20.00	10.00	25.00
Money ball	10.00	12.50	6.00	15.00
Stratford teacup	8.00	10.00	5.00	12.00

Note: *Standing by Pram*, CT6 is combined with *Picking Daisies*, CT4 on Albion 1 pint and ½ pint jugs.

FEEDING THE BABY

Feeding the Baby (HW13)

Design No.: HW13
Designer: Barbara Vernon
Issued: By 1937 - by 1967
Combined with: *Bedtime in Bunks,* SF3
Cycling, HW15R
Family at Breakfast, HW12
Footballer, HW13R
Golfer, HW4R
Going Shopping, SF10
Kissing under the Mistletoe, HW11R
Leapfrog, HW12R
Pressing Trousers, HW14
Pulling on Trousers, HW2
Raising Hat, Style One, HW16R
Santa Claus, SF9
Sleeping in a Rocking Chair, EC1
Top Hat, HW14R
Trumpeter, EC5
Washing in the Open Air, HW10R

Shape	U.S. $	Can. $	U.K. £	Aust. $
Baby plate, round, small				
with signature	50.00	60.00	30.00	65.00
without signature	30.00	35.00	17.50	40.00
Candle holder	1,500.00	1,800.00	850.00	1,900.00
Casino jug, 36s				
with signature	300.00	350.00	175.00	375.00
without signature	250.00	300.00	150.00	325.00
Casino jug, 42s				
with signature	250.00	300.00	150.00	325.00
without signature	200.00	250.00	115.00	275.00
Casino saucer				
with signature	75.00	90.00	45.00	95.00
without signature	50.00	60.00	30.00	65.00
Casino sugar bowl, 30s				
with signature	200.00	250.00	115.00	275.00
without signature	150.00	180.00	90.00	190.00
Casino teacup				
with signature	75.00	90.00	45.00	95.00
without signature	50.00	60.00	30.00	65.00
Casino teapot, 36s				
with signature	250.00	300.00	150.00	325.00
without signature	225.00	275.00	125.00	300.00
Cup / mug, large	800.00	975.00	475.00	1,075.00
Don beaker				
with signature	65.00	80.00	40.00	85.00
without signature	35.00	45.00	20.00	50.00

Shape	U.S. $	Can. $	U.K. £	Aust. $
Don beaker, one handle				
with signature	65.00	80.00	40.00	85.00
without signature	35.00	45.00	20.00	50.00
Don mug, one handle				
with silver rim	350.00	425.00	200.00	450.00
with signature	50.00	60.00	30.00	65.00
without signature	15.00	20.00	10.00	25.00
Don mug, two handles				
with signature	50.00	60.00	30.00	65.00
without signature	15.00	20.00	10.00	25.00
Jaffa fruit saucer				
plain rim	50.00	60.00	30.00	65.00
wavy rim	75.00	90.00	45.00	95.00
Jam pot	1,500.00	1,800.00	850.00	1,900.00
Lid of hot water plate				
with signature	100.00	125.00	60.00	135.00
without signature	75.00	90.00	45.00	95.00
Plate, 6 ½”				
with signature	30.00	35.00	17.50	40.00
without signature	20.00	25.00	12.00	30.00
Sugar bowl with handles	3,500.00	4,250.00	2,000.00	5,250.00
FINE WHITE CHINA				
Saucer	300.00	350.00	175.00	375.00
Teacup	300.00	350.00	175.00	375.00

FIRE STATION THEME – Frank Endersby

Washing the Fire Engine (10)

WASHING THE FIRE ENGINE

Design No.: 10 Washing the Fire Engine
Designer: Frank Endersby
Issued: 1995 to the present

Shape	U.S. $	Can. $	U.K. £	Aust. $
Baby plate, round, small	25.00	30.00	15.00	35.00
Cereal / oatmeal bowl	15.00	20.00	10.00	25.00
Jaffa fruit saucer	15.00	20.00	10.00	25.00
Plate, 6 ½"	10.00	12.00	6.00	15.00
Plate, 8"	15.00	20.00	10.00	25.00

Pumping Water (11)

PUMPING WATER / TRYING ON HAT

Design No.: Front — 11 Pumping Water
Reverse — 12 Trying on Hat
Designer: Frank Endersby
Issued: 1995 to the present
Combined with: **Carrying Net*, (6)

Shape	U.S. $	Can. $	U.K. £	Aust. $
Hug-a-mug, one handle	20.00	25.00	12.00	30.00
Hug-a-mug, two handles	20.00	25.00	12.00	30.00
Divider dish	50.00	60.00	30.00	65.00
Malvern beaker	15.00	20.00	10.00	25.00
Money ball	25.00	30.00	15.00	35.00
Stratford teacup	8.00	10.00	5.00	12.00

* Indicates scenes on divider dish.

Trying on Hat (12)

FISHING THEME – Frank Endersby

FISHING AT THE POND

Design No.: 4 Fishing at the Pond
Designer: Frank Endersby
Issued: 1995 to the present

Shape	U.S. $	Can. $	U.K. £	Aust. $
Baby plate, round, small	15.00	20.00	10.00	25.00
Jaffa fruit saucer	15.00	20.00	10.00	25.00
Plate, 6 ½"	10.00	12.00	6.00	15.00
Plate, 8"	15.00	20.00	10.00	25.00

Fishing at the Pond (4)

Resting by Pond (5)

RESTING BY POND / CARRYING NET

Design No.: Front — 5 Resting by Pond
Reverse — 6 Carrying Net
Designer: Frank Endersby
Issued: 1995 to the present
Combined with: **Playing with Balloons*, (33)

Shape	U.S. $	Can. $	U.K. £	Aust. $
Hug-a-mug, one handle	20.00	25.00	12.00	30.00
Hug-a-mug, two handles	20.00	25.00	12.00	30.00
Divider dish	50.00	60.00	30.00	65.00
Money ball	25.00	30.00	15.00	35.00
Stratford teacup	8.00	10.00	5.00	12.00

* Indicates scene on divider dish.

Carrying Net (6)

Fishing in the Goldfish Bowl (HW3R)

FISHING IN THE GOLDFISH BOWL

Design No.:	HW3R
Designer:	Barbara Vernon
Issued:	By 1937 - by 1952
Combined with:	*Artist*, HW1
	Fixing Braces, HW3
	Mr. Piggly's Stores, SF14
	Netting a Cricket, HW6
	Playing with Cup and Spoon, EC6
	Pressing Trousers, HW14
	Pulling on Trousers, HW2
	Sheltering Under an Umbrella, EC3

Shape	U.S. $	Can. $	U.K. £	Aust. $
Casino jug, 24s	475.00	575.00	270.00	600.00
Casino jug, 36s	300.00	350.00	175.00	375.00
Casino teacup	75.00	90.00	45.00	95.00
Don beaker	150.00	180.00	90.00	190.00
Don mug, one handle	75.00	90.00	45.00	95.00
FINE WHITE CHINA				
Teacup	300.00	350.00	175.00	375.00

Note: This design should appear with the Barbara Vernon facsimile signature.

FISHING ON THE PIER

Design No.:	LF3
Designer:	Barbara Vernon
Issued:	By 1940 - by 1952

Shape	U.S. $	Can. $	U.K. £	Aust. $
Baby plate, round, large				
with silver rim		Rare		
with signature	400.00	475.00	225.00	500.00
without signature	350.00	425.00	200.00	450.00
Bread and butter plate				
with signature	500.00	600.00	285.00	625.00
without signature	400.00	475.00	225.00	500.00
Cereal / oatmeal bowl				
with signature	200.00	250.00	115.00	275.00
without signature	175.00	200.00	100.00	225.00
Plate, 6 ½"				
with signature	250.00	300.00	150.00	325.00
without signature	200.00	250.00	115.00	275.00
Plate, 8 ½"				
with signature	300.00	350.00	175.00	375.00
without signature	250.00	300.00	150.00	325.00
Porridge plate				
with signature	300.00	350.00	175.00	375.00
without signature	250.00	300.00	150.00	325.00

Fishing on the Pier (LF3)

FIXING BRACES

Design No.: HW3
Designer: Barbara Vernon
Issued: By 1937 - by 1952
Combined with: *Chicken Pulling a Cart*, SF8
Cycling, HW15R
Embracing at a Window, HW5
Family at Breakfast, HW12
Fishing in the Goldfish Bowl, HW3R
Going Shopping, SF10
Leapfrog, HW12R
Smoking in the Doorway, SF2

Fixing Braces (HW3)

Shape	U.S. $	Can. $	U.K. £	Aust. $
Candle holder	1,500.00	1,800.00	850.00	1,900.00
Casino jug, 24s	400.00	475.00	225.00	500.00
Casino jug, 36s	300.00	350.00	175.00	375.00
Casino saucer	75.00	90.00	45.00	95.00
Casino teacup	75.00	90.00	45.00	95.00
Cup / mug, large			Rare	
Don beaker	65.00	80.00	40.00	85.00
Don beaker, one handle	65.00	80.00	40.00	85.00
Don mug, one handle	50.00	60.00	30.00	65.00
Don mug, two handles	50.00	60.00	30.00	65.00
Jaffa fruit saucer				
plain rim	50.00	60.00	30.00	65.00
wavy rim	75.00	90.00	45.00	95.00
Plate, 6 ½"	30.00	35.00	17.50	40.00
FINE WHITE CHINA				
Night light		Very Rare		
Rex mug, small	750.00	900.00	425.00	950.00

Note: This design should appear with the Barbara Vernon facsimile signature.

Flying Kites (SF133)

FLYING KITES

Design No.: SF133
Designer: Walter Hayward
Issued: 1967 - by 1998
Combined with: *Playing with Doll and Pram,* HW115

Shape	U.S. $	Can. $	U.K. £	Aust. $
Albion jug, 1 pint	100.00	125.00	60.00	135.00
Baby plate, round, small	20.00	25.00	12.00	30.00
Cake stand	150.00	180.00	90.00	190.00
Casino saucer	8.00	10.00	5.00	12.00
Cereal / oatmeal bowl	15.00	20.00	10.00	25.00
Jaffa fruit saucer (plain)	15.00	20.00	10.00	25.00
Hot water plate	75.00	90.00	45.00	95.00
Picture plaque, large	20.00	25.00	12.00	30.00
Plate, 6 ½"	15.00	20.00	10.00	25.00
Plate, 8"	15.00	20.00	10.00	25.00

Footballer (HW13R)

FOOTBALLER

Design No.: HW13R
Designer: Barbara Vernon
Issued: By 1937 - by 1967
Combined with: *Cuddling under a Mushroom*, HW4
Family at Breakfast, HW12
Family with Pram, Style One, HW15
Feeding the Baby, HW13
Gardening, Style One (HW9)
Lambeth Walk, HW16
Pressing Trousers, HW14
Proposal, HW11
Reading the Times, HW2R
Santa Claus, SF9
Sleeping in a Rocking Chair, EC1

Shape	U.S. $	Can. $	U.K. £	Aust. $
Beaker Cover	65.00	80.00	40.00	85.00
Casino jug, 42s				
with signature	250.00	300.00	150.00	325.00
without signature	200.00	250.00	115.00	275.00
Casino sugar bowl, 36s				
with signature	175.00	200.00	100.00	225.00
without signature	125.00	150.00	75.00	160.00
Casino teacup				
with signature	75.00	90.00	45.00	95.00
without signature	50.00	60.00	30.00	65.00
Don beaker				
with signature	65.00	80.00	40.00	85.00
without signature	35.00	45.00	20.00	50.00
Don beaker, one handle				
with signature	65.00	80.00	40.00	85.00
without signature	35.00	45.00	20.00	50.00
Don mug, one handle				
with silver rim		Rare		
with signature	50.00	60.00	30.00	65.00
without signature	15.00	20.00	10.00	25.00
Don mug, two handles				
with signature	50.00	60.00	30.00	65.00
without signature	15.00	20.00	10.00	25.00
Lid of hot water plate				
with signature	100.00	125.00	65.00	135.00
without signature	75.00	90.00	45.00	95.00
Sugar bowl with handles		Very rare		
FINE WHITE CHINA				
Rex mug, small	750.00	900.00	425.00	950.00
Teacup	300.00	350.00	175.00	375.00

Note: **1.** The Rex mug can be found combined with one of the following: *Pressing Trousers* (HW14), *Proposal* (HW11) or *Lambeth Walk*, First Version (HW16).
2. Fine white china prices are indications only due to the scarcity of the shapes, prices will vary.

FRIGHTENING SPIDER

Design No.:	SF4
Designer:	Barbara Vernon
Issued:	By 1937 - by 1952
Combined with:	*Conducting the Orchestra*, LF5
	Greetings, HW7
	Medicine Time, SF1
	Pressing Trousers, HW14

Shape	U.S. $	Can. $	U.K. £	Aust. $
Baby plate, round, large	100.00	125.00	60.00	135.00
Baby plate, round, small	50.00	60.00	30.00	35.00
Casino jug, 24s	400.00	475.00	225.00	500.00
Casino jug, 30s	225.00	275.00	125.00	300.00
Casino jug, 36s	300.00	350.00	175.00	375.00
Casino saucer	75.00	90.00	45.00	95.00
Casino teapot, 24s	375.00	450.00	210.00	475.00
Casino teapot, 30s	325.00	400.00	185.00	425.00
Cereal / oatmeal bowl	35.00	45.00	20.00	50.00
Jaffa fruit saucer				
plain rim	50.00	60.00	30.00	65.00
wavy rim	75.00	90.00	45.00	95.00
Hot water plate	125.00	150.00	75.00	160.00
Plate, 6 ½"	30.00	35.00	17.50	40.00
Plate, 7"	65.00	80.00	40.00	85.00
Plate, 7 ½"	65.00	80.00	40.00	85.00
Plate, 8"	75.00	90.00	45.00	95.00
FINE WHITE CHINA				
Saucer	300.00	350.00	175.00	375.00
Teacup	300.00	350.00	175.00	375.00

Note: This design should appear with the Barbara Vernon facsimile signature. A round baby plate has been recorded featuring the facsimile name of Dorothy Vernon instead of Barbara Vernon.

Frightening Spider (SF4)

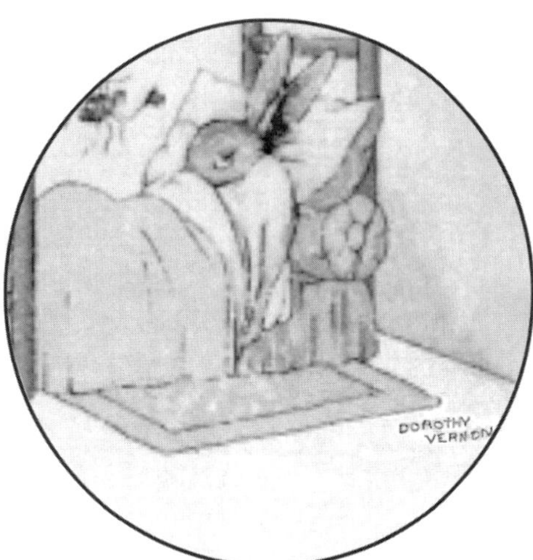

Frightening Spider with
"Dorothy Vernon" facsimile name

Fun in the Snow

FUN IN THE SNOW
CHRISTMAS TREE ORNAMENT

This Christmas tree ornament, which has a rabbit-shaped rim, was commissioned by Royal Doulton U.S.A. and produced in the U.S.A. The words Fun in the Snow appear on the reverse.

Design No.: None
Designer: Frank Endersby
Issued: 1995 - 1995
Series: Christmas Tree Ornaments

Shape	U.S. $	Can. $	U.K. £	Aust. $
Christmas tree ornament	25.00	30.00	15.00	35.00

Note: For other Christmas ornaments in this series see page 42, 44, 143 and 165.

Game of Golf (SF11)

GAME OF GOLF

Design No.: SF11
Designer: Barbara Vernon
Issued: By 1940 - by 1952
Combined with: *Gardening*, Style One, HW9
Picnic, Second Version, LF10
Pulling on Trousers, HW2

Shape	U.S. $	Can. $	U.K. £	Aust. $
Baby plate, round, large				
with signature	100.00	125.00	60.00	135.00
without signature	75.00	90.00	45.00	95.00
Baby plate, round, small				
with signature	50.00	60.00	30.00	65.00
without signature	30.00	35.00	17.50	40.00
Casino jug, 36s				
with signature	300.00	350.00	175.00	375.00
without signature	250.00	300.00	150.00	325.00
Casino saucer				
with signature	75.00	90.00	45.00	95.00
without signature	50.00	60.00	30.00	65.00
Casino teapot, 24s				
with signature	375.00	450.00	210.00	475.00
without signature	300.00	350.00	175.00	375.00
Casino teapot, 30s				
with signature	400.00	475.00	225.00	500.00
without signature	300.00	350.00	175.00	375.00
Cereal / oatmeal bowl				
with signature	35.00	45.00	20.00	50.00
without signature	25.00	30.00	15.00	35.00
Hot water plate	150.00	180.00	90.00	190.00
Jaffa fruit saucer				
plain rim	50.00	60.00	30.00	65.00
wavy rim	75.00	90.00	45.00	95.00
Lid for hot water plate				
with signature	100.00	125.00	60.00	135.00
without signature	75.00	90.00	45.00	95.00
Plate, 6 ½"				
with signature	30.00	35.00	17.50	40.00
without signature	20.00	25.00	12.00	30.00
Plate, 7 ½"				
with signature	65.00	80.00	40.00	85.00
without signature	25.00	30.00	15.00	35.00

Note: See also *Golfer* (HW4R) page 87.

GARAGE THEME – Frank Endersby

PETROL IN THE SPORTS CAR

Design No.: 37 Petrol in the Sports Car
Designer: Frank Endersby
Issued: 1995 to the present

Shape	U.S. $	Can. $	U.K. £	Aust. $
Baby plate, round, small	25.00	30.00	15.00	35.00
Plate, 6 ½"	10.00	12.00	6.00	15.00
Plate, 8"	15.00	20.00	10.00	25.00

Petrol in the Sports Car (37)

Pumping Tyre (38)

PUMPING TYRE / SITTING ON OIL DRUM

Design No.: Front — 38 Pumping Tyre
Reverse — 39 Sitting on Oil Drum
Designer: Frank Endersby
Issued: 1995 to the present
Combined with: *Pillar Money Box*

Shape	U.S. $	Can. $	U.K. £	Aust. $
Hug-a-mug, one handle	20.00	25.00	12.00	30.00
Hug-a-mug, two handles	20.00	25.00	12.00	30.00
Malvern beaker	15.00	25.00	10.00	25.00

Sitting on Oil Drum (39)

Gardener with Wheelbarrow (HW9R)

GARDENER WITH WHEELBARROW

Design No.:	HW9R
Designer:	Barbara Vernon
Issued:	By 1937 - by 1967
Combined with:	*Chicken Pulling a Cart,* SF8
	Gardening, Style One, HW9
	Leapfrog, HW12R
	Netting a Cricket, HW6

Shape	U.S. $	Can. $	U.K. £	Aust. $
Casino jug, 42s				
with signature	250.00	300.00	150.00	325.00
without signature	200.00	250.00	115.00	275.00
Casino sugar bowl, 30s				
with signature	200.00	250.00	115.00	275.00
without signature	150.00	180.00	90.00	190.00
Casino sugar bowl, 36s				
with signature	175.00	200.00	100.00	225.00
without signature	125.00	150.00	75.00	160.00
Casino teacup				
with signature	75.00	90.00	45.00	95.00
without signature	50.00	60.00	30.00	65.00
Cup / mug, large		Rare		
Don beaker				
with signature	60.00	70.00	35.00	75.00
without signature	35.00	45.00	20.00	50.00
Don mug, one handle				
with silver rim		Rare		
with signature	50.00	60.00	30.00	65.00
without signature	15.00	20.00	10.00	25.00
Don mug, two handles				
with signature	50.00	60.00	30.00	65.00
without signature	15.00	20.00	10.00	25.00
Lid of hot water plate				
with signature	100.00	125.00	60.00	135.00
without signature	75.00	90.00	45.00	95.00

Note: **1.** Retirement dates are all approximate. When a design is retired all remaining stocks of the retired litho prints are used until exhausted.
2. Condition is important. Prices listed are based on nurseryware in mint condition. Items in less than mint condition will command lower prices.

GARDENING
Style One

Gardening, Style One (HW9)

Design No.: HW9
Designer: Barbara Vernon
Issued: By 1937 - by 1967

Combined with: *Asleep in the Open Air*, HW10
Footballer, HW13R
Game of Golf, SF11
Gardener with Wheelbarrow, HW9R
Greetings, HW7
Leapfrog, HW12R
Washing in the Open Air, HW10R

Shape	U.S. $	Can. $	U.K. £	Aust. $
Baby plate, round, small				
with signature	200.00	250.00	115.00	275.00
without signature	150.00	180.00	90.00	190.00
Casino jug, 36s				
with signature	300.00	350.00	175.00	375.00
without signature	275.00	325.00	160.00	350.00
Casino jug, 42s				
with signature	275.00	325.00	160.00	350.00
without signature	200.00	250.00	115.00	275.00
Casino saucer				
with signature	75.00	90.00	45.00	95.00
without signature	50.00	60.00	30.00	65.00
Casino sugar bowl, 36s				
with signature	200.00	250.00	115.00	275.00
without signature	175.00	200.00	100.00	225.00
Casino teacup				
with signature	75.00	90.00	45.00	95.00
without signature	50.00	60.00	30.00	65.00
Casino teapot, 24s				
with signature	375.00	450.00	210.00	475.00
without signature	300.00	350.00	175.00	375.00
Casino teapot, 30s				
with signature	250.00	300.00	150.00	325.00
without signature	225.00	275.00	125.00	300.00
Cereal / oatmeal bowl				
with signature	100.00	125.00	60.00	135.00
without signature	90.00	110.00	50.00	120.00

Shape	U.S. $	Can. $	U.K. £	Aust. $
Don beaker				
with signature	150.00	180.00	90.00	190.00
without signature	100.00	125.00	60.00	135.00
Don beaker, one handle				
with signature	150.00	180.00	90.00	190.00
without signature	100.00	125.00	60.00	135.00
Don mug, one handle				
with silver rim	350.00	425.00	200.00	450.00
with signature	100.00	125.00	60.00	135.00
without signature	75.00	90.00	45.00	95.00
Don mug, two handles				
with signature	75.00	90.00	45.00	95.00
without signature	35.00	45.00	20.00	50.00
Jaffa fruit saucer				
plain rim	95.00	115.00	55.00	125.00
wavy rim	125.00	150.00	75.00	160.00
Jam pot	1,500.00	1,800.00	850.00	1,900.00
Lid of hot water plate				
with signature	175.00	200.00	100.00	225.00
without signature	125.00	150.00	75.00	160.00
Plate, 6 ½"				
with signature	60.00	70.00	35.00	75.00
without signature	35.00	45.00	20.00	50.00

GARDENING THEME – Frank Endersby

Gardening, Style Two (55)

GARDENING
Style Two

Design No.: 55 Gardening
Designer: Frank Endersby
Issued: 1995 - 2003

Shape	U.S. $	Can. $	U.K. £	Aust. $
Baby plate, round, small	25.00	30.00	15.00	35.00
Cake stand	150.00	180.00	90.00	190.00
Plate, 6 ½"	10.00	12.00	6.00	15.00
Plate, 8"	15.00	20.00	10.00	25.00
Plate, 10 ½"	25.00	30.00	15.00	35.00

Playing in Tree House (56)

PLAYING IN TREE HOUSE / RESTING IN WHEELBARROW

Design No.: Front — 56 Playing in Tree House
Reverse — 57 Resting in Wheelbarrow
Designer: Frank Endersby
Issued: 1995 - 2003
Combined with: **Butterfly Net*, (6)

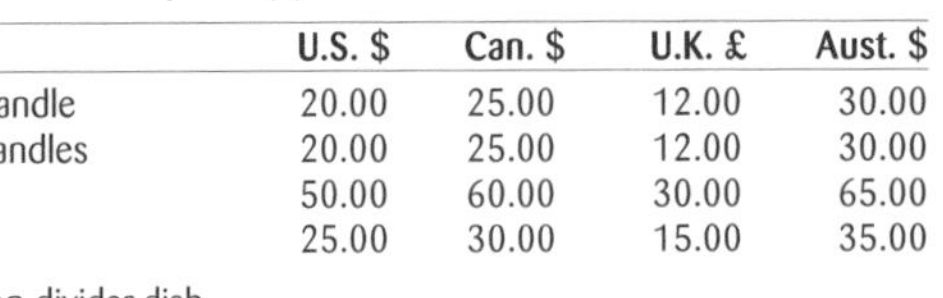

Shape	U.S. $	Can. $	U.K. £	Aust. $
Hug-a-mug, one handle	20.00	25.00	12.00	30.00
Hug-a-mug, two handles	20.00	25.00	12.00	30.00
Divider Dish	50.00	60.00	30.00	65.00
Money Ball	25.00	30.00	15.00	35.00

* Indicates scene on divider dish.

Resting in Wheelbarrow (57)

GEOGRAPHY LESSON

Design No.: LF17
Designer: Walter Hayward
Issued: 1954 - 1970

Shape	U.S. $	Can. $	U.K. £	Aust. $
Baby plate, oval, large				
with signature	200.00	250.00	115.00	275.00
without signature	150.00	180.00	90.00	190.00
Baby plate, round, large				
with signature	100.00	125.00	60.00	135.00
without signature	75.00	90.00	45.00	95.00
Bread and butter plate				
with signature	250.00	300.00	150.00	325.00
without signature	200.00	250.00	115.00	275.00
Cereal / oatmeal bowl				
with signature	35.00	45.00	20.00	50.00
without signature	25.00	30.00	15.00	35.00
Plate, 8"	75.00	90.00	45.00	95.00
Plate, 8 ½"				
with signature	75.00	90.00	45.00	95.00
without signature	25.00	30.00	15.00	35.00
Porridge plate				
with signature	110.00	135.00	65.00	145.00
without signature	85.00	100.00	50.00	110.00

Geography Lesson (LF17)

GETTING DRESSED

Design No.: LF2
Designer: Barbara Vernon
Issued: By 1940 - by 1952

Shape	U.S. $	Can. $	U.K. £	Aust. $
Baby plate, round, large				
with signature	400.00	475.00	225.00	500.00
without signature	350.00	425.00	200.00	450.00
Bread / butter plate, handles				
with signature	500.00	600.00	285.00	625.00
without signature	400.00	475.00	225.00	500.00
Hot water plate				
with signature	375.00	450.00	210.00	475.00
without signature	325.00	400.00	185.00	425.00
Plate, 8 ½"				
with signature	400.00	475.00	225.00	500.00
without signature	350.00	425.00	200.00	450.00
Porridge plate				
with signature	300.00	350.00	175.00	375.00
without signature	250.00	300.00	150.00	325.00

Getting Dressed (LF2)

Going Shopping (SF10)

GOING SHOPPING

Design No.: SF10
Designer: Barbara Vernon
Issued: By 1940 - by 1952
Combined with: *Chicken Pulling a Cart*, SF8
Engine Pulling a Carriage, HW17
Feeding the Baby, HW13
Fixing Braces, HW3
Kissing Under the Mistletoe, First Version, HW11R
Lambeth Walk, second version, HW16
Pulling on Trousers, HW2

Shape	U.S. $	Can. $	U.K. £	Aust. $
Baby plate, round, small				
with signature	50.00	60.00	30.00	65.00
without signature	30.00	35.00	17.50	40.00
Casino jug, 30s				
with signature	300.00	350.00	175.00	375.00
without signature	225.00	275.00	125.00	300.00
Casino jug, 36s				
with signature	275.00	325.00	160.00	350.00
without signature	225.00	275.00	125.00	300.00
Casino saucer				
with signature	75.00	90.00	45.00	95.00
without signature	50.00	60.00	30.00	65.00
Casino sugar bowl, 30s				
with signature	175.00	200.00	100.00	225.00
without signature	125.00	150.00	75.00	160.00
Casino teapot, 24s				
with signature	375.00	450.00	210.00	475.00
without signature	300.00	350.00	175.00	375.00
Casino teapot, 36s				
with signature	325.00	400.00	185.00	425.00
without signature	250.00	300.00	150.00	325.00
Cereal / oatmeal bowl				
with signature	35.00	45.00	20.00	50.00
without signature	25.00	30.00	15.00	35.00
Don beaker				
with signature	65.00	80.00	40.00	85.00
without signature	35.00	45.00	20.00	50.00
Don beaker, one handle				
with signature	65.00	80.00	40.00	85.00
without signature	35.00	45.00	20.00	50.00
Jaffa fruit saucer (wavy)				
with signature	75.00	90.00	45.00	95.00
without signature	50.00	60.00	30.00	65.00
Hot water plate				
with signature	125.00	150.00	75.00	160.00
without signature	100.00	125.00	60.00	135.00
Plate, 6 ½"				
with signature	30.00	35.00	17.50	40.00
without signature	20.00	25.00	12.50	30.00
Plate, 7 ½"				
with signature	65.00	80.00	40.00	85.00
without signature	25.00	30.00	15.00	35.00
FINE WHITE CHINA				
Cereal / oatmeal bowl			Very Rare	
Plate, 6"	650.00	775.00	375.00	800.00

Note: **1.** Early Don beakers may come with a border of running rabbits inside the beaker, a little down from the rim.
2. Condition is important. Prices listed are based on nurseryware in mint condition. Items in less than mint condition will command lower prices.

BUNNYKINS

DB1 – Family Photograph Bunnykins, *First Variation*

DB2 – Buntie Bunnykins Helping Mother

DB3 – Billie Bunnykins Cooling Off

DB4 – Billie & Buntie Bunnykins Sleigh Ride, *First Variation*

DB5 – Mr. Bunnykins Autumn Days

DB6 – Mrs. Bunnykins Clean Sweep

DB7 – Daisie Bunnykins Spring Time

DB8 – Dollie Bunnykins Playtime *First Variation*

DB9 – Storytime Bunnykins *First Variation*

DB10 – Busy Needles Bunnykins

DB11 – Rise and Shine Bunnykins

DB12 – Tally Ho! Bunnykins *First Variation*

DB13 – The Artist Bunnykins

DB14 – Grandpa's Story Bunnykins

DB15 – Sleepytime Bunnykins

DB16 – Mr. Bunnybeat Strumming

DB17 – Santa Bunnykins Happy Christmas

DB18 – Mr. Bunnykins at the Easter Parade, *First Variation*

DB19 – Mrs. Bunnykins at the Easter Parade, *First Variation*

DB20 – Astro Bunnykins Rocket Man

DB21 – Happy Birthday Bunnykins

DB22 – Jogging Bunnykins

DB23 – Sousaphone Bunnykins *First Variation*

DB24 – Trumpeter Bunnykins *First Variation*

BUNNYKINS

DB25 – Cymbals Bunnykins
First Variation

DB26A – Drummer Bunnykins
Style One, First Variation

DB26B – Drummer Bunnykins
Style One, Second Variation

DB27 – Drum-Major
Bunnykins, *First Variation*

DB28A – Olympic Bunnykins
First Variation

DB28B – Olympic Bunnykins
Second Variation

DB29A – Touchdown Bunnykins
First Variation

DB29B – Touchdown Bunnykins
Second Variation (Boston College)

DB30 – Knockout Bunnykins

DB31 – Downhill Bunnykins

DB32 – Bogey Bunnykins

DB33 – Tally Ho!
Music Box

DB34 – Santa Bunnykins
Music Box

DB35 – Astro Bunnykins
Rocket Man, Music Box

DB36 – Happy Birthday
Bunnykins, Music Box

DB37 – Jogging Bunnykins
Music Box

DB38 – Mr. Bunnybeat Strumming
Music Box

DB39 – Mrs. Bunnykins at the
Easter Parade, Music Box

DB40 – Aerobic Bunnykins

DB41 – Freefall Bunnykins

DB42 – Ace Bunnykins

DB43 – Home Run Bunnykins

DB45 – King John
First Variation

DB46 – Queen Sophie
First Variation

Note: DB44 Ballet Bunnykins not issued

DB47 – Princess Beatrice
First Variation

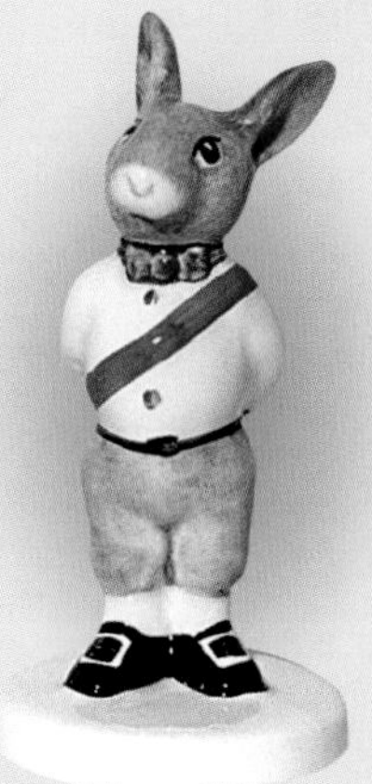

DB48 – Prince Frederick
First Variation

DB49 – Harry The Herald
First Variation

DB50 – Uncle Sam Bunnykins
First Variation

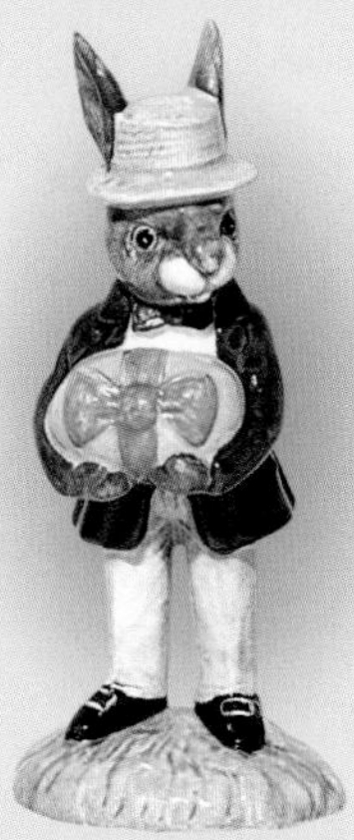

DB51 – Mr. Bunnykins
at the Easter Parade
Second Variation

DB52 – Mrs. Bunnykins
at the Easter Parade
Second Variation

DB53 – Carol Singer Bunnykins
Music Box

DB54 – Collector Bunnykins

DB55 – Bedtime Bunnykins
First Variation

DB56 – Be Prepared Bunnykins

DB57 – Schooldays Bunnykins

DB58 – Australian Bunnykins

DB59 Storytime Bunnykins
Second Variation

DB60 Schoolmaster Bunnykins

DB61 – Brownie Bunnykins

DB62 – Santa Bunnykins
Happy Christmas
Christmas Tree Ornament

DB63 – Bedtime Bunnykins
Second Variation

DB64 – Policeman Bunnykins

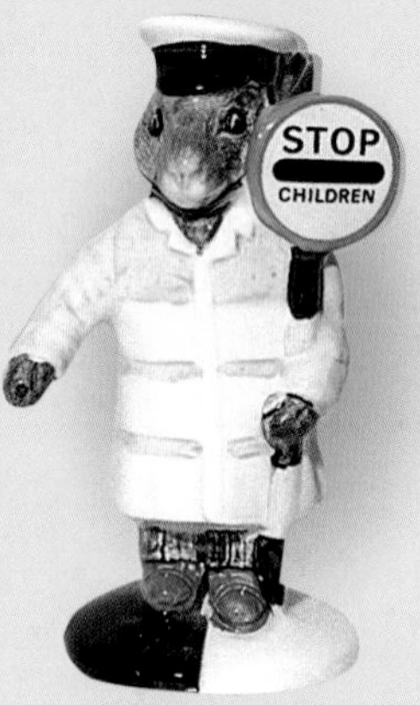

DB65 – Lollipopman Bunnykins

DB66 – Schoolboy Bunnykins

DB67 – Family Photograph
Bunnykins, *Second Variation*

DB68 – Father, Mother &
Victoria Bunnykins

DB69 – William Bunnykins

DB70 – Susan Bunnykins

BUNNYKINS

DB71 – Polly Bunnykins

DB72 – Tom Bunnykins

DB73 – Harry Bunnykins

DB74A – Nurse Bunnykins
First Variation

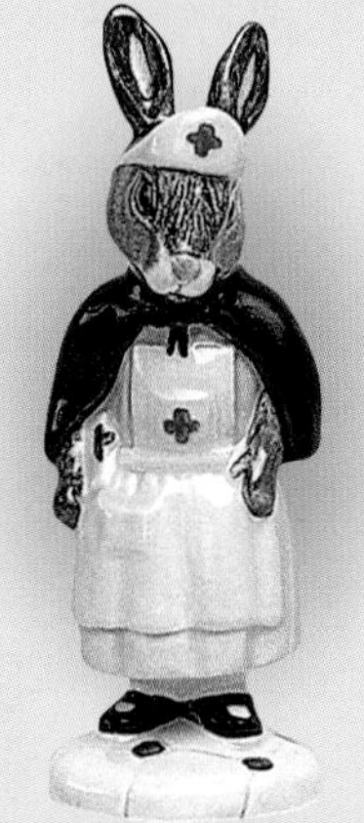
DB74B – Nurse Bunnykins
Second Variation

DB75 – Fireman Bunnykins
First Variation

DB76 – Postman Bunnykins
Style One

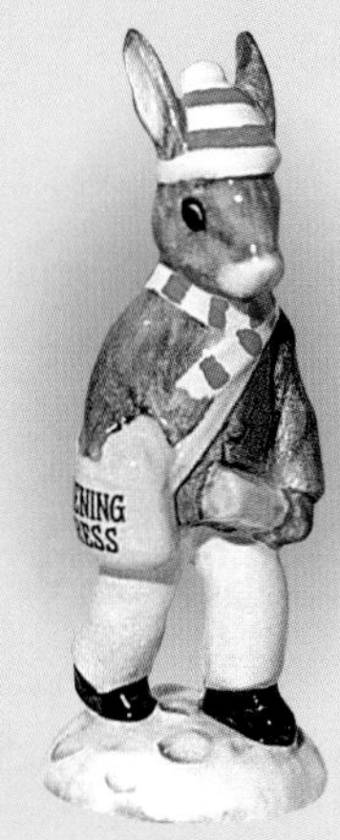
DB77 – Paperboy Bunnykins

DB78 – Tally Ho! Bunnykins
Second Variation

DB79 – Bedtime Bunnykins
Third Variation

DB80 – Dolly Bunnykins Playtime
Second Variation

DB81 – Billie & Buntie Bunnykins
Sleigh Ride, *Second Variation*

DB82 – Ice Cream Bunnykins

DB83 – Susan Bunnykins as Queen of the May

DB84 – Fisherman Bunnykins
Style One

DB85 – Cook Bunnykins

DB86 – Sousaphone Bunnykins, *Second Variation*

DB87 – Trumpeter Bunnykins
Second Variation

DB88 – Cymbals Bunnykins
Second Variation

DB89 – Drummer Bunnyk
Style One, Third Variatio

DB90 – Drum-Major Bunnykins
Second Variation

DB91 – King John
Second Variation

DB92 – Queen Sophie
Second Variation

DB93 – Princess Beatric
Second Variation

GOLFER

Design No.:	HW4R
Designer:	Barbara Vernon
Issued:	By 1937 - by 1952
Combined with:	
Cuddling under a Mushroom, HW4	*Pressing Trousers*, HW14
Cycling, HW15R	*Proposal*, HW11
Family at Breakfast, HW12	*Pulling on Trousers*, HW2
Feeding the Baby, HW13	*Reading the Times*, HW2R

Shape	U.S. $	Can. $	U.K. £	Aust. $
Casino jug, 36s	300.00	350.00	175.00	375.00
Casino jug, 42s	250.00	300.00	150.00	325.00
Casino teacup	75.00	90.00	45.00	95.00
Don beaker	65.00	80.00	40.00	85.00
Don beaker, one handle	65.00	80.00	40.00	85.00
Don mug, one handle	50.00	60.00	30.00	65.00
Don mug, two handles	50.00	60.00	30.00	65.00
FINE WHITE CHINA				
Rex mug, small	750.00	900.00	425.00	950.00

Golfer (HW4R)

Note: 1. This design should appear with the Barbara Vernon facsimile signature. See also *Game of Golf* (SF11) page 80.
2. *Golfer* (HW4R) is combined with *Proposal* (HW11) on the Rex mug.

Greetings (HW7)

GREETINGS

Design No.:	HW7
Designer:	Barbara Vernon
Issued:	By 1937 - by 1952
Combined with:	*Artist*, HW1
	Dunce, HW1R
	Fixing Braces, HW3
	Frightening Spider, SF4
	Gardening, Style One, HW9
	Pulling on Trousers, HW2

Shape	U.S. $	Can. $	U.K. £	Aust. $
Baby plate, round, small	50.00	60.00	30.00	65.00
Casino jug, 30s	350.00	425.00	200.00	450.00
Casino jug, 36s	300.00	350.00	175.00	375.00
Casino jug, 42s	250.00	300.00	150.00	325.00
Casino saucer	75.00	90.00	45.00	95.00
Casino teacup	75.00	90.00	45.00	95.00
Casino teapot, 24s	375.00	450.00	210.00	475.00
Casino teapot, 30s	325.00	400.00	185.00	425.00
Cereal / oatmeal bowl	35.00	45.00	20.00	50.00
Don beaker	125.00	150.00	75.00	160.00
Don beaker, one handle	100.00	125.00	60.00	135.00
Don mug, one handle	50.00	60.00	30.00	65.00
Don mug, two handles	50.00	60.00	30.00	65.00
Jaffa fruit saucer				
plain rim	50.00	60.00	30.00	65.00
wavy rim	75.00	90.00	45.00	95.00
Lid of hot water plate	100.00	125.00	60.00	135.00
Plate, 6 ½"	30.00	35.00	17.50	40.00
Plate, 7 ½"	65.00	80.00	40.00	85.00
FINE CHINA				
Plate, 5"	650.00	775.00	375.00	800.00
Plate, 7"	650.00	775.00	375.00	800.00
Rex mug, small	750.00	900.00	425.00	950.00

Note: This design should appear with the Barbara Vernon facsimile signature.

HAPPY BIRTHDAY FROM BUNNYKINS – Walter Hayward

Happy Birthday From Bunnykins,
Style One, (SF136)

Reverse Birthday Inscription

Style One

Design No.: Front — SF136 Happy Birthday from Bunnykins
Reverse — Birthday Inscription

Designer: Walter Hayward

Issued: 1982 - 1989

Inscription: "Birthdays are lots and lots of fun,
With cards and gifts for everyone
There are cakes and jellies and lots to eat,
Parties and games and your favourite treat.
So on this your very special day
The Bunnykins wish you a Happy Birthday"

Shape	U.S. $	Can. $	U.K. £	Aust. $
Plate, 8"	15.00	20.00	10.00	25.00

HAPPY BIRTHDAY FROM BUNNYKINS – Colin Twinn

Style Two, First Version

The rhyme used on the reverse of this plate is the same as that used on style one, however a new border and copyright date are shown.

Design No.: Front — CT37 Happy Birthday from Bunnykins
Reverse — CT64 Birthday Inscription
Designer: Colin Twinn
Issued: 1990 - 1992
Inscription: Birthdays are lots and lots of fun,
With cards and gifts for everyone
There are cakes and jellies and lots to eat
Parties and games and your favourite treat.
So on this your very special day
The Bunnykins wish you a Happy Birthday

Shape	U.S. $	Can. $	U.K. £	Aust. $
Cake plate, footed, 11"	175.00	225.00	100.00	250.00
Plate, 8"	15.00	20.00	10.00	25.00

Happy Birthday from Bunnykins
Style Two, First Version (CT37)

Birthday Inscription (CT64)

Happy Birthday from Bunnykins
Style Two, Second Version (CT60)

Style Two, Second Version

Design No.: Front — CT60 Happy Birthday from Bunnykins
Reverse — CT61 Inscription
Designer: Colin Twinn
Issued: 1992 - 1992

Shape	U.S. $	Can. $	U.K. £	Aust. $
Hug-a-mug, one handle	10.00	12.00	6.00	15.00

Happy Birthday Bunnykins
Inscription (CT61)

Note: See page 191 for two money balls issued for the 1992 U.S. Special Events Tour.

HAPPY EASTER FROM BUNNYKINS – Colin Twinn

Happy Easter from Bunnykins
First Version (CT40)

First Version, Large Design

Design No.: Front — CT40 Happy Easter from Bunnykins
Reverse no. one - without inscription
Reverse no. two — CT67 with inscription
Designer: Colin Twinn
Issued: 1990 - 1992
Rhyme: The Easter Bunnykins romp and play,
Loving the joy of this Easter Day.
Gone is the frost, the long winter lost,
The sunshine brings light and new blossoms bright,
So Bunnykins send you this warm invitation
To Easter party, a grand celebration.

Shape	U.S. $	Can. $	U.K. £	Aust. $
Plate, 8"	15.00	20.00	10.00	25.00

Happy Easter from Bunnykins
Second Version (CT62)

Second Version, Small Design

Design No.: Front — CT62 Happy Easter from Bunnykins
Reverse — CT63 Happy Easter Inscription
Designer: Colin Twinn
Issued: 1992 - 1992

Shape	U.S. $	Can. $	U.K. £	Aust. $
Hug-a-mug, one handle	10.00	12.00	6.00	15.00

Happy Easter Inscription (CT63)

HAT SHOP / TRYING ON HATS

Hat Shop (HW28)

Trying on Hats (HW28R)

Design No.: Front — HW28 Hat Shop
Reverse — HW28R Trying on Hats
Designer: Walter Hayward
Issued: *Hat Shop*: 1954 - by 1998
Trying on Hats: 1954 - 2003

Combined with: *Afternoon Tea*, HW116
Bedtime with Dollies, EC125
Dancing with Doll, HW115R
Drummer and Bugler, EC126
Serving Tea, HW116R
Trumpeter, EC5

Shape	U.S. $	Can. $	U.K. £	Aust. $
Albion cream jug	35.00	45.00	20.00	50.00
Albion jug, ½ pint	85.00	100.00	50.00	110.00
Albion jug, 1 pint	100.00	125.00	60.00	135.00
Albion teapot	50.00	60.00	30.00	65.00
Casino jug, 30s				
with signature	200.00	250.00	115.00	275.00
without signature	150.00	180.00	90.00	190.00
Casino jug, 36s				
with signature	175.00	200.00	100.00	225.00
without signature	125.00	150.00	75.00	160.00
Casino jug, 42s				
with signature	150.00	180.00	90.00	190.00
without signature	100.00	125.00	60.00	135.00
Casino saucer				
with signature	15.00	20.00	10.00	25.00
without signature	8.00	10.00	5.00	12.00
Casino teacup				
with signature	15.00	20.00	10.00	25.00
without signature	8.00	10.00	5.00	12.00
Divider dish	50.00	60.00	30.00	65.00
Don beaker				
with signature	50.00	60.00	30.00	65.00
without signature	25.00	35.00	15.00	35.00
Don beaker, one handle				
with signature	50.00	60.00	30.00	65.00
without signature	25.00	30.00	15.00	35.00

Shape	U.S. $	Can. $	U.K. £	Aust. $
Don mug, one handle				
with signature	40.00	50.00	25.00	55.00
without signature	10.00	12.50	6.00	15.00
Don mug, two handles				
with signature	40.00	50.00	25.00	55.00
without signature	10.00	12.00	6.00	15.00
Egg box				
small	175.00	200.00	100.00	225.00
medium	200.00	250.00	115.00	275.00
large	225.00	275.00	125.00	300.00
Hug-a-mug, one handle	10.00	12.00	6.00	15.00
Hug-a-mug, two handles	10.00	12.00	6.00	15.00
Jaffa fruit saucer (plain)	15.00	20.00	10.00	25.00
Lamp	50.00	60.00	30.00	65.00
Lid of hot water plate				
with signature	75.00	90.00	45.00	95.00
without signature	50.00	60.00	30.00	65.00
Malvern beaker	15.00	20.00	10.00	25.00
Money ball	10.00	12.00	6.00	15.00
Picture plaque, small	20.00	25.00	12.50	30.00
Plate, 6 ½"				
with signature	25.00	30.00	15.00	35.00
without signature	15.00	20.00	10.00	25.00
Savings book	15.00	20.00	10.00	25.00
Stratford straight beaker	15.00	20.00	10.00	25.00
Stratford teacup	8.00	10.00	5.00	12.00

Note: *Trying on Hats* (HW28R) is paired with *Dancing with Doll* (HW115R) on the Savings book. The divider dish combines *Afternoon Tea* (HW116), *Serving Tea* (HW116R) and *Trying on Hats* (HW28R) and the lid of the hot water plate combines *Hat Shop* (HW28), *Trying on Hats* (HW28R) and *Drummer and Bugler* (EC126).

HAYMAKING / LUNCH BREAK

Haymaking (HW29)

Lunch Break (HW29R)

Design No.: Front — HW29 Haymaking
Reverse — HW29R Lunch Break
Designer: Walter Hayward
Issued: 1954 - by 1998

Combined with: *Apple Picking*, SF25
Dancing with Doll, HW115R
Holding Hat and Coat, EC4
Sleeping in a Rocking Chair, EC1
Toast for Tea Today, SF3

Shape	U.S. $	Can. $	U.K. £	Aust. $
Albion cream jug	35.00	45.00	20.00	50.00
Albion jug, ½ pint	85.00	100.00	50.00	110.00
Albion jug, 1 pint	100.00	125.00	60.00	135.00
Albion teapot	50.00	60.00	30.00	65.00
Casino jug, 36s				
with signature	175.00	200.00	100.00	225.00
without signature	125.00	150.00	75.00	160.00
Casino jug, 42s				
with signature	150.00	180.00	90.00	190.00
without signature	100.00	125.00	60.00	135.00
Casino saucer				
with signature	15.00	20.00	10.00	25.00
without signature	8.00	10.00	5.00	12.00
Casino sugar, 30s				
with signature	175.00	200.00	100.00	225.00
without signature	125.00	150.00	75.00	160.00
Casino teacup				
with signature	15.00	20.00	10.00	25.00
without signature	8.00	10.00	5.00	12.00
Casino teapot, 24s				
with signature	300.00	350.00	175.00	375.00
without signature	225.00	275.00	125.00	300.00
Casino teapot, 30s				
with signature	250.00	300.00	150.00	325.00
without signature	150.00	180.00	90.00	190.00
Don beaker				
with signature	50.00	60.00	30.00	65.00
without signature	25.00	30.00	15.00	35.00
Don beaker, one handle				
with signature	50.00	60.00	30.00	65.00
without signature	25.00	30.00	15.00	35.00

Shape	U.S. $	Can. $	U.K. £	Aust. $
Don mug, one handle				
with signature	40.00	50.00	25.00	55.00
without signature	10.00	12.50	6.00	15.00
Don mug, two handles				
with signature	40.00	50.00	25.00	55.00
without signature	10.00	12.50	6.00	15.00
Egg box				
small	175.00	200.00	100.00	225.00
medium	200.00	250.00	115.00	275.00
large	225.00	275.00	125.00	300.00
Hug-a-mug, one handle	10.00	12.00	6.00	15.00
Hug-a-mug, two handles	10.00	12.00	6.00	15.00
Jaffa fruit saucer (plain)	15.00	20.00	10.00	25.00
Lamp	50.00	60.00	30.00	65.00
Lid of hot water plate				
with signature	75.00	90.00	45.00	95.00
without signature	50.00	60.00	30.00	65.00
Malvern beaker	15.00	20.00	10.00	25.00
Money ball	10.00	12.00	6.00	15.00
Picture plaque, small	20.00	25.00	12.50	30.00
Plate, 6 ½"				
with signature	25.00	30.00	15.00	35.00
without signature	15.00	20.00	10.00	25.00
Savings book	15.00	20.00	10.00	25.00
Stratford straight beaker	15.00	20.00	10.00	25.00
Stratford teacup	8.00	10.00	5.00	12.00

HIKERS

Hikers (EC124)

Design No.:	EC124
Designer:	Walter Hayward
Issued:	1959 to the present
Combined with:	*Afternoon Tea,* HW116
	Bedtime with Dollies, EC125
	Daisy Chains, HW25
	The Doll's House, HW120
	Drummer, EC2
	Drummer and Bugler, EC126
	Hobby Horse, Style Two, EC121
	Holding Hat and Coat, EC4
	Nipped by a Crab, HW21R
	Playing with Cup and Spoon, EC6
	Playing with Doll and Pram, EC123
	Playing with Doll and Teddy, HW120R
	Playing with Dolls and Prams, HW115
	Raising Hat, Style Two, EC7
	Reading, EC122
	Row Boat, HW21
	Sheltering Under an Umbrella, EC3
	Sleeping in a Rocking Chair, EC1
	Trumpeter, EC5

Shape	U.S. $	Can. $	U.K. £	Aust. $
Albion sugar bowl	30.00	35.00	17.50	40.00
Beaker cover	65.00	80.00	40.00	85.00
Egg cup				
Style One	30.00	35.00	17.50	40.00
Style Two	40.00	50.00	25.00	55.00
Style Three	10.00	12.00	6.00	15.00
Lid of hot water plate	50.00	60.00	30.00	65.00
Money Ball	25.00	30.00	15.00	35.00

Note: This scene was combined with *Daisy Chains*, (HW25) on a Hug-a-mug for the U.S. Special Events Tour in 1993, see page 192.

Hobby Horse, Style Two (EC121)

HOBBY HORSE
Style Two

Design No.:	EC121
Designer:	Walter Hayward
Issued:	1959 to the present
Combined with:	*Cowboy on Rocking Horse*, HW140R *Cowboys and Indians*, HW140 *Drummer,* EC2 *Drummer and Bugler*, EC126 *Hikers,* EC124 *Holding Hat and Coat,* EC4 *Lasso Games*, HW117 *Lassoing*, HW117R *Playing with Cup and Spoon*, EC6 *Playing with Doll and Pram*, EC123 *Raising Hat*, Style Two, EC7 *Reading*, EC122 *Sheltering Under an Umbrella*, EC3 *Sleeping in a Rocking Chair*, EC1 *Trumpeter,* EC5

Shape	U.S. $	Can. $	U.K. £	Aust. $
Albion sugar bowl	30.00	35.00	17.50	40.00
Beaker cover	65.00	80.00	40.00	85.00
Egg cup				
Style One	30.00	35.00	17.50	40.00
Style Two	40.00	50.00	25.00	55.00
Style Three	10.00	12.00	6.00	15.00
Lid of hot water plate	50.00	60.00	30.00	65.00

Fine white china teacup combining *Pulling on Trousers* (HW2) and *Proposal* (HW11)

HOLDING HAT AND COAT

Holding Hat and Coat (EC4)

Design No.: EC4
Designer: Barbara Vernon
Issued: 1937 - 2003
Combined with: *Bedtime with Dollies*, EC125
Drummer, EC2
Drummer and Bugler, EC126
Haymaking, HW29
Hikers, EC124
Hobby Horse, Style Two, EC121
Lunch Break, HW29R
Netting a Cricket, HW6
Playing with Cup and Spoon, EC6
Playing with Doll and Pram, EC123
Pressing Trousers, HW14
Proposal, HW11
Pulling on Trousers, HW2
Raising Hat, Style Two, EC7
Sheltering Under an Umbrella, EC3
Skipping, HW20R
Swinging, HW20
Trumpeter, EC5
Wheelbarrow Race, Style One, HW22

Shape	U.S. $	Can. $	U.K. £	Aust. $
Albion sugar bowl	30.00	35.00	17.50	40.00
Beaker cover				
with signature	75.00	90.00	45.00	95.00
without signature	65.00	80.00	40.00	85.00
Casino sugar bowl, 36s				
with signature	125.00	150.00	75.00	160.00
without signature	100.00	125.00	60.00	135.00
Egg cup				
Style One	30.00	35.00	17.50	40.00
Style Two				
with signature	50.00	60.00	30.00	65.00
without signature	40.00	50.00	25.00	55.00
Style Three	10.00	12.00	6.00	15.00
Lid of hot water plate				
with signature	75.00	90.00	45.00	95.00
without signature	50.00	60.00	30.00	65.00
Money ball	10.00	12.00	6.00	15.00

FINE CHINA

Beaker cover
with signature — Very Rare

Home Decorating (SF131)

HOME DECORATING

Design No.: SF131
Designer: Walter Hayward
Issued: 1967 - by 1998

Shape	U.S. $	Can. $	U.K. £	Aust. $
Baby plate, round, small	20.00	25.00	12.00	30.00
Cake stand	150.00	180.00	90.00	190.00
Casino saucer	8.00	10.00	5.00	12.00
Cereal / oatmeal bowl	15.00	20.00	10.00	25.00
Coupe plate, 6 ¾"		Very Rare		
Hot water plate	75.00	90.00	45.00	95.00
Jaffa fruit saucer (plain)	15.00	20.00	10.00	25.00
Picture plaque, large	20.00	25.00	12.00	30.00
Plate, 6 ½"	15.00	20.00	10.00	25.00
Plate, 8"	15.00	20.00	10.00	25.00
Plate, 10 ½"	20.00	25.00	12.00	30.00

HOME FROM FISHING
First Variation, Large Size

Design No.: CT18 Home from Fishing
Designer: Colin Twinn
Issued: 1990 - 1993

Shape	U.S. $	Can. $	U.K. £	Aust. $
Albion cream jug	35.00	45.00	20.00	50.00
Albion jug, 1 pint	100.00	125.00	60.00	135.00
Baby plate, round, small	20.00	25.00	12.50	30.00
Divider dish	75.00	90.00	45.00	95.00
Jaffa fruit saucer	15.00	20.00	10.00	25.00
Picture plaque, large	20.00	25.00	12.00	30.00
Picture plaque, small	20.00	25.00	12.00	30.00
Plate, 8"	15.00	20.00	10.00	25.00

Home from Fishing, First Variation (CT18)

HOME FROM FISHING
Second Variation, Small Size / FATHER BUNNYKINS WITH FISHING ROD

Design No.: Front — CT26 Home from Fishing
Reverse — CT27 Father Bunnykins with Fishing Rod
Designer: Colin Twinn
Issued: 1990 - 1993
Combined with: *Bunny on Rocking Horse*, CT29
Family with Pram, Style Two, CT14
Standing by Pram, CT6

Shape	U.S. $	Can. $	U.K. £	Aust. $
Albion cream jug	35.00	45.00	20.00	50.00
Albion jug, ½ pint	85.00	100.00	50.00	110.00
Albion jug, 1 pint	100.00	125.00	60.00	135.00
Albion teapot	50.00	60.00	30.00	65.00
Hug-a-mug, one handle	10.00	12.00	6.00	15.00
Hug-a-mug, two handles	10.00	12.00	6.00	15.00
Lamp	50.00	60.00	30.00	65.00
Malvern beaker	15.00	20.00	10.00	25.00
Money ball	10.00	12.00	6.00	15.00
Picture plaque, small	20.00	25.00	12.50	30.00
Savings book	15.00	20.00	10.00	25.00
Stratford straight beaker	15.00	20.00	10.00	25.00
Stratford teacup	8.00	10.00	5.00	12.00

Note: *Bunny on Rocking Horse* (CT29) is combined with *Home from Fishing* (CT26) on a savings book.

Home from Fishing, Second Variation (CT26)

Father Bunnykins with Fishing Rod (CT27)

Hoopla (LF129)

HOOPLA

Design No.: LF129
Designer: Walter Hayward
Issued: 1967 - 1970

Shape	U.S. $	Can. $	U.K. £	Aust. $
Baby plate, oval, large	450.00	550.00	260.00	575.00
Baby plate, round, large	350.00	425.00	200.00	450.00
Plate, 8 ½"	225.00	275.00	125.00	300.00
Porridge Plate	250.00	300.00	150.00	325.00

ICE CREAM THEME – Colin Twinn

Ice Cream Seller, First Variation (CT5)

ICE CREAM SELLER
First Variation, Large Size

Design No.: CT5 Ice Cream Seller
Designer: Colin Twinn
Issued: 1989 - 1993
Combined with: *Pushing the Wheelbarrow*, CT3
Splashing at Sink, CT33
Washing Up, CT32

Shape	U.S. $	Can. $	U.K. £	Aust. $
Albion teapot	50.00	60.00	30.00	65.00
Hug-a-mug, one handle	10.00	12.00	6.00	15.00
Hug-a-mug, two handles	10.00	12.00	6.00	15.00
Lamp	50.00	60.00	30.00	65.00
Malvern beaker	15.00	20.00	10.00	25.00
Money ball	10.00	12.00	6.00	15.00
Picture plaque, small	25.00	30.00	15.00	35.00
Stratford straight beaker	15.00	20.00	10.00	25.00
Stratford teacup	8.00	10.00	5.00	12.00

ICE CREAM SELLER
Second Variation, Small Size

Design No.: CT11 Ice Cream Seller
Designer: Colin Twinn
Issued: 1989 - 1993
Combined with: *Bunny on Trike*, CT23
Picking Daisies, CT4

Shape	U.S. $	Can. $	U.K. £	Aust. $
Albion cream jug	35.00	45.00	20.00	50.00
Albion jug, ½ pint	85.00	100.00	50.00	110.00
Albion jug, 1 pint	100.00	125.00	60.00	135.00
Albion teapot	50.00	60.00	30.00	65.00
Baby plate, round, small	20.00	25.00	12.00	30.00
Cake stand	150.00	180.00	90.00	190.00
Cereal / oatmeal bowl	15.00	20.00	10.00	25.00
Plate, 6"	15.00	20.00	10.00	25.00

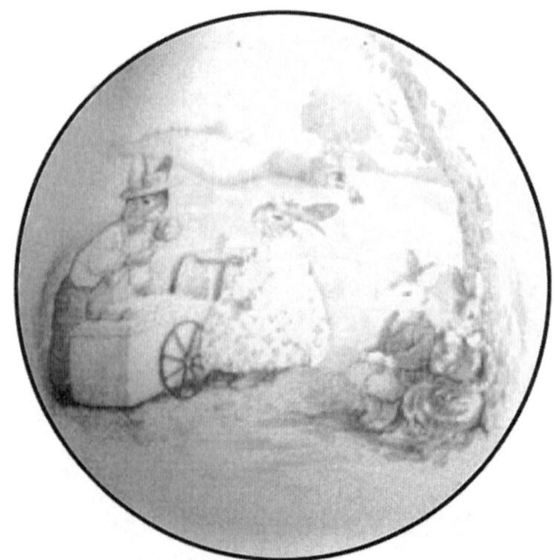

Ice Cream Seller, Second Variation (CT11)

ICE CREAM VENDOR / HIKER RESTING WITH ICE CREAM

Ice Cream Vendor (HW23)

Hiker Resting with Ice Cream (HW23R)

Design No.: Front — HW23 Ice Cream Vendor
Reverse — HW23R Hiker Resting with Ice Cream
Designer: Walter Hayward
Issued: By 1952 - by 1998

Combined with: *Daisy Chains*, HW25
**Peashooter*, HW118
Playing on the River, SF16
**Skipping Game*, HW139R
Sleeping on a Rocking Chair, EC1
**Snowball Fight*, HW141R

Shape	U.S. $	Can. $	U.K. £	Aust. $
Albion cream jug	35.00	45.00	20.00	50.00
Albion jug, ½ pint	85.00	100.00	50.00	110.00
Albion jug, 1 pint	100.00	125.00	60.00	135.00
Albion teapot	50.00	60.00	30.00	65.00
Baby plate, round, small				
with signature	30.00	35.00	17.50	40.00
without signature	20.00	25.00	12.00	30.00
Casino jug, 30s				
with signature	250.00	300.00	150.00	325.00
without signature	150.00	180.00	90.00	190.00
Casino jug, 36s				
with signature	175.00	200.00	100.00	225.00
without signature	125.00	150.00	75.00	160.00
Casino jug, 42s				
with signature	150.00	180.00	90.00	190.00
without signature	100.00	125.00	60.00	135.00
Casino saucer				
with signature	15.00	20.00	10.00	25.00
without signature	8.00	10.00	5.00	12.00
Casino sugar bowl, 30s				
with signature	175.00	200.00	100.00	225.00
without signature	125.00	150.00	75.00	160.00
Casino sugar bowl, 36s				
with signature	150.00	180.00	90.00	190.00
without signature	100.00	125.00	60.00	135.00
Casino teacup				
with signature	15.00	20.00	10.00	25.00
without signature	8.00	10.00	5.00	12.00
Casino teapot, 30s				
with signature	250.00	300.00	150.00	325.00
without signature	150.00	180.00	90.00	190.00
Divider dish	50.00	60.00	30.00	65.00
Don beaker				
with signature	50.00	60.00	30.00	65.00

Shape	U.S. $	Can. $	U.K. £	Aust. $
Don beaker				
without signature	25.00	30.00	15.00	35.00
Don beaker, one handle				
with signature	50.00	60.00	30.00	65.00
without signature	25.00	30.00	15.00	35.00
Don mug, one handle				
with signature	40.00	50.00	25.00	55.00
without signature	10.00	12.00	6.00	15.00
Don mug, two handles				
with signature	40.00	50.00	25.00	55.00
without signature	10.00	12.00	6.00	15.00
Egg box				
small	125.00	200.00	100.00	225.00
medium	200.00	250.00	115.00	275.00
large	225.00	275.00	125.00	300.00
Hug-a-mug, one handle	10.00	12.00	6.00	15.00
0Hug-a-mug, two handles	10.00	12.00	6.00	15.00
Jaffa fruit saucer				
plain rim	15.00	20.00	12.00	25.00
wavy rim	35.00	45.00	20.00	50.00
Lamp	50.00	60.00	30.00	65.00
Lid of hot water plate				
with signature	75.00	90.00	45.00	95.00
without signature	50.00	60.00	30.00	65.00
Malvern Beaker	25.00	30.00	15.00	35.00
Money ball	15.00	20.00	10.00	25.00
Picture plaque, small	20.00	25.00	12.00	30.00
Plate, 6 ½"				
with signature	25.00	30.00	15.00	35.00
without signature	15.00	20.00	10.00	25.00
Savings book	15.00	20.00	10.00	25.00
Stratford straight beaker	15.00	20.00	10.00	25.00
Stratford teacup	8.00	10.00	5.00	12.00

* Indicates scene on divider dish

Ice Skating (SF24)

ICE SKATING

Design No.: SF24
Designer: Walter Hayward
Issued: 1954 - 1967

Shape	U.S. $	Can. $	U.K. £	Aust. $
Baby plate, round, small				
with signature	50.00	60.00	30.00	65.00
without signature	30.00	35.00	17.50	40.00
Baby plate, round, large				
with signature	100.00	125.00	60.00	135.00
without signature	75.00	90.00	45.00	95.00
Casino jug, 24s				
with signature	400.00	475.00	225.00	500.00
without signature	350.00	425.00	200.00	450.00
Casino saucer				
with signature	75.00	90.00	45.00	95.00
without signature	50.00	60.00	30.00	65.00
Casino sugar bowl, 36s				
with signature	150.00	180.00	90.00	190.00
without signature	135.00	160.00	75.00	170.00
Cereal / oatmeal bowl				
with signature	35.00	45.00	20.00	50.00
without signature	25.00	30.00	15.00	35.00
Hot water plate				
with signature	125.00	150.00	75.00	160.00
without signature	100.00	125.00	60.00	135.00
Jaffa fruit saucer (plain)	30.00	35.00	17.50	40.00
Plate, 6 ½"				
with signature	30.00	35.00	17.50	40.00
without signature	20.00	25.00	12.50	30.00
Plate, 7 ½"				
with signature	60.00	70.00	35.00	75.00
without signature	25.00	30.00	15.00	35.00
Plate, 8 ½"				
with signature	75.00	90.00	45.00	95.00
without signature	25.00	30.00	15.00	35.00

Note: Retirement dates are all approximate. When a design is retired all remaining stocks of the retired litho prints are used until exhausted.

JACK AND JILL

Design No.: Front — CT9 Jack and Jill
Reverse — CT10 Jack and Jill Nursery Rhyme
Designer: Colin Twinn
Issued: 1989 - 1993

Shape	U.S. $	Can. $	U.K. £	Aust. $
Hug-a-mug, one handle	10.00	12.00	6.00	15.00

Jack and Jill (CT9)

Jack and Jill Nursery Rhyme (CT10)

JUGGLING

Design No.: LF127
Designer: Walter Hayward
Issued: 1967 - 1970

Shape	U.S. $	Can. $	U.K. £	Aust. $
Baby plate, oval, large	450.00	550.00	260.00	575.00
Baby plate, round, large	300.00	350.00	175.00	375.00
Plate, 8 ½"	225.00	275.00	125.00	300.00
Porridge plate	250.00	300.00	150.00	325.00

Juggling (LF127)

Kissing Under the Mistletoe
(with mistletoe)

KISSING UNDER THE MISTLETOE
First Version, With Mistletoe

Design No.: HW11R
Designer: Barbara Vernon
Issued: By 1937 - by 1947
Combined with: *Cycling*, HW15R
Family at Breakfast, HW12
Feeding the Baby, HW13
Going Shopping, SF10
Lambeth Walk, First Version, HW16
Medicine Time, SF1
Proposal, HW11
Reading the Times, HW2R

Shape	U.S. $	Can. $	U.K. £	Aust. $
Casino jug, 30s	250.00	300.00	150.00	325.00
Casino jug, 36s	300.00	350.00	175.00	375.00
Casino jug, 42s	275.00	325.00	160.00	350.00
Casino sugar bowl	200.00	250.00	115.00	275.00
Casino teacup	75.00	90.00	45.00	95.00
Don beaker	150.00	180.00	90.00	190.00
Don beaker, one handle	150.00	180.00	90.00	190.00
Don mug, one handle	75.00	90.00	45.00	95.00
Don mug, two handles	75.00	90.00	45.00	95.00
FINE WHITE CHINA				
Teacup	300.00	350.00	175.00	375.00

Kissing Under the Mistletoe
(without mistletoe)

KISSING UNDER THE MISTLETOE
Second Version, Without Mistletoe

Design No.: HW11R
Designer: Barbara Vernon
Issued: By 1947 - by 1967
Combined with: *Cycling*, HW15R
Family at Breakfast, HW12
Feeding the Baby, HW13
Medicine Time, SF1
Proposal, HW11
Reading the Times, HW2R

Shape	U.S. $	Can. $	U.K. £	Aust. $
Beaker cover	75.00	90.00	45.00	95.00
Casino jug, 42s				
with signature	150.00	180.00	90.00	190.00
without signature	100.00	125.00	60.00	135.00
Casino teacup				
with signature	75.00	90.00	45.00	95.00
without signature	50.00	60.00	30.00	65.00
Don beaker				
with signature	65.00	80.00	40.00	85.00
without signature	35.00	45.00	20.00	50.00
Don beaker, one handle				
with signature	65.00	80.00	40.00	85.00
without signature	35.00	45.00	20.00	50.00
Don mug, one handle				
with signature	50.00	60.00	30.00	65.00
without signature	15.00	20.00	10.00	25.00
Don mug, two handles				
with signature	50.00	60.00	30.00	65.00
without signature	15.00	20.00	10.00	25.00
FINE WHITE CHINA				
Rex mug, small	750.00	900.00	425.00	950.00

LAMBETH WALK
First Version, Lambeth Walk on Music Sheet

Lambeth Walk, First Version (HW16)

Design No.:	HW16
Designer:	Barbara Vernon
Issued:	By 1937 - by 1949
Combined with:	**Cycling*, HW15R *Family at Breakfast,* HW12 *Footballer*, HW13R *Kissing Under the Mistletoe,* First Version, HW1R *Leapfrog*, HW12R *Raising Hat*, Style One, HW16R Sleeping in a Rocking Chair, EC1 *Top Hat*, HW14R **Trumpeter,* EC5 *Wedding,* LFd

Shape	U.S. $	Can. $	U.K. £	Aust. $
Baby plate, round, small	50.00	60.00	30.00	65.00
Candle holder	1,500.00	1,800.00	850.00	1,900.00
Casino jug, 30s	300.00	350.00	175.00	375.00
Casino jug, 36s	250.00	300.00	150.00	325.00
Casino saucer	75.00	90.00	45.00	95.00
Casino sugar bowl, 36s	200.00	250.00	115.00	275.00
Casino teacup	100.00	125.00	60.00	135.00
Casino teapot, 36s	250.00	300.00	150.00	325.00
Don beaker	65.00	80.00	40.00	85.00
Don mug, one handle	50.00	60.00	30.00	65.00
Don mug, two handles	50.00	60.00	30.00	65.00
Jam pot	1,500.00	1,800.00	850.00	1,900.00
Lid of hot water plate	100.00	125.00	60.00	135.00
Plate, 6 ½"	75.00	90.00	45.00	95.00
FINE WHITE CHINA				
Rex mug, small	750.00	900.00	425.00	950.00
Saucer	300.00	350.00	175.00	375.00

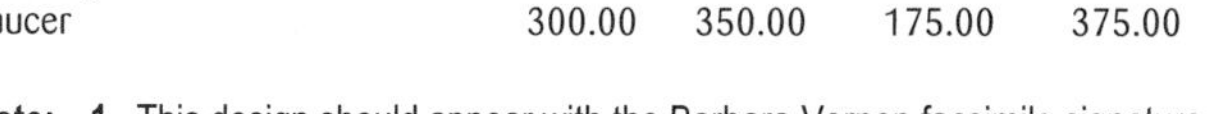

Note:
1. This design should appear with the Barbara Vernon facsimile signature.
2. On the Rex mug *Lambeth Walk*, first version (HW16) is combined with *Cycling* (HW15R) or *Footballer* (HW13R)
3. * Indicates a design on a lid of a hot water plate.

A rare Bunnykins vegetable tureen
Family at Breakfast, (HW12); *Lambeth Walk* (HW16)

Lambeth Walk, Second Version (HW16)

LAMBETH WALK, Second Version, Musical Score on Music Sheet, Bird Sits Atop Sheet

After 1949 the words Lambeth Walk were replaced by a musical score, and a small bird sat atop the music sheet.

Design No.: HW16
Designer: Barbara Vernon
Issued: By 1949 - 1967
Combined with: *Bedtime with Dollies*, EC125
Cycling, HW15R
Footballer, HW13R
Going Shopping, SF10
Leapfrog, HW12R
Playing with Dolls, EC123
Raising Hat, Style One, HW16R
Santa Claus, SF9
Sleeping in a Rocking Chair, EC1
Soldiers Marching, HW18R
Top Hat, HW14R
Trumpeter, EC5

Shape	U.S. $	Can. $	U.K. £	Aust. $
Baby plate, round, small				
with signature	50.00	60.00	30.00	65.00
without signature	30.00	35.00	17.50	40.00
Candle holder	1,500.00	1,800.00	850.00	1,900.00
Casino jug, 30s				
with signature	200.00	250.00	115.00	275.00
without signature	150.00	180.00	90.00	190.00
Casino jug, 36s				
with signature	150.00	180.00	90.00	190.00
without signature	125.00	150.00	75.00	160.00
Casino jug, 42s				
with signature	125.00	150.00	75.00	160.00
without signature	100.00	125.00	60.00	135.00
Casino saucer				
with signature	15.00	20.00	10.00	25.00
without signature	8.00	10.00	5.00	12.00
Casino sugar bowl, 30s				
with signature	200.00	250.00	115.00	275.00
without signature	175.00	200.00	100.00	225.00
Casino teacup				
with signature	15.00	20.00	10.00	25.00
without signature	8.00	10.00	5.00	12.00
Casino teapot, 24s				
with signature	275.00	325.00	160.00	350.00
without signature	175.00	200.00	100.00	225.00
Cup / mug, large	350.00	425.00	200.00	450.00

Shape	U.S. $	Can. $	U.K. £	Aust. $
Don beaker				
with signature	65.00	80.00	40.00	85.00
without signature	35.00	45.00	20.00	50.00
Don beaker, one handle				
with signature	65.00	80.00	40.00	85.00
without signature	35.00	45.00	20.00	50.00
Don mug, one handle				
with signature	50.00	60.00	30.00	65.00
without signature	15.00	20.00	10.00	25.00
Don mug, two handles				
with signature	50.00	60.00	30.00	65.00
without signature	15.00	20.00	10.00	25.00
Egg cup				
Style One	40.00	50.00	25.00	55.00
Style Two	75.00	90.00	45.00	95.00
Style Three	20.00	25.00	12.00	30.00
Jam pot	1,500.00	1,800.00	850.00	1,900.00
Lid of hot water plate				
with signature	100.00	125.00	60.00	135.00
without signature	75.00	90.00	45.00	95.00
Plate, 6 ½"				
with signature	30.00	35.00	17.50	40.00
without signature	20.00	25.00	12.00	30.00
Sugar bowl with handles		Extremely rare		
FINE WHITE CHINA				
Rex mug, small	750.00	900.00	425.00	950.00

Note: On the Rex mug *Lambeth Walk* is combined with *Proposal* (HW11).

LASSO GAMES / LASSOING

Design No.: Front — HW117 Lasso Games
Reverse — HW117R Lassoing
Designer: Walter Hayward
Issued: 1959 - 1967
Combined with: *Hobby Horse*, Style Two, EC121
Watering the Flowers, SF15

Shape	U.S. $	Can. $	U.K. £	Aust. $
Casino teacup	50.00	60.00	30.00	65.00
Casino teapot, 30s	325.00	400.00	185.00	425.00
Don beaker	35.00	45.00	20.00	50.00
Don beaker, one handle	35.00	45.00	20.00	50.00
Don mug, one handle	15.00	20.00	12.00	25.00
Don mug, two handles	15.00	20.00	12.00	25.00
Jaffa fruit saucer (plain)	30.00	35.00	17.50	40.00
Lid of hot water plate	75.00	90.00	45.00	95.00
Plate, 6 ½"	20.00	25.00	12.00	30.00

Lasso Games (HW117)

LEAPFROG

Design No.: HW12R
Designer: Barbara Vernon
Issued: By 1937 - by 1952
Combined with:
Asleep in the Open Air, HW10
Chicken Pulling a Cart, SF8
Convalescing, SF5
Embracing at a Window, HW5
Family at Breakfast, HW12
Feeding the Baby, HW13
Fixing Braces, HW3
Gardener with Wheelbarrow, HW9R
Family Going out on Washing Day, HW8
Family with Pram, Style One, HW15
Gardening, Style One, HW9
Lambeth Walk, HW16
Pressing Trousers, HW14
Proposal, HW11
Raising Hat, Style Two, EC7
Reading the Times, HW2R
Washing in the Open Air, HW10R

Shape	U.S. $	Can. $	U.K. £	Aust. $
Beaker cover	75.00	90.00	45.00	95.00
Casino jug, 36s				
with signature	300.00	350.00	175.00	375.00
without signature	250.00	300.00	150.00	325.00
Casino jug, 42s				
with signature	250.00	300.00	150.00	325.00
without signature	200.00	250.00	115.00	275.00
Casino sugar bowl, 30s				
with signature	200.00	250.00	115.00	275.00
without signature	150.00	180.00	90.00	190.00
Casino teacup				
with signature	75.00	90.00	45.00	95.00
without signature	50.00	60.00	30.00	65.00
Casino teapot 36s				
with signature	275.00	325.00	160.00	350.00
without signature	200.00	250.00	115.00	275.00
Don beaker				
with signature	65.00	80.00	40.00	85.00
without signature	35.00	45.00	20.00	50.00
Don beaker, one handle				
with signature	65.00	80.00	40.00	85.00
without signature	35.00	45.00	20.00	50.00
Don mug, one handle				
with signature	50.00	60.00	30.00	65.00
without signature	15.00	20.00	10.00	25.00
Egg cup, Style One	50.00	60.00	30.00	65.00
Jam pot	1,500.00	1,800.00	850.00	1,900.00
FINE WHITE CHINA				
Rex mug, small	750.00	900.00	425.00	950.00
Saucer	300.00	350.00	175.00	375.00
Teacup	300.00	350.00	175.00	375.00

Lassoing (HW117R)

Leapfrog (HW12R)

Note: *Leapfrog* is combined with *Footballer* (HW13R) on the Rex mug.

Letterbox (SF13)

LETTERBOX

Design No.: SF13
Designer: Walter Hayward after Barbara Vernon
Issued: By 1952 - by 1998
Combined with: *Engine Pulling a Carriage*, HW17

Shape	U.S. $	Can. $	U.K. £	Aust. $
Baby plate, round, small				
with signature	30.00	35.00	17.50	40.00
without signature	20.00	25.00	12.00	30.00
Cake stand	150.00	180.00	90.00	190.00
Casino jug, 30s				
with signature	200.00	250.00	115.00	275.00
without signature	175.00	200.00	100.00	225.00
Casino saucer				
with signature	15.00	20.00	10.00	25.00
without signature	8.00	10.00	5.00	12.00
Casino teapot, 24s				
with signature	275.00	325.00	160.00	350.00
without signature	175.00	200.00	100.00	225.00
Cereal / oatmeal bowl				
with signature	25.00	30.00	15.00	35.00
without signature	15.00	20.00	10.00	25.00
Hot water plate				
with signature	100.00	125.00	60.00	135.00
without signature	75.00	90.00	45.00	95.00
Jaffa fruit saucer (plain)				
with signature	25.00	30.00	15.00	35.00
without signature	15.00	20.00	10.00	25.00
Plate, 6 ½"				
with signature	25.00	30.00	15.00	35.00
without signature	10.00	12.00	6.00	15.00
Plate, 7 ½"				
with signature	30.00	35.00	17.50	40.00
without signature	15.00	20.00	10.00	25.00
Plate, 8"				
with signature	30.00	35.00	17.50	40.00
without signature	15.00	20.00	10.00	25.00

Note: A money box in the same shape of a post box was modelled but not put into production. Two examples have been recorded, one in the Royal Doulton Archives and another in a private collection. A Money Box was produced for the Millennium Bunnykins Extravaganza. For illustration of post box see page 2.

MEDICINE TIME

Design No.: SF1
Designer: Barbara Vernon
Issued: By 1937 - by 1952
Combined with: *Dunce*, HW1R
Frightening Spider, SF4
Kissing Under the Mistletoe, HW11R
Proposal, HW11

Shape	U.S. $	Can. $	U.K. £	Aust. $
Baby plate, round, small				
with signature	200.00	250.00	115.00	275.00
without signature	150.00	180.00	90.00	190.00
Baby plate, round, large				
with signature	250.00	300.00	150.00	325.00
without signature	200.00	250.00	115.00	275.00
Candle holder	1,500.00	1,800.00	850.00	1,900.00
Casino jug, 30s				
with signature	375.00	450.00	210.00	475.00
without signature	300.00	350.00	175.00	375.00
Casino jug, 42s				
with signature	325.00	400.00	185.00	425.00
without signature	250.00	300.00	150.00	325.00
Casino saucer				
with signature	75.00	90.00	45.00	95.00
without signature	50.00	60.00	30.00	65.00
Casino teapot, 30s				
with signature	375.00	450.00	210.00	475.00
without signature	300.00	350.00	175.00	375.00
Cereal / oatmeal bowl				
with signature	100.00	125.00	60.00	135.00
without signature	90.00	110.00	50.00	120.00
Hot water plate				
with signature	200.00	250.00	115.00	275.00
without signature	150.00	180.00	90.00	190.00
Plate, 6 ½"				
with signature	90.00	110.00	50.00	120.00
without signature	65.00	80.00	40.00	85.00
Plate, 7"				
with signature	90.00	110.00	50.00	120.00
without signature	65.00	80.00	40.00	85.00
Plate, 8"	75.00	90.00	45.00	95.00
FINE WHITE CHINA				
Coupe	650.00	775.00	375.00	800.00
Night light		Very Rare		
Plate, 6"	650.00	775.00	375.00	800.00
Plate, 7"	650.00	775.00	375.00	800.00

Medicine Time (SF1)

MERRY CHRISTMAS FROM BUNNYKINS – Walter Hayward

Merry Christmas from Bunnykins,
Style One (SF137)

Reverse Inscription (SF137)

Style One

The reverse decoration on this plate has a single holly leaf wreath border and a 1936 copyright date.

Design No.:	Front — SF137 Merry Christmas from Bunnykins Reverse — Inscription
Designer:	Walter Hayward
Issued:	1981 - 1989
Rhyme:	'Bunnykins are just like you For they love Christmas too, They sing and dance as you can see And play around the Christmas tree, And each year they always say We wish it were Christmas every day'

Shape	U.S. $	Can. $	U.K. £	Aust. $
Plate, 8"	15.00	20.00	10.00	25.00

MERRY CHRISTMAS FROM BUNNYKINS – Colin Twinn

Style Two
First Variation, Large Size

The reverse decoration on this plate has a multiple holly leaf wreath border.

Design No.: Front — CT39 Merry Christmas from Bunnykins
Reverse — CT66 Inscription
Designer: Colin Twinn
Issued: 1990 - 1993
Rhyme: ´Bunnykins are just like you
For they love Christmas too.
They sing and dance as you can see
And play around the Christmas tree
And each year they always say
"We wish it were Christmas every day."

Shape	U.S. $	Can. $	U.K. £	Aust. $
Plate, 8"	15.00	20.00	10.00	25.00

Merry Christmas from Bunnykins
First Variation (CT39)

Merry Christmas from Bunnykins
Second Variation (CT43)

Style Two
Second Variation, Small Size

Design No.: Front — CT43 Merry Christmas from Bunnykins
Reverse — CT44 Inscription
Designer: Colin Twinn
Issued: 1992 - 1994

Shape	U.S. $	Can. $	U.K. £	Aust. $
Hug-a-mug, one handle	10.00	12.00	6.00	15.00

Family Christmas Scene, First Version (CT72)

Style Three
FAMILY CHRISTMAS SCENE
First Version, Large Size

Design No.:	CT72 Family Christmas Scene CT73 Christmas Inscription
Designer:	Colin Twinn
Issued:	1993 - 1994
Inscription:	´Bunnykins are just like you For they love Christmas too. They sing and dance as you can see And play around the Christmas tree And each year they always say "We wish it were Christmas every day."

Shape	U.S. $	Can. $	U.K. £	Aust. $
Plate, 8"	15.00	20.00	10.00	25.00

Christmas Inscription, First Version (CT73)

Family Christmas Scene
Second Version (CT74)

Style Three
FAMILY CHRISTMAS SCENE
Second Version, Small Size

Design No.:	Front — CT74 Family Christmas Scene Reverse — CT75 Merry Christmas from Bunnykins Inscription
Designer:	Colin Twinn
Issued:	1993 - 1994

Shape	U.S. $	Can. $	U.K. £	Aust. $
Hug-a-mug, one handle	10.00	12.00	6.00	15.00
Malvern beaker	15.00	20.00	10.00	25.00
Money ball	10.00	12.00	6.00	15.00

Merry Christmas Inscription,
Second Version (CT75)

MR. PIGGLY'S STORES

Design No.: SF14
Designer: Walter Hayward after Barbara Vernon
Issued: By 1952 - by 1998
Combined with: *Dress Making*, HW 26
Fishing in the Goldfish Bowl, HW3R
Playing on the River, SF16
See-saw, Style One, SFS17
Swinging, HW 20
Toast for Tea Today, SF23

Mr. Piggly's Stores (SF14)

Shape	U.S. $	Can. $	U.K. £	Aust. $
Baby plate, small, round				
with signature	30.00	35.00	17.50	40.00
without signature	20.00	25.00	12.00	30.00
Bread and butter plate				
with signature	200.00	250.00	115.00	275.00
without signature	125.00	150.00	75.00	160.00
Casino jug, 24s				
with signature	300.00	350.00	175.00	375.00
without signature	175.00	200.00	100.00	225.00
Casino saucer				
with signature	15.00	20.00	10.00	25.00
without signature	8.00	10.00	5.00	12.00
Casino sugar, 30s				
with signature	150.00	180.00	90.00	190.00
without signature	100.00	125.00	60.00	135.00
Casino teapot, 30s				
with signature	250.00	300.00	150.00	325.00
without signature	150.00	180.00	90.00	190.00
Cereal / oatmeal bowl				
with signature	25.00	30.00	15.00	35.00
without signature	15.00	20.00	10.00	25.00
Hot water plate				
with signature	100.00	125.00	60.00	135.00
without signature	75.00	90.00	45.00	95.00
Jaffa fruit saucer (plain)				
with signature	25.00	30.00	15.00	35.00
without signature	15.00	20.00	10.00	25.00
Picture plaque, large	20.00	25.00	12.00	30.00
Plate, 6 ½"				
with signature	25.00	30.00	15.00	35.00
without signature	15.00	20.00	10.00	25.00
Plate, 7 ½"				
with signature	30.00	35.00	17.50	40.00
without signature	15.00	20.00	10.00	25.00
Plate, 8 ½"				
with signature	30.00	35.00	17.50	40.00
without signature	15.00	20.00	10.00	25.00
Porridge plate				
with signature	90.00	110.00	50.00	120.00
without signature	70.00	85.00	40.00	90.00

Mrs. Moppet's Tea Room (LF6)

MRS. MOPPET'S TEA ROOM

Design No.: LF6
Designer: Barbara Vernon
Issued: By 1940 - by 1952

Shape	U.S. $	Can. $	U.K. £	Aust. $
Baby plate, oval, large				
with signature	350.00	425.00	200.00	450.00
without signature	300.00	350.00	175.00	375.00
Baby plate, round, large				
with silver rim			Rare	
with signature	250.00	300.00	150.00	325.00
without signature	200.00	250.00	115.00	275.00
Bread / butter plate, handles				
with signature	400.00	475.00	225.00	500.00
without signature	350.00	425.00	200.00	450.00
Cereal / oatmeal bowl				
with signature	100.00	125.00	60.00	135.00
without signature	90.00	110.00	50.00	120.00
Plate, 8 ½"				
with signature	100.00	125.00	60.00	135.00
without signature	75.00	90.00	45.00	95.00
Porridge plate				
with signature	125.00	150.00	75.00	160.00
without signature	100.00	125.00	60.00	135.00

Fine White China Sugar Bowl
Proposal (HW11) / *Pulling on Trousers* (HW14)

NETTING A CRICKET

Design No.: HW6
Designer: Barbara Vernon
Issued: By 1937 - by 1952
Combined with: *Artist*, HW1
Cuddling under a Mushroom, HW4
Dunce, HW1R
Family Going out on Washing Day, HW8
Fishing in the Goldfish Bowl, HW3R
Gardener with Wheelbarrow, HW9R
Holding Hat and Coat, EC4
Pressing Trousers, HW14
Proposal, HW11
Pulling on Trousers, HW2
Reading the Times, HW2R

Netting a Cricket (HW6)

Shape	U.S. $	Can. $	U.K. £	Aust. $
Casino jug, 24s				
with signature	350.00	425.00	200.00	450.00
without signature	300.00	350.00	175.00	375.00
Casino sugar bowl, 30s				
with signature	200.00	250.00	115.00	275.00
without signature	125.00	150.00	75.00	160.00
Casino sugar bowl, 36s				
with signature	150.00	180.00	90.00	190.00
without signature	125.00	150.00	75.00	160.00
Casino teacup				
with signature	75.00	90.00	45.00	95.00
without signature	50.00	60.00	30.00	65.00
Cup / mug, large				
with signature	600.00	725.00	340.00	750.00
without signature	500.00	600.00	285.00	625.00
Don beaker				
with signature	150.00	180.00	90.00	190.00
without signature	100.00	125.00	60.00	135.00
Don beaker, one handle				
with signature	150.00	180.00	90.00	190.00
without signature	100.00	125.00	60.00	135.00
Don mug, one handle				
with signature	75.00	90.00	45.00	95.00
without signature	35.00	45.00	20.00	50.00
Don mug, two handles				
with signature	75.00	90.00	45.00	95.00
without signature	35.00	45.00	20.00	50.00
Jaffa fruit saucer				
plain rim	35.00	45.00	20.00	50.00
wavy rim	65.00	80.00	40.00	85.00
Jam pot	1,500.00	1,800.00	850.00	1,900.00
Lid of hot water plate	100.00	125.00	60.00	135.00
Plate, 6 ½"				
with signature	90.00	110.00	50.00	120.00
without signature	65.00	80.00	40.00	85.00

FINE WHITE CHINA

Shape	U.S. $	Can. $	U.K. £	Aust. $
Don mug, one handle	300.00	350.00	175.00	375.00

Note: Retirement dates are all approximate. When a design is retired all remaining stocks of the retired litho prints are used until exhausted.

NEW ARRIVAL THEME — Colin Twinn

Family Group with Father Standing (CT97)

FAMILY GROUP WITH FATHER STANDING

Design No.: CT97 Family Group with Father Standing
Designer: Colin Twinn
Issued: 1995 - 1997

Shape	U.S. $	Can. $	U.K. £	Aust. $
Baby plate, round, small	25.00	30.00	15.00	35.00
Cereal / oatmeal bowl	15.00	20.00	10.00	25.00
Plate, 8"	15.00	20.00	10.00	25.00

Family Group with Father Kneeling (CT98)

FAMILY GROUP WITH FATHER KNEELING

Design No.: Front — CT98 Family Group with Father Kneeling
Reverse — CT99 New Arrival Inscription
Designer: Colin Twinn
Issued: 1995 - 1997

Shape	U.S. $	Can. $	U.K. £	Aust. $
Hug-a-mug, one handle	10.00	12.00	6.00	15.00
Money ball	10.00	12.00	6.00	15.00

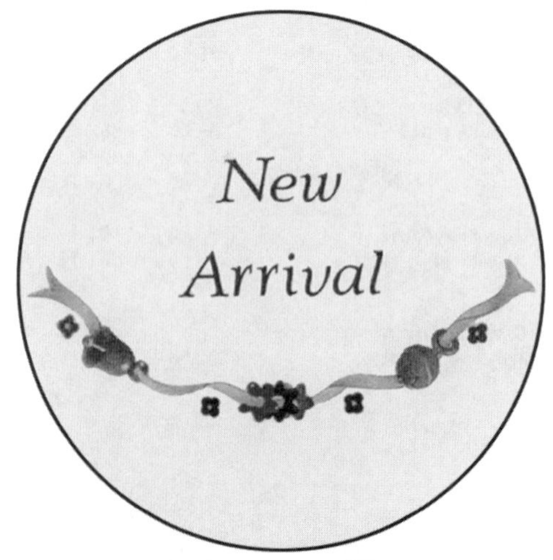

New Arrival Inscription (CT99)

NEW BABY THEME – Frank Endersby

SHOWING BABY AT WINDOW

Design No.: 40 Showing Baby at Window
Designer: Frank Endersby
Issued: 1996 to the present

Shape	U.S. $	Can. $	U.K. £	Aust. $
Plate, 6 ½"	10.00	12.00	6.00	15.00
Plate, 8"	15.00	20.00	10.00	25.00

Showing Baby at Window (40)

Pushing Pram (41)

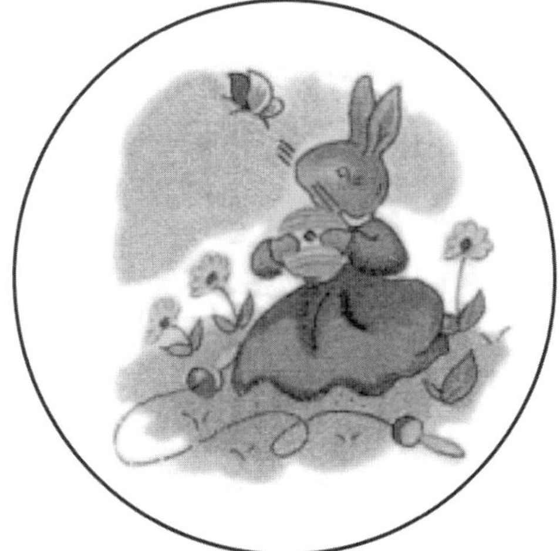
Playing with Ball (42)

PUSHING PRAM / PLAYING WITH BALL

Design No.: Front — 41 Pushing Pram
Reverse — 42 Playing with Ball
Designer: Frank Endersby
Issued: 1996 to the present
Combined with: **Carrying Letter* (30)
**Decorating the Cake,* (9)
**Playing and reading,* (15)

Shape	U.S. $	Can. $	U.K. £	Aust. $
Hug-a-mug, one handle	20.00	25.00	12.00	30.00
Hug-a-mug, two handles	20.00	25.00	12.00	30.00
Divider dish	50.00	60.00	30.00	65.00
Malvern beaker	15.00	20.00	10.00	25.00
Money ball	25.00	30.00	15.00	35.00
Stratford teacup	8.00	10.00	5.00	12.00

* Indicates scene on divider dish.

NURSERY THEME — Colin Twinn

Nursery, First Version (CT19)

NURSERY
First Version, Small Size

Design No.:	CT19 Nursery
Designer:	Colin Twinn
Issued:	1990 - 1993
Combined with:	*Family with Pram*, Style Two, CT14
	Standing by Pram, CT6

Shape	U.S. $	Can. $	U.K. £	Aust. $
Albion jug, 1 pint	100.00	125.00	60.00	135.00
Baby plate, round, small	20.00	25.00	12.00	30.00
Cake stand	150.00	180.00	90.00	190.00
Cereal / oatmeal bowl	15.00	20.00	10.00	25.00
Lamp	50.00	60.00	30.00	65.00
Money ball	10.00	12.50	6.00	15.00
Picture plaque, large	20.00	25.00	12.00	30.00
Picture plaque, small	20.00	25.00	12.00	30.00
Plate, 6 ½"	15.00	20.00	10.00	25.00
Plate, 8"	15.00	20.00	10.00	25.00

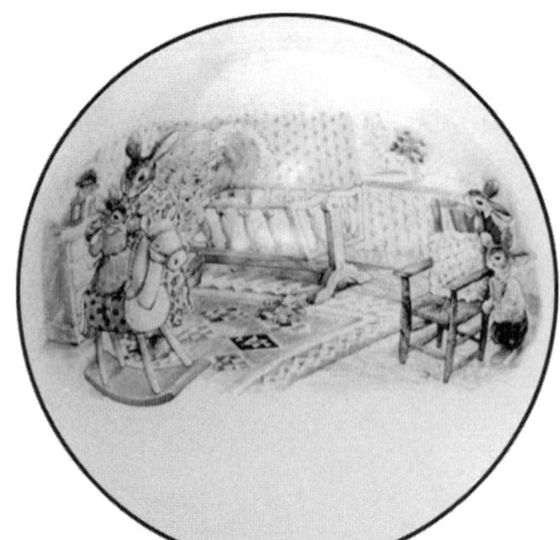

Nursery, Second Version (CT28)

NURSERY
Second Version, Large Size / BUNNY ON ROCKING HORSE

Design No.:	Front — CT28 Nursery
	Reverse — CT29 Bunny on Rocking Horse
Designer:	Colin Twinn
Issued:	1990 - 1993
Combined with:	*Family with Pram*, Style Two, CT14
	Father Bunnykins with Fishing Rod, (CT27)

Shape	U.S. $	Can. $	U.K. £	Aust. $
Albion cream jug	35.00	45.00	20.00	50.00
Albion jug, ½ pint	85.00	100.00	50.00	110.00
Albion jug, 1 pint	100.00	125.00	60.00	135.00
Albion teapot	50.00	60.00	30.00	65.00
Egg cup				
Style Three	10.00	12.00	6.00	15.00
Hug-a-mug, one handle	10.00	12.00	6.00	15.00
Hug-a-mug, two handles	10.00	12.00	6.00	15.00
Money ball	10.00	12.00	6.00	15.00
Picture plaque, small	20.00	25.00	12.00	30.00
Savings book	15.00	20.00	10.00	25.00
Stratford straight beaker	15.00	20.00	10.00	25.00
Stratford teacup	8.00	10.00	5.00	12.00

Bunny on Rocking Horse (CT29)

BUNNY WITH MIRROR

Design No.: Front — CT35 Bunny with Mirror
Designer: Colin Twinn
Issued: 1990 - 1993
Combined with: *Bunnies in the Bath*, Second Version, CT34
Classroom Scene, Style Two, First version, CT36
Classroom Scene, Style Two, Second version, CT16
Picking Daisies, CT4

Shape	U.S. $	Can. $	U.K. £	Aust. $
Albion cream jug	35.00	45.00	20.00	50.00
Albion sugar bowl	30.00	35.00	17.50	40.00
Divider dish	75.00	90.00	45.00	95.00
Egg cup				
Style Three	10.00	12.00	6.00	15.00

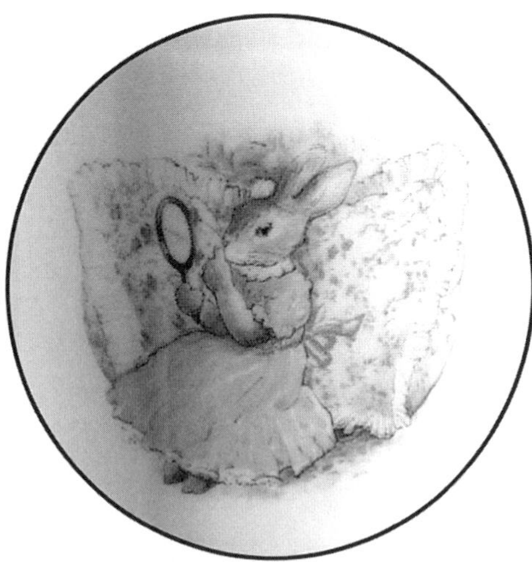

Bunny with Mirror (CT35)

Fine White China Beaker (Large)
Artist (HW1)

Earthernware Don Beaker
Going Shopping (SF10)

Orange Vendor (SF12)

ORANGE VENDOR

Design No.: SF12
Designer: Walter Hayward after Barbara Vernon
Issued: By 1952 - 1967
Combined with: *Family at Breakfast*, HW12
Family Going Out on Washing Day, HW8
Soldiers Marching to the Music, HW18
Wheelbarrow Race, HW22
Writing Letters, HW19R

Shape	U.S. $	Can. $	U.K. £	Aust. $
Baby plate, round, small				
with signature	30.00	35.00	17.50	40.00
without signature	20.00	25.00	12.50	30.00
Baby plate, round, large				
with signature	75.00	90.00	45.00	95.00
without signature	50.00	60.00	30.00	65.00
Casino jug, 30s				
with signature	200.00	250.00	115.00	275.00
without signature	150.00	180.00	90.00	190.00
Casino jug, 36s				
with signature	150.00	180.00	90.00	190.00
without signature	100.00	125.00	60.00	135.00
Casino saucer				
with signature	15.00	20.00	12.00	25.00
without signature	8.00	10.00	5.00	12.00
Casino teapot, 30s				
with signature	250.00	300.00	150.00	325.00
without signature	150.00	180.00	90.00	190.00
Casino teapot, 36s				
with signature	200.00	250.00	115.00	275.00
without signature	100.00	125.00	60.00	135.00
Cereal / oatmeal bowl				
with signature	25.00	30.00	15.00	35.00
without signature	15.00	20.00	10.00	25.00
Hot water plate				
with signature	100.00	125.00	60.00	135.00
without signature	75.00	90.00	45.00	95.00
Jaffa fruit saucer (plain)				
with signature	25.00	30.00	15.00	35.00
without signature	15.00	20.00	10.00	25.00
Plate, 6 ½"				
with signature	25.00	30.00	15.00	35.00
without signature	15.00	20.00	10.00	25.00
Plate, 7 ½"				
with signature	30.00	35.00	17.50	40.00
without signature	15.00	20.00	10.00	25.00
Plate, 8 ½"				
with signature	30.00	35.00	17.50	40.00
without signature	15.00	20.00	10.00	25.00

Note: Retirement dates are all approximate. When a design is retired all remaining stocks of retired litho prints are used until exhausted.

PICNIC
Style One, First Version (without trees)

Design No.: Unknown
Designer: Walter Hayward after Barbara Vernon
Issued: 1940

Shape	U.S. $	Can. $	U.K. £	Aust. $
Baby plate, oval, small	500.00	600.00	285.00	625.00
Baby plate, round, large	400.00	475.00	225.00	500.00
Bread and butter plate	500.00	600.00	285.00	625.00
Plate, 8 ½"	225.00	275.00	125.00	300.00

Note: This design should appear with the Barbara Vernon facsimile signature.

Picnic, Style One, First Version

Picnic, Style One, Second Version (LF10)

PICNIC
Style One, Second Version (with trees)

This scene was redrawn to better fit, or conform to round shapes.

Design No.: LF10
Designer: Walter Hayward after Barbara Vernon
Issued: By 1940 - 1970
Combined with: *Game of Golf,* SF11

Shape	U.S. $	Can. $	U.K. £	Aust. $
Baby plate, oval, large				
with signature	200.00	250.00	115.00	275.00
without signature	150.00	180.00	90.00	190.00
Baby plate, round, large				
with signature	100.00	125.00	60.00	135.00
without signature	75.00	90.00	45.00	95.00
Bread and butter plate				
with signature	250.00	300.00	150.00	325.00
without signature	200.00	250.00	115.00	275.00
Casino teapot, 30s				
with signature	200.00	250.00	115.00	275.00
without signature	150.00	180.00	90.00	190.00
Cereal / oatmeal bowl				
with signature	35.00	45.00	20.00	50.00
without signature	25.00	30.00	15.00	35.00
Hot water plate				
with signature	125.00	150.00	75.00	160.00
without signature	100.00	125.00	60.00	135.00
Plate, 8 ½"				
with signature	75.00	90.00	45.00	95.00
without signature	25.00	30.00	15.00	35.00
Porridge plate				
with signature	110.00	135.00	65.00	145.00
without signature	85.00	100.00	50.00	110.00

PICNIC CAKE STALL THEME – Colin Twinn

Picnic and Cake Stall (CT2)

PICNIC AND CAKE STALL

Design No.: CT2 Picnic and Cake Stall
Designer: Colin Twinn
Issued: 1989 - 1993

Shape	U.S. $	Can. $	U.K. £	Aust. $
Plate, 8"	30.00	35.00	17.50	40.00
Plate 10 ½"	35.00	45.00	20.00	50.00

Cake Stall (CT12)

CAKE STALL / PICKING DAISIES

Design No.: Front — CT12 Cake Stall
Reverse — CT4 Picking Daisies
Designer: Colin Twinn
Issued: 1989 - 1993
Combined with: *Bunny with Mirror*, CT35
Classroom Scene, Style Two, Second Version, CT16
Ice Cream Seller, Second Variation, CT11
Pushing the Wheelbarrow, CT3
Queen of the May, First Variation, CT7
Queen of the May, Second Variation, CT13
Standing by Pram, CT6

Shape	U.S. $	Can. $	U.K. £	Aust. $
Albion cream jug	35.00	45.00	20.00	50.00
Albion jug, ½ pint	85.00	100.00	50.00	110.00
Albion jug, 1 pint	100.00	125.00	60.00	135.00
Albion teapot	50.00	60.00	30.00	65.00
Hug-a-mug, one handle	10.00	12.00	6.00	15.00
Hug-a-mug, two handles	10.00	12.00	6.00	15.00
Malvern beaker	15.00	20.00	10.00	25.00
Stratford straight beaker	15.00	20.00	10.00	25.00
Stratford teacup	8.00	10.00	5.00	12.00

Picking Daisies (CT4)

Note: *Cake Stall*, (CT12) is combined with *Standing by Pram*, (CT6) on Albion, ½ and 1 pint jugs.

PICNIC THEME – Frank Endersby

PICNIC
Style Two

Design No.: 16 Picnic
Designer: Frank Endersby
Issued: 1995 to the present

Shape	U.S. $	Can. $	U.K. £	Aust. $
Baby plate, round, small	25.00	30.00	15.00	35.00
Cereal / oatmeal bowl	15.00	20.00	10.00	25.00
Plate, 6 ½"	10.00	12.00	6.00	15.00
Plate, 8"	15.00	20.00	10.00	25.00

Picnic, Style Two (16)

Playing Badminton (17)

Resting, Style One (18)

PLAYING BADMINTON / RESTING, Style One

Design No.: Front —17 Playing Badminton
Reverse — 18 Resting, Style One
Designer: Frank Endersby
Issued: 1995 to the present

Shape	U.S. $	Can. $	U.K. £	Aust. $
Hug-a-mug, one handle	20.00	25.00	12.00	30.00
Hug-a-mug, two handles	20.00	25.00	12.00	30.00
Money ball	25.00	30.00	15.00	35.00
Stratford straight beaker	15.00	20.00	10.00	25.00
Stratford teacup	8.00	10.00	5.00	12.00

Note: It is unusual to find the Stratford beaker with this design as this shape was officially withdrawn in 1993, two years before this Frank Endersby design was introduced.

Pillow Fight (SF7)

PILLOW FIGHT
Style One

Design No.:	SF7
Designer:	Barbara Vernon
Issued:	By 1940 - by 1952
Combined with:	*Chicken Pulling a Cart*, SF8

Shape	U.S. $	Can. $	U.K. £	Aust. $
Baby plate, oval, small				
with signature	200.00	250.00	115.00	275.00
without signature	150.00	180.00	90.00	190.00
Casino teapot, 24s				
with signature	375.00	450.00	210.00	475.00
without signature	300.00	350.00	175.00	375.00
Cereal / oatmeal bowl				
with signature	35.00	45.00	20.00	50.00
without signature	25.00	30.00	15.00	35.00
Hot water plate				
with signature	125.00	150.00	75.00	160.00
without signature	100.00	125.00	60.00	135.00
Plate, 6 ½"				
with signature	30.00	35.00	17.50	40.00
without signature	20.00	25.00	12.00	30.00
Plate, 7 ½"				
with signature	65.00	80.00	40.00	85.00
without signature	25.00	30.00	15.00	35.00

Egg Cup Tray (9 ¾" x 6" dated July 1937)
Holds four style one egg cups.

PLAYING ON THE RIVER

Design No.: SF16
Designer: Walter Hayward after Barbara Vernon
Issued: By 1952 - by 1998
Combined with: *Ice Cream Vendor,* HW23
Mr. Piggly's Stores, SF14

Shape	U.S. $	Can. $	U.K. £	Aust. $
Baby plate, round, small				
with signature	30.00	35.00	17.50	40.00
without signature	20.00	25.00	12.00	30.00
Cake stand	150.00	180.00	90.00	190.00
Casino jug, 30s				
with signature	200.00	250.00	115.00	275.00
without signature	125.00	150.00	75.00	160.00
Casino saucer				
with signature	15.00	20.00	12.00	25.00
without signature	8.00	10.00	5.00	12.00
Casino teapot, 30s				
with signature	250.00	300.00	150.00	325.00
without signature	150.00	180.00	90.00	190.00
Cereal / oatmeal bowl				
with signature	25.00	30.00	15.00	35.00
without signature	15.00	20.00	10.00	25.00
Hot water plate				
with signature	100.00	125.00	60.00	135.00
without signature	75.00	90.00	45.00	95.00
Jaffa fruit saucer (plain)				
with signature	25.00	30.00	15.00	35.00
without signature	15.00	20.00	10.00	25.00
Picture plaque, large	20.00	25.00	12.00	30.00
Plate, 6 ½"				
with signature	25.00	30.00	15.00	35.00
without signature	15.00	20.00	10.00	25.00
Plate, 7 ½"				
with signature	30.00	35.00	17.50	40.00
without signature	15.00	20.00	10.00	25.00
Plate, 8"				
with signature	30.00	35.00	17.50	40.00
without signature	15.00	20.00	10.00	25.00

Note: Condition is important. Prices listed are based on nurseryware in mint condition. Items in less than mint condition will command lower prices.

Playing on the River (SF16)

Playing with Cup and Spoon (EC6)

PLAYING WITH CUP AND SPOON

Design No.: EC6
Designer: Barbara Vernon
Issued: 1937 to the present
Combined with: *Artist,* HW1
Bedtime with Dollies, EC125
Daisy Chains, HW25
Drummer, EC2
Drummer and Bugler, EC126
Dunce, HW1R
Fishing in the Goldfish Bowl, HW3R
Hikers, EC124
Hobby Horse, Style Two, EC121
Holding Hat and Coat, EC4
Nipped by a Crab, HW21R
Playing with Doll and Pram, EC123
Proposal, HW11
Raising Hat, Style Two, EC7
Reading, EC122
Rowboat, HW21
Sheltering Under an Umbrella, EC3
Sleeping in a Rocking Chair, EC1
Trumpeter, EC5

Shape	U.S. $	Can. $	U.K. £	Aust. $
Albion sugar bowl	30.00	35.00	17.50	40.00
Beaker cover	65.00	80.00	40.00	85.00
Casino sugar bowl, 30s				
with signature	250.00	300.00	150.00	325.00
without signature	175.00	200.00	100.00	225.00
Casino sugar bowl, 36s				
with signature	175.00	200.00	100.00	225.00
without signature	125.00	150.00	75.00	160.00
Casino teacup				
with signature	15.00	20.00	10.00	25.00
without signature	8.00	10.00	5.00	12.00
Egg cup				
Style One	30.00	35.00	17.50	40.00
Style Two	40.00	50.00	25.00	55.00
Style Three	10.00	12.50	6.00	15.00
Lid of hot water plate	50.00	60.00	30.00	65.00
Money ball	25.00	30.00	15.00	35.00
FINE WHITE CHINA				
Night light			Very Rare	
Saucer	300.00	350.00	175.00	375.00
Teacup	300.00	350.00	175.00	375.00

Note: Fine white china prices are indications only due to the scarcity of the shapes. Prices will vary.

PLAYING WITH DOLL AND PRAM

Design No.: EC123
Designer: Walter Hayward
Issued: 1959 to the present
Combined with: *Bedtime with Dollies*, EC125
Building Sand Castles, HW138
Dancing with Doll, HW115R
Drummer, EC2
Drummer and Bugler, EC126
Flying Kites, SF133
Hikers, EC124
Hobby Horse, Style Two, EC121
Holding Hat and Coat, EC4
Playing with Cup and Spoon, EC6
Playing with Dolls and Prams, HW115
Reading, EC122
Sailing Boats, HW138R
Sheltering Under an Umbrella, EC3
Sleeping in a Rocking Chair, EC1

Playing with Doll and Pram (EC123)

Shape	U.S. $	Can. $	U.K. £	Aust. $
Albion cream jug	35.00	45.00	20.00	50.00
Albion jug, ½ pint	85.00	100.00	50.00	110.00
Albion jug, 1 pint	100.00	125.00	60.00	135.00
Albion sugar bowl	30.00	35.00	17.50	40.00
Beaker cover	65.00	80.00	40.00	85.00
Egg cup				
Style One	30.00	35.00	17.50	40.00
Style Two	40.00	50.00	25.00	55.00
Style Three	10.00	12.00	6.00	15.00
Hug-a-mug, two handles	10.00	12.00	6.00	15.00
Lid of hot water plate	50.00	60.00	30.00	65.00

Playing with Dolls and Prams (HW115)

Dancing with Doll (HW115R)

PLAYING WITH DOLLS AND PRAMS / DANCING WITH DOLL

Design No.:	Front — HW115 Playing with Dolls and Prams Reverse — HW115R Dancing with Doll
Designer:	Walter Hayward
Issued:	1959 - by 1998
Combined with:	*Broken Umbrella*, HW27R *Disturbing Sleeping Father*, HW118 *Hikers*, EC124 *Ice Cream on the Beach*, HW136R *Lunch Break*, HW29R *Playing with Doll and Pram*, EC123 **Playing with Doll and Teddy*, HW120R **Roller Skating Arm in Arm*, HW137R *Serving Tea*, HW116R *Trying on Hats*, HW28R

Shape	U.S. $	Can. $	U.K. £	Aust. $
Albion cream jug	35.00	45.00	20.00	50.00
Albion jug, ½ pint	85.00	100.00	50.00	110.00
Albion jug, 1 pint	100.00	125.00	60.00	135.00
Albion teapot	50.00	60.00	30.00	65.00
Casino saucer	8.00	10.00	5.00	12.00
Casino teacup	8.00	10.00	5.00	12.00
Divider dish	50.00	60.00	30.00	65.00
Don beaker	25.00	30.00	15.00	35.00
Don beaker, one handle	25.00	30.00	15.00	35.00
Don mug, one handle	10.00	12.00	6.00	15.00
Don mug, two handles	10.00	12.00	6.00	15.00
Egg box				
small	175.00	200.00	100.00	225.00
medium	200.00	250.00	115.00	275.00
large	225.00	275.00	125.00	300.00
Hug-a-mug, one handle	10.00	12.00	6.00	15.00
Hug-a-mug, two handles	10.00	12.00	6.00	15.00
Jaffa fruit saucer (plain)	15.00	20.00	10.00	25.00
Lamp	50.00	60.00	30.00	65.00
Lid of hot water plate	50.00	60.00	30.00	65.00
Money ball	10.00	12.50	6.00	15.00
Picture plaque, small	20.00	25.00	12.00	30.00
Plate, 6 ½"	15.00	20.00	10.00	25.00
Savings book	15.00	20.00	10.00	25.00
Stratford straight beaker	15.00	20.00	10.00	25.00
Stratford teacup	8.00	10.00	5.00	12.00

* Indicates scene on divider dish.

Note: The savings book can have a combined design of *Dancing with Doll* (HW115R) and *Trying on Hats* (HW28R) or *Dancing with Doll* (HW115R) and *Lunch Break* (HW29R).

PLAYTIME THEME – Frank Endersby

SEE-SAW
Style Two

Design No.:	52 See-saw
Designer:	Frank Endersby
Issued:	1995 - 2003

Shape	U.S. $	Can. $	U.K. £	Aust. $
Baby plate, round, small	20.00	25.00	12.00	30.00
Plate, 6 ½"	15.00	20.00	10.00	25.00
Plate, 8"	15.00	20.00	10.00	25.00

See-saw, Style Two (52)

Pushing Swing (53)

Bunny on Swing (54)

PUSHING SWING / BUNNY ON SWING

Design No.:	Front — 53 Pushing Swing Reverse — 54 Bunny on Swing
Designer:	Frank Endersby
Issued:	1995 - 2003

Shape	U.S. $	Can. $	U.K. £	Aust. $
Hug-a-mug, one handle	10.00	12.00	6.00	15.00
Hug-a-mug, two handles	10.00	12.00	6.00	15.00

Portrait Painter (SF20)

PORTRAIT PAINTER

Design No.:	SF20
Designer:	Walter Hayward
Issued:	1954 - by 1998
Combined with:	*Dancing Round the Barrel Organ*, HW139 *Rocking Horse*, HW24

Shape	U.S. $	Can. $	U.K. £	Aust. $
Albion jug, 1 pint	75.00	90.00	45.00	95.00
Baby plate, round, small				
with signature	30.00	35.00	17.50	40.00
without signature	20.00	25.00	12.00	30.00
Cake stand	150.00	180.00	90.00	190.00
Casino saucer				
with signature	15.00	20.00	10.00	25.00
without signature	8.00	10.00	5.00	12.00
Casino teapot, 24s				
with signature	375.00	450.00	210.00	475.00
without signature	325.00	400.00	185.00	425.00
Casino teapot, 30s				
with signature	350.00	425.00	200.00	450.00
without signature	300.00	350.00	175.00	375.00
Cereal / oatmeal bowl				
with signature	25.00	30.00	15.00	35.00
without signature	15.00	20.00	10.00	25.00
Hot water plate				
with signature	100.00	125.00	60.00	135.00
without signature	75.00	90.00	45.00	95.00
Jaffa fruit saucer (plain)				
with signature	25.00	30.00	15.00	35.00
without signature	15.00	20.00	10.00	25.00
Plate, 6 ½"				
with signature	25.00	30.00	15.00	35.00
without signature	15.00	20.00	10.00	25.00
Plate, 7 ½"				
with signature	30.00	35.00	17.50	40.00
without signature	15.00	20.00	10.00	25.00
Plate, 8"	15.00	20.00	10.00	25.00

POST OFFICE THEME – Frank Endersby

POSTING LETTERS

Design No.: 28 Posting Letters
Designer: Frank Endersby
Issued: 1995 to the present

Shape	U.S. $	Can. $	U.K. £	Aust. $
Cereal bowl	15.00	20.00	10.00	25.00
Money ball	15.00	20.00	10.00	25.00
Plate, 6 ½"	10.00	12.00	6.00	15.00
Plate, 8"	15.00	20.00	10.00	25.00

Posting Letters (28)

Letter Box (29)

LETTER BOX / CARRYING LETTER

Design No.: Front — 29 Letter Box
Reverse — 30 Carrying Letter
Designer: Frank Endersby
Issued: 1995 to the present
Combined with: **Playing with Balloons*, (33)
**Trying on Hat*, (12)

Shape	U.S. $	Can. $	U.K. £	Aust. $
Hug-a-mug, one handle	20.00	25.00	12.00	30.00
Hug-a-mug, two handles	20.00	25.00	12.00	30.00
Divider dish	50.00	60.00	30.00	65.00
Stratford teacup	8.00	10.00	5.00	12.00

* Indicates scene on divider dish.

Carrying Letter (30)

Postman Delivering Letters (HW19)

Writing Letters (HW19R)

POSTMAN DELIVERING LETTERS / WRITING LETTERS

Design No.: Front — HW19 Postman Delivering Letters
Reverse — HW19R Writing Letters
Designer: Walter Hayward after Barbara Vernon
Issued: By 1952 - 1967
Combined with: *Orange Vendor,* SF12

Shape	U.S. $	Can. $	U.K. £	Aust. $
Baby plate, round, small				
with signature	200.00	250.00	115.00	275.00
without signature	150.00	180.00	90.00	190.00
Casino jug, 24s				
with signature	475.00	575.00	270.00	600.00
without signature	400.00	475.00	225.00	500.00
Casino jug, 36s				
with signature	300.00	350.00	175.00	375.00
without signature	275.00	325.00	160.00	350.00
Casino jug, 42s				
with signature	275.00	325.00	160.00	350.00
without signature	200.00	250.00	115.00	275.00
Casino saucer				
with signature	75.00	90.00	45.00	95.00
without signature	50.00	60.00	30.00	65.00
Casino sugar bowl, 30s				
with signature	200.00	250.00	115.00	275.00
without signature	125.00	150.00	75.00	160.00
Casino teacup				
with signature	75.00	90.00	45.00	95.00
without signature	50.00	60.00	30.00	65.00
Casino teapot, 24s				
with signature	375.00	450.00	210.00	475.00
without signature	300.00	350.00	175.00	375.00
Casino teapot, 30s				
with signature	300.00	350.00	175.00	375.00
without signature	225.00	275.00	125.00	300.00
Don beaker				
with signature	150.00	180.00	90.00	190.00
without signature	100.00	125.00	60.00	135.00
Don beaker, one handle				
with signature	150.00	180.00	90.00	190.00
without signature	100.00	125.00	60.00	135.00
Don mug, one handle				
with signature	75.00	90.00	45.00	95.00
without signature	35.00	45.00	20.00	50.00
Don mug, two handles				
with signature	75.00	90.00	45.00	95.00
without signature	35.00	45.00	20.00	50.00
Lid of hot water plate				
with signature	175.00	200.00	100.00	225.00
without signature	125.00	150.00	75.00	160.00
Plate, 6 ½"				
with signature	90.00	110.00	50.00	120.00
without signature	65.00	80.00	40.00	85.00

PRESSING TROUSERS

Design No.: HW14
Designer: Barbara Vernon
Issued: By 1937 - 1967
Combined with: *Cycling*, HW15R
Dunce, HW1R
Feeding the Baby, HW13
Fishing in the Gold Fish Bowl, HW3R
Footballer, HW13R
Frightening Spider, SF4
Golfer, HW4R
Holding Hat and Coat, EC4
Leapfrog, HW12R
Kissing Under the Mistletoe, HW11R
Netting a Cricket, HW6
Pulling on Trousers, HW2
Raising Hat, Style One, HW16R
Santa Claus, SF9
Top Hat, HW14R
Washing Day, HW8R
Watering the Flowers, SF15
Wedding, LFd

Pressing Trousers (HW14)

Shape	U.S. $	Can. $	U.K. £	Aust. $
Baby plate, round, small				
with signature	50.00	60.00	30.00	65.00
without signature	30.00	35.00	17.50	40.00
Casino jug, 24s				
with signature	300.00	350.00	175.00	375.00
without signature	250.00	300.00	150.00	325.00
Casino jug, 30s				
with signature	300.00	350.00	175.00	375.00
without signature	225.00	275.00	125.00	300.00
Casino jug, 36s				
with signature	400.00	475.00	225.00	500.00
without signature	350.00	425.00	200.00	450.00
Casino saucer				
with signature	75.00	90.00	45.00	95.00
without signature	50.00	60.00	30.00	65.00
Casino sugar bowl, 36s				
with signature	150.00	180.00	90.00	190.00
without signature	100.00	125.00	60.00	135.00
Casino teacup				
with signature	75.00	90.00	45.00	95.00
without signature	50.00	60.00	30.00	65.00
Casino teapot, 30s				
with signature	325.00	400.00	185.00	425.00
without signature	250.00	300.00	150.00	325.00
Casino teapot, 36s				
with signature	250.00	300.00	150.00	325.00
without signature	225.00	275.00	125.00	300.00
Cup / mug, large				
with signature	200.00	250.00	115.00	275.00
without signature	150.00	180.00	90.00	190.00
Don beaker				
with signature	65.00	80.00	40.00	85.00
without signature	35.00	45.00	20.00	50.00

Shape	U.S. $	Can. $	U.K. £	Aust. $
Don beaker, one handle				
with signature	65.00	80.00	40.00	85.00
without signature	35.00	45.00	20.00	50.00
Don mug, one handle				
with signature	50.00	60.00	30.00	65.00
without signature	15.00	20.00	10.00	25.00
Don mug, two handles				
with signature	50.00	60.00	30.00	65.00
without signature	15.00	20.00	10.00	25.00
Jaffa fruit saucer				
plain rim	50.00	60.00	30.00	65.00
wavy rim	75.00	90.00	45.00	95.00
Jam pot	1,500.00	1,800.00	850.00	1,900.00
Lid of hot water plate				
with signature	100.00	125.00	60.00	135.00
without signature	75.00	90.00	45.00	95.00
Plate, 6 ½"				
with signature	30.00	35.00	17.50	40.00
without signature	20.00	25.00	12.00	30.00

FINE WHITE CHINA

Shape	U.S. $	Can. $	U.K. £	Aust. $
Baby bowl	Very Rare			
Bread and butter plate	300.00	350.00	175.00	375.00
Cereal/oatmeal bowl	Very Rare			
Coupe	Very Rare			
Plate, 5"	200.00	250.00	115.00	275.00
Rex mug, small	750.00	900.00	425.00	950.00
Saucer	300.00	350.00	175.00	375.00
Sugar bowl	1,200.00	1,500.00	700.00	1,600.00
Teacup	300.00	350.00	175.00	375.00

Note: The Rex mug combines *Pressing Trousers* (HW14) with *Cycling* (HW15R).

Proposal (HW11)

PROPOSAL

Design No.:	HW11
Designer:	Barbara Vernon
Issued:	By 1937 - by 1967
Combined with:	*Bedtime in Bunks,* SF3
	Cycling, HW15R
	Dress Making, HW26
	Dunce, HW1R
	Family at Breakfast, HW12
	Family with Pram, Style One, HW15
	Footballer, HW13R
	Golfer, HW4R
	Holding Hat and Coat, EC4
	Kissing Under the Mistletoe, HW11R
	Leapfrog, HW12R
	Netting a Cricket, HW6
	Playing with Cup and Spoon, EC6
	Pulling on Trousers, HW2
	Raising Hat, Style One, HW16R
	Santa Claus, SF9
	Wedding, LFd

Shape	U.S. $	Can. $	U.K. £	Aust. $
Baby plate, round, small				
with signature	50.00	60.00	30.00	65.00
without signature	30.00	35.00	17.50	40.00
Candle holder	1,500.00	1,800.00	850.00	1,900.00
Casino jug, 30s				
with signature	500.00	600.00	285.00	625.00
without signature	450.00	550.00	260.00	575.00
Casino jugs, 36s				
with signature	300.00	350.00	175.00	375.00
without signature	250.00	300.00	150.00	325.00
Casino jug, 42s				
with signature	250.00	300.00	150.00	325.00
without signature	200.00	250.00	115.00	275.00
Casino saucer				
with signature	75.00	90.00	45.00	95.00
without signature	50.00	60.00	30.00	65.00
Casino sugar bowl, 30s				
with signature	200.00	250.00	115.00	275.00
without signature	150.00	180.00	90.00	190.00
Casino sugar bowl, 36s				
with signature	250.00	300.00	150.00	325.00
without signature	200.00	250.00	115.00	275.00
Casino teacup				
with signature	75.00	90.00	45.00	95.00
without signature	50.00	60.00	30.00	65.00
Casino teapot, 24s				
with signature	375.00	450.00	210.00	475.00
without signature	300.00	350.00	175.00	375.00
Casino teapot, 30s				
with signature	325.00	400.00	185.00	425.00
without signature	250.00	300.00	150.00	325.00
Cereal/oatmeal bowl				
with signature	35.00	45.00	20.00	50.00
without signature	25.00	30.00	15.00	35.00
Coupe dish, 6 ¾"				
with signature	200.00	250.00	115.00	275.00
without signature	150.00	180.00	90.00	190.00

Shape	U.S. $	Can. $	U.K. £	Aust. $
Don beaker				
with signature	65.00	80.00	40.00	85.00
without signature	35.00	45.00	20.00	50.00
Don beaker, one handle				
with signature	65.00	80.00	40.00	85.00
without signature	35.00	45.00	20.00	50.00
Don mug, one handle				
with silver rim	350.00	425.00	200.00	450.00
with signature	50.00	60.00	30.00	65.00
without signature	15.00	20.00	10.00	25.00
Don mug, two handles				
with signature	50.00	60.00	30.00	65.00
without signature	15.00	20.00	10.00	25.00
Jaffa fruit saucer				
plain rim	50.00	60.00	30.00	65.00
wavy rim	75.00	90.00	40.00	95.00
Jam pot	1,500.00	1,800.00	850.00	1,900.00
Lid of hot water plate				
with signature	100.00	125.00	60.00	135.00
without signature	75.00	90.00	45.00	95.00
Plate, 6 ½"				
with signature	30.00	35.00	17.50	40.00
without signature	20.00	25.00	12.00	30.00

FINE WHITE CHINA

Shape	U.S. $	Can. $	U.K. £	Aust. $
Baby bowl	Very rare			
Beaker	300.00	350.00	175.00	375.00
Plate, 5"	650.00	775.00	375.00	800.00
Plate, 6"	250.00	300.00	150.00	325.00
Prince sugar bowl	2,500.00	3,000.00	1,400.00	4,000.00
Rex mug, small	750.00	900.00	425.00	950.00
Rex mug, large	Very rare			
Saucer	300.00	350.00	175.00	375.00
Teacup	300.00	350.00	175.00	375.00

PULLING ON TROUSERS

Design No.: HW2
Designer: Barbara Vernon
Issued: By 1937 - by 1952
Combined with: *Artist*, HW1
Bedtime in Bunks, SF3
Family at Breakfast, HW12
Family with Pram, Style One, HW15
Feeding the Baby, HW
Fishing in the Goldfish Bowl, HW3R
Game of Golf, SF11
Going Shopping, SF10
Golfer, HW4R
Holding Hat and Coat, EC4
Netting a Cricket, HW6
Pressing Trousers, HW14
Proposal, HW11
Raising Hat, Style One, HW16R
Reading the Times, HW2R
Santa Claus, SF9

Pulling on Trousers (HW2)

Shape	U.S. $	Can. $	U.K. £	Aust. $
Casino jug, 30s				
with signature	300.00	350.00	175.00	375.00
without signature	225.00	275.00	125.00	300.00
Casino jug, 36s				
with signature	300.00	350.00	175.00	375.00
without signature	250.00	300.00	150.00	325.00
Casino jug, 42s				
with signature	250.00	300.00	150.00	325.00
without signature	200.00	250.00	115.00	275.00
Casino saucer				
with signature	75.00	90.00	45.00	95.00
without signature	50.00	60.00	30.00	55.00
Casino sugar bowl, 30s				
with signature	200.00	250.00	115.00	275.00
without signature	150.00	180.00	90.00	190.00
Casino sugar bowl, 36s				
with signature	150.00	180.00	90.00	190.00
without signature	100.00	125.00	60.00	135.00
Casino teacup				
with signature	75.00	90.00	45.00	95.00
without signature	50.00	60.00	30.00	55.00
Cup / mug, large			Rare	
Don beaker				
with signature	65.00	80.00	40.00	85.00
without signature	35.00	45.00	20.00	50.00
Don beaker, one handle				
with signature	65.00	80.00	40.00	85.00
without signature	35.00	45.00	20.00	50.00
Don mug, one handle				
with signature	50.00	60.00	30.00	55.00
without signature	15.00	20.00	10.00	25.00
Don mug, two handles				
with signature	50.00	60.00	30.00	55.00
without signature	15.00	20.00	10.00	25.00
Jaffa fruit saucer				
plain rim	50.00	60.00	30.00	55.00
wavy rim	75.00	90.00	45.00	95.00
Jam pot	1,500.00	1,800.00	850.00	1,900.00
Lid of hot water plate				
with signature	100.00	125.00	60.00	135.00
without signature	75.00	90.00	45.00	95.00
Plate, 6 ½"				
with signature	30.00	35.00	17.50	40.00
without signature	20.00	25.00	12.00	30.00
FINE WHITE CHINA				
Prince sugar bowl	2,500.00	3,000.00	1,400.00	4,000.00
Rex mug, large			Very rare	
Teacup	300.00	350.00	175.00	375.00

Punch and Judy Show (HW136)

Ice Cream on the Beach (HW136R)

PUNCH AND JUDY SHOW / ICE CREAM ON THE BEACH

Design No.: Front — HW136 Punch and Judy Show
Reverse — HW136R Ice Cream on the Beach
Designer: Walter Hayward
Issued: 1967 - by 1998
Combined with: **Cowboy on Rocking Horse*, HW140R
Playing with Dolls and Prams, HW115
**Roller Skating*, HW137R
Sailing Boats, HW138R
Serving Tea, HW116R
To the Station, HW17R

Shape	U.S. $	Can. $	U.K. £	Aust. $
Albion cream jug	35.00	45.00	20.00	50.00
Albion jug, ½ pint	85.00	100.00	50.00	110.00
Albion jug, 1 pint	100.00	125.00	60.00	135.00
Albion teapot	50.00	60.00	30.00	65.00
Cake stand	150.00	180.00	90.00	190.00
Casino saucer	8.00	10.00	5.00	12.00
Casino teacup	8.00	10.00	5.00	12.00
Casino teapot, 30s	150.00	180.00	90.00	190.00
Divider dish	50.00	60.00	30.00	65.00
Don beaker	25.00	30.00	15.00	35.00
Don beaker, one handle	25.00	30.00	15.00	35.00
Don mug, one handle	10.00	12.00	6.00	15.00
Don mug, two handles	10.00	12.00	6.00	15.00
Egg box				
small	175.00	200.00	100.00	225.00
medium	200.00	250.00	115.00	275.00
large	225.00	275.00	125.00	300.00
Hug-a-mug, one handle	10.00	12.00	6.00	15.00
Hug-a-mug, two handles	10.00	12.00	6.00	15.00
Jaffa fruit saucer (plain)	15.00	20.00	10.00	25.00
Lamp	50.00	60.00	30.00	65.00
Malvern beaker	15.00	20.00	10.00	25.00
Money ball	10.00	12.00	6.00	15.00
Picture plaque, small	20.00	25.00	12.00	30.00
Savings book	15.00	20.00	10.00	25.00
Stratford straight beaker	15.00	20.00	10.00	25.00
Stratford teacup	8.00	10.00	5.00	12.00

* Indicates scene on divider dish.

QUEEN OF THE MAY – Colin Twinn

First Variation, Small Size

Design No.:	Front — CT7 Queen of the May Reverse — CT8 Counting Motif
Designer:	Colin Twinn
Issued:	1988 - 1993
Combined with:	*Picking Daisies*, CT4

Shape	U.S. $	Can. $	U.K. £	Aust. $
Albion cream jug	35.00	45.00	20.00	50.00
Albion jug, ½ pint	85.00	100.00	50.00	110.00
Albion jug, 1 pint	100.00	125.00	60.00	135.00
Albion teapot	75.00	90.00	45.00	95.00
Baby plate, small, round	20.00	25.00	12.00	30.00
Hug-a-mug, one handle	10.00	12.00	6.00	15.00
Hug-a-mug, two handles	10.00	12.00	6.00	15.00
Picture plaque, small	20.00	25.00	12.00	30.00
Malvern beaker	15.00	20.00	10.00	25.00

Queen of the May, First Variation (CT7)

Note: Two money balls were issued for the U.S. Special Events Tour in 1992. This design was featured on the Spring tour with no special inscription. *Happy Birthday from Bunnykins* (CT60) was featured on the Fall tour. *Queen of the May* (CT17) is combined with *Picking Daisies* (CT4) on a one handled, hug-a-mug, see page 191.

1 One

Can you find
Susan's crown?

Counting Motif (CT8)

Queen of the May, Second Variation (CT13)

Second Variation, Large Size

Design No.:	CT13 Queen of the May
Designer:	Colin Twinn
Issued:	1989- 1993
Combined with:	*Picking Daisies*, CT13

Shape	U.S. $	Can. $	U.K. £	Aust. $
Albion jug, 1 pint	100.00	125.00	60.00	135.00
Baby plate, round, small	15.00	20.00	10.00	25.00
Cake stand	150.00	180.00	90.00	190.00
Cereal / oatmeal bowl	15.00	20.00	10.00	25.00
Lamp	50.00	60.00	30.00	65.00
Picture plaque, small	20.00	25.00	12.00	30.00
Picture plaque, large	20.00	25.00	12.00	30.00
Plate, 8"	15.00	20.00	10.00	25.00

Raft (SF111)

RAFT

Design No.: SF111
Designer: Walter Hayward after Penelope Hollinshead
Issued: 1959 - 2003

Shape	U.S. $	Can. $	U.K. £	Aust. $
Baby plate, round, small	20.00	25.00	12.00	30.00
Casino saucer	8.00	10.00	5.00	12.00
Casino teapot, 30s	150.00	180.00	90.00	190.00
Cereal / oatmeal bowl	15.00	20.00	10.00	25.00
Coupe plate, 6 ¾"		Very Rare		
Hot water plate	75.00	90.00	45.00	95.00
Jaffa fruit saucer (plain)	15.00	20.00	10.00	25.00
Picture plaque, large	20.00	25.00	12.00	30.00
Plate, 6 ½"	15.00	20.00	10.00	25.00
Plate, 7 ½"	15.00	20.00	10.00	25.00
Plate, 8"	15.00	20.00	10.00	25.00

Note: **1.** Retirement dates are all approximate. When a design is retired all remaining stocks of the retired litho prints are used until exhausted.
2. Condition is important. Prices listed are based on nurseryware in mint condition. Items in less than mint condition will command lower prices.

RAISING HAT
Style One

Design No.: HW16R
Designer: Barbara Vernon
Issued: By 1937 - by 1952
Combined with: *Family at Breakfast*, HW12
Family with Pram, Style One, HW15
Feeding the Baby, HW13
Lambeth Walk, HW16
Pressing Trousers, HW14
Proposal, HW11
Pulling on Trousers, HW2
Sleeping in a Rocking Chair, EC1
Wedding, LFd

Shape	U.S. $	Can. $	U.K. £	Aust. $
Beaker cover				
with signature	75.00	90.00	45.00	95.00
without signature	65.00	80.00	40.00	85.00
Casino jug, 42s				
with signature	250.00	300.00	150.00	325.00
without signature	200.00	250.00	115.00	275.00
Casino teacup				
with signature	75.00	90.00	45.00	95.00
without signature	50.00	60.00	30.00	65.00
Casino teapot, 30s				
with signature	325.00	400.00	185.00	425.00
without signature	250.00	300.00	150.00	325.00
Casino teapot, 36s				
with signature	250.00	300.00	150.00	325.00
without signature	225.00	275.00	125.00	300.00
Don beaker				
with signature	65.00	80.00	40.00	85.00
without signature	35.00	45.00	20.00	50.00
Don beaker, one handle				
with signature	65.00	80.00	40.00	85.00
without signature	35.00	45.00	20.00	50.00
Don mug, one handle				
with signature	50.00	60.00	30.00	65.00
without signature	15.00	20.00	10.00	25.00
Jam pot	1,500.00	1,800.00	850.00	1,900.00
Lid of hot water plate				
with signature	75.00	90.00	45.00	95.00
without signature	50.00	60.00	30.00	65.00

Raising Hat, Style One (HW16R)

Note: *Raising Hat* (HW16R) is combined with *Family with Pram*, Style One, (HW15) on a large round and an oval baby plate, and also a 7 ½" plate. For an illustration see page 71.

Raising Hat, Style Two (EC7)

RAISING HAT
Style Two

Design No.: EC7
Designer: Barbara Vernon
Issued: 1937 to the present
Combined with: *Bedtime with Dollies*, EC125
Building Sandcastles, HW138
Drummer, EC2
Drummer and Bugler, EC126
Engine Pulling a Carriage, HW17
Family with Pram, Style One, HW15
Hikers, EC124
Hobby Horse, Style Two, EC121
Holding Hat and Coat, EC4
Playing with Cup and Spoon, EC6
Playing with Doll and Pram, EC123
Reading, EC122
Sheltering Under an Umbrella, EC3
Sleeping in a Rocking Chair, EC1
To the Station, HW17R
Trumpeter, EC5

Shape	U.S. $	Can. $	U.K. £	Aust. $
Albion sugar bowl	30.00	35.00	17.50	40.00
Beaker cover	65.00	80.00	40.00	85.00
Casino sugar bowl, 30s	150.00	180.00	90.00	190.00
Egg cup				
Style One	30.00	35.00	17.50	40.00
Style Two	40.00	50.00	25.00	55.00
Style Three	10.00	12.00	6.00	15.00
Lid of hot water plate	50.00	60.00	30.00	65.00
Money Ball	25.00	30.00	15.00	35.00

READING

Design No.: EC122
Designer: Walter Hayward
Issued: 1959 to the present
Combined with: *Bedtime with Dollies*, EC125
The Doll's House, HW120
Drummer, EC2
Drummer and Bugler, EC126
Hikers, EC124
Hobby Horse, Style One, HW24R
Hobby Horse, Style Two, EC121
Playing with Cup and Spoon, EC6
Playing with Doll and Pram, EC123
Raising Hat, Style Two, EC7
Sheltering Under an Umbrella, EC3
Sledging, Style One, HW141
Sleeping in a Rocking Chair, EC1
Trumpeter, EC5

Shape	U.S. $	Can. $	U.K. £	Aust. $
Albion sugar bowl	30.00	35.00	17.50	40.00
Beaker cover	65.00	80.00	40.00	85.00
Egg cup				
Style One	30.00	35.00	17.50	40.00
Style Two	40.00	50.00	25.00	55.00
Style Three	10.00	12.00	6.00	15.00
Lid of hot water plate	50.00	60.00	30.00	65.00
Money ball	10.00	12.00	6.00	15.00

Reading (EC122)

READING THE TIMES

Design No.: HW2R
Designer: Barbara Vernon
Issued: By 1937 - by 1952
Combined with: *Cycling*, HW15R
Footballer, HW13R
Golfer, HW4R
Kissing Under the Mistletoe, HW11R
Leapfrog, HW12R
Netting a Cricket, HW6
Pulling on Trousers, HW2
Smoking in the Doorway, SF2

Shape	U.S. $	Can. $	U.K. £	Aust. $
Beaker Cover	75.00	90.00	45.00	95.00
Casino jug, 42s	275.00	325.00	160.00	350.00
Casino teacup	75.00	90.00	45.00	95.00
Cup / mug, large	350.00	425.00	200.00	450.00
Don beaker	150.00	180.00	90.00	190.00
Don beaker, one handle	150.00	180.00	90.00	190.00
Don mug, one handle	100.00	125.00	60.00	135.00
Don mug, two handles	100.00	125.00	60.00	135.00

Reading the Times (HW2R)

Note: This design should appear with the Barbara Vernon facsimile signature.

Ring-a-Ring o'Roses (SF21)

RING-A-RING O'ROSES

Design No.: SF21
Designer: Walter Hayward
Issued: 1954 - by 1998

Shape	U.S. $	Can. $	U.K. £	Aust. $
Baby plate, round, small				
with signature	30.00	35.00	17.50	40.00
without signature	20.00	25.00	12.00	30.00
Cake stand	150.00	180.00	90.00	190.00
Casino saucer				
with signature	15.00	20.00	10.00	25.00
without signature	8.00	10.00	5.00	12.00
Casino teapot, 24s				
with signature	275.00	325.00	160.00	350.00
without signature	175.00	200.00	100.00	225.00
Cereal / oatmeal bowl				
with signature	25.00	30.00	15.00	35.00
without signature	15.00	20.00	10.00	25.00
Hot water plate				
with signature	100.00	125.00	60.00	135.00
without signature	75.00	90.00	45.00	95.00
Jaffa fruit saucer (plain)				
with signature	25.00	30.00	15.00	35.00
without signature	15.00	20.00	10.00	25.00
Picture plaque, large	20.00	25.00	12.00	30.00
Plate, 6 ½"				
with signature	25.00	30.00	15.00	35.00
without signature	15.00	20.00	10.00	25.00
Plate, 7 ½"				
with signature	30.00	35.00	17.50	40.00
without signature	15.00	20.00	10.00	25.00
Plate, 8"				
with signature	30.00	35.00	17.50	40.00
without signature	15.00	20.00	10.00	25.00

ROCKING HORSE / HOBBY HORSE, Style One

Rocking Horse (HW24)

Hobby Horse (HW24R)

Design No.:	Front — HW24 Rocking Horse Reverse — HW24R Hobby Horse
Designer:	Walter Hayward after Barbara Vernon
Issued:	1954 - 1967
Combined with:	*Portrait Painter*, SF20 *Reading*, EC122 *Trumpeter*, EC5

Shape	U.S. $	Can. $	U.K. £	Aust. $
Beaker cover				
with signature	75.00	90.00	45.00	95.00
without signature	65.00	80.00	40.00	85.00
Casino jug, 42s				
with signature	225.00	275.00	125.00	300.00
without signature	150.00	180.00	90.00	190.00
Casino teacup				
with signature	75.00	90.00	45.00	95.00
without signature	50.00	60.00	30.00	65.00
Casino teapot, 24s				
with signature	375.00	450.00	210.00	475.00
without signature	325.00	400.00	185.00	425.00
Don beaker				
with signature	100.00	125.00	60.00	135.00
without signature	50.00	60.00	30.00	65.00
Don beaker, one handle				
with signature	100.00	125.00	60.00	135.00
without signature	50.00	60.00	30.00	65.00
Don mug, one handle				
with signature	75.00	90.00	45.00	95.00
without signature	35.00	45.00	20.00	50.00
Don mug, two handles				
with signature	75.00	90.00	45.00	95.00
without signature	35.00	45.00	20.00	50.00
Egg cup, Style Two	50.00	60.00	30.00	50.00
Jaffa fruit saucer (plain)				
with signature	50.00	60.00	30.00	65.00
without signature	30.00	35.00	17.50	40.00
Lamp	50.00	60.00	30.00	65.00
Lid of hot water plate				
with signature	100.00	125.00	60.00	135.00
without signature	75.00	90.00	45.00	95.00
Money ball	10.00	12.00	6.00	15.00
Plate, 6 ½"				
with signature	30.00	35.00	17.50	40.00
without signature	20.00	25.00	12.50	30.00

Note: *Hobby Horse* (HW24R) is combined with *Reading* (EC122) on the Egg cup, style two.

ROLLER SKATING RACE / ROLLER SKATING ARM IN ARM

Design No.: Front — HW137 Roller Skating Race
Reverse — HW137R Roller Skating Arm in Arm
Designer: Walter Hayward
Issued: 1967 - by 1998
Combined with: *Building Sand Castles*, HW138
Dancing with Doll, HW115R
Nipped by a Crab, HW22R
Playing with Dolls and Prams, HW115
Sailing Boats, HW138R
Trumpeter, EC5

Shape	U.S. $	Can. $	U.K. £	Aust. $
Albion cream jug	35.00	45.00	20.00	50.00
Albion jug, 1 pint	100.00	125.00	60.00	135.00
Albion teapot	50.00	60.00	30.00	65.00
Cake stand	150.00	180.00	90.00	190.00
Casino teacup	8.00	10.00	5.00	12.00
Casino teapot, 36s	125.00	150.00	75.00	160.00
Divider dish	50.00	60.00	30.00	65.00
Don beaker	25.00	30.00	15.00	35.00
Don beaker, one handle	25.00	30.00	15.00	35.00
Don mug, one handle	10.00	12.00	6.00	15.00
Don mug, two handles	10.00	12.00	6.00	15.00
Egg box				
small	175.00	200.00	100.00	225.00
medium	200.00	250.00	115.00	275.00
large	225.00	275.00	125.00	300.00
Hug-a-mug, one handle	10.00	12.00	6.00	15.00
Hug-a-mug, two handles	10.00	12.00	6.00	15.00
Jaffa fruit saucer (plain)	15.00	20.00	10.00	25.00
Lamp	50.00	60.00	30.00	65.00
Lid of hot water plate	225.00	275.00	125.00	300.00
Malvern beaker	15.00	20.00	10.00	25.00
Money ball	10.00	12.00	6.00	15.00
Picture plaque, small	20.00	25.00	12.00	30.00
Plate, 6 ½"	15.00	20.00	10.00	25.00
Savings book	15.00	20.00	10.00	25.00
Stratford straight beaker	15.00	20.00	10.00	25.00
Stratford teacup	8.00	10.00	5.00	12.00

Roller Skating Race (HW137)

Roller Skating Arm in Arm (HW137R)

ROW BOAT / NIPPED BY A CRAB

Row Boat (HW21)

Nipped by a Crab (HW21R)

Design No.: Front — HW21 Row Boat
Reverse — HW21R Nipped by a Crab
Designer: Walter Hayward
Issued: By 1952 - by 1998
Combined with: *Cricketer*, HW22R
Family with Pram, Style One, HW15
Hikers, EC124
Playing with Cup and Spoon, EC6
Roller Skating Arm in Arm, HW133
Swinging, HW20
Trumpeter, EC5
Wheelbarrow Race, Style One, HW22

Shape	U.S. $	Can. $	U.K. £	Aust. $
Albion jug, ½ pint	85.00	100.00	50.00	110.00
Albion jug, 1 pint	100.00	125.00	60.00	135.00
Albion teapot	50.00	60.00	30.00	65.00
Casino jug, 36s				
with signature	175.00	200.00	100.00	225.00
without signature	125.00	150.00	75.00	160.00
Casino saucer				
with signature	15.00	20.00	10.00	25.00
without signature	8.00	10.00	5.00	12.00
Casino sugar bowl, 36s				
with signature	150.00	180.00	90.00	190.00
without signature	125.00	150.00	75.00	160.00
Casino teacup				
with signature	15.00	20.00	10.00	25.00
without signature	8.00	10.00	5.00	12.00
Casino teapot, 24s				
with signature	275.00	325.00	160.00	350.00
without signature	175.00	200.00	100.00	225.00
Casino teapot, 36s				
with signature	225.00	275.00	125.00	300.00
without signature	150.00	180.00	90.00	190.00
Divider dish	50.00	60.00	30.00	65.00
Don beaker				
with signature	50.00	60.00	30.00	65.00
without signature	25.00	30.00	15.00	35.00
Don beaker, one handle				
with signature	50.00	60.00	30.00	65.00
without signature	25.00	30.00	15.00	35.00

Shape	U.S. $	Can. $	U.K. £	Aust. $
Don mug, one handle				
with signature	40.00	50.00	25.00	55.00
without signature	10.00	12.00	6.00	15.00
Don mug, two handles				
with signature	40.00	50.00	25.00	55.00
without signature	10.00	12.00	6.00	15.00
Egg box				
small	175.00	200.00	100.00	225.00
medium	200.00	250.00	115.00	275.00
large	225.00	275.00	125.00	300.00
Hug-a-mug, one handle	10.00	12.00	6.00	15.00
Hug-a-mug, two handles	10.00	12.00	6.00	15.00
Jaffa fruit saucer (plain)				
with signature	25.00	30.00	15.00	35.00
without signature	15.00	20.00	10.00	25.00
Lamp	50.00	60.00	30.00	65.00
Lid of hot water plate				
with signature	75.00	90.00	45.00	95.00
without signature	50.00	60.00	30.00	65.00
Malvern beaker	15.00	20.00	10.00	25.00
Money ball	10.00	12.00	6.00	15.00
Picture plaque, small	20.00	20.00	10.00	25.00
Plate, 6 ½"				
with signature	25.00	30.00	15.00	35.00
without signature	15.00	20.00	10.00	25.00
Savings book	15.00	20.00	10.00	25.00
Stratford straight beaker	15.00	20.00	10.00	25.00
Stratford teacup	8.00	10.00	5.00	12.00

Note: 1. A Casino jug combines *Rowboat (*HW21), with *Swinging* (HW20).
2. Indicates a scene on a lid of a hot water plate.

SANTA BUNNYKINS CHRISTMAS TREE ORNAMENT

Design No.:	Front — CT68 Santa Bunnykins Reverse — CT69 Christmas 1991
Designer:	Colin Twinn
Issued:	1991 - 1991
Series:	Christmas Tree Ornaments

Shape	U.S. $	Can. $	U.K. £	Aust. $
Christmas Tree Ornament	15.00	20.00	10.00	25.00

Note: For other Christmas tree ornaments in this series see pages 42, 44, 80, and 165.

Santa Bunnykins Christmas Tree Ornament (CT68)

Christmas 1991 (CT69)

Santa Claus (SF9)

SANTA CLAUS

Design No.: SF9
Designer: Barbara Vernon
Issued: By 1940 - by 1952
Combined with: *Feeding the Baby*, HW13
Footballer, HW13R
Pressing Trousers, HW14
Proposal, HW11
Pulling on Trousers, HW2

Shape	U.S. $	Can. $	U.K. £	Aust. $
Baby plate, oval, small				
with signature	200.00	250.00	115.00	275.00
without signature	150.00	180.00	90.00	190.00
Baby plate, round, small				
with signature	50.00	60.00	30.00	65.00
without signature	30.00	35.00	17.50	40.00
Candle holder	2,000.00	2,500.00	1,100.00	2,750.00
Casino jug, 30s				
with signature	250.00	300.00	150.00	325.00
without signature	200.00	250.00	115.00	275.00
Casino jug, 36s				
with signature	250.00	300.00	150.00	325.00
without signature	175.00	200.00	100.00	225.00
Casino teapot, 30s				
with signature	325.00	400.00	185.00	425.00
without signature	250.00	300.00	150.00	325.00
Cereal / oatmeal bowl				
with signature	35.00	45.00	20.00	50.00
without signature	25.00	30.00	15.00	35.00
Don beaker, one handle				
with signature	100.00	125.00	60.00	135.00
without signature	50.00	60.00	30.00	65.00
Hot water plate				
with signature	125.00	150.00	75.00	160.00
without signature	100.00	125.00	60.00	135.00
Jaffa fruit saucer				
plain rim	50.00	60.00	30.00	65.00
wavy rim	75.00	90.00	45.00	95.00
Plate, 6 ½"				
with signature	30.00	35.00	17.50	40.00
without signature	20.00	25.00	12.00	30.00
Plate, 7"				
with signature	65.00	80.00	40.00	85.00
without signature	25.00	30.00	15.00	35.00
Plate, 7 ½"				
with signature	65.00	80.00	40.00	85.00
without signature	25.00	30.00	15.00	35.00
Plate, 8 ½"				
with signature	75.00	90.00	45.00	95.00
without signature	25.00	30.00	15.00	35.00
FINE WHITE CHINA				
Cereal bowl	350.00	425.00	200.00	450.00
Plate, 5"	650.00	775.00	375.00	800.00
Plate, 7"	650.00	775.00	375.00	800.00

Note: Fine white china prices are indications only due to the scarcity of the shapes. Prices will vary.

SCHOOL THEME – Frank Endersby

MATHS LESSON

Design No.:	25 Maths Lesson
Designer:	Frank Endersby
Issued:	1995 to the present

Shape	U.S. $	Can. $	U.K. £	Aust. $
Baby plate, round, small	25.00	30.00	15.00	35.00
Plate, 6 ½"	10.00	12.00	6.00	15.00
Plate, 8"	15.00	20.00	10.00	25.00

Maths Lesson (25)

Teacher Scolding (26)

Bunny with Bag (27)

TEACHER SCOLDING / BUNNY WITH BAG

Design No.:	Front — 26 Teacher Scolding
	Reverse — 27 Bunny with Bag
Designer:	Frank Endersby
Issued:	1995 to the present
Combined with:	**Carrying Letter, (30)*

Shape	U.S. $	Can. $	U.K. £	Aust. $
Hug-a-mug, one handle	20.00	25.00	12.00	30.00
Hug-a-mug, two handles	20.00	25.00	12.00	30.00
Divider dish	50.00	60.00	30.00	65.00

* Indicates scene on divider dish.

SCHOOL DINNER THEME — Colin Twinn

School Dinner, First Variation (CT17)

First Variation, Small Size

Design No.: CT17 School Dinner
Designer: Colin Twinn
Issued: 1990 - 1993

Shape	U.S. $	Can. $	U.K. £	Aust. $
Albion jug, 1 pint	100.00	125.00	60.00	135.00
Baby plate, round, small	20.00	25.00	12.50	30.00
Cake stand	150.00	180.00	90.00	190.00
Cereal / oatmeal bowl	15.00	20.00	12.00	25.00
Jaffa fruit saucer (plain)	15.00	20.00	12.00	25.00
Plate, 8"	15.00	20.00	12.00	25.00

School Dinner, Second Variation (CT30)

Second Variation, Large Size / COOK AND BUNNY

Design No.: Front — CT30 School Dinner
Reverse — CT31 Cook and Bunny
Designer: Colin Twinn
Issued: 1990 - 1993

Shape	U.S. $	Can. $	U.K. £	Aust. $
Albion cream jug	35.00	45.00	20.00	50.00
Albion jug, 1 pint	100.00	125.00	60.00	135.00
Albion teapot	50.00	60.00	30.00	65.00
Hug-a-mug, one handle	10.00	12.00	6.00	15.00
Hug-a-mug, two handles	10.00	12.00	6.00	15.00
Lamp	50.00	60.00	30.00	65.00
Malvern beaker	15.00	20.00	10.00	25.00
Money ball	10.00	12.00	6.00	15.00
Savings book	15.00	20.00	10.00	22.50
Stratford teacup	8.00	10.00	5.00	12.00

Cook and Bunny (CT31)

SCHOOL GATES THEME – Colin Twinn

First Variation, Large Size

Design No.:	CT20 School Gates
Designer:	Colin Twinn
Issued:	1991 - 1993

Shape	U.S. $	Can. $	U.K. £	Aust. $
Albion jug, 1 pint	100.00	125.00	60.00	135.00
Baby plate, round, small	100.00	125.00	60.00	135.00
Cereal / oatmeal bowl	15.00	20.00	10.00	25.00
Lamp	50.00	60.00	30.00	65.00
Picture plaque, large	20.00	25.00	12.00	30.00
Plate, 6"	15.00	20.00	10.00	25.00
Plate, 8"	15.00	20.00	10.00	25.00

School Gates, First Variation (CT20)

School Gates, Second Variation (CT22)

Bunny on Trike (CT23)

SCHOOL GATES
Second Variation, Small Size / BUNNY ON TRIKE

Design No.:	Front — CT22 School Gates
Designer:	Reverse — CT23 Bunny on Trike
Issued:	1991 - 1993
Combined with:	*Bathtime Scene*, Style Two, Second Variation, CT24
	Bunnies in the Bath, First Version, CT25
	Classrooom Scene, Style Two, Second Version, CT16
	Ice Cream Seller, Second Variation, CT11

Shape	U.S. $	Can. $	U.K. £	Aust. $
Albion jug, ½ pint	85.00	100.00	50.00	110.00
Albion teapot	50.00	60.00	30.00	65.00
Hug-a-mug, one handle	10.00	12.00	6.00	15.00
Hug-a-mug, two handles	10.00	12.00	6.00	15.00
Lamp	50.00	60.00	30.00	65.00
Money ball	10.00	12.00	6.00	15.00
Picture plaque, small	20.00	25.00	12.00	30.00
Stratford straight beaker	15.00	20.00	10.00	25.00

See-saw, Style One (SF17)

SEE-SAW
Style One

Design No.: SF17
Designer: Walter Hayward
Issued: By 1952 - by 1998
Combined with: *Engine Pulling a Carriage*, HW17
Mr. Piggly's Stores, SF14
To the Station, HW17R

Shape	U.S. $	Can. $	U.K. £	Aust. $
Albion jug, ½ pint	85.00	100.00	50.00	110.00
Albion jug, 1 pint	100.00	125.00	60.00	135.00
Baby plate, round, small				
with signature	30.00	35.00	17.50	40.00
without signature	20.00	25.00	12.00	30.00
Cake stand	150.00	180.00	90.00	190.00
Casino sugar bowl, 36s				
with signature	150.00	180.00	90.00	190.00
without signature	125.00	150.00	75.00	160.00
Cereal / oatmeal bowl				
with signature	25.00	30.00	15.00	35.00
without signature	15.00	20.00	10.00	25.00
Coupe plate, 6 ¾"			Very Rare	
Hot water plate				
with signature	100.00	125.00	60.00	135.00
without signature	75.00	90.00	45.00	95.00
Jaffa fruit saucer (plain)				
with signature	25.00	30.00	15.00	35.00
without signature	15.00	20.00	10.00	25.00
Picture plaque, large	20.00	25.00	12.00	30.00
Plate, 6 ½"				
with signature	25.00	30.00	15.00	35.00
without signature	15.00	20.00	10.00	25.00
Plate, 7 ½"				
with signature	30.00	35.00	17.50	40.00
without signature	15.00	20.00	10.00	25.00
Plate, 8"	15.00	20.00	10.00	25.00

Note: **1.** Casino sugar bowl combines *See-Saw* (SF17) and *To The Station* (HW17R).
2. Condition is important. Prices listed are based on nurseryware in mint condition. Items in less than mint condition will command lower prices.

SHELTERING UNDER AN UMBRELLA

Sheltering Under an Umbrella (EC3)

Design No.: EC3
Designer: Barbara Vernon
Issued: 1937 to the present
Combined with: *Afternoon Tea*, HW116
Bedtime with Dollies, EC125
Drummer, EC2
Family Going Out on Washing Day, HW8
Fishing in the Goldfish Bowl, HW3R
Hikers, EC124
Hobby Horse, Style Two, EC121
Holding Hat and Coat, EC4
Playing with Cup and Spoon, EC6
Playing with Doll and Pram, EC123
Raising Hat, Style Two, EC7
Reading, EC122
Serving Tea, HW116R
Sleeping in a Rocking Chair, EC1
Trumpeter, EC5
Washing Day, HW8R

Shape	U.S. $	Can. $	U.K. £	Aust. $
Albion sugar bowl	30.00	35.00	17.50	40.00
Beaker cover				
with signature	75.00	90.00	45.00	95.00
without signature	65.00	80.00	40.00	85.00
Casino sugar bowl, 30s				
with signature	150.00	180.00	90.00	190.00
without signature	125.00	150.00	75.00	160.00
Casino sugar bowl, 36s				
with signature	125.00	150.00	75.00	160.00
without signature	100.00	125.00	60.00	135.00
Egg cup				
Style One				
with signature	40.00	50.00	25.00	55.00
without signature	30.00	35.00	17.50	40.00
Style Two	40.00	50.00	25.00	55.00
Style Three	10.00	12.00	6.00	15.00
Lid of hot water plate				
with signature	75.00	90.00	45.00	95.00
without signature	50.00	60.00	30.00	65.00

FINE WHITE CHINA

Teacup	Very rare

SHOPPING THEME – Frank Endersby

Shopping (1)

SHOPPING

Design No.: 1 Shopping
Designer: Frank Endersby
Issued: 1995 to the present

Shape	U.S. $	Can. $	U.K. £	Aust. $
Baby plate, round, small	20.00	25.00	12.00	30.00
Jaffa fruit saucer	15.00	20.00	10.00	25.00
Plate, 6 ½"	10.00	12.50	6.00	15.00
Plate, 8"	15.00	20.00	10.00	25.00

Vegetable Stall (2)

VEGETABLE STALL / EATING APPLES

Design No.: Front — 2 Vegetable Stall
Reverse — 3 Eating Apples
Designer: Frank Endersby
Issued: 1995 to the present
Combined with: **Resting*, Style Two, (21)

Shape	U.S. $	Can. $	U.K. £	Aust. $
Hug-a-mug, one handle	20.00	25.00	12.00	30.00
Hug-a-mug, two handles	20.00	25.00	12.00	30.00
Divider dish	50.00	60.00	30.00	65.00
Stratford teacup	8.00	10.00	5.00	12.00

* Indicates scene on divider dish.

Eating Apples (3)

SLEDGING, Style One / SNOWBALL FIGHT

Design No.: Front — HW141 Sledging
Reverse — HW141R Snowball Fight
Designer: Walter Hayward
Issued: 1967 - by 1998
Combined with: *Engine Pulling a Carriage*, HW17
**Pea Shooter*, HW118R
Reading, EC122
Serving Tea, HW116R

Shape	U.S. $	Can. $	U.K. £	Aust. $
Albion cream jug	35.00	45.00	20.00	50.00
Albion jug, ½ pint	85.00	100.00	50.00	110.00
Albion jug, 1 pint	100.00	125.00	60.00	135.00
Albion teapot	50.00	60.00	30.00	65.00
Casino teacup	8.00	10.00	5.00	12.00
Divider dish	50.00	60.00	30.00	65.00
Don beaker	25.00	30.00	15.00	35.00
Don beaker, one handle	25.00	30.00	15.00	35.00
Don mug, one handle	10.00	12.00	6.00	15.00
Don mug, two handles	10.00	12.00	6.00	15.00
Egg box				
small	175.00	200.00	100.00	225.00
medium	200.00	250.00	115.00	275.00
large	225.00	275.00	125.00	300.00
Hug-a-mug, one handle				
Christmas 1988 - 1991	10.00	12.00	6.00	15.00
regular issue	10.00	12.00	6.00	15.00
Hug-a-mug, two handles				
Christmas 1988 - 1991	10.00	12.00	6.00	15.00
regular issue	10.00	12.00	6.00	15.00
Jaffa fruit saucer (plain)	15.00	20.00	10.00	25.00
Lamp	50.00	60.00	30.00	65.00
Malvern beaker	15.00	20.00	10.00	25.00
Money ball	10.00	12.00	6.00	15.00
Picture plaque, small	20.00	25.00	12.00	30.00
Savings book	15.00	20.00	10.00	25.00
Stratford straight beaker	15.00	20.00	10.00	25.00
Stratford teacup	8.00	10.00	5.00	12.00

* Indicates scene on divider dish.

Sledging, Style One (HW141)

Snowball Fight (HW141R)

Note: A Merry Christmas from Bunnykins was added to the hug-a-mugs as part of the Christmas set issued between 1988 - 1991. *Sledging*, Style One (HW141) was combined with *Reading* (EC122) on a money ball and *Engine Pulling a Carriage* (HW17) is combined with *Snowball Fight* (HW141R) on a Don mug with two handles.

Sleeping in a Rocking Chair (EC1)

SLEEPING IN A ROCKING CHAIR

Design No.: EC1
Designer: Barbara Vernon
Issued: 1937 to the present
Combined with: *Bugler with Toy Donkey*, HW26R
Dress Making, HW26
Drummer, EC2
Drummer and Bugler, EC126
Engine Pulling a Carriage, HW17
Feeding the Baby, HW13
Footballer, HW13R
Haymaking, HW29
Hiker Resting with Ice Cream, HW23R
Hikers, EC124
Hobby Horse, Style Two, EC121
Ice Cream Vendor, HW23
Lambeth Walk, First Version and Second Version, HW16
Lunch Break, HW29R
Playing with Cup and Spoon, EC6
Playing with Doll and Pram, EC123
Raising Hat, Style One, HW16R
Raising Hat, Style Two, EC7
Reading, EC122
Sheltering Under an Umbrella, EC3
Skipping, HW20R
Swinging, HW20
To the Station, HW17R
Trumpeter, EC5

Shape	U.S. $	Can. $	U.K. £	Aust. $
Albion sugar bowl	30.00	35.00	17.50	40.00
Beaker cover				
with signature	75.00	90.00	45.00	95.00
without signature	65.00	80.00	40.00	85.00
Casino sugar bowl, 30s				
with signature	150.00	180.00	90.00	190.00
without signature	125.00	150.00	75.00	160.00
Casino sugar bowl, 36s	200.00	250.00	115.00	275.00
Egg cup				
Style One				
with signature	40.00	50.00	25.00	55.00
without signature	30.00	35.00	17.50	40.00
Style Two				
with signature	50.00	65.00	30.00	70.00
without signature	40.00	50.00	25.00	55.00
Style Three	10.00	12.00	6.00	15.00
Lid of hot water plate				
with signature	75.00	90.00	45.00	95.00
without signature	50.00	60.00	30.00	65.00

SMOKING IN THE DOORWAY

Design No.: SF2
Designer: Barbara Vernon
Issued: 1937 - by 1952
Combined with: *Family at Breakfast*, HW12
Fixing Braces, HW3
Pulling on Trousers, HW2
Reading the Times, HW2R

Shape	U.S. $	Can. $	U.K. £	Aust. $
Baby plate, oval, small	350.00	425.00	200.00	450.00
Baby plate, round, small	200.00	250.00	115.00	275.00
Candle holder	2,000.00	2,500.00	1,100.00	2,750.00
Casino jug, 24s	475.00	575.00	270.00	600.00
Casino jug, 36s	425.00	500.00	250.00	525.00
Casino saucer	75.00	90.00	45.00	95.00
Casino teapot, 30s	300.00	350.00	175.00	375.00
Cereal / oatmeal bowl	100.00	125.00	60.00	135.00
Don beaker, one handle	150.00	180.00	90.00	190.00
Hot water plate	200.00	250.00	115.00	275.00
Jaffa fruit saucer				
plain rim	95.00	115.00	55.00	125.00
wavy rim	125.00	150.00	75.00	160.00
Plate, 6 ½"	90.00	110.00	50.00	120.00
Plate, 7 ½"	100.00	125.00	60.00	135.00
Porridge plate	125.00	150.00	75.00	160.00

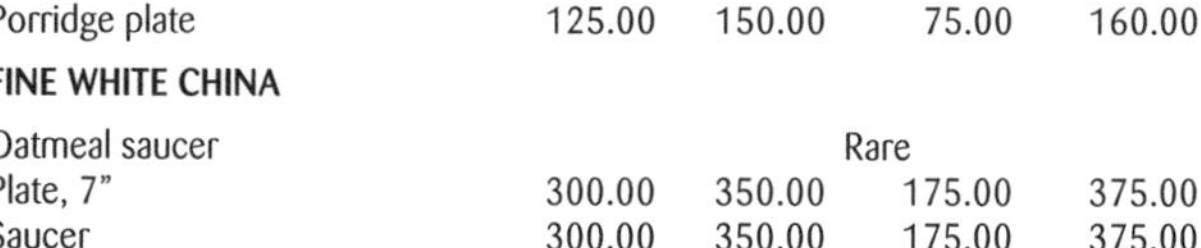

FINE WHITE CHINA

Shape	U.S. $	Can. $	U.K. £	Aust. $
Oatmeal saucer		Rare		
Plate, 7"	300.00	350.00	175.00	375.00
Saucer	300.00	350.00	175.00	375.00

Smoking in the Doorway (SF2)

Note: This design should appear with the Barbara Vernon facsimile signature.

A very rare combination of a Bunnykins design on a Series Ware shape.

SNOW SCENES THEME – Frank Endersby

Snow Scene (58)

SNOW SCENE

Design No.: 58 Snow Scene
Designer: Frank Endersby
Issued: 1995 - 2003

Shape	U.S. $	Can. $	U.K. £	Aust. $
Jaffa fruit saucer	15.00	20.00	10.00	25.00
Plate, 6 ½"	15.00	20.00	10.00	25.00
Plate, 8"	15.00	20.00	10.00	25.00

Building Snowman (59)

BUILDING SNOWMAN / SLEDGING, STYLE TWO

Design No.: Front — 59 Building Snowman
Reverse — 60 Sledging
Designer: Frank Endersby
Issued: 1995 - 2003
Combined with: **Resting in Wheelbarrow*, (57)

Shape	U.S. $	Can. $	U.K. £	Aust. $
Hug-a-mug, one handle	10.00	12.00	6.00	15.00
Hug-a-mug, two handles	10.00	12.00	6.00	15.00
Divider dish	50.00	60.00	30.00	65.00
Malvern beaker	15.00	20.00	10.00	25.00
Money ball	10.00	12.00	6.00	15.00
Stratford teacup	8.00	10.00	5.00	12.00

* Indicates scene on divider dish.

Sledging, Style Two (60)

SOLDIERS MARCHING TO THE MUSIC / SOLDIER MARCHING

Design No.:	Front — HW18 Soldiers Marching to the Music Reverse — HW18R Soldier Marching
Designer:	Walter Hayward after Barbara Vernon
Issued:	By 1952 - 1967
Combined with:	*Baking*, SF19 *Convalescing*, SF5 *Lambeth Walk*, Second Version, HW16 *Orange Vendor*, SF12

Shape	U.S. $	Can. $	U.K. £	Aust. $
Casino jug, 30s				
with signature	300.00	350.00	175.00	375.00
without signature	200.00	250.00	115.00	275.00
Casino jug, 42s				
with signature	200.00	250.00	115.00	275.00
without signature	175.00	200.00	100.00	225.00
Casino saucer				
with signature	75.00	90.00	45.00	95.00
without signature	50.00	60.00	30.00	65.00
Casino teacup				
with signature	75.00	90.00	45.00	95.00
without signature	50.00	60.00	30.00	65.00
Casino teapot, 30s				
with signature	300.00	350.00	175.00	375.00
without signature	250.00	300.00	150.00	325.00
Casino teapot, 36s				
with signature	250.00	300.00	150.00	325.00
without signature	225.00	275.00	125.00	300.00
Don beaker				
with signature	65.00	80.00	40.00	85.00
without signature	35.00	45.00	20.00	50.00
Don beaker, one handle				
with signature	65.00	80.00	40.00	85.00
without signature	35.00	45.00	20.00	50.00
Don mug, one handle				
with signature	50.00	60.00	30.00	65.00
without signature	15.00	20.00	10.00	25.00
Don mug, two handles				
with signature	50.00	60.00	30.00	65.00
without signature	15.00	20.00	10.00	25.00
Jaffa fruit saucer (plain)				
with signature	50.00	60.00	30.00	65.00
without signature	30.00	35.00	17.50	40.00
Lid of hot water plate				
with signature	100.00	125.00	60.00	135.00
without signature	75.00	90.00	45.00	95.00
Plate, 6 ½"				
with signature	30.00	35.00	17.50	40.00
without signature	20.00	25.00	12.00	30.00

Soldiers Marching to the Music (HW18)

Soldier Marching (HW18R)

SPACE ROCKET LAUNCH

Design No.: SF132
Designer: Walter Hayward
Issued: 1967 - by 1998

Shape	U.S. $	Can. $	U.K. £	Aust. $
Albion cream jug	35.00	45.00	20.00	50.00
Albion jug, 1 pint	100.00	125.00	60.00	135.00
Baby plate, round, small	20.00	25.00	12.00	30.00
Cake stand	150.00	180.00	90.00	190.00
Casino saucer	8.00	10.00	5.00	12.00
Cereal / oatmeal bowl	15.00	20.00	10.00	25.00
Hot water plate	75.00	90.00	45.00	95.00
Jaffa fruit saucer (plain)	15.00	20.00	10.00	25.00
Picture plaque, large	20.00	25.00	12.00	30.00
Plate 6 ½"	15.00	20.00	10.00	25.00
Plate 7 ½"	15.00	20.00	10.00	25.00
Plate 8"	15.00	20.00	10.00	25.00

Space Rocket Launch (SF132)

SPRING CLEANING

Design No.: LF14
Designer: Walter Hayward
Issued: By 1952 - 1970

Shape	U.S. $	Can. $	U.K. £	Aust. $
Baby plate, oval, large				
with signature	200.00	250.00	115.00	275.00
without signature	150.00	180.00	90.00	190.00
Baby plate, round, large				
with signature	100.00	125.00	60.00	135.00
without signature	75.00	90.00	45.00	95.00
Bread and butter plate				
with signature	250.00	300.00	150.00	325.00
without signature	200.00	250.00	115.00	275.00
Cereal / oatmeal bowl				
with signature	35.00	45.00	20.00	50.00
without signature	25.00	30.00	15.00	35.00
Hot water plate				
with signature	125.00	150.00	75.00	160.00
without signature	100.00	125.00	60.00	135.00
Plate, 8 ½"				
with signature	75.00	90.00	45.00	95.00
without signature	25.00	30.00	15.00	35.00
Porridge plate				
with signature	110.00	135.00	65.00	145.00
without signature	85.00	100.00	50.00	110.00

Spring Cleaning (LF14)

SPRING CLEANING THEME – Frank Endersby

DUSTING

Design No.: 19 Dusting
Designer: Frank Endersby
Issued: 1995 to the present

Shape	U.S. $	Can. $	U.K. £	Aust. $
Baby plate, round, small	25.00	30.00	15.00	35.00
Plate, 6 ½"	10.00	12.00	6.00	15.00
Plate, 8"	15.00	20.00	10.00	25.00

Dusting (19)

Beating Carpet (20)

BEATING CARPET / RESTING, Style Two

Design No.: Front — 20 Beating Carpet
Reverse — 21 Resting, Style Two
Designer: Frank Endersby
Issued: 1995 to the present
Combined with: **Eating Apples,* (3)

Shape	U.S. $	Can. $	U.K. £	Aust. $
Hug-a-mug, one handle	20.00	25.00	12.00	30.00
Hug-a-mug, two handles	20.00	25.00	12.00	30.00
Divider dish	50.00	60.00	30.00	65.00

* Indicates scene on divider dish.

Resting, Style Two (21)

Storytime (SF110)

STORYTIME

Design No.: SF110
Designer: Walter Hayward
Issued: 1959 - 1967

Shape	U.S. $	Can. $	U.K. £	Aust. $
Baby plate, round, small	150.00	180.00	90.00	190.00
Casino Jug, 36s	275.00	325.00	160.00	350.00
Casino saucer	50.00	60.00	30.00	65.00
Cereal / oatmeal bowl	90.00	110.00	50.00	120.00
Hot water plate	150.00	180.00	90.00	190.00
Plate 6 ½"	65.00	80.00	40.00	85.00
Plate 7 ½"	75.00	90.00	45.00	95.00
Plate 8"	75.00	90.00	45.00	95.00

Casino Cup, *Fishing in the Goldfish Bowl* (HW3R)

SWINGING / SKIPPING

Swinging (HW20)

Skipping (HW20R)

Design No.: Front — HW20 Swinging
Reverse — HW20R Skipping
Designer: Walter Hayward
Issued: By 1952 - 1967
Combined with: *Chicken Pulling a Cart*, SF8
Dress Making, HW26
Holding Hat and Coat, EC4
Mr. Piggly's Store, SF14
Nipped by a Crab, HW22R
Row Boat, HW21
Sleeping in a Rocking Chair, EC1

Shape	U.S. $	Can. $	U.K. £	Aust. $
Casino jug, 24s				
with signature	350.00	425.00	200.00	475.00
without signature	300.00	350.00	175.00	375.00
Casino jug, 30s				
with signature	300.00	350.00	175.00	375.00
without signature	250.00	300.00	150.00	325.00
Casino jug, 36s				
with signature	250.00	300.00	150.00	325.00
without signature	175.00	200.00	100.00	225.00
Casino saucer				
with signature	75.00	90.00	45.00	95.00
without signature	50.00	60.00	30.00	65.00
Casino sugar bowl, 36s				
with signature	175.00	200.00	100.00	225.00
without signature	125.00	150.00	75.00	160.00
Casino teacup				
with signature	75.00	90.00	45.00	95.00
without signature	50.00	60.00	30.00	65.00
Casino teapot, 36s				
with signature	250.00	300.00	150.00	325.00
without signature	225.00	275.00	125.00	300.00
Divider dish	50.00	60.00	30.00	65.00
Don beaker				
with signature	65.00	80.00	40.00	85.00
without signature	35.00	45.00	20.00	50.00
Don beaker, one handle				
with signature	65.00	80.00	40.00	85.00
without signature	35.00	45.00	20.00	50.00
Don mug, one handle				
with signature	50.00	60.00	30.00	65.00
without signature	15.00	20.00	10.00	25.00
Don mug, two handles				
with signature	50.00	60.00	30.00	65.00
without signature	15.00	20.00	10.00	25.00
Egg box				
small	175.00	200.00	100.00	225.00
Jaffa fruit saucer (plain)				
with signature	50.00	60.00	30.00	65.00
without signature	30.00	35.00	17.50	40.00
Lid of hot water plate				
with signature	100.00	125.00	60.00	135.00
without signature	75.00	90.00	45.00	95.00
Plate, 6 ½"				
with signature	30.00	35.00	17.50	40.00
without signature	20.00	25.00	12.00	30.00

Note: A Casino jug combines *Swinging,* (HW20) with *Rowboat* (HW21).

Television Time (SF112)

TELEVISION TIME

Design No.: SF112
Designer: Walter Hayward
Issued: 1959 - by 1998

Shape	U.S. $	Can. $	U.K. £	Aust. $
Baby plate, round, small	20.00	25.00	12.00	30.00
Cake stand	150.00	180.00	90.00	190.00
Casino saucer	8.00	10.00	5.00	12.00
Cereal / oatmeal bowl	15.00	20.00	8.00	25.00
Hot water plate	75.00	90.00	45.00	95.00
Jaffa fruit saucer				
plain	15.00	20.00	10.00	25.00
wavy	35.00	45.00	20.00	50.00
Picture plaque, large	20.00	25.00	12.00	30.00
Plate, 6 ½"	15.00	20.00	10.00	25.00
Plate, 7 ½"	15.00	20.00	10.00	25.00
Plate, 8"	15.00	20.00	10.00	25.00

TENNIS

A boxed Bunnykins for Grown Ups Set containing a cereal bowl and a hug-a-mug with one handle with the *Aerobics/Jogging* design, a 6" plate with the *Aeroplane* design, an 8" plate with the *Breakfast Time* design and a cereal bowl with the *Tennis* design was distributed mainly in the U.S.A.

Design No.: None
Designer: Walter Hayward
Issued: 1986 - 1988
Series: Bunnykins for Grown-Ups

Shape	U.S. $	Can. $	U.K. £	Aust. $
Cereal / oatmeal bowl	40.00	50.00	25.00	55.00
Complete set (M.I.B.)	180.00	220.00	110.00	240.00

Note: See also *Aerobics / Jogging* and *Aeroplane* page 14 and *Breakfast Time* page 32.

Tennis

TICKET QUEUE

Design No.: SF109
Designer: Walter Hayward
Issued: 1959 - by 1998

Shape	U.S. $	Can. $	U.K. £	Aust. $
Baby plate, round, small	20.00	25.00	12.00	30.00
Casino saucer	8.00	10.00	5.00	12.00
Cereal / oatmeal bowl	15.00	20.00	10.00	25.00
Hot water plate	75.00	90.00	45.00	95.00
Picture plaque, large	20.00	25.00	12.00	30.00
Plate, 6 ½"	15.00	20.00	10.00	25.00
Plate, 7 ½"	15.00	20.00	10.00	25.00
Plate, 8"	15.00	20.00	10.00	25.00
Plate, 10 ½"	20.00	25.00	12.00	30.00

Ticket Queue (SF109)

TOAST FOR TEA TODAY

Design No.: SF23
Designer: Walter Hayward
Issued: 1954 - 1967
Combined with: *Daisy Chains,* HW25
Dress Making, HW26
Dressing Up, First Version, SF22
Haymaking, HW29
Mr. Piggly's Stores, SF14
Windy Day, HW27

Shape	U.S. $	Can. $	U.K. £	Aust. $
Baby plate, round, small				
with signature	50.00	60.00	30.00	65.00
without signature	30.00	35.00	17.50	40.00
Casino jug, 24s				
with signature	275.00	325.00	160.00	350.00
without signature	225.00	275.00	125.00	300.00
Casino saucer				
with signature	75.00	90.00	45.00	95.00
without signature	50.00	60.00	30.00	65.00
Casino teapot, 24s				
with signature	375.00	450.00	210.00	475.00
without signature	300.00	350.00	175.00	375.00
Casino teapot, 30s				
with signature	325.00	400.00	185.00	425.00
without signature	250.00	300.00	150.00	325.00
Cereal / oatmeal bowl				
with signature	35.00	45.00	20.00	50.00
without signature	25.00	30.00	15.00	35.00
Hot water plate				
with signature	125.00	150.00	75.00	160.00
without signature	100.00	125.00	60.00	135.00
Jaffa fruit saucer (plain)				
with signature	50.00	60.00	30.00	65.00
without signature	30.00	35.00	17.50	40.00
Plate, 6 ½"				
with signature	30.00	35.00	17.50	40.00
without signature	20.00	25.00	12.00	30.00
Porridge Bowl	85.00	100.00	50.00	110.00

Toast for Tea Today (SF23)

Top Hat (HW14R)

TOP HAT

Design No.:	HW14R
Designer:	Barbara Vernon
Issued:	By 1937 - 1967
Combined with:	*Embracing at a Window*, HW5 *Family at Breakfast*, HW12 *Feeding the Baby*, HW13 *Lambeth Walk*, HW16 *Pressing Trousers*, HW14 *Trumpeter*, EC5

Shape	U.S. $	Can. $	U.K. £	Aust. $
Casino jug, 36s				
with signature	150.00	180.00	90.00	190.00
without signature	125.00	150.00	75.00	160.00
Casino jug, 42s				
with signature	125.00	150.00	75.00	160.00
without signature	100.00	125.00	60.00	135.00
Casino sugar bowl, 36s				
with signature	150.00	180.00	90.00	190.00
without signature	100.00	125.00	60.00	135.00
Casino teacup				
with signature	15.00	20.00	10.00	25.00
without signature	8.00	10.00	5.00	12.00
Don beaker				
with signature	50.00	60.00	30.00	65.00
without signature	25.00	30.00	15.00	35.00
Don beaker, one handle				
with signature	50.00	60.00	30.00	65.00
without signature	25.00	30.00	15.00	35.00
Don mug, one handle				
with signature	40.00	50.00	25.00	55.00
without signature	10.00	12.00	6.00	15.00
Don mug, two handles				
with signature	40.00	50.00	25.00	55.00
without signature	10.00	12.00	6.00	15.00
FINE WHITE CHINA				
Saucer	300.00	350.00	175.00	375.00
Teacup	300.00	350.00	175.00	375.00

TOPPLING THE FRUIT CART

Design No.:	SF134
Designer:	Walter Hayward
Issued:	1967 - by 1998

Shape	U.S. $	Can. $	U.K. £	Aust. $
Albion jug, 1 pint	100.00	125.00	60.00	135.00
Baby plate, round, small	20.00	25.00	12.00	30.00
Cake stand	150.00	180.00	90.00	190.00
Casino saucer	8.00	10.00	5.00	12.00
Cereal / oatmeal bowl	15.00	20.00	10.00	25.00
Hot water plate	75.00	90.00	45.00	95.00
Jaffa fruit saucer (plain)	15.00	20.00	10.00	25.00
Picture plaque, large	20.00	25.00	12.00	30.00
Plate, 6 ½"	15.00	20.00	10.00	25.00
Plate, 7 ½"	15.00	20.00	10.00	25.00
Plate, 8"	15.00	20.00	10.00	25.00

Toppling the Fruit Cart (SF134)

TOY SHOP

Design No.: SF114
Designer: Walter Hayward after Barbara Vernon
Issued: 1959 - 1967
Combined with: *Hat Shop*, HW28

Shape	U.S. $	Can. $	U.K. £	Aust. $
Baby plate, round, small	30.00	35.00	17.50	40.00
Casino jug, 30s	50.00	60.00	30.00	65.00
Casino saucer	20.00	25.00	12.00	30.00
Cereal / oatmeal bowl	25.00	30.00	15.00	35.00
Hot water plate	100.00	125.00	60.00	135.00
Jaffa fruit saucer (plain)	30.00	35.00	17.50	40.00
Plate, 6 ½"	20.00	25.00	12.00	30.00
Plate, 7 ½"	25.00	30.00	15.00	35.00

Toy Shop (SF114)

A busy Hug-a-mug

TRAIN STATION THEME – Frank Endersby

Waiting for Train (49)

WAITING FOR TRAIN

Design No.: 49 Waiting for Train
Designer: Frank Endersby
Issued: 1995 - 2003

Shape	U.S. $	Can. $	U.K. £	Aust. $
Baby plate, round, small	20.00	25.00	12.00	30.00
Jaffa fruit saucer	15.00	20.00	10.00	25.00
Plate, 6 ½"	15.00	20.00	10.00	25.00
Plate, 8"	15.00	20.00	10.00	25.00

Ticket Office (50)

TICKET OFFICE / SITTING ON SUITCASE

Design No.: Front — 50 Ticket Office
Reverse — 51 Sitting on Suitcase
Designer: Frank Endersby
Issued: 1995 - 2003

Shape	U.S. $	Can. $	U.K. £	Aust. $
Hug-a-mug, one handle	10.00	12.00	6.00	15.00
Hug-a-mug, two handles	10.00	12.00	6.00	15.00

Sitting on Suitcase (51)

TRIMMING THE TREE
CHRISTMAS TREE ORNAMENT

Design No.:	Front — CT80 Trimming the Tree Reverse — CT81 Christmas 1994
Designer:	Colin Twinn
Issued:	1994 - 1994
Series:	Christmas Tree Ornaments

Shape	U.S. $	Can. $	U.K. £	Aust. $
Christmas tree ornaments	15.00	20.00	10.00	25.00

Note: For other Christmas tree ornaments in this series see pages 42, 44, 80 and 165.

Trimming the Tree Christmas Tree Ornament (CT80)

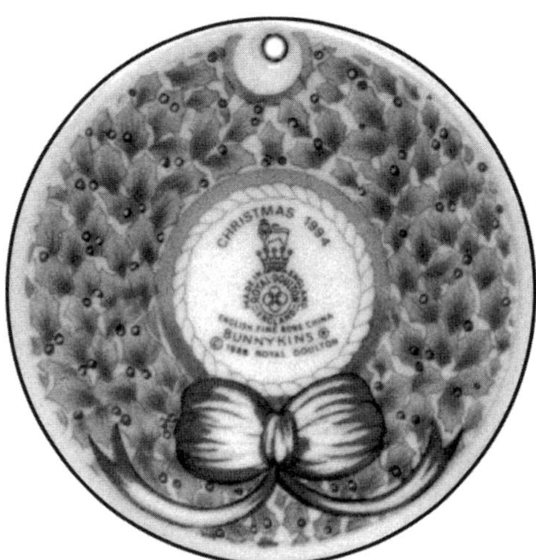

Christmas 1994 (CT81)

Trumpeter (EC5)

TRUMPETER

Design No.: EC5
Designer: Barbara Vernon
Issued: 1937 to the present
Combined with: *Cycling*, HW15R
Bedtime with Dollies, EC125
Drummer, EC2
Drummer and Bugler, EC126
Family at Breakfast, HW12
Family Going out on Washing Day, HW8
Feeding the Baby, HW13
Hat Shop, HW28
Hikers, EC124
Hobby Horse, Style One, HW24R
Hobby Horse, Style Two, EC121
Holding Hat and Coat, EC4
Lambeth Walk, HW15R
Playing with Cup and Spoon, EC6
Raising Hat, Style Two, EC7
Reading, EC122
Rocking Horse, HW24
Sheltering Under an Umbrella, EC3
Sleeping in a Rocking Chair, EC1
Top Hat, HW14R
Washing Day, HW8R

Shape	U.S. $	Can. $	U.K. £	Aust. $
Albion sugar bowl	30.00	35.00	17.50	40.00
Beaker cover				
with signature	75.00	90.00	45.00	95.00
without signature	65.00	80.00	40.00	85.00
Casino sugar bowl, 36s				
with signature	100.00	125.00	60.00	135.00
without signature	80.00	95.00	45.00	100.00
Egg cup				
Style One				
with signature	40.00	50.00	25.00	55.00
without signature	30.00	35.00	17.50	40.00
Egg cup				
Style Two				
with signature	50.00	60.00	30.00	65.00
without signature	40.00	50.00	25.00	55.00
Style Three	10.00	12.00	6.00	15.00
Lid of hot water plate				
with signature	75.00	90.00	45.00	95.00
without signature	50.00	60.00	30.00	65.00
Money ball	25.00	30.00	15.00	35.00

TUG OF WAR

Design No.: LF1
Designer: Barbara Vernon
Issued: By 1937 - by 1952

Shape	U.S. $	Can. $	U.K. £	Aust. $
Bread / butter plate, handles				
with signature	500.00	600.00	285.00	625.00
without signature	400.00	475.00	225.00	500.00
Plate, 7 ½"				
with signature	350.00	425.00	200.00	450.00
without signature	300.00	350.00	175.00	375.00
Plate, 8 ½"				
with signature	225.00	275.00	125.00	300.00
without signature	175.00	200.00	100.00	225.00
Porridge plate				
with signature	300.00	350.00	175.00	375.00
without signature	250.00	300.00	150.00	325.00
FINE WHITE CHINA				
Bread and butter plate	800.00	975.00	475.00	1,075.00

Tug of War (LF1)

UNRAVELLING THE KNITTING / TRYING ON KNITTING

Design No.:	Front — HW119 Unravelling the Knitting Reverse — HW119R Trying on Knitting
Designer:	Walter Hayward
Issued:	1959 - 1992
Combined with:	*Bedtime with Dollies*, EC125 *Broken Umbrella*, HW27R *Sleeping in a Rocking Chair*, EC1 *Windy Day*, HW27

Unravelling the Knitting (HW119)

Shape	U.S. $	Can. $	U.K. £	Aust. $
Albion cream jug	35.00	45.00	20.00	50.00
Albion jug, ½ pint	85.00	100.00	50.00	110.00
Albion jug, 1 pint	100.00	125.00	60.00	135.00
Albion teapot	50.00	60.00	30.00	65.00
Cake stand	150.00	180.00	90.00	190.00
Casino jug, 30s	150.00	180.00	90.00	190.00
Casino jug, 36s	125.00	150.00	75.00	160.00
Casino jug, 42s	100.00	125.00	60.00	135.00
Casino saucer	8.00	10.00	5.00	12.00
Casino sugar bowl, 36s	100.00	125.00	60.00	135.00
Casino teacup	8.00	10.00	5.00	12.00
Casino teapot, 30s	150.00	180.00	90.00	190.00
Don beaker	25.00	30.00	15.00	35.00
Don beaker, one handle	25.00	30.00	15.00	35.00
Don mug, one handle	10.00	12.00	6.00	15.00
Don mug, two handles	10.00	12.00	6.00	15.00
Egg box				
small	175.00	200.00	100.00	225.00
medium	200.00	250.00	115.00	275.00
large	225.00	275.00	125.00	300.00
Hug-a-mug, one handle	10.00	12.00	6.00	15.00
Hug-a-mug, two handles	10.00	12.00	6.00	15.00
Jaffa fruit saucer (plain)	15.00	20.00	10.00	25.00
Lamp	50.00	60.00	30.00	65.00
Lid of hot water plate	50.00	60.00	30.00	65.00
Malvern beaker / mug	15.00	20.00	10.00	25.00
Money ball	10.00	12.00	6.00	15.00
Picture plaque, small	20.00	25.00	12.00	30.00
Plate, 6 ½"	15.00	20.00	10.00	25.00
Savings book	15.00	20.00	10.00	25.00
Stratford straight beaker	15.00	20.00	10.00	25.00
Stratford teacup	8.00	10.00	5.00	12.00

Trying on Knitting (HW119R)

Note: Retirement dates are all approximate. When a design is retired all remaining stocks of retired litho prints are used until exhausted.

Visiting the Cottage, First Version (SF6a)

VISITING THE COTTAGE
First Version

Design No.:	SF6a
Designer:	Barbara Vernon
Issued:	By 1940 - c.1949

Shape	U.S. $	Can. $	U.K. £	Aust. $
Baby plate, round, small	350.00	425.00	200.00	450.00
Baby plate, round, large	400.00	475.00	225.00	500.00
Bread and butter plate	500.00	600.00	285.00	625.00
Hot water plate	375.00	450.00	210.00	475.00
Plate, 6 ½"	225.00	275.00	125.00	300.00
Plate, 7 ½"	225.00	275.00	125.00	300.00
Plate, 8 ½"	225.00	275.00	125.00	300.00
Porridge plate	300.00	350.00	175.00	375.00

Note: This design should appear with the Barbara Vernon facsimile signature.

VISITING THE COTTAGE
Second Version

Design No.:	SF6b
Designer:	Barbara Vernon
Issued:	c.1949 - 1952

Shape	U.S. $	Can. $	U.K. £	Aust. $
Baby plate, round, small	200.00	250.00	115.00	275.00
Baby plate, round, large	250.00	300.00	150.00	325.00
Bread / butter plate	400.00	475.00	225.00	500.00
Casino saucer	75.00	90.00	45.00	95.00
Casino jug, 24s	475.00	575.00	270.00	600.00
Cereal / oatmeal bowl	100.00	125.00	60.00	135.00
Jaffa fruit saucer				
plain rim	95.00	115.00	55.00	125.00
wavy rim	125.00	150.00	75.00	160.00
Plate, 6 ½"	90.00	110.00	50.00	120.00
Plate, 7 ½"	100.00	125.00	60.00	135.00
Plate, 8 ½"	100.00	125.00	60.00	135.00
Porridge plate	125.00	150.00	75.00	160.00

Visiting the Cottage, Second Version (SF6b)

Note: This design should appear with the Barbara Vernon facsimile signature.

WASHING DAY

Design No.: HW8R
Designer: Barbara Vernon
Issued: By 1937 - by 1967
Combined with: *Family at Breakfast*, HW12
Family Going out on Washing Day, HW8
Pressing Trousers, HW14
Sheltering Under an Umbrella, EC3
Trumpeter, EC5

Shape	U.S. $	Can. $	U.K. £	Aust. $
Casino jug, 30s				
with signature	450.00	550.00	260.00	575.00
without signature	400.00	475.00	225.00	500.00
Casino jug, 36s				
with signature	400.00	475.00	225.00	500.00
without signature	350.00	425.00	200.00	450.00
Casino sugar bowl, 36s				
with signature	175.00	200.00	100.00	225.00
without signature	125.00	150.00	75.00	160.00
Casino teacup				
with signature	75.00	90.00	45.00	95.00
without signature	50.00	60.00	30.00	65.00
Casino teapot, 30s				
with signature	325.00	400.00	185.00	425.00
without signature	250.00	300.00	150.00	325.00
Casino teapot, 36s				
with signature	250.00	300.00	150.00	325.00
without signature	225.00	275.00	125.00	300.00
Don beaker, one handle				
with signature	65.00	80.00	40.00	85.00
without signature	35.00	45.00	20.00	50.00
Don mug, one handle				
with signature	50.00	60.00	30.00	65.00
without signature	15.00	20.00	10.00	25.00
Don mug, two handles				
with signature	50.00	60.00	30.00	65.00
without signature	15.00	20.00	10.00	25.00

Washing Day (HW8R)

Washing in the Open Air (HW10R)

WASHING IN THE OPEN AIR

Design No.: HW10R
Designer: Barbara Vernon
Issued: By 1937 - by 1967
Combined with: *Asleep in the Open Air*, HW10
Convalescing, SF5
Family with Pram, Style One, HW15
Feeding the Baby, HW13
Gardening, Style One, HW9
Leapfrog, HW12R

Shape	U.S. $	Can. $	U.K. £	Aust. $
Casino jug, 30s				
with signature	375.00	450.00	210.00	475.00
without signature	300.00	350.00	175.00	375.00
Casino jug, 36s				
with signature	300.00	350.00	175.00	375.00
without signature	275.00	325.00	160.00	350.00
Casino sugar bowl, 30s				
with signature	200.00	250.00	115.00	275.00
without signature	125.00	150.00	75.00	160.00
Casino teacup				
with signature	75.00	90.00	45.00	95.00
without signature	50.00	60.00	30.00	65.00
Don beaker, one handle				
with signature	150.00	180.00	90.00	190.00
without signature	100.00	125.00	60.00	135.00
Don mug, one handle				
with signature	75.00	90.00	45.00	95.00
without signature	35.00	45.00	20.00	50.00
Don mug, two handles				
with signature	75.00	90.00	45.00	95.00
without signature	35.00	45.00	20.00	50.00

WASHING UP THEME – Colin Twinn

First Variation, Large Size

Design No.: CT15 Washing Up
Designer: Colin Twinn
Issued: 1990 - 1993

Shape	U.S. $	Can. $	U.K. £	Aust. $
Albion jug, 1 pint	100.00	125.00	60.00	135.00
Baby bowl, round, small	20.00	25.00	12.00	30.00
Cake stand	150.00	180.00	90.00	190.00
Cereal / oatmeal bowl	25.00	30.00	15.00	35.00
Picture plaque, large	20.00	25.00	12.00	30.00
Plate, 6½"	15.00	20.00	10.00	25.00
Plate, 8"	15.00	20.00	10.00	25.00

Washing Up, First Variation (CT15)

Washing Up, Second Variation (CT32)

Splashing at Sink (CT33)

Second Variation, Small Size / SPLASHING AT SINK

Design No.: Front — CT32 Washing Up
Reverse — CT33 Splashing at Sink
Designer: Colin Twinn
Issued: 1990 - 1993
Combined with: *Ice Cream Seller*, First Variation, CT5
Pushing the Wheelbarrow, CT3

Shape	U.S. $	Can. $	U.K. £	Aust. $
Albion teapot	50.00	60.00	30.00	65.00
Divider dish	75.00	90.00	45.00	95.00
Hug-a-mug, one handle	10.00	12.00	6.00	15.00
Hug-a-mug, two handles	10.00	12.00	6.00	15.00
Lamp	50.00	60.00	30.00	65.00
Malvern beaker	15.00	20.00	10.00	25.00
Money ball	10.00	12.00	6.00	15.00
Savings book	15.00	20.00	10.00	25.00

Watering the Flowers (SF15)

WATERING THE FLOWERS

Design No.:	SF15
Designer:	Walter Hayward after Barbara Vernon
Issued:	By 1952 - 1967
Combined with:	*Cricketer,* HW22R
	Pressing Trousers, HW14
	Lasso Games, HW117
	Wheelbarrow Race, Style One, HW22

Shape	U.S. $	Can. $	U.K. £	Aust. $
Baby plate, round, small				
with signature	50.00	60.00	30.00	65.00
without signature	30.00	35.00	17.50	40.00
Casino jug, 30s				
with signature	300.00	350.00	175.00	375.00
without signature	225.00	275.00	125.00	300.00
Casino saucer				
with signature	75.00	90.00	45.00	95.00
without signature	50.00	60.00	30.00	65.00
Casino sugar bowl				
with signature	175.00	200.00	100.00	225.00
without signature	150.00	180.00	90.00	190.00
Casino teapot, 24s				
with signature	375.00	450.00	210.00	475.00
without signature	300.00	350.00	175.00	375.00
Casino teapot, 30s				
with signature	325.00	400.00	185.00	425.00
without signature	250.00	300.00	150.00	325.00
Cereal / oatmeal bowl				
with signature	35.00	45.00	20.00	50.00
without signature	25.00	30.00	15.00	35.00
Hot water plate				
with signature	125.00	150.00	75.00	160.00
without signature	100.00	125.00	60.00	135.00
Jaffa fruit saucer (plain)				
with signature	50.00	60.00	30.00	65.00
without signature	30.00	35.00	17.50	40.00
Plate, 6 ½				
with signature	30.00	35.00	17.50	40.00
without signature	20.00	25.00	12.00	30.00
Plate, 7 ½"				
with signature	65.00	80.00	40.00	85.00
without signature	25.00	30.00	15.00	35.00

WEDDING

Design No.: LFd
Designer: Barbara Vernon
Issued: 1937 - by 1952
Combined with: *Family at Breakfast*, HW12
Lambeth Walk, First Version, HW16
Pressing Trousers, HW14
Proposal, HW11
Raising Hat, Style One, HW16R

Shape	U.S. $	Can. $	U.K. £	Aust. $
Baby plate, oval, small	350.00	425.00	200.00	450.00
Baby plate, round, large	400.00	475.00	225.00	500.00
Casino teapot, 24s	600.00	725.00	340.00	750.00
Casino teapot, 30s	400.00	475.00	225.00	500.00
Casino teapot, 36s	450.00	550.00	260.00	575.00
Hot water plate	375.00	450.00	210.00	475.00
Plate, 7 ½"	375.00	450.00	210.00	475.00
Plate, 8 ½"	225.00	275.00	125.00	300.00
Porridge plate	300.00	350.00	175.00	375.00
FINE WHITE CHINA				
Plate, 5"	650.00	775.00	375.00	800.00
Plate 7"	650.00	775.00	375.00	800.00

Wedding (LFd)

Note: This design should appear with the Barbara Vernon facsimile signature.

Casino teapot (24s), combining *Proposal* (HW11) and *Wedding* (LFd), exists with a silver rimmed lid and a crackle finish, this is considered extremely rare.

WHEELBARROW RACE, Style One / CRICKETER

Wheelbarrow Race, Style One (HW22)

Cricketer (HW22R)

Design No.: Front — HW22 Wheelbarrow Race
Reverse — HW22R Cricketer
Designer: Walter Hayward
Issued: By 1952 - by 1998
Combined with: *Asleep in the Open Air*, HW10
Baking, SF19
Bedtime with Dollies, EC125
Drummer, EC2
Holding Hat and Coat, EC4
Nipped by a Crab, HW121R
Orange Vendor, HW12
Pea Shooter, HW118R
Row Boat, HW21
Watering the Flowers, SF15

Shape	U.S. $	Can. $	U.K. £	Aust. $
Albion cream jug	35.00	45.00	20.00	50.00
Albion jug, ½ pint	85.00	100.00	50.00	110.00
Albion jug, 1 pint	100.00	125.00	60.00	135.00
Albion teapot	50.00	60.00	30.00	65.00
Casino jug, 24s				
with signature	300.00	350.00	175.00	375.00
without signature	175.00	200.00	100.00	225.00
Casino jug, 30s				
with signature	250.00	300.00	150.00	325.00
without signature	150.00	180.00	90.00	190.00
Casino jug, 42s				
with signature	150.00	180.00	90.00	190.00
without signature	100.00	125.00	60.00	135.00
Casino jug, 36s				
with signature	200.00	250.00	115.00	275.00
without signature	125.00	150.00	75.00	160.00
Casino saucer				
with signature	15.00	20.00	10.00	25.00
without signature	8.00	10.00	5.00	12.00
Casino sugar bowl, 30s				
with signature	150.00	180.00	90.00	190.00
without signature	125.00	150.00	75.00	160.00
Casino teacup				
with signature	15.00	20.00	10.00	25.00
without signature	8.00	10.00	5.00	12.00
Casino teapot, 30s				
with signature	250.00	300.00	150.00	325.00
without signature	150.00	180.00	90.00	190.00
Casino teapot, 36s				
with signature	250.00	300.00	150.00	325.00
without signature	150.00	180.00	90.00	190.00
Divider dish	50.00	60.00	30.00	65.00

Shape	U.S. $	Can. $	U.K. £	Aust. $
Don beaker				
with signature	50.00	60.00	30.00	65.00
without signature	25.00	30.00	15.00	35.00
Don beaker, one handle				
with signature	50.00	60.00	30.00	65.00
without signature	25.00	30.00	15.00	35.00
Don mug, one handle				
with signature	40.00	50.00	25.00	55.00
without signature	10.00	12.00	6.00	15.00
Don mug, two handles				
with signature	40.00	50.00	25.00	55.00
without signature	10.00	12.00	6.00	15.00
Egg box				
small	175.00	200.00	100.00	225.00
medium	200.00	250.00	115.00	275.00
large	225.00	275.00	125.00	300.00
Hug-a-mug, one handle	10.00	12.00	6.00	15.00
Hug-a-mug, two handles	10.00	12.00	6.00	15.00
Jaffa fruit saucer (plain)	15.00	20.00	10.00	25.00
Lamp	50.00	60.00	30.00	65.00
Lid of hot water plate	50.00	60.00	30.00	65.00
Malvern beaker	15.00	20.00	10.00	25.00
Money ball	10.00	12.00	6.00	15.00
Picture plaque, small	20.00	25.00	12.00	30.00
Plate, 6 ½"				
with signature	25.00	30.00	15.00	35.00
without signature	15.00	20.00	10.00	25.00
Savings book	15.00	20.00	10.00	25.00
Stratford teacup	8.00	10.00	5.00	12.00

WHEELBARROW RACE
Style Two

Design No.: CT1
Designer: Colin Twinn
Issued: 1988 - 1993
Combined with: *Pushing the Wheelbarrow*, CT3

Shape	U.S. $	Can. $	U.K. £	Aust. $
Albion jug, ½ jug	85.00	100.00	50.00	110.00
Albion jug, 1 pint	100.00	125.00	60.00	135.00
Baby plate, round, small	20.00	25.00	12.00	30.00
Cake stand	150.00	180.00	90.00	190.00
Cereal / oatmeal bowl	15.00	20.00	10.00	25.00
Jaffa fruit saucer	15.00	20.00	10.00	25.00
Picture plaque, large	20.00	25.00	12.00	30.00
Plate, 6 ½"	15.00	20.00	10.00	25.00
Plate, 8"	15.00	20.00	10.00	25.00

Wheelbarrow Race, Style Two (CT1)

PUSHING THE WHEELBARROW

Design No.: CT3
Designer: Colin Twinn
Issued: 1988 - 1993
Combined with: *Bunnies in the Bath*, Second Version, CT34
Ice Cream Seller, First Variation, CT5
Picking Daisies, CT4
Splashing at Sink, CT33
Washing Up, CT32
Wheelbarrow Race, Style Two, CT1

Shape	U.S. $	Can. $	U.K. £	Aust. $
Albion sugar bowl	30.00	35.00	17.50	40.00
Albion teapot	50.00	60.00	30.00	65.00
Egg cup				
Style Three	10.00	12.00	6.00	15.00
Hug-a-mug, one handle	10.00	12.00	6.00	15.00
Hug-a-mug, two handles	10.00	12.00	6.00	15.00
Lamp	50.00	60.00	30.00	65.00
Malvern beaker	15.00	20.00	10.00	25.00
Stratford teacup	8.00	10.00	5.00	12.00

Pushing the Wheelbarrow (CT3)

WINDY DAY / BROKEN UMBRELLA

Windy Day (HW27)

Broken Umbrella (HW27R)

Design No.: Front — HW27 Windy Day
Reverse — HW27R Broken Umbrella
Designer: Walter Hayward
Issued: 1952 - by 1998
Combined with: *Apple Picking,* SF25
Dress Making, HW26

Combined with: *Drummer*, EC2
Toast for Tea Today, SF23
Trying on Knitting, HW119R
Playing with Doll and Teddy, HW120R
Unravelling the Knitting, HW119

Shape	U.S. $	Can. $	U.K. £	Aust. $
Albion cream jug	35.00	45.00	20.00	50.00
Albion jug, 1 pint	100.00	125.00	60.00	135.00
Albion jug, ½ pint	85.00	100.00	50.00	110.00
Albion teapot	50.00	60.00	30.00	65.00
Casino jug, 36s				
with signature	175.00	200.00	100.00	225.00
without signature	125.00	150.00	75.00	160.00
Casino jug, 42s				
with signature	150.00	180.00	90.00	190.00
without signature	100.00	125.00	60.00	135.00
Casino saucer				
with signature	15.00	20.00	10.00	25.00
without signature	8.00	10.00	5.00	12.00
Casino teacup				
with signature	15.00	20.00	10.00	25.00
without signature	8.00	10.00	5.00	12.00
Casino teapot, 24s				
with signature	275.00	325.00	160.00	350.00
without signature	175.00	200.00	100.00	225.00
Casino teapot, 36s				
with signature	250.00	300.00	150.00	325.00
without signature	150.00	180.00	90.00	190.00
Divider dish	50.00	60.00	30.00	65.00
Don beaker				
with signature	50.00	60.00	30.00	65.00
without signature	25.00	30.00	15.00	35.00
Don beaker, one handle				
with signature	50.00	60.00	30.00	65.00

Shape	U.S. $	Can. $	U.K. £	Aust. $
Don Beaker, One handle				
without signature	25.00	30.00	15.00	35.00
Don mug, one handle				
with signature	40.00	50.00	25.00	55.00
without signature	10.00	12.00	6.00	15.00
Don mug, two handles				
with signature	40.00	50.00	25.00	55.00
without signature	10.00	12.00	6.00	15.00
Egg box				
small	175.00	200.00	100.00	225.00
medium	200.00	250.00	115.00	275.00
large	225.00	275.00	125.00	300.00
Hug-a-mug, one handle	10.00	12.00	6.00	15.00
Hug-a-mug, two handles	10.00	12.00	6.00	15.00
Jaffa fruit saucer (plain)				
with signature	25.00	30.00	15.00	35.00
without signature	15.00	20.00	10.00	25.00
Lamp	50.00	60.00	30.00	65.00
Lid of hot water plate	50.00	60.00	30.00	65.00
Malvern beaker	15.00	20.00	10.00	25.00
Money ball	10.00	12.00	6.00	15.00
Picture plaque, small	20.00	25.00	12.00	30.00
Plate, 6 ½"				
with signature	25.00	30.00	15.00	35.00
without signature	15.00	20.00	10.00	25.00
Savings book	15.00	20.00	10.00	25.00
Stratford straight beaker	15.00	20.00	10.00	25.00
Stratford teacup	8.00	10.00	5.00	12.00

Note: *Toast for Tea Today* (SF23) and *Dress Making* (HW25) are combined with *Windy Day* (HW27) on the Casino teapot.

WINNING POST

Design No.: LF106
Designer: Walter Hayward after Barbara Vernon
Issued: 1959 - 1970

Shape	U.S. $	Can. $	U.K. £	Aust. $
Baby plate, oval, large	250.00	300.00	150.00	325.00
Baby plate, round, small	150.00	180.00	90.00	190.00
Baby plate, round, large	200.00	250.00	115.00	275.00
Plate, 8 ½"	75.00	90.00	45.00	95.00
Porridge plate	100.00	125.00	60.00	135.00

Winning Post (LF106)

XMAS MENU

Design No.: LF8
Designer: Barbara Vernon
Issued: 1940 - by 1952

Shape	U.S. $	Can. $	U.K. £	Aust. $
Baby plate, oval , large				
with signature	500.00	600.00	285.00	625.00
without signature	450.00	550.00	260.00	575.00
Baby plate, round, large				
with signature	400.00	475.00	225.00	500.00
without signature	350.00	425.00	200.00	450.00
Bread and butter plate				
with signature	500.00	600.00	285.00	625.00
without signature	400.00	475.00	225.00	500.00
Cereal / oatmeal bowl				
with signature	200.00	250.00	115.00	275.00
without signature	175.00	200.00	100.00	225.00
Plate, 8 ½"				
with signature	225.00	275.00	125.00	300.00
without signature	175.00	200.00	100.00	225.00
Porridge plate				
with signature	300.00	350.00	175.00	375.00
without signature	250.00	300.00	150.00	325.00

FINE WHITE CHINA

Shape	U.S. $	Can. $	U.K. £	Aust. $
Bread and butter plate	800.00	975.00	475.00	1,075.00

Xmas Menu (LF8)

On left; Rex mug, large size, *Proposal,* (HW11)
On right; Rex mug, small size, *Pressing Trousers,* (HW14)

On left; Rex mug, large size, *Pulling on Trousers,* (HW2)
On right; Rex mug, small size, *Golfer*, (HW4R)

BUNNYKINS BREAKFAST SET

Issues of 1939 - 1945

D6010
TEAPOT

Designer: Charles Noke
Height: 4 ¾", 12.1 cm
Colour: Brown rabbit; green leaves
Issued: 1939 - by 1945

Doulton Number	Price U.S. $	Can. $	U.K. £	Aust. $
D6010	2,000.00	2,500.00	1,100.00	2,750.00

D6034
EGG CUP
Style One

Designer: Charles Noke
Height: 1 ¾", 4.5 cm
Colour: Brown rabbit
Issued: 1939 - by 1939

Doulton Number	Price U.S. $	Can. $	U.K. £	Aust. $
D6034	2,250.00	2,750.00	1,275.00	3,250.00

D6040
SUGAR SIFTER

Designer: Charles Noke
Height: 2 ¾", 7.0 cm
Colour: Brown rabbit, blue sweater , red trousers
Issued: 1939 - by 1945

Doulton Number	Price U.S. $	Can. $	U.K. £	Aust. $
D6040	3,000.00	3,750.00	1,750.00	4,750.00

Note: Designed by Charles Noke in 1939, this breakfast set comprises six pieces. Production started in 1940 but was soon halted due to wartime needs.

D6056
SUGAR BOWL

Designer: Charles Noke
Height: 1 ¾", 4.5 cm
Colour: Brown rabbit; green leaves
Issued: 1939 - by 1945

Doulton Number	Price U.S. $	Can. $	U.K. £	Aust. $
D6056	850.00	1,000.00	500.00	1,200.00

D6057
CREAM JUG

Designer: Charles Noke
Height: 2 ¾", 7.0 cm
Colour: Brown rabbit; green leaves
Issued: 1939 - by 1945

Doulton Number	Price U.S. $	Can. $	U.K. £	Aust. $
D6057	3,000.00	3,750.00	1,750.00	4,750.00

Note: The pieces comprising the Bunnykins Breakfast Set, due to the short production period, are scarce items and thus prices may vary. Prices listed above should be treated as indications only.

BUNNYKINS TEAPOTS

Issues of 1994 - 1998

D6966
LONDON CITY GENT BUNNYKINS TEAPOT

Modeller: Martyn Alcock
Height: 8", 20.3 cm
Colour: Brown and black
Issued: 1994 in a special edition of 2,500

U.S.	$100.00
Can.	$125.00
U.K.	£ 60.00
Aust.	$150.00

D6996
U.S.A. PRESIDENT BUNNYKINS TEAPOT

Modeller: Shane Ridge
Height: 8", 20.3 cm
Colour: Red, white and blue
Issued: 1995 in a special edition of 2,500

U.S.	$100.00
Can.	$125.00
U.K.	£ 60.00
Aust.	$150.00

Backstamp not available at press time

D7027
AUSSIE EXPLORER BUNNYKINS TEAPOT

Modeller: Shane Ridge
Height: 7 ¾", 19.7 cm
Colour: Brown, yellow, green and orange
Issued: 1996 in a special edition of 2,500
Series: Bunnykins Teapots of the World

U.S.	$100.00
Can.	$125.00
U.K.	£ 60.00
Aust.	$150.00

D7126
GEISHA GIRL BUNNYKINS TEAPOT

Designer: Caroline Dadd
Modeller: Martyn Alcock
Height: 7 ¾", 19.7 cm
Colour: Brown, lilac, green, yellow , black, cream and red
Issued: 1998 in a special edition of 2,500

U.S.	$100.00
Can.	$125.00
U.K.	£ 60.00
Aust.	$150.00

BUNNYKINS TEA SET

Issues of 1998 - 2001

COOKIE JAR

Height:	13 ½", 34.3 cm
Colour:	Brown bunny, blue dress, white collar and apron, pink hat, red flowers in basket
Issued:	1998 - 2001
U.S.	$20.00
Can.	$25.00
U.K.	£12.00
Aust.	$30.00

CREAMER

Height:	4 ½", 11.9 cm
Colour:	White dress with blue polka dots Deep pink jacket, pale pink jumper, brown trousers, white and black cow
Issued:	1998 - 2001
U.S.	$30.00
Can.	$35.00
U.K.	£17.50
Aust.	$40.00

SALT AND PEPPER SET

Height:	Salt 5 ¾", 14.6 cm Pepper 6", 15.0 cm
Colour:	Salt – white dress with blue polka dots Pepper – deep pink jacket, pink jumper, brown trousers
Issued:	1998 - 2001
U.S.	$30.00
Can.	$35.00
U.K.	£17.50
Aust.	$40.00

SUGAR DISH

Height:	5 ½", 14.0 cm
Colour:	Blue dress, white collar and apron; brown sugar dish with white lid and spoon
Issued:	1998 - 2001
U.S.	$20.00
Can.	$25.00
U.K.	£12.00
Aust.	$30.00

TEAPOT

Height:	9 ½", 24.0 cm
Colour:	Brown bunny, green jacket, yellow shirt, deep pink bow tie, black belt and spectacles
Issued:	1998 - 2001
U.S.	$20.00
Can.	$25.00
U.K.	£12.00
Aust.	$30.00

DB94 – Prince Frederick
Second Variation

DB95 – Harry The Herald
Second Variation

DB96 – Touchdown
Bunnykins, *Third Variation*

DB97 – Touchdown
Bunnykins, *Fourth Variation*

DB98 – Touchdown
Bunnykins, *Fifth Variation*

DB99 – Touchdown
Bunnykins, *Sixth Variation*

DB100 – Touchdown
Bunnykins, *Seventh Variation*

DB101 – Bride Bunnykins

DB102 – Groom Bunnykins

DB103 – Bedtime
Bunnykins, *Fourth Variation*

DB104 – Carol Singer
Bunnykins

DB105 – Sousaphone
Bunnykins, *Third Variation*

DB106 – Trumpeter Bunnykins
Third Variation

DB107 – Cymbals Bunnykins
Third Variation

DB108 – Drummer Bunnykins
Style One, Fourth Variation

DB109 – Drum-Major Bunnykins
Third Variation

DB115 – Harry The Herald
Third Variation

DB116 – Goalkeeper Bunnykins
First Variation

DB117 – Footballer Bunnykins
First Variation

DB118 – Goalkeeper Bunnykins
Second Variation

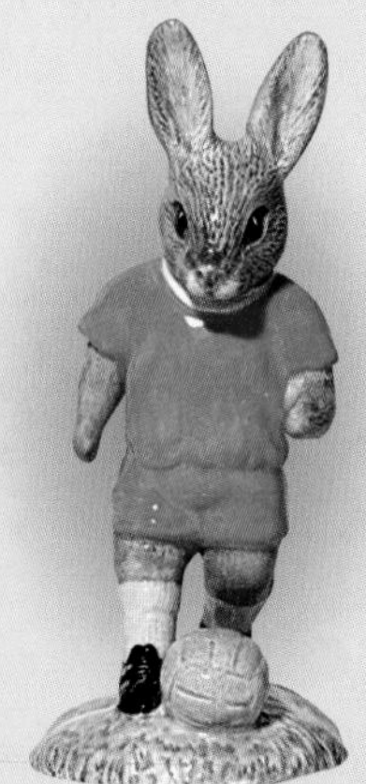

DB119 – Footballer Bunnykins
Second Variation

DB120 – Goalkeeper Bunnykins
Third Variation

DB121 – Footballer Bunnykins
Third Variation

DB122 – Goalkeeper Bunnykins
Fourth Variation

Note: DB110 to 114 not allocated

BUNNYKINS

DB123 – Soccer Player Bunnykins

DB124 – Rock and Roll Bunnykins

DB125 – Milkman Bunnykins

DB126 – Magician Bunnykins
First Variation

DB127 – Guardsman Bunnykins

DB128 – Clown Bunnykins
First Variation

DB129 – Clown Bunnykins
Second Variation

DB130 – Sweetheart Bunnykins
First Variation

DB131 – Master Potter Bunnykins

DB132 – Halloween Bunnykins

DB133 – Aussie Surfer Bunnykins

DB134 – John Bull Bunnykins

DB135 – Mountie Bunnykins

DB136 – Sergeant Mountie Bunnykins

DB137 – 60th Anniversary Bunnykins

DB142 – Cheerleader Bunnykins
First Variation

DB143 – Cheerleader Bunnykins
Second Variation

DB144 – Batsman Bunnykins

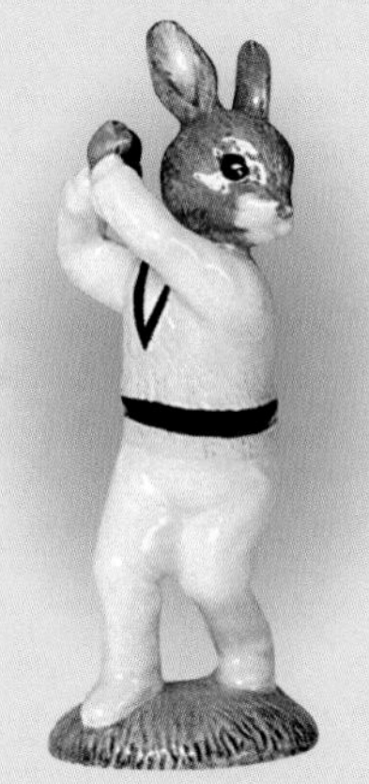
DB145 – Bowler Bunnykins

DB146 – Christmas Surprise Bunnykins

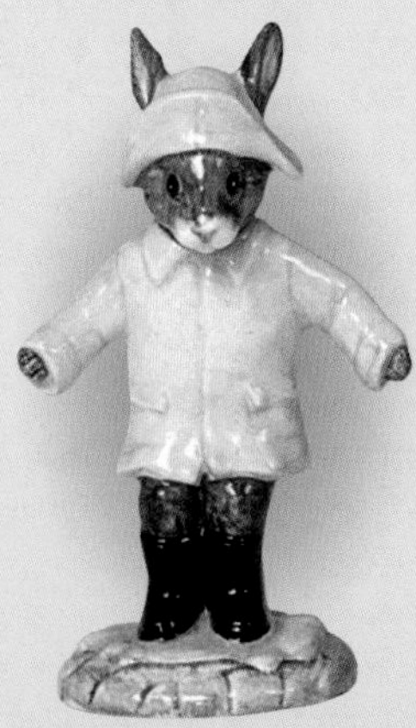
DB147 – Rainy Day Bunnykins

DB148 – Bathtime Bunnykins

DB149 – Easter Greetings Bunnykins

DB150 – Wicketkeeper Bunnykins

Note: DB138 to 141 not allocated

DB151 – Partners in Collecting

DB152 – Boy Skater Bunnykins
First Variation

DB153 – Girl Skater Bunnykins

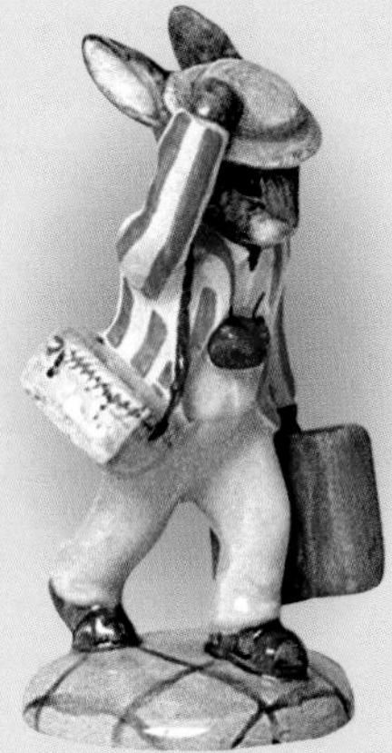
DB154 – Father Bunnykins
Style One

DB155 – Mother's Day Bunnykins

DB156 – Gardener Bunnykins

DB157 – Goodnight Bunnykins

DB158 – New Baby Bunnykins

DB159 – Magician Bunnykins
Second Variation

DB160 – Out for a Duck Bunnykins

DB161 – Jester Bunnykins

DB162 – Trick or Treat Bunnykins

DB163 – Beefeater Bunnykins

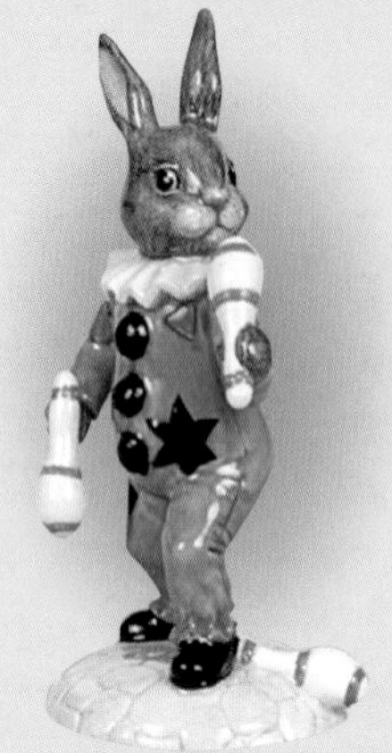
DB164 – Juggler Bunnykins

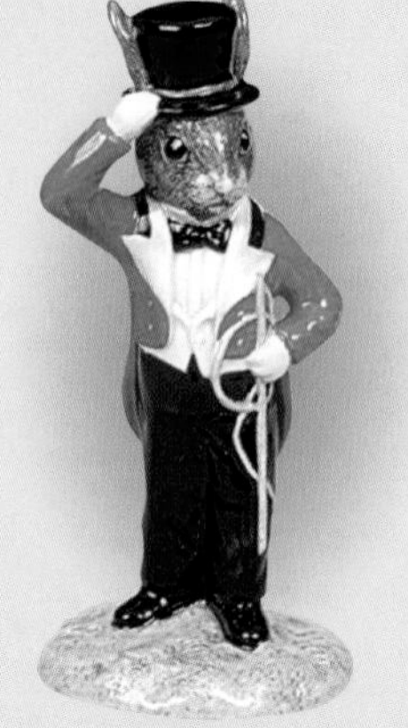
DB165 – Ringmaster Bunnykins

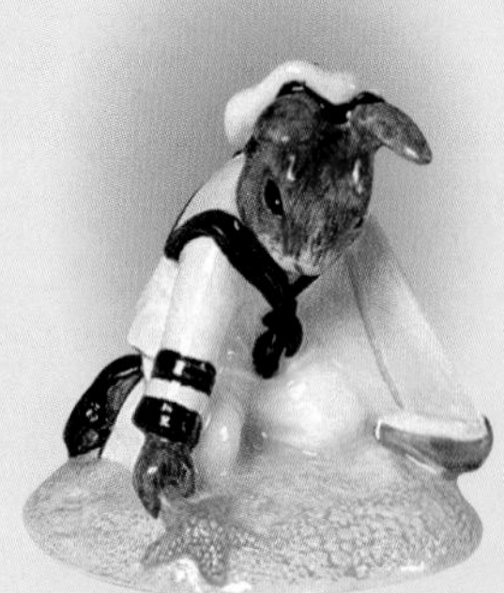
DB166 – Sailor Bunnykins

DB167 – Mother and Baby Bunnykins, *Style One*

DB168 – Wizard Bunnykins

DB169 – Jockey Bunnykins

DB170 – Fisherman Bunnykins *Style Two*

DB171 – Joker Bunnykins

DB172 – Welshlady Bunnykins

DB173 – Bridesmaid Bunnykins

DB174 – Sweetheart Bunnykins *Second Variation*

BUNNYKINS

DB175 – Uncle Sam Bunnykins
Second Variation

DB176 – Ballerina Bunnykins

DB177 – Seaside Bunnykins

DB178 – Irishman Bunnykins

DB179 – Cavalier Bunnykins

DB180 – Scotsman Bunnykins

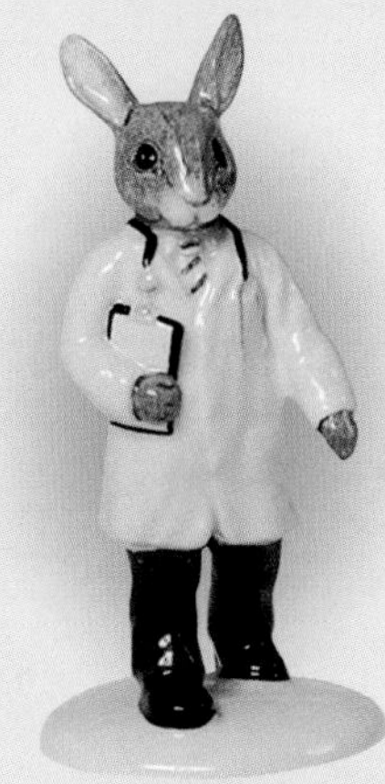
DB181 – Doctor Bunnykins
Style One

DB182 – Banjo Player Bunnykins

DB183 – Fireman Bunnykins
Style One, Second Variation

DB184 – Clarinet Player Bunnykins

DB185 – Double Bass Player Bunnykins

DB186 – Saxophone Player Bunnykins

DB187 Boy Skater Bunnykins
Second Variation

DB188 – Judge Bunnykins

DB189 – Mother Bunnykins

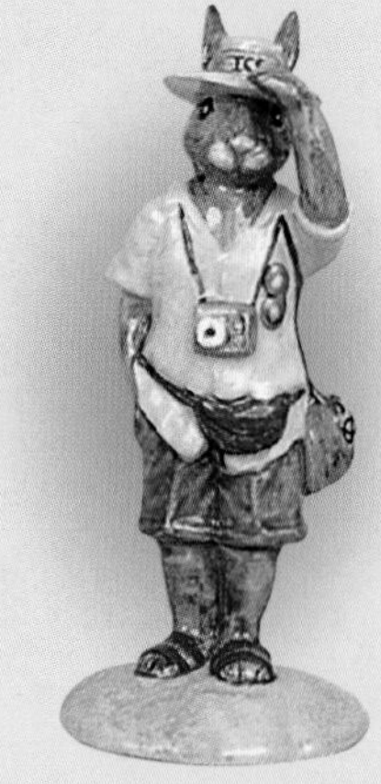

DB190 – Tourist Bunnykins

DB191 – Piper Bunnykins

DB192 – Santa's Helper Bunnykins

DB193 – Detective Bunnykins

DB195 – Sydney Bunnykins

DB194 – Merry Christmas Bunnykins Tableau

DB196 – Angel Bunnykins

DB197 – Mystic Bunnykins

COUNTRY MANOR TEA SET

Issues of 2003

DBD1
LORD OF THE MANOR COFFEE POT

Designer: Shane Ridge
Height: 7 ½", 19.1 cm
Colour: Green, black, white brown, tan, silver
Issued: 2003 in a limited edition of 1,500

U.S. $100.00
Can. $125.00
U.K. £ 60.00
Aust. $135.00

DBD2
LADY OF THE MANOR TEAPOT

Designer: Shane Ridge
Height: 6 ¾", 17.2 cm
Colour: Yellow, white, brown, peach, green and black
Issued: 2003 in a limited edition of 1,500

U.S. $100.00
Can. $125.00
U.K. £ 60.00
Aust. $135.00

DBD3
MASTER OF THE MANOR CUP AND SAUCER

Designer: Shane Ridge
Height: 4 ¼", 11.0 cm
Colour: Grey, brown, white, black, yellow, blue, red and purple
Issued: 2003 in a limited edition of 1,500

U.S. $100.00
Can. $125.00
U.K. £ 60.00
Aust. $135.00

DBD4
MISS OF THE MANOR CUP AND SAUCER

Designer: Shane Ridge
Height: 4 ¼", 11.0 cm
Colour: Brown, black, blue, white, red, green, yellow and blue
Issued: 2003 in a limited edition of 1,500

U.S. $100.00
Can. $125.00
U.K. £ 60.00
Aust. $135.00

DBD5
COUNTRY MANOR BUTLER CREAM JUG

Designer: Shane Ridge
Height: 4 ¼", 11.0 cm
Colour: Black, white, grey, gold, red and brown
Issued: 2003 in a limited edition of 1,500

U.S. $75.00
Can. $90.00
U.K. £45.00
Aust. $95.00

DBD6
COUNTRY MANOR MAID COVERED SUGAR

Designer: Shane Ridge
Height: 4 ¼", 11.0 cm
Colour: Black, white, yellow and brown
Issued: 2003 in a limited edition of 1,500

U.S. $75.00
Can. $90.00
U.K. £45.00
Aust. $95.00

DBD7
COUNTRY MANOR CHEF CANDY BOX

Designer: Shane Ridge
Height: 5", 12.5 cm
Colour: Red, white, brown and orange
Issued: 2003 in a limited edition of 1,500

U.S. $ 85.00
Can. $100.00
U.K. £ 50.00
Aust. $110.00

BUNNYKINS TOBY JUGS

Issues of 1999 - 2003

D7157
FORTUNE TELLER BUNNYKINS™

Designer:	Kimberley Curtis
Modeller:	Warren Platt
Height:	5 ½", 14.0 cm
Colour:	Black, blue, brown, mauve, pink, white and yellow
Issued:	1999 in a limited edition of 1,500
U.S.	$110.00
Can.	$135.00
U.K.	£ 65.00
Aust.	$145.00

D7160
PARTY-TIME BUNNYKINS™

Designer:	Caroline Dadd
Modeller:	Warren Platt
Height:	6", 15 cm
Colour:	Blue pants; yellow shirt; red hat and balloons
Issued:	2000 in a limited edition of 1,500
U.S.	$110.00
Can.	$135.00
U.K.	£ 65.00
Aust.	$145.00

Backstamp not available at press time

D7166
WITCHING TIME BUNNYKINS™

Designer:	Caroline Dadd
Modeller:	Warren Platt
Height:	6", 15 cm
Colour:	Black, yellow and red
Issued:	2001 in a limited edition of 1,500
U.S.	$110.00
Can.	$135.00
U.K.	£ 65.00
Aust.	$145.00

Backstamp not available at press time

D7185
TOY SOLDIER BUNNYKINS ™

Designer:	Caroline Dadd
Modeller:	Warren Platt
Height:	6 ¼", 15.9 cm
Colour:	Red, blue, brown, yellow, white and grey
Issued:	2003 in a limited edition of 1,500
U.S.	$125.00
Can.	$150.00
U.K.	£ 75.00
Aust.	$160.00

BUNNYKINS BANKS 186
Issues of 1967 - 1981
BUNNYKINS COMMEMORATIVES 188
Issues of 1982 - 2003
BUNNYKINS ENAMEL BOXES 198
Issues of 1999

BUNNYKINS BANKS

Issues of 1967 - 1981

D6615A
BUNNYBANK
First Version

Designer:	Unknown
Modeller:	John Bromley and David Biggs
Height:	9 ¼", 23.5 cm
Coin Slot:	1 ½", 3.84 cm
Colour:	Brown rabbit; grey-blue jacket with white collar and buttons, pale yellow epaulettes and strap, grey-blue cap trimmed with white band; yellow straps on drum
Issued:	1967 - Unknown

Doulton Number	U.S. $	Price Can. $	U.K. £	Aust. $
D6615A			Rare	

D6615B
BUNNYBANK
Second Version, First Variation

Designer:	Unknown
Modeller:	John Bromley and David Biggs
Height:	8 ¼" to 8 ¾", 21.0 cm to 22.2 cm
Coin Slot:	1 ¼", 3.1 cm
Colour:	Brown rabbit; dark green jacket with cream collar and buttons, deep yellow epaulettes and strap, dark green cap trimmed with yellow band; cream straps on drum, deep yellow fasteners
Issued:	1967 - 1977

Doulton Number	U.S. $	Price Can. $	U.K. £	Aust. $
D6615B	200.00	250.00	115.00	275.00

D6615C
BUNNYBANK
Second Version, Second Variation

Designer:	Unknown
Modeller:	John Bromley and David Biggs
Height:	9" to 9 ¼", 22.9 cm to 23.5 cm
Coin Slot:	1 ¾", 4.4 cm
Colour:	Brown rabbit; dark green jacket with cream collar and buttons, deep yellow buttons and strap, dark green cap trimmed with yellow band; cream straps on drum, deep yellow fasteners
Issued:	1977 - 1981

Doulton Number	U.S. $	Price Can. $	U.K. £	Aust. $
D6615C	175.00	225.00	100.00	250.00

BUNNYKINS COMMEMORATIVES

Issues 1982 - 2002

TO CELEBRATE THE BIRTH OF THE FIRST CHILD OF T.R.H. THE PRINCE & PRINCESS OF WALES 1982

The following is a list of designs known to appear on these shapes; more may exist.

Design No.: HW17, HW17R, HW21, HW21R, HW22, HW22R, HW23, HW23R, HW26, HW26R, HW27R, HW28R, HW29R, HW119, HW119R, HW136, HW136R, HW137, HW137R, HW139, HW139R, HW141, HW141R, EC1, EC3, EC4, EC6, EC121, EC123, EC124, EC125, EC126

Issued: 1982

Shape	U.S. $	Can. $	U.K. £	Aust. $
Hug-a-mug, one handle	50.00	60.00	30.00	65.00
Hug-a-mug, two handles	50.00	60.00	30.00	65.00
Money ball	50.00	60.00	30.00	65.00
Savings book	50.00	60.00	30.00	65.00

Birth of the First Child of T.R.H. The Prince & Princess of Wales 1982

To T.R.H. The Prince and Princess of Wales A Second Child 1984

TO T.R.H. THE PRINCE AND PRINCESS OF WALES A SECOND CHILD 1984 IN JOYFUL CELEBRATION

The following is a list of designs known to appear on these shapes, more may exist.

Design No.: HW22, HW22R, HW23, HW27, HW27R, HW29, HW29R, HW120R

Issued: 1984

Shape	U.S. $	Can. $	U.K. £	Aust. $
Hug-a-mug, one handle	25.00	30.00	15.00	35.00
Hug-a-mug, two handles	25.00	30.00	15.00	35.00
Savings book	50.00	60.00	30.00	65.00

BUNNYKINS CELEBRATE THEIR GOLDEN JUBILEE 1934 - 1984

Birthday Cake

Design No.: SF140 — Birthday Cake
Designer: Walter Hayward
Issued: 1984 - 1984
Backstamp: Golden Jubilee Celebration

Shape	U.S. $	Can. $	U.K. £	Aust. $
Baby plate, round, small				
with inscription	50.00	60.00	30.00	65.00
without inscription	30.00	35.00	17.50	40.00
Cereal bowl				
with inscription	50.00	60.00	30.00	65.00
without inscription	30.00	35.00	17.50	40.00
Plate, 8"				
with inscription	50.00	60.00	30.00	65.00
without inscription	30.00	35.00	17.50	40.00

Note: The inscription was removed from the design after the Jubilee and the design was sold on baby plates, cereal bowls and the 8" plate.

Chicken Pulling A Cart

This scene was first issued in 1940 and discontinued by 1952. It was reissued in 1984 to commemorate the fiftieth anniversary of Bunnykins and was issued in two variations, with and without the inscription.

Design No.: SF141 — Chicken Pulling a Cart
Designer: After a design by Barbara Vernon (SF8)
Issued: 1984 - 1984
Backstamp: Golden Jubilee Celebration.

Shape	U.S. $	Can. $	U.K. £	Aust. $
Plate, 8"				
with inscription	80.00	95.00	45.00	100.00
without inscription	60.00	70.00	35.00	75.00

Note: For the complete listing on SF141 see page 43.

TO CELEBRATE THE MARRIAGE OF THE PRINCE ANDREW WITH MISS SARAH FERGUSON WESTMINSTER ABBEY, WEDNESDAY, 23RD JULY 1986

The following is a list of designs known to appear on these shapes; more may exist.

Design No.: HW26, HW26R, HW27, HW29, HW29R, HW115, HW115R, HW116, HW116R, HW118, HW118R, HW119, HW119R, HW120, HW136, HW136R, HW139, HW139R
Issued: 1986

Shape	U.S. $	Can. $	U.K. £	Aust. $
Hug-a-mug, one handle.	50.00	60.00	30.00	65.00
Money ball	50.00	60.00	30.00	65.00

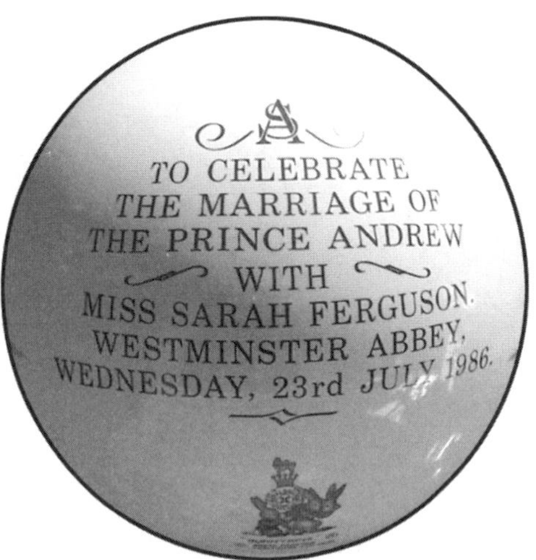

Marriage of The Prince Andrew with Miss Sarah Ferguson

Bunnykins Celebrate Australia's Bicentenary 1788 - 1988

TO CELEBRATE AUSTRALIA' S BICENTENARY 1788-1988

Design No.: None
Designer: Walter Hayward
Issued: 1987 - 1988
Backstamp: The Australian Bicentenary 1788-1988

Shape	U.S. $	Can. $	U.K. £	Aust. $
Plate, 8"	60.00	70.00	35.00	75.00

Dancing in the Moonlight, Second Version
First Variation (CT91)

To COMMEMORATE BUNNYKINS 60th ANNIVERSARY 1994

Dancing in the Moonlight
Second Version, First Variation, Large Size

Design No.:
Front — CT91 Dancing in the Moonlight
Designer: Justin Clarke based on a design by Barbara Vernon
Issued: 1994 - 1994
Backstamp:
Dancing in the Moonlight Bunnykins 60th Anniversary

Shape	U.S. $	Can. $	U.K. £	Aust. $
Baby plate, round, small	25.00	30.00	15.00	35.00
Plate, 8"	25.00	30.00	15.00	35.00

Note: See also *Dancing in the Moonlight*, Style One, page 53.

Dancing in the Moonlight
Second Version, Second Variation, Small Size

Design No.: Front — CT92 Dancing in the Moonlight
Reverse — CT93 Bunnykins 60th Anniversary inscription
Designer: Justin Clarke based on a design by Barbara Vernon
Issued: 1994 - 1994

Shape	U.S. $	Can. $	U.K. £	Aust. $
Hug-a-mug, one handle	15.00	20.00	8.00	25.00
Money ball	40.00	50.00	25.00	55.00

Dancing in the Moonlight, Second Version, Second Variation (CT92)

Bunnykins 60th Anniversary Inscription (CT93)

1990 U.S. SPECIAL EVENTS TOUR

An 8" plate was issued for the U.S. Special Events Tour, 1990. The year 1990 was incorporated under the design. The reverse is inscribed 'To' and 'From' to be completed by customer, and 'Special Events Tour 1990.

Designer: Walter Hayward
Diameter: 8", 20.3 cm
Colour: Cream / multicoloured print
Issued: 1990
Scene: *Apple Picking* (SF25)

Shape	U.S. $	Can. $	U.K. £	Aust. $
Plate, 8"	30.00	35.00	17.50	40.00

1992 U.S. SPECIAL EVENTS TOUR

Two money balls were issued for the U.S. Special Events Tour in 1992. This design was featured on the Spring tour with no special inscription. "Happy Birthday from Bunnykins" (CT60) was featured on the Fall tour.

Money Ball

Designer: Colin Twinn
Height: 3", 7.6 cm
Colour: Cream / multicoloured print
Issued: 1992
Scenes: Spring: *Queen of the May* (CT7)
Fall: *Happy Birthday Bunnykins*, Style Two, Second Version (CT60)

Description	U.S. $	Can. $	U.K. £	Aust. $
Spring: Queen of the May	15.00	20.00	10.00	25.00
Fall: Happy Birthday Bunnykins	15.00	20.00	10.00	25.00

1993 U.S. SPECIAL EVENTS TOUR

A Hug-a-mug (two handles) was issued for the U.S. Special Event Tour in 1993. The front illustrates *Daisy Chains* (HW25), and the back *Hikers* (EC124) with the words 'U.S. Special Events Tour 1993.'

Designer: Walter Hayward
Height: 3", 7.6 cm
Colour: Cream / multicoloured print
Issued: 1993
Scenes: *Daisy Chains* (HW25)
Hikers (EC124)

Shape	U.S. $	Can. $	U.K. £	Aust. $
Hug-a-mug	10.00	12.00	6.00	15.00

1994 U.S. SPECIAL EVENTS TOUR

A savings book was issued for the U.S. Special Events Tour 1994. The front features *Skipping Game* (HW139R) and the reverse is inscribed 'To' and 'From' for the customer to complete and 'U.S. Special Events Tour 1994.'

Designer: Walter Hayward
Height: 4 ¼", 10.8 cm
Colour: Cream / multicoloured print
Issued: 1994
Scene: *Skipping Game* (HW139R)

Shape	U.S .$	Can. $	U.K. £	Aust. $
Savings Bank	15.00	20.00	10.00	25.00

TO CELEBRATE THE MILLENNIUM EXHIBITION HELD APRIL 15TH TO MAY 31ST, 2000 AT THE ROYAL DOULTON VISITOR CENTRE

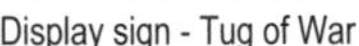
Display sign - Tug of War

Key fob - Tug of War

Desk clock - Sleeping in a Rocking Chair

ITEM:	**Display Sign**	**Key Fob**	**Desk Clock**	**Desk Clock Scenes:**
Designer:	Unknown	Unknown	Unknown	*Drummer, EC2*
Modeller:	Unknown	Unknown	Unknown	*Drummer and Bugler, EC126*
Height:	2 ¼", 6 cm	2½" x 2", 6.4 x5.0 cm	4 ¼", 11 cm	*Hikers, EC124*
Colour:	Multicoloured print	Multicoloured print	Multicoloured print	*Hobby Horse, EC121*
				Playing with Cup and Spoon, EC6
Issue:	1,250	1,250	1,000	*Playing with Doll and Pram*, EC123
				Raising Hat, EC7
				Reading, EC122
				Sheltering Under an Umbrella, EC3
				Sleeping in a Rocking Chair, EC1
				Trumpeter, EC5

Shape	Issue Price U.K. £	U.S. $	Can. $	U.K. £	Aust. $
Desk clock	45.00	70.00	85.00	40.00	90.00
Display sign	15.00	25.00	30.00	15.00	35.00
Key Fob	5.00	10.00	12.00	6.00	15.00

Note: Please see DB200 which was also part of the exhibition page 269.

TO COMMEMORATE THE AUSTRALIAN TOUR, 2000

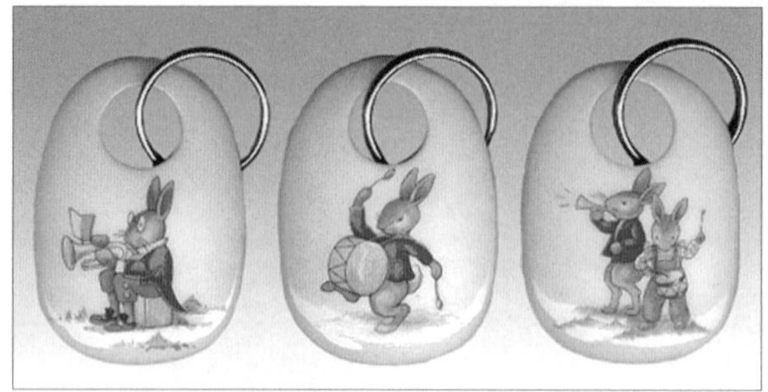

ITEM:	Scenes:	Designer:	Height:	Colour:
Key Fob	*Trumpeter*, EC4	Barbara Vernon	2½" x 2", 6.4 x 5.0 cm	Cream/multicoloured print
Key Fob	*Drummer*, EC2	Barbara Vernon	2½" x 2", 6.4 x 5.0 cm	Cream/multicoloured print
Key Fob	*Drummer and Bugler*, EC126	Walter Hayward	2½" x 2", 6.4 c 5.0 cm	Cream/multicoloured print

Shape	Issue Price Aust. $	U.S. $	Can. $	U.K. £	Aust. $
Key fobs, set of three	30.00	60.00	70.00	35.00	75.00

ROYAL DOULTON BUNNYKINS EXTRAVAGANZA FAIR, OCTOBER 2001

Mantle clock

Pillar Money Box

Commemorative tray 2001

ITEM:	**Mantle Clock**	**Piller Money Box**	**Commemorative Tray 2001**
Designer:	Unknown	Unknown	Unknown
Height/diameter:	4", 10.1 cm	5 ½", 14 cm	5 ¼", 13.5 cm
Colour:	Multicoloured print	Multicoloured print	Multicoloured print
Issue:	1,000	1,000	300
Scenes:	144 different combinations of 14 designs	*Posting Letters*, (28) *Sitting on Oil Drum*, (39)	*Letter Box*, (29)

Shape	Issue Price U.K. £	U.S. $	Can. $	U.K. £	Aust. $
Mantle clock	45.00	65.00	80.00	40.00	85.00
Pillar Money Box	45.00	65.00	80.00	40.00	85.00
Commemorative Tray	10.00	15.00	20.00	8.00	25.00

TO COMMEMORATE THE 65TH ANNIVERSARY OF NURSERY WARES AND 30TH ANNIVERSARY OF DB NUMBERS HELD AT THE ROYAL DOULTON VISITOR CENTRE, APRIL 2002

Rex mug

Commemorative tray 2002

30th Anniversary of DB Numbers Key Fob

ITEM:	**Rex Mug**	**Commemorative Tray**	**Key Fob**
Designer:	Unknown	Unknown	Unknown
Height/Diameter:	3", 7.5 cm	5 ¼", 13.5 cm	2 ½" x 2", 6.4 x 5.0 cm
Colour:	Multicoloured print	Multicoloured print	Multicoloured print
Issue:	325	700	Unknown
Scenes:	Unknown	*Beating Carpet*, (20)	30th Anniversary Crest

Shape	Issus Price U.K. £	U.S. $	Can. $	U.K. £	Aust. $
Rex mug	25.00	40.00	50.00	25.00	55.00
Commemorative tray	15.00	25.00	30.00	15.00	35.00
Key Fob	5.00	10.00	12.00	6.00	15.00

TO COMMEMORATE THE GOLDEN JUBILEE OF QUEEN ELIZABETH II, 1953 - 2003 DOULTON, BESWICK COLLECTORS FAIR OCTOBER 20TH, 2002.

Designer: Frank Endersby
Diameter: 10 ½", 26.7 cm
Colour: Cream/multicoloured print
Issued: 2002 in a limited edition of 50 (in presentation box)
Scenes: *Swinging*, HW138R
(Other scenes may be available)

Shape	Issue Price	U.S. $	Can. $	U.K. £	Aust. $
Plate, 10"	150.00	300.00	350.00	175.00	375.00

ROYAL DOULTON BUNNYKINS EXTRAVAGANZA, MAY 10TH AND 11TH, 2003

The May event was held at the Royal Doulton Visitor Centre in Burslem.

Designer: Colin Twinn
Diameter: 6 ½", 16.5 cm
Colour: Cream and multicoloured print
Issued: 2003 in a limited edition of 200
Scenes: *ABCDEF*, CT94

Shape	Issue Price	U.S. $	Can. $	U.K. £	Aust. $
Plate, 6 ½"	10.00	25.00	30.00	15.00	35.00

BUNNYKINS ENAMEL BOXES

THE BUNNYKINS™ MILLENNIUM BOX

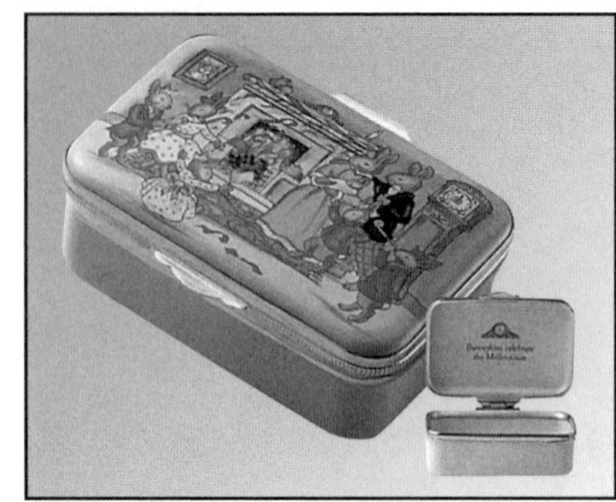

Hand crafted and painted rectangular enamelled, commemorative box which shows the Bunnykin Family gathering at the fireside as the grandfather clock strikes the arrival of the new millennium.

Modeller: Unknown
Size: 2 ½" x 2" x 1", 6.4 x 5.0 x 2.5 cm
Colour: Cream, multicoloured print
Issued: 1999 in a limited edition of 500
Comm. by: Lawleys by Post

Description	U.S. $	Can. $	U.K. £	Aust. $
Millenium box	325.00	400.00	185.00	425.00

THE BUNNYKINS FAMILY™

Lawleys by Post issued a specially commissioned set of five enamelled boxes depicting each of the Bunnykins Family. Father, sitting in the garden; Mother, picking vegetables; Polly, smelling the flowers; William, playing with an aeroplane and Baby sleeping. The hand made metal boxes are hand painted and come in a special edition of 500, with matching numbers, in a presentation box.

Modeller: Unknown
Size: 1. Father/Mother; 1 ¾", 4.5 cm
2. Polly/William; 1", 2.5 cm
3. Baby; ¾", 1.9 cm
Colour: Cream, multicoloured print
Issued: 1999 in a limited edition of 500
Comm. by: Lawleys by Post

Description	U.S. $	Can. $	U.K. £	Aust. $
Father	90.00	110.00	50.00	120.00
Mother	90.00	110.00	50.00	120.00
Polly	60.00	80.00	40.00	85.00
William	60.00	80.00	40.00	85.00
Baby	50.00	60.00	30.00	65.00
Set of five boxes	350.00	440.00	210.00	475.00

BUNNYKINS FIGURINES

EARTHENWARE
Issues of 1939 - 1940 203
Issues of 1972 - 2005 205
RESIN
Issues of 1996 - 1997 331

BUNNYKINS FIGURINE BACKSTAMPS

The Bunnykins backstamps have been reclassified due to design changes over the last three years. The stamps are whole numbers in the order of their appearance. They are then subdivided into "Standard" and "Modified." A "Standard" and "Special" stamp are the same except the "Special" serves to indicate a Limited Edition, Event, etc. A "Modified" backstamp is the "Standard" altered so it may be adapted to the base of the particular model to which it is to be applied. Flexibility must be allowed in dating by use of backstamps due to the over or under use of the backstamp lithos. Royal Doulton consumed all inventories of lithos before changing to a new style.

BK-1. Standard 1972 - 1975
Doulton & Co. Limited

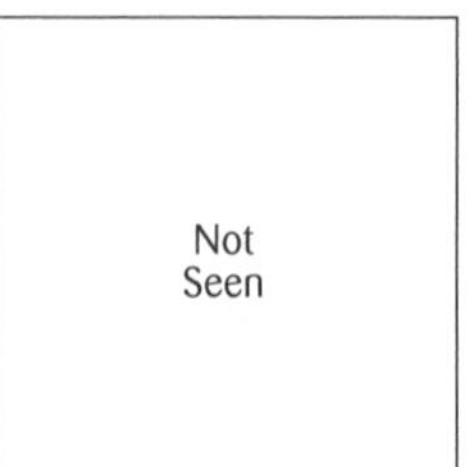

BK-1 Modified

BK-2 Standard 1976 - 1983
Doulton Tableware Ltd.

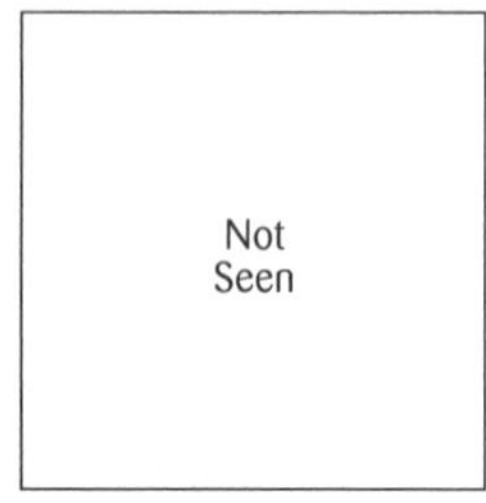

BK-2 Modified

BK-3 Standard 1984
Golden Jubilee Celebration

BK-3 Modified

BK-4 Standard 1985 - 1986
Royal Doulton (U.K.)

BK-4a Modified

BK-5 Standard 1987 - 1997
Royal Doulton 1987 - 1997

BK-5a Modified 1987 - 1997

BK-5 Special

BK-5a Special

BK-6 Standard 1998

BK-6a Modified 1998

BK-6 Special

BK-6a Special

Royal Doulton Crown and Lion logo with the 1998 folded umbrella date cypher.

SYDNEY BUNNYKINS
DB 195
PRODUCED EXCLUSIVELY FOR
Dalbry Antiques
Melbourne, Australia
IN A SPECIAL EDITION OF 2,500
© 1999 ROYAL DOULTON

SUNDIAL BUNNYKINS
DB 213
BUNNYKINS OF THE YEAR 2000
FIRST IN THE 'TIME' SERIES
© 1999 ROYAL DOULTON

SYDNEY BUNNYKINS
DB 195
PRODUCED EXCLUSIVELY FOR
Dalbry Antiques
Melbourne, Australia
IN A SPECIAL EDITION OF 2,500
© 1999 ROYAL DOULTON

BK-7 Standard 1999 | **BK-7a Modified 1999** | **BK-7 Special 1999** | **BK-7a Special 1999**

Royal Doulton, Crown and Lion logo with 1999 Top Hay cypher.

Not Seen

BK-8 Standard 2000 | **BK-8a Modified 2000** | **BK-8a Modified 2000** | **BK-8 Special 2000**

Royal Doulton, Crown and Lion logo with Millennium 2000 stamp and different date cyphers.

BK-9 Standard 2000 | **BK-9 Modified 2000** | **BK-9 Special 2000** | **BK-9a Special 2000**

Royal Doulton, Crown and Lion logo with 2000 Fob Watch cypher.

BK-10 Standard 2000 | **BK-10a Modified 2000** | **BK-10 Special 2000** | **BK-10a Special 2000**

Royal Doulton, oval backstamp designs with 2000 Fob Watch cypher.

HAND MADE AND HAND DECORATED
Bunnykins
by ROYAL DOULTON
SHOPPER
BUNNYKINS
DB 233
MADE IN ENGLAND © 2000 ROYAL DOULTON

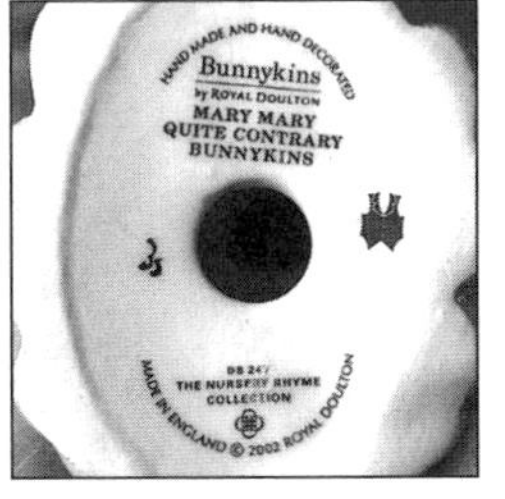

BK-11 Standard 2001 | **BK-11a Modified 2001** | **BK-11 Special 2001** | **BK-11a Special 2001**

Royal Doulton, oval backstamp with 2001 Vest cypher.

BK-12 Standard 2002

BK12a Modified 2002

Royal Doulton, round backstamp with 2002 Boot cypher.

BK-12 Special 2002

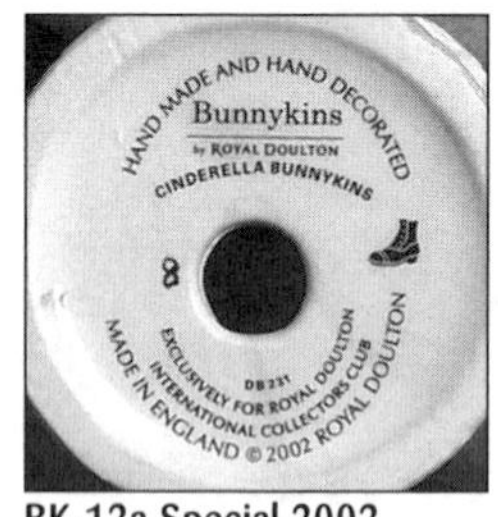

BK-12a Special 2002

BK-13a Special 2003
Glove Cypher

BK-14 Special 2004
Bottle Oven Cypher

Not Seen

BK-15a Special 2005
Henry Doulton Cypher

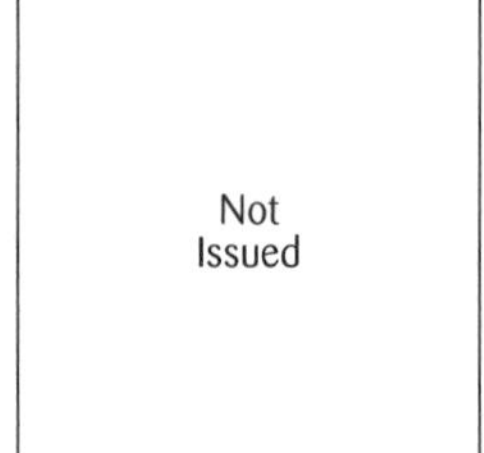

Not
Seen

BK-16 Standard 2003

BK-16a Modified 2003

Royal Doulton, Running Bunny / Interlocking "D" logo

BK-16 Special 2003

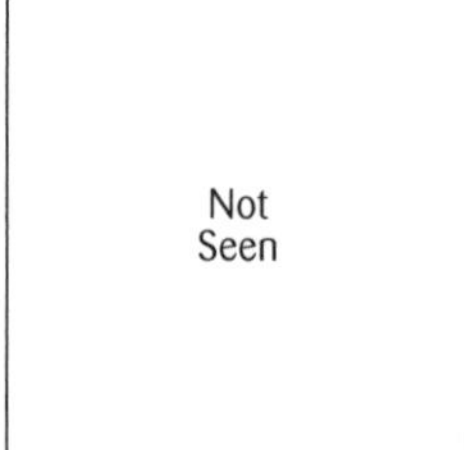

BK-16a Special 2003

BK-17 Standard
2003-2005

BK-17a Modified
2003-2005

Royal Doulton, Running Bunny logo

BK-17 Special
2003-2005

BK-17a Special
2003-2005

EARTHENWARE ISSUES

1939 - 1940

D6001
BILLY BUNNYKIN™

Designer: Charles Noke
Height: 4 ½", 11.9 cm
Colour: Red trousers, blue jacket, white bow tie with blue spots
Issued: 1939-c.1940

Doulton Number	U.S. $	Price Can. $	U.K. £	Aust. $
D6001	1,250.00	1,500.00	700.00	1,600.00

D6002
MARY BUNNYKIN™

Designer: Charles Noke
Height: 6 ½", 16.5 cm
Colour: Red bodice, dark blue collar; pale blue skirt, white apron
Issued: 1939-c.1940

Doulton Number	U.S. $	Price Can. $	U.K. £	Aust. $
D6002	2,000.00	2,500.00	1,200.00	2,750.00

D6003
FARMER BUNNYKIN™

Designer: Charles Noke
Height: 7 ½", 19.1 cm
Colour: Green coat, blue and white smock, yellow bow tie, red handkerchief with white dots
Issued: 1939-c.1940

Doulton Number	U.S. $	Price Can. $	U.K. £	Aust. $
D6003	2,000.00	2,500.00	1,200.00	2,750.00

Note: A prototype Farmer Bunnykin exists which has a straw coloured smock and red bow tie, white handkerchief with blue dots.

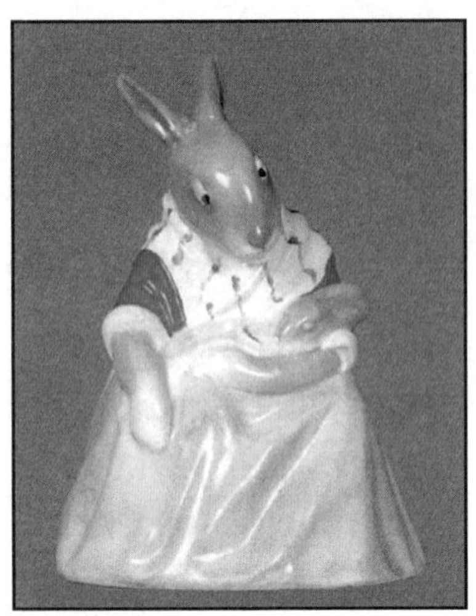

D6004
MOTHER BUNNYKIN™

Designer:	Charles Noke
Height:	7", 17.8 cm
Colour:	Blue skirt, red jacket, white shawl with blue stripes
Issued:	1939-c.1940

Doulton Number	U.S. $	Can. $	U.K. £	Aust. $
	Price			
D6004	1,750.00	2,000.00	1,000.00	2,250.00

D6024
FREDDIE BUNNYKIN™

Designer:	Charles Noke
Height:	3 ¾", 9.5 cm
Colour:	Green trousers, red jacket and yellow bow tie
Issued:	1939-c.1940

Doulton Number	U.S. $	Can. $	U.K. £	Aust. $
	Price			
D6024	3,500.00	4,250.00	2,000.00	4,500.00

D6025
REGGIE BUNNYKIN™

Designer:	Charles Noke
Height:	3 ¾", 9.5 cm
Colour:	Blue smock; red bow tie
Issued:	1939-c.1940

Doulton Number	U.S. $	Can. $	U.K. £	Aust. $
	Price			
D6025	3,500.00	4,250.00	2,000.00	4,500.00

EARTHENWARE ISSUES

1972 to 2005

DB1
FAMILY PHOTOGRAPH BUNNYKINS™
First Variation

Designer:	Based on a design by Walter Hayward
Modeller:	Albert Hallam
Height:	4 ½", 11.9 cm
Colour:	Blue, white, burgundy and grey
Issued:	1972 - 1988
Varieties:	DB67; also called Father, Mother and Victoria Bunnykins, DB68

Back Stamp	U.S. $	Price Can. $	U.K. £	Aust. $
BK-1 to BK-5	120.00	150.00	70.00	150.00

DB2
BUNTIE BUNNYKINS HELPING MOTHER™

Designer:	Based on a design by Walter Hayward
Modeller:	Albert Hallam
Height:	3 ½", 8.9 cm
Colour:	Rose-pink and yellow
Issued:	1972 - 1993

BUNTIE BUNNYKINS
"Helping Mother"
DB2
COPR. 1972
DOULTON & CO. LIMITED
Rd. No. 956234
Rd. No. 12900
R.S.A Rd. No. 193/72

Back Stamp	U.S. $	Price Can. $	U.K. £	Aust. $
BK-1 to BK-5	80.00	100.00	50.00	110.00

DB3
BILLIE BUNNYKINS COOLING OFF™

Designer:	Based on a design by Walter Hayward
Modeller:	Albert Hallam
Height:	3 ¾", 9.5 cm
Colour:	Burgundy, yellow and green-grey
Issued:	1972 - 1987

Back Stamp	U.S. $	Price Can. $	U.K. £	Aust. $
BK-1 to BK-5	175.00	220.00	100.00	220.00

Note: A colourway variation exists with white boots.

DB4
BILLIE & BUNTIE BUNNYKINS SLEIGH RIDE™
First Variation

Designer:	Based on a design by Walter Hayward
Modeller:	Albert Hallam
Height:	3 ¼", 8.3 cm
Colour:	Blue, maroon and yellow
Issued:	1972 - 1997
Varieties:	DB81

Back Stamp	U.S. $	Price Can. $	U.K. £	Aust. $
BK-1 to BK-5	45.00	55.00	25.00	60.00

Note: Colour variations exist in Buntie's dress.

DB5
MR. BUNNYKINS AUTUMN DAYS™

Designer:	Based on a design by Walter Hayward
Modeller:	Albert Hallam
Height:	4", 10.1 cm
Colour:	Maroon, yellow and blue
Issued:	1972 - 1982

Back Stamp	U.S. $	Price Can. $	U.K. £	Aust. $
BK-1 to BK-2	250.00	300.00	150.00	325.00

DB6
MRS. BUNNYKINS CLEAN SWEEP™

Designer:	Based on a design by Walter Hayward
Modeller:	Albert Hallam
Height:	4", 10.1 cm
Colour:	Blue and white
Issued:	1972 - 1991

Back Stamp	U.S. $	Price Can. $	U.K. £	Aust. $
BK-1 to BK-5	90.00	110.00	55.00	115.00

DB7
DAISIE BUNNYKINS SPRING TIME™

Designer:	Based on a design by Walter Hayward
Modeller:	Albert Hallam
Height:	3 ½", 8.9 cm
Colour:	Blue, white and yellow
Issued:	1972 - 1983

DAISIE BUNNYKINS
"Spring Time"
DB7
COPR. 1972
DOULTON & CO. LIMITED
Rd. No. 956231
Rd. No. 12906
R.S.A. Rd. No. 186/72

Back Stamp	U.S. $	Price Can. $	U.K. £	Aust. $
BK-1 to BK-2	275.00	325.00	160.00	350.00

DB8
DOLLIE BUNNYKINS PLAYTIME™
First Variation

Designer:	Based on a design by Walter Hayward
Modeller:	Albert Hallam
Height:	4", 10.1 cm
Colour:	White dress with pink design, blue dress
Issued:	1972 - 1993
Varieties:	DB80

DOLLIE BUNNYKINS
"Playtime"
DB8
COPR. 1972
DOULTON & CO. LIMITED
Rd. No. 956229
Rd. No. 12906
R.S.A. Rd. No. 187/72

Back Stamp	U.S. $	Price Can. $	U.K. £	Aust. $
BK-1 to BK-5	80.00	100.00	50.00	110.00

DB9
STORYTIME BUNNYKINS™
First Variation

Designer:	Based on a design by Walter Hayward
Modeller:	Albert Hallam
Height:	3", 7.6 cm
Colour:	White dress with blue design, pink dress
Issued:	1972 - 1997
Varieties:	DB59; also called Partners in Collecting, DB151

Back Stamp	U.S. $	Price Can. $	U.K. £	Aust. $
BK-1 to BK-5	40.00	50.00	25.00	55.00

MADE IN ENGLAND
ROYAL DOULTON
ENGLAND
BUNNYKINS
"Busy Needles"
DB 10
COPR 1974
DOULTON & CO.LIMITED
Rd No 963542
RSA Rd No 73/0974

DB10
BUSY NEEDLES BUNNYKINS™

Designer: Based on a design by Walter Hayward
Modeller: Albert Hallam
Height: 3 ¼", 8.3 cm
Colour: White, green and maroon
Issued: 1973 - 1988
Varieties: Also called Susan Bunnykins, DB70

Back Stamp	U.S. $	Price Can. $	U.K. £	Aust. $
BK-1 to BK-5	80.00	100.00	50.00	110.00

DB11
RISE AND SHINE BUNNYKINS™

Designer: Based on a design by Walter Hayward
Modeller: Albert Hallam
Height: 3 ¾", 9.5 cm
Colour: Maroon, yellow and blue
Issued: 1973 - 1988

MADE IN ENGLAND
ROYAL DOULTON
ENGLAND
BUNNYKINS ®
"Rise and Shine"
DB 11
© ROYAL DOULT
TABLEWARE LT 197

Back Stamp	U.S. $	Price Can. $	U.K. £	Aust. $
BK-1 to BK-5	110.00	135.00	65.00	150.00

DB12
TALLY HO! BUNNYKINS™
First Variation

Designer: Based on a design by Walter Hayward
Modeller: Albert Hallam
Height: 3 ¾", 9.5 cm
Colour: Burgundy, yellow, blue, white and green
Issued: 1973 - 1988
Varieties: DB78; also called William Bunnykins, DB69

Back Stamp	U.S. $	Price Can. $	U.K. £	Aust. $
BK-1 to BK-5	100.00	120.00	60.00	130.00

Note: A colourway variation exists with a white jacket and black trousers.

DB13
THE ARTIST BUNNYKINS™

Designer:	Based on a design by Walter Hayward
Modeller:	Alan Maslankowski
Height:	3 ¾", 9.5 cm
Colour:	Burgundy, yellow and blue
Issued:	1975 - 1982

MADE IN ENGLAND ROYAL DOULTON
BUNNYKINS ®
The Artist
D B 13
© ROYAL DOULTON
TABLEWARE LTD 1975

Back Stamp	U.S. $	Price Can. $	U.K. £	Aust. $
BK-1 to BK-3	275.00	325.00	160.00	350.00

DB14
GRANDPA'S STORY BUNNYKINS™

Designer:	Based on a design by Walter Hayward
Modeller:	Alan Maslankowski
Height:	4", 10.1 cm
Colour:	Burgundy, grey, yellow blue and green
Issued:	1975 - 1983

MADE IN ENGLAND ROYAL DOULTON
BUNNYKINS
Grandpa's Story
D B 14
© ROYAL DOULTON
TABLEWARE LTD 1975

Back Stamp	U.S. $	Price Can. $	U.K. £	Aust. $
BK-1 to BK-3	275.00	325.00	160.00	350.00

DB15
SLEEPYTIME BUNNYKINS™

Designer:	Based on a design by Walter Hayward
Modeller:	Alan Maslankowski
Height:	1 ¾", 4.7 cm
Colour:	Brown, white, yellow, blue and red
Issued:	1975 - 1993

MADE IN ENGLAND ROYAL DOULTON
BUNNYKINS ®
"Sleepytime"
D B 15
© ROYAL DOULTON
TABLEWARE LTD 1975

Back Stamp	U.S. $	Price Can. $	U.K. £	Aust. $
BK-1 to BK-5	60.00	70.00	35.00	75.00

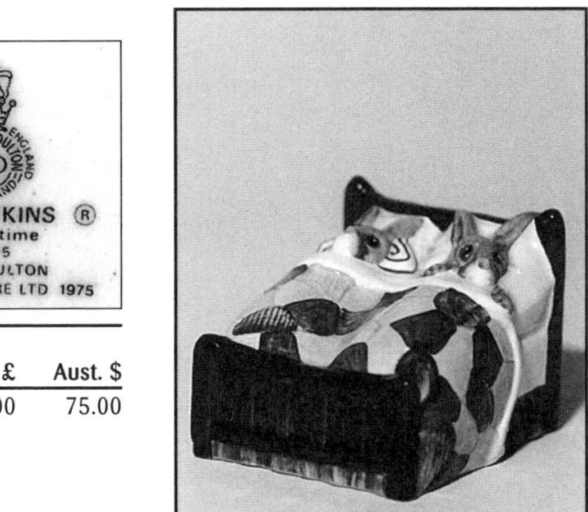

DB16
MR. BUNNYBEAT STRUMMING™

MADE IN ENGLAND ROYAL DOULTON ENGLAND
MR. BUNNYBEAT
"Strumming"
DB 16
© ROYAL DOULTON
TABLEWARE LTD. 19..

Designer:	Harry Sales
Modeller:	David Lyttleton
Height:	4 ½", 11.9 cm
Colour:	Pink and yellow coat, blue and white stripped trousers, white with blue polka-dot neck bow
Issued:	1982 - 1988
Varieties:	Also called Rock and Roll Bunnykins, DB124

Back Stamp	U.S. $	Price Can. $	U.K. £	Aust. $
BK-2 to BK-5	200.00	250.00	125.00	275.00

DB17
SANTA BUNNYKINS HAPPY CHRISTMAS™

MADE IN ENGLAND ROYAL DOULTON ENGLAND
SANTA BUNNYKINS
"Happy Christmas"
DB 17
© ROYAL DOULTON
TABLEWARE LTD. 1981

Designer:	Harry Sales
Modeller:	David Lyttleton
Height:	4 ½", 11.9 cm
Colour:	Red, white and brown
Issued:	1981 - 1996

Back Stamp	U.S. $	Price Can. $	U.K. £	Aust. $
BK-2 to BK-5	50.00	60.00	30.00	65.00

DB18
MR. BUNNYKINS AT THE EASTER PARADE™
First Variation

Designer:	Harry Sales
Modeller:	David Lyttleton
Height:	5", 12.7 cm
Colour:	Red, yellow and brown
Issued:	1982 - 1993
Varieties:	DB51

Back Stamp	U.S. $	Price Can. $	U.K. £	Aust. $
BK-2 to BK-5	85.00	100.00	50.00	110.00

DB19
MRS. BUNNYKINS
AT THE EASTER PARADE™
First Variation

MRS BUNNYKINS
"At The Easter Parade"
DB 19
© ROYAL DOULTON
TABLEWARE LTD 1982

Designer:	Harry Sales
Modeller:	David Lyttleton
Height:	4 ½", 11.9 cm
Colour:	Pale blue and maroon
Issued:	1982 - 1996
Varieties:	DB52

Back Stamp	Price U.S. $	Can. $	U.K. £	Aust. $
BK-2 to BK-5	50.00	60.00	30.00	65.00

DB20
ASTRO BUNNYKINS ROCKET MAN™

ASTRO BUNNYKINS
Rocket Man
DB 20
© ROYAL DOULTON
TABLEWARE LTD 1982

Designer:	Harry Sales
Modeller:	David Lyttleton
Height:	4 ¼", 10.8 cm
Colour:	White, red, blue and yellow
Issued:	1983 - 1988

Back Stamp	Price U.S. $	Can. $	U.K. £	Aust. $
BK-2 to BK-5	135.00	160.00	80.00	175.00

DB21
HAPPY BIRTHDAY BUNNYKINS™

Designer:	Harry Sales
Modeller:	Graham Tongue
Height:	3 ¾", 9.5 cm
Colour:	Red and blue
Issued:	1983 - 1997

Back Stamp	Price U.S. $	Can. $	U.K. £	Aust. $
BK-2 to BK-5	40.00	55.00	25.00	60.00

DB22
JOGGING BUNNYKINS™

Designer:	Harry Sales
Modeller:	David Lyttleton
Height:	2 ½", 6.4 cm
Colour:	Yellow, blue and white
Issued:	1983 - 1989

Back Stamp	U.S. $	Price Can. $	U.K. £	Aust. $
BK-2 to BK-5	110.00	135.00	65.00	150.00

DB23
SOUSAPHONE BUNNYKINS™
First Variation

Designer:	Harry Sales
Modeller:	David Lyttleton
Height:	3 ½", 8.9 cm
Colour:	Red, blue and yellow
Issued:	1984 - 1990
Varieties:	DB86, DB105
Series:	Bunnykins Oompah Band

Back Stamp	U.S. $	Price Can. $	U.K. £	Aust. $
BK-2 to BK-5	110.00	135.00	65.00	150.00
Set DB23 - 27 (5pcs.)	550.00	825.00	325.00	750.00

DB24
TRUMPETER BUNNYKINS™
First Variation

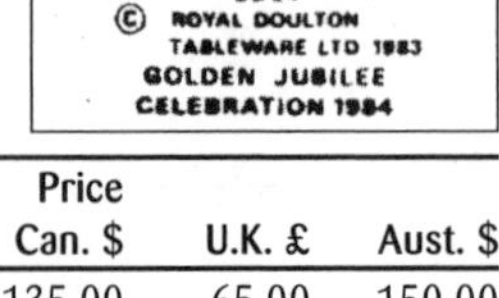

Designer:	Harry Sales
Modeller:	David Lyttleton
Height:	3 ½", 8.9 cm
Colour:	Red, blue and yellow
Issued:	1984 - 1990
Varieties:	DB87, DB106
Series:	Bunnykins Oompah Band

Back Stamp	U.S. $	Price Can. $	U.K. £	Aust. $
BK-2 to BK-5	110.00	135.00	65.00	150.00

DB25
CYMBALS BUNNYKINS™
First Variation

"CYMBALS BUNNYKINS"
FROM THE OOMPAH BAND
DB 25
© ROYAL DOULTON
TABLEWARE LTD. 1983
GOLDEN JUBILEE
CELEBRATION 1984

Designer:	Harry Sales
Modeller:	David Lyttleton
Height:	3 ½", 8.9 cm
Colour:	Red, blue and yellow
Issued:	1984 - 1990
Varieties:	DB88, DB107
Series:	Bunnykins Oompah Band

Back Stamp	U.S. $	Price Can. $	U.K. £	Aust. $
BK-2 to BK-5	110.00	135.00	65.00	150.00

DB26A
DRUMMER BUNNYKINS™
Style One, First Variation
50th Anniversary Edition

"DRUMMER BUNNYKINS"
FROM THE OOMPAH BAND
DB 26
© ROYAL DOULTON
TABLEWARE LTD. 1983
GOLDEN JUBILEE
CELEBRATION 1984

Designer:	Harry Sales
Modeller:	David Lyttleton
Height:	3 ½", 8.9 cm
Colour:	Blue, yellow, red and cream
Issued:	1984 - 1984
Series:	Bunnykins Oompah Band

Back Stamp	U.S. $	Price Can. $	U.K. £	Aust. $
BK-3	150.00	175.00	90.00	195.00

DB26B
DRUMMER BUNNYKINS™
Style One, Second Variation

"DRUMMER BUNNYKINS"
FROM THE OOMPAH BAND
DB 26
© ROYAL DOULTON
TABLEWARE LTD. 1983

Designer:	Harry Sales
Modeller:	David Lyttleton
Height:	3 ¾", 9.5 cm
Colour:	Blue, yellow, red and cream
Issued:	1984 - 1990
Varieties:	DB89, DB108
Series:	Bunnykins Oompah Band

Back Stamp	U.S. $	Price Can. $	U.K. £	Aust. $
BK-2 to BK-5	110.00	135.00	65.00	150.00

DB27
DRUM-MAJOR BUNNYKINS™
First Variation

Designer: Harry Sales
Modeller: David Lyttleton
Height: 3 ½", 8.9 cm
Colour: Red, blue and yellow
Issued: 1984 - 1990
Varieties: DB90, DB109
Series: Bunnykins Oompah Band

Back Stamp	U.S. $	Price Can. $	U.K. £	Aust. $
BK-2 to BK-5	110.00	135.00	65.00	150.00

DB28A
OLYMPIC BUNNYKINS™
First Variation

Designer: Harry Sales
Modeller: David Lyttleton
Height: 3 ¾", 9.5 cm
Colour: White and blue
Issued: 1984 - 1988

Back Stamp	U.S. $	Price Can. $	U.K. £	Aust. $
BK-2 to BK-5	135.00	170.00	80.00	195.00

DB28B
OLYMPIC BUNNYKINS™
Second Variation

Designer: Harry Sales
Modeller: David Lyttleton
Height: 3 ½", 8.9 cm
Colour: Gold and green
Issued: 1984 - 1984

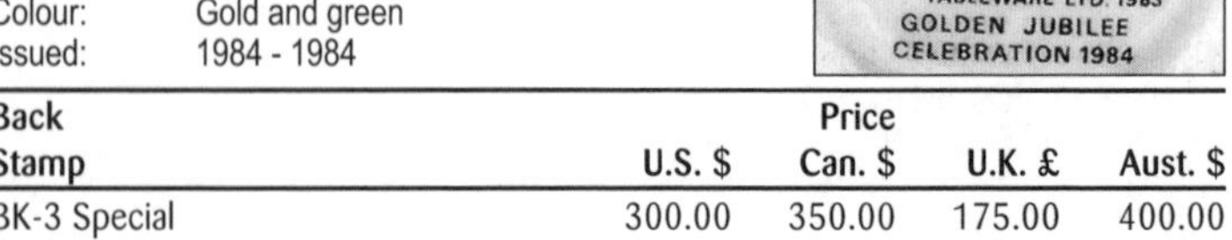

Back Stamp	U.S. $	Price Can. $	U.K. £	Aust. $
BK-3 Special	300.00	350.00	175.00	400.00

DB29A
TOUCHDOWN BUNNYKINS™
First Variation

Designer:	Harry Sales
Modeller:	David Lyttleton
Height:	3 ¼", 8.3 cm
Colour:	Blue and white
Issued:	1985 - 1988
Varieties:	DB29B, DB96, DB97, DB98, DB99, DB100

"TOUCHDOWN BUNNYKINS"
DB 29
© ROYAL DOULTON
TABLEWARE LTD 1984
GOLDEN JUBILEE
CELEBRATION 1984

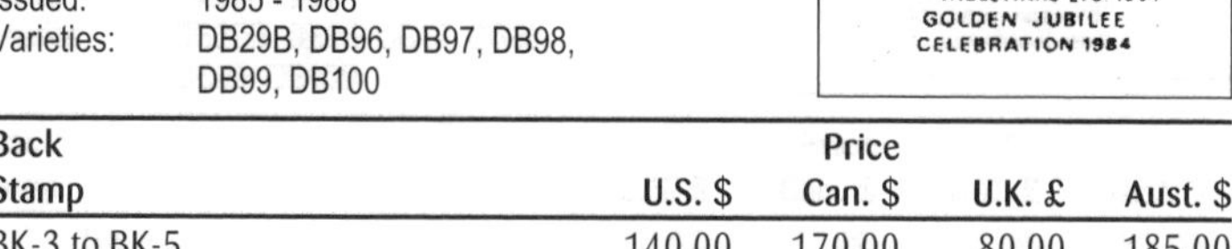

Back Stamp	U.S. $	Price Can. $	U.K. £	Aust. $
BK-3 to BK-5	140.00	170.00	80.00	185.00

DB29B
TOUCHDOWN BUNNYKINS™
Second Variation (Boston College)

Designer:	Harry Sales
Modeller:	David Lyttleton
Height:	3 ¼", 8.3 cm
Colour:	Maroon, gold and white
Issued:	1985 in a limited edition of 50
Varieties:	DB29A, DB96, DB97, DB98, DB99, DB100

TOUCHDOWN BUNNYKINS"
DB 29
© ROYAL DOULTON
TABLEWARE LTD 1984

Back Stamp	U.S. $	Price Can. $	U.K. £	Aust. $
BK-2	1,750.00	2,100.00	1,000.00	2,200.00

DB30
KNOCKOUT BUNNYKINS™

Designer:	Harry Sales
Modeller:	David Lyttleton
Height:	4", 10.1 cm
Colour:	Yellow, green and white
Issued:	1984 - 1988

Back Stamp	U.S. $	Price Can. $	U.K. £	Aust. $
BK-3 to BK-5	220.00	265.00	125.00	275.00

DB31
DOWNHILL BUNNYKINS™

"DOWNHILL BUNNYKINS"
DB 31
© ROYAL DOULTON
TABLEWARE LTD 1984

Designer:	Harry Sales
Modeller:	Graham Tongue
Height:	2 ½", 6.4 cm
Colour:	Yellow, green, maroon and grey
Issued:	1985 - 1988

Back Stamp	U.S. $	Price Can. $	U.K. £	Aust. $
BK-3 to BK-5	175.00	200.00	100.00	225.00

DB32
BOGEY BUNNYKINS™

"BOGEY BUNNYKINS"
DB 32
© ROYAL DOULTON
TABLEWARE LTD 1984

Designer:	Harry Sales
Modeller:	David Lyttleton
Height:	4", 10.1 cm
Colour:	Green, brown and yellow
Issued:	1984 - 1992

Back Stamp	U.S. $	Price Can. $	U.K. £	Aust. $
BK-2 to BK-5	100.00	120.00	60.00	120.00

DB33A
TALLY HO!™
Music Box
First Variation, Tally-Ho! Figurine

Designer:	Based on a design by Walter Hayward
Modeller:	Albert Hallam
Height:	7", 17.8 cm
Colour:	Light blue coat, yellow sweater
Issued:	1984 - 1993
Tune:	'Rock A Bye Baby'

Back Stamp	U.S. $	Price Can. $	U.K. £	Aust. $
Tug of War	175.00	200.00	100.00	225.00

Note: For Tug of War backstamp see Tableware Section page 5 and 6.

DB33B
TALLY HO!™
Music Box
Second Variation, William Bunnykins Figurine

Designer:	Based on a design by Walter Hayward
Modeller:	Albert Hallam
Height:	7", 17.8 cm
Colour:	Red coat and brown trousers
Issued:	1988 - 1991
Tune:	'Rock A Bye Baby'

Back Stamp	U.S. $	Price Can. $	U.K. £	Aust. $
Tug of War	175.00	200.00	100.00	225.00

DB34
SANTA BUNNYKINS™
Music Box

Designer:	Harry Sales
Modeller:	David Lyttleton
Height:	7 ¼", 18.4 cm
Colour:	Red, white and brown
Issued:	1984 - 1991
Tune:	'White Christmas'

Back Stamp	U.S. $	Price Can. $	U.K. £	Aust. $
Tug of War	175.00	200.00	100.00	225.00

DB35
ASTRO BUNNYKINS ROCKET MAN™
Music Box

Designer:	Harry Sales
Modeller:	David Lyttleton
Height:	7", 17.8 cm
Colour:	White, red and blue
Issued:	1984 - 1989
Tune:	'Fly Me To The Moon'

Back Stamp	U.S. $	Price Can. $	U.K. £	Aust. $
Tug of War	175.00	200.00	100.00	225.00

DB36
HAPPY BIRTHDAY BUNNYKINS™
Music Box

Designer: Harry Sales
Modeller: Graham Tongue
Height: 7", 17.8 cm
Colour: Red and white
Issued: 1984 - 1991
Tune: 'Happy Birthday To You'

Backstamp not available at press time

Back Stamp	Price U.S. $	Can. $	U.K. £	Aust. $
Tug of War	175.00	200.00	100.00	225.00

DB37
JOGGING BUNNYKINS™
Music Box

Designer: Harry Sales
Modeller: David Lyttleton
Height: 5 ½", 14.0 cm
Colour: Yellow and blue
Issued: 1987 - 1989
Tune: 'King of the Road'

Backstamp not available at press time

Back Stamp	Price U.S. $	Can. $	U.K. £	Aust. $
Tug of War	175.00	200.00	100.00	225.00

DB38
MR. BUNNYBEAT STRUMMING™
Music Box

Designer: Harry Sales
Modeller: David Lyttleton
Height: 7 ½", 19.1 cm
Colour: Pink, white and yellow
Issued: 1987 - 1989
Tune: 'Hey Jude'

Backstamp not available at press time

Back Stamp	Price U.S. $	Can. $	U.K. £	Aust. $
Tug of War	175.00	200.00	100.00	225.00

DB39
MRS. BUNNYKINS
AT THE EASTER PARADE™
Music Box

Designer:	Harry Sales
Modeller:	David Lyttleton
Height:	7", 17.8 cm
Colour:	Blue, yellow and maroon
Issued:	1987 - 1991
Tune:	'Easter Parade'

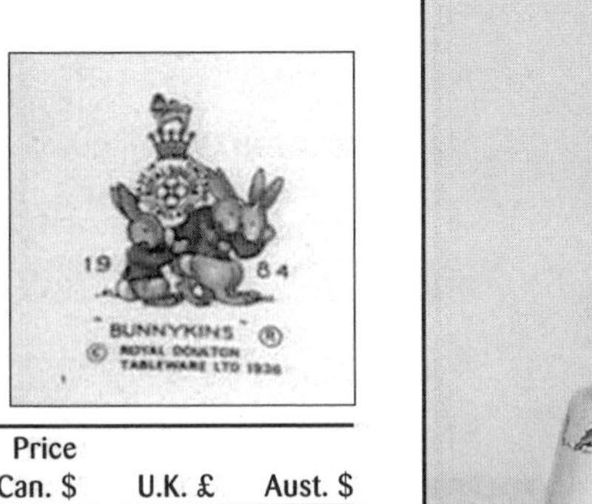

Back Stamp	U.S. $	Price Can. $	U.K. £	Aust. $
Tug of War	175.00	200.00	100.00	225.00

DB40
AEROBIC BUNNYKINS™

Designer:	Harry Sales
Modeller:	David Lyttleton
Height:	2 ¾", 7.0 cm
Colour:	Yellow and pale blue
Issued:	1985 - 1988

MADE IN ENGLAND ROYAL DOULTON ENGLAND
"AEROBIC BUNNYKINS"
DB 40
© ROYAL DOULTON (UK) 1984

Back Stamp	U.S. $	Price Can. $	U.K. £	Aust. $
BK-4 to BK-5	175.00	200.00	100.00	225.00

DB41
FREEFALL BUNNYKINS™

Designer:	Harry Sales
Modeller:	David Lyttleton
Height:	2 ¼", 5.7 cm
Colour:	Grey, yellow and white
Issued:	1986 - 1989

Back Stamp	U.S. $	Price Can. $	U.K. £	Aust. $
BK-4 to BK-5	250.00	300.00	150.00	325.00

Note: Different colourway variations exist, dark grey to light grey suits.

DB42
ACE BUNNYKINS™

Designer:	Harry Sales
Modeller:	David Lyttleton
Height:	3 ¾", 9.5 cm
Colour:	White and blue
Issued:	1986 - 1989

Back Stamp	U.S. $	Price Can. $	U.K. £	Aust. $
BK-4 to BK-5	200.00	250.00	120.00	275.00

DB43
HOME RUN BUNNYKINS™
(1 on Back of Jersey)

Designer:	Harry Sales
Modeller:	David Lyttleton
Height:	4", 10.1 cm
Colour:	Blue, yellow and white
Issued:	1986 - 1993

Back Stamp	U.S. $	Price Can. $	U.K. £	Aust. $
BK-4 to BK-5	85.00	100.00	50.00	110.00

DB44: ASSIGNED TO BALLET BUNNYKINS BUT NOT ISSUED.

DB45
KING JOHN™
First Variation

Designer:	Harry Sales
Modeller:	David Lyttleton
Height:	4", 10.1 cm
Colour:	Red, yellow and blue
Issued:	1986 - 1990
Varieties:	DB91
Series:	Bunnykins Royal Family

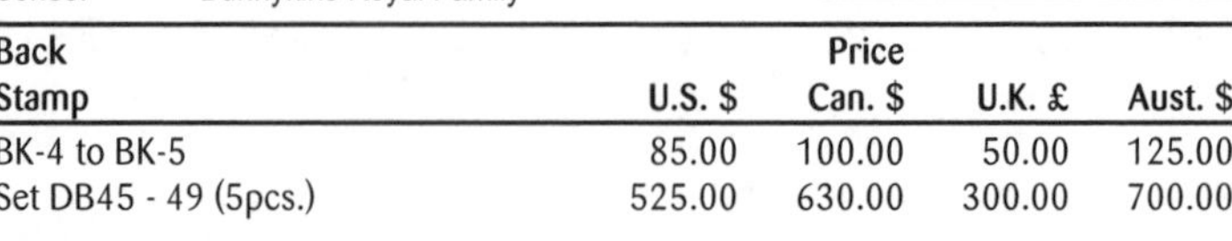

Back Stamp	U.S. $	Price Can. $	U.K. £	Aust. $
BK-4 to BK-5	85.00	100.00	50.00	125.00
Set DB45 - 49 (5pcs.)	525.00	630.00	300.00	700.00

DB46
QUEEN SOPHIE™
First Variation

Designer:	Harry Sales
Modeller:	David Lyttleton
Height:	4 ½", 11.9 cm
Colour:	Blue and red
Issued:	1986 - 1990
Varieties:	DB92
Series:	Bunnykins Royal Family

Back Stamp	U.S. $	Price Can. $	U.K. £	Aust. $
BK-4 to 5	100.00	120.00	60.00	130.00

DB47
PRINCESS BEATRICE™
First Variation

Designer:	Harry Sales
Modeller:	David Lyttleton
Height:	3 ½", 8.9 cm
Colour:	Pale green
Issued:	1986 - 1990
Varieties:	DB93
Series:	Bunnykins Royal Family

Back Stamp	U.S. $	Price Can. $	U.K. £	Aust. $
BK-4a to BK-5a	100.00	120.00	60.00	130.00

DB48
PRINCE FREDERICK™
First Variation

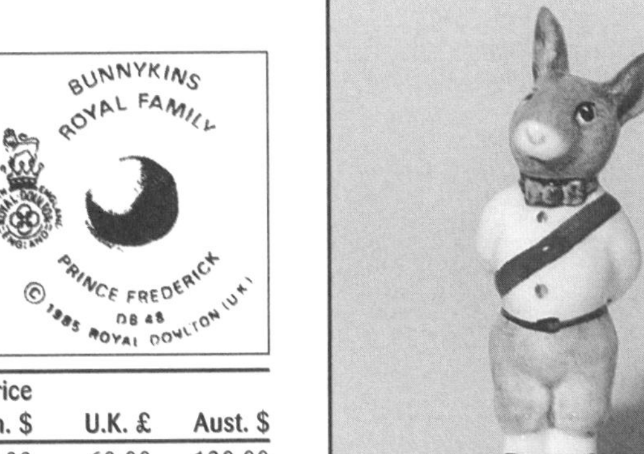

Designer:	Harry Sales
Modeller:	David Lyttleton
Height:	3 ½", 8.9 cm
Colour:	Green, white and red
Issued:	1986 - 1990
Varieties:	DB94
Series:	Bunnykins Royal Family

Back Stamp	U.S. $	Price Can. $	U.K. £	Aust. $
BK-4a to BK-5a	100.00	120.00	60.00	130.00

DB49
HARRY THE HERALD™
First Variation

Designer:	Harry Sales
Modeller:	David Lyttleton
Height:	3 ½", 8.9 cm
Colour:	Maroon, white and tan
Issued:	1986 - 1990
Varieties:	DB95, DB115
Series:	Bunnykins Royal Family

Back Stamp	U.S. $	Price Can. $	U.K. £	Aust. $
BK-4a to BK-5a	140.00	170.00	80.00	185.00

DB50
UNCLE SAM BUNNYKINS™
First Variation

Designer:	Harry Sales
Modeller:	David Lyttleton
Height:	4 ½", 11.9 cm
Colour:	Blue, red and white
Issued:	1986 - 2001
Varieties:	DB175

Back Stamp	U.S. $	Price Can. $	U.K. £	Aust. $
BK-4a to BK-5a	60.00	75.00	35.00	75.00

Note: Prototype exists with yellow bowtie; and a colourway variation exists with a dark blue jacket, and an all white model is also known.

DB51
MR. BUNNYKINS AT THE EASTER PARADE™
Second Variation

Designer:	Harry Sales
Modeller:	David Lyttleton
Height:	5", 12.7 cm
Colour:	Maroon coat, light grey trousers, blue bowtie, yellow straw hat, yellow egg with pink ribbon
Issued:	1986 - 1986
Varieties:	DB18

Back Stamp	U.S. $	Price Can. $	U.K. £	Aust. $
BK-4	975.00	1,175.00	550.00	1,275.00

DB52
MRS. BUNNYKINS AT THE EASTER PARADE™
Second Variation

Designer: Harry Sales
Modeller: David Lyttleton
Height: 4 ½", 11.9 cm
Colour: Pink dress, white bodice, white cap with blue ribbon, yellow basket with multicoloured eggs
Issued: 1986 - 1986
Varieties: DB19
Series: Special Events 1986

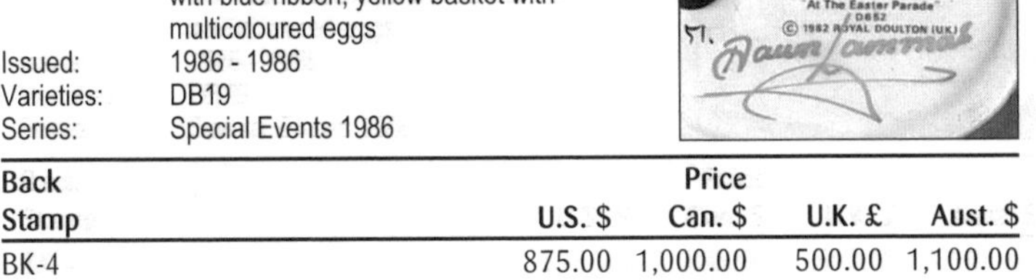

Back Stamp	Price U.S. $	Can. $	U.K. £	Aust. $
BK-4	875.00	1,000.00	500.00	1,100.00

DB53
CAROL SINGER BUNNYKINS™
Music Box

Designer: Harry Sales
Modeller: David Lyttleton
Height: 7", 17.8 cm
Colour: Red, yellow, blue and grey
Issued: 1986 - 1990
Tune: 'Silent Night'

Backstamp not available at press time

Back Stamp	Price U.S. $	Can. $	U.K. £	Aust. $
BK-9a to BK-10a	350.00	425.00	200.00	450.00

DB54
COLLECTOR BUNNYKINS™

Designer: Harry Sales
Modeller: David Lyttleton
Height: 4 ¼", 10.8 cm
Colour: Brown, blue, yellow and grey
Issued: 1987 - 1987
Series: ICC Members Exclusive

Back Stamp	Price U.S. $	Can. $	U.K. £	Aust. $
BK-5 Special	475.00	575.00	275.00	600.00

DB55
BEDTIME BUNNYKINS™
First Variation

Designer:	Graham Tongue
Modeller:	David Lyttleton
Height:	3 ¼", 8.3 cm
Colour:	Blue and white stripped pyjamas, brown teddy bear
Issued:	1987 - 1998
Varieties:	DB63, DB79, DB103

Back Stamp	U.S. $	Price Can. $	U.K. £	Aust. $
BK-5a	40.00	50.00	25.00	55.00

Note: A colourway variation exists with a white bear.

DB56
BE PREPARED BUNNYKINS™

Designer:	Graham Tongue
Modeller:	David Lyttleton
Height:	4", 10.1 cm
Colour:	Dark green, grey and red
Issued:	1987 - 1996

Back Stamp	U.S. $	Price Can. $	U.K. £	Aust. $
BK-5a	70.00	85.00	40.00	85.00

DB57
SCHOOLDAYS BUNNYKINS™

Designer:	Graham Tongue
Modeller:	David Lyttleton
Height:	3 ½", 8.9 cm
Colour:	Dark green, white and yellow
Issued:	1987 - 1994

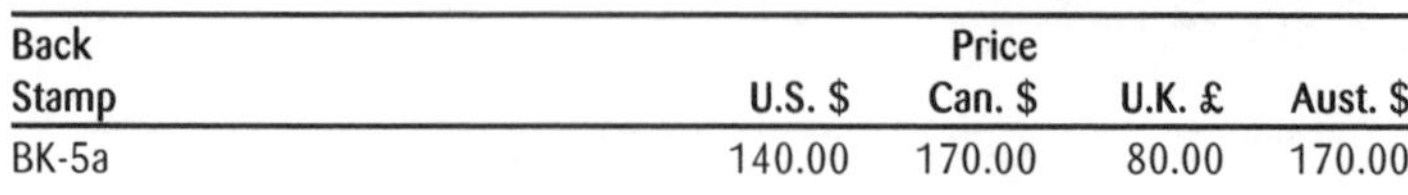

Back Stamp	U.S. $	Price Can. $	U.K. £	Aust. $
BK-5a	140.00	170.00	80.00	170.00

DB58
AUSTRALIAN BUNNYKINS™

Designer:	Harry Sales
Modeller:	Warren Platt
Height:	4", 10.1 cm
Colour:	Gold and green
Issued:	1988 - 1988

Back Stamp	U.S. $	Price Can. $	U.K. £	Aust. $
BK-5a Special	350.00	425.00	200.00	425.00

DB59
STORYTIME BUNNYKINS™
Second Variation

Designer:	Based on a design by Walter Hayward
Modeller:	Albert Hallam
Height:	3", 7.6 cm
Colour:	Left - green design on white dress, yellow shoes Right - yellow dress, green shoes
Issued:	1987 - 1987
Varieties:	DB9; also called Partners in Collecting, DB151
Series:	Special Events 1987

MADE IN ENGLAND ROYAL DOULTON ENGLAND
BUNNYKINS ®
"Storytime"
DB 59
(C 1974 ROYAL DOULTON

Back Stamp	U.S. $	Price Can. $	U.K. £	Aust. $
BK-5	300.00	360.00	175.00	375.00

DB60
SCHOOLMASTER BUNNYKINS™

Designer:	Graham Tongue
Modeller:	Warren Platt
Height:	4", 10.1 cm
Colour:	Black, green and white
Issued:	1987 - 1996

Back Stamp	U.S. $	Price Can. $	U.K. £	Aust. $
BK-5a	85.00	100.00	50.00	110.00

DB61
BROWNIE BUNNYKINS™

Designer:	Graham Tongue
Modeller:	Warren Platt
Height:	4", 10.1 cm
Colour:	Brown uniform, yellow neck-tie
Issued:	1987 - 1993

BROWNIE BUNNYKINS
DB 61
© 1987 ROYAL DOULTON

Back Stamp	U.S. $	Price Can. $	U.K. £	Aust. $
BK-5a	125.00	150.00	70.00	175.00

Note: Models with unpainted belts exist.

DB62
SANTA BUNNYKINS HAPPY CHRISTMAS™
Christmas Tree Ornament

Designer:	Harry Sales
Modeller:	David Lyttleton
Height:	3 ¾", 9.5 cm
Colour:	Red, white, brown, blue and yellow
Issued:	1987 in a limited edition of 1,551

SANTA BUNNYKINS
Happy Christmas
DB 62
© 1981 ROYAL DOULTON

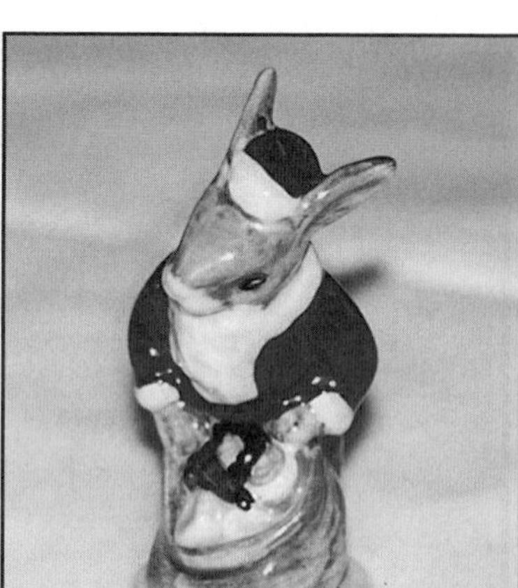

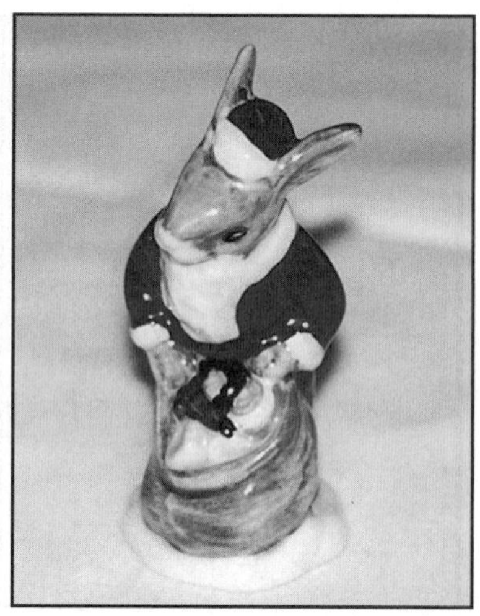

Back Stamp	U.S. $	Price Can. $	U.K. £	Aust. $
BK-5	775.00	950.00	450.00	1,000.00

Note: A colourway variation exists with a white jacket and trousers.

DB63
BEDTIME BUNNYKINS™
Second Variation

Designer:	Graham Tongue
Modeller:	David Lyttleton
Height:	3 ¼", 8.3 cm
Colour:	Red and white stripped pyjamas, white teddy bear
Issued:	1987 - 1987
Varieties:	DB55, DB79, DB103

BEDTIME BUNNYKINS
DB 63
© 1986 ROYAL DOULTON

Back Stamp	U.S. $	Price Can. $	U.K. £	Aust. $
BK-5a Special	275.00	325.00	160.00	350.00

DB64
POLICEMAN BUNNYKINS™

Designer:	Graham Tongue
Modeller:	Martyn Alcock
Height:	4 ¼", 10.8 cm
Colour:	Dark blue uniform
Issued:	1988 - 2000

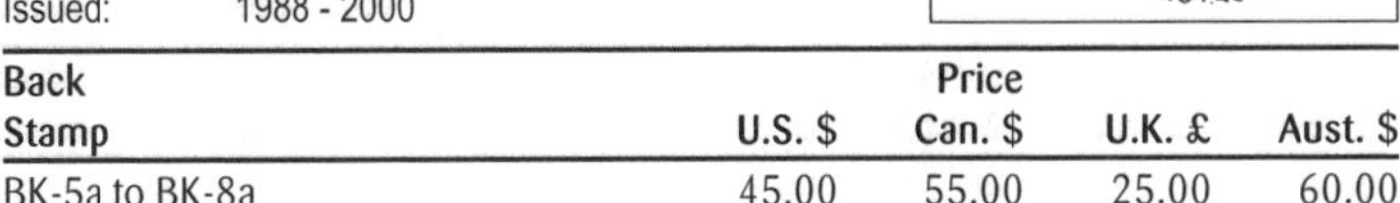

Back Stamp	U.S. $	Price Can. $	U.K. £	Aust. $
BK-5a to BK-8a	45.00	55.00	25.00	60.00

DB65
LOLLIPOPMAN BUNNYKINS™

Designer:	Graham Tongue
Modeller:	Martyn Alcock
Height:	3 ¾", 9.5 cm
Colour:	Yellow, white, black and red
Issued:	1988 - 1991

Back Stamp	U.S. $	Price Can. $	U.K. £	Aust. $
BK-5a	200.00	250.00	120.00	275.00

Note: Two colourway variations in the sign exist, one with a red rim and the other with a white rim.

DB66
SCHOOLBOY BUNNYKINS™

Designer:	Graham Tongue
Modeller:	Martyn Alcock
Height:	4", 10.1 cm
Colour:	Blue, white and grey
Issued:	1988 - 1991

Back Stamp	U.S. $	Price Can. $	U.K. £	Aust. $
BK-5a	250.00	300.00	140.00	325.00

DB67
FAMILY PHOTOGRAPH BUNNYKINS™
Second Variation

Designer:	Based on a design by Walter Hayward
Modeller:	Albert Hallam
Height:	4 ½", 11.9 cm
Colour:	Pink, black and white
Issued:	1988 - 1988
Varieties:	DB1; also called Father, Mother and Victoria Bunnykins, DB68
Series:	Special Events 1988

Back Stamp	U.S. $	Price Can. $	U.K. £	Aust. $
BK-5 Special	250.00	300.00	150.00	325.00

DB68
FATHER, MOTHER & VICTORIA BUNNYKINS™

Designer:	Based on design Family Photograph by Walter Hayward
Modeller:	Martyn Alcock
Height:	4 ½", 11.9 cm
Colour:	Blue, grey, maroon and yellow
Issued:	1988 - 1996
Varieties:	Also called Family Photograph Bunnykins, DB1, DB67

FATHER, MOTHER & VICTORIA BUNNYKINS
DB 68
© 1988 ROYAL DOULTON

Back Stamp	U.S. $	Price Can. $	U.K. £	Aust. $
BK-5	75.00	90.00	45.00	100.00

DB69
WILLIAM BUNNYKINS™

Designer:	Based on a design by Walter Hayward
Modeller:	Martyn Alcock
Height:	4", 10.1 cm
Colour:	Red and white
Issued:	1988 - 1993
Varieties:	Also called Tally Ho! Bunnykins, DB12, DB78

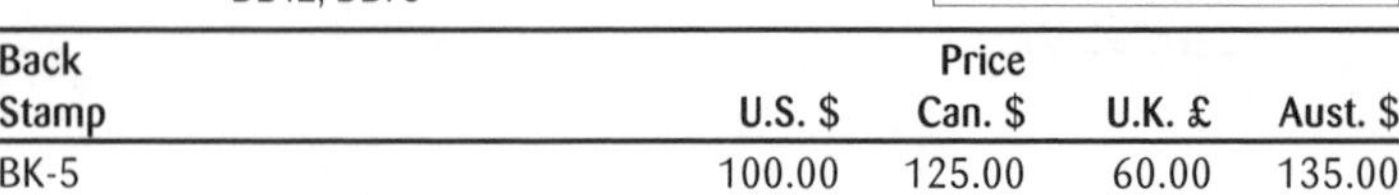

Back Stamp	U.S. $	Price Can. $	U.K. £	Aust. $
BK-5	100.00	125.00	60.00	135.00

DB70
SUSAN BUNNYKINS™

Designer:	Based on the design Busy Needles by Walter Hayward
Modeller:	Martyn Alcock
Height:	3 ¼", 8.3 cm
Colour:	White dress with blue design, yellow knitting
Issued:	1988 - 1993
Varieties:	Also called Busy Needles Bunnykins, DB10

Back Stamp	Price U.S. $	Can. $	U.K. £	Aust. $
BK-5a	120.00	150.00	70.00	150.00

DB71
POLLY BUNNYKINS™

Designer:	Graham Tongue
Modeller:	Martyn Alcock
Height:	3 ½", 8.9 cm
Colour:	Pink
Issued:	1988 - 1993

Back Stamp	Price U.S. $	Can. $	U.K. £	Aust. $
BK-5a	100.00	125.00	60.00	125.00

DB72
TOM BUNNYKINS™

Designer:	Graham Tongue
Modeller:	Martyn Alcock
Height:	3", 7.6 cm
Colour:	Browns, white and blue
Issued:	1988 - 1993

Back Stamp	Price U.S. $	Can. $	U.K. £	Aust. $
BK-5a	100.00	125.00	60.00	125.00

DB73
HARRY BUNNYKINS™

Designer:	Graham Tongue
Modeller:	Martyn Alcock
Height:	3", 7.9 cm
Colour:	Blue, brown, white and yellow
Issued:	1988 - 1993

Back Stamp	U.S. $	Price Can. $	U.K. £	Aust. $
BK-5a	85.00	100.00	50.00	110.00

DB74A
NURSE BUNNYKINS™
Style One, First Variation (Red Cross)

Designer:	Graham Tongue
Modeller:	Martyn Alcock
Height:	4 ¼", 10.8 cm
Colour:	Dark and light blue and white, red cross
Issued:	1989 - 1994
Varieties:	DB74B

Back Stamp	U.S. $	Price Can. $	U.K. £	Aust. $
BK-5a	200.00	250.00	120.00	275.00

DB74B
NURSE BUNNYKINS™
Style One, Second Variation (Green Cross)

Designer:	Graham Tongue
Modeller:	Martyn Alcock
Height:	4 ¼", 10.8 cm
Colour:	Dark and light blue and white, green cross
Issued:	1994 - 2000
Varieties:	DB74A

Back Stamp	U.S. $	Price Can. $	U.K. £	Aust. $
BK-5a to BK-8a	45.00	55.00	25.00	60.00

DB75
FIREMAN BUNNYKINS™
Style One, First Variation

Designer:	Graham Tongue
Modeller:	Martyn Alcock
Height:	4 ¼", 10.8 cm
Colour:	Dark blue and yellow
Issued:	1989 - 2001
Varieties:	DB183; Also called American Firefighter Bunnykins, DB268

FIREMAN BUNNYKINS
DB 75
© 1989 ROYAL DOULTON

Back Stamp	U.S. $	Price Can. $	U.K. £	Aust. $
BK-5 to BK-10	45.00	55.00	25.00	60.00

DB76
POSTMAN BUNNYKINS™
Style One

Designer:	Graham Tongue
Modeller:	Martyn Alcock
Height:	4 ½", 11.9 cm
Colour:	Dark blue and red
Issued:	1989 - 1993

POSTMAN BUNNYKINS
DB 76
© 1989 ROYAL DOULTON

Back Stamp	U.S. $	Price Can. $	U.K. £	Aust. $
BK-5	135.00	165.00	80.00	175.00

DB77
PAPERBOY BUNNYKINS™

Designer:	Graham Tongue
Modeller:	Martyn Alcock
Height:	4", 10.1 cm
Colour:	Green, yellow, red and white
Issued:	1989 - 1993

Back Stamp	U.S. $	Price Can. $	U.K. £	Aust. $
BK-5	125.00	150.00	70.00	160.00

DB78
TALLY HO! BUNNYKINS™
Second Variation

Designer:	Based on a design by Walter Hayward
Modeller:	Albert Hallam
Height:	4", 10.1 cm
Colour:	Light blue coat, yellow sweater
Issued:	1988 - 1988
Varieties:	DB12; also called William Bunnykins, DB69

BUNNYKINS®
"Tally Ho!"
DB78
© 1974 ROYAL DOULTON
SPECIAL COMMISSION
COLOURWAY

Back Stamp	U.S. $	Price Can. $	U.K. £	Aust. $
BK-5 Special	175.00	220.00	100.00	250.00

DB79
BEDTIME BUNNYKINS™
Third Variation

Designer:	Graham Tonge
Modeller:	David Lyttleton
Height:	3 ¼", 8.3 cm
Colour:	Light blue and white striped pyjamas, white teddy bear
Issued:	1988 - 1988
Varieties:	DB55, DB63, DB103

BEDTIME BUNNYKINS
DB 79
© 1986 ROYAL DOULTON
100/1988 - 1988
SPECIAL COMMISSION COLOURWAY

Back Stamp	U.S. $	Price Can. $	U.K. £	Aust. $
BK-5 Special	525.00	650.00	300.00	700.00

Note: This was a limited colourway commissioned by Belk's Department Stores.

DB80
DOLLIE BUNNYKINS PLAYTIME™
Second Variation

Designer:	Based on a design by Walter Hayward
Modeller:	Albert Hallam
Height:	4", 10.1 cm
Colour:	White and yellow
Issued:	1988 in a limited edition of 250
Varieties:	DB8

DOLLIE BUNNYKINS
"Playtime"
DB 80
© 1972 ROYAL DOULTON
SPECIAL COLOURWAY COMMISSION
FOR D H HOLMES

Back Stamp	Store	U.S. $	Price Can. $	U.K. £	Aust. $
BK-5 Special	Higbee	175.00	225.00	100.00	275.00
BK-5 Special	Holmes	175.00	225.00	100.00	275.00
BK-5 Special	Hornes	175.00	225.00	100.00	275.00
BK-5 Special	Strawbridge	175.00	225.00	100.00	275.00

DB81
BILLIE & BUNTIE BUNNYKINS SLEIGH RIDE™
Second Variation

Designer:	Based on a design by Walter Hayward
Modeller:	Albert Hallam
Height:	3 ½", 8.9 cm
Colour:	Green, yellow and red
Issued:	1989 - 1989
Varieties:	DB4
Series:	Special Events 1989

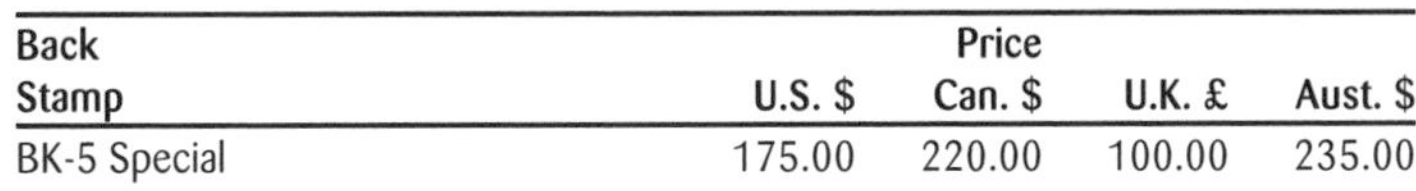

Back Stamp	U.S. $	Price Can. $	U.K. £	Aust. $
BK-5 Special	175.00	220.00	100.00	235.00

DB82
ICE CREAM BUNNYKINS™

Designer:	Graham Tongue
Modeller:	Warren Platt
Height:	4 ½", 11.9 cm
Colour:	White, blue and green
Issued:	1990 - 1993

Back Stamp	U.S. $	Price Can. $	U.K. £	Aust. $
BK-5	150.00	175.00	80.00	175.00

DB83
SUSAN BUNNYKINS AS QUEEN OF THE MAY™

Designer:	Graham Tongue
Modeller:	Martyn Alcock
Height:	4", 10.1 cm
Colour:	White dress with blue design, pink and brown chair
Issued:	1990 - 1992

Back Stamp	U.S. $	Price Can. $	U.K. £	Aust. $
BK-5	150.00	175.00	80.00	175.00

DB84
FISHERMAN BUNNYKINS™
Style One

Designer:	Graham Tongue
Modeller:	Warren Platt
Height:	4 ¼", 10.8 cm
Colour:	Maroon, yellow and grey
Issued:	1990 - 1993

MADE IN ENGLAND
ROYAL DOULTON
ENGLAND
FISHERMAN BUNNYKINS
DB 84
© 1990 ROYAL DOULTON

Back Stamp	U.S. $	Price Can. $	U.K. £	Aust. $
BK-5	150.00	175.00	80.00	200.00

DB85
COOK BUNNYKINS™

Designer:	Graham Tongue
Modeller:	Warren Platt
Height:	4 ¼", 10.8 cm
Colour:	White and green
Issued:	1990 - 1994

MADE IN ENGLAND
ROYAL DOULTON
ENGLAND
COOK BUNNYKINS
DB 85
© 1990 ROYAL DOULTON

Back Stamp	U.S. $	Price Can. $	U.K. £	Aust. $
BK-5	100.00	125.00	60.00	135.00

DB86
SOUSAPHONE BUNNYKINS™
Second Variation

Designer:	Harry Sales
Modeller:	David Lyttleton
Height:	3 ½", 8.9 cm
Colour:	Blue uniform and yellow sousaphone
Issued:	1990 in a limited edition of 250
Varieties:	DB23, DB105
Series:	Bunnykins Oompah Band

"SOUSAPHONE BUNNYKINS"
FROM THE OOMPAH BAND
DB 86
© 1990 ROYAL DOULTON

Back Stamp	U.S. $	Price Can. $	U.K. £	Aust. $
BK-5	425.00	500.00	250.00	550.00
DB86 to 90 (5pcs.)	2,125.00	2,500.00	1,250.00	2,750.00

DB87
TRUMPETER BUNNYKINS™
Second Variation

"TRUMPETER BUNNYKINS"
FROM THE OOMPAH BAND
DB 87
© 1990 ROYAL DOULTON

Designer:	Harry Sales
Modeller:	David Lyttleton
Height:	3 ¾", 9.5 cm
Colour:	Blue uniform and yellow trumpet
Issued:	1990 in a limited edition of 250
Varieties:	DB24, DB106
Series:	Bunnykins Oompah Band

Back Stamp	U.S. $	Price Can. $	U.K. £	Aust. $
BK-5	425.00	500.00	250.00	550.00

DB88
CYMBALS BUNNYKINS™
Second Variation

"CYMBAL BUNNYKINS"
FROM THE OOMPAH BAND
DB 88
© 1990 ROYAL DOULTON

Designer:	Harry Sales
Modeller:	David Lyttleton
Height:	3 ½", 8.9 cm
Colour:	Blue uniform and yellow cymbals
Issued:	1990 in a limited edition of 250
Varieties:	DB25, DB107
Series:	Bunnykins Oompah Band

Back Stamp	U.S. $	Price Can. $	U.K. £	Aust. $
BK-5	425.00	500.00	250.00	550.00

DB89
DRUMMER BUNNYKINS™
Style One, Third Variation

"DRUMMER BUNNYKINS"
FROM THE OOMPAH BAND
DB 89
SPECIAL COLOURWAY EDITION OF 250 SETS
EXCLUSIVE FOR UK FAIRS LTD.
© 1990 ROYAL DOULTON

Designer:	Harry Sales
Modeller:	David Lyttleton
Height:	3 ¾", 9.5 cm
Colour:	Blue trousers and sleeves, yellow vest, cream and red drum
Issued:	1990 in a limited edition of 250
Varieties:	DB26B, DB108
Series:	Bunnykins Oompah Band

Back Stamp	U.S. $	Price Can. $	U.K. £	Aust. $
BK-5 Special	425.00	500.00	250.00	550.00

ROYAL DOULTON
Collectors
Band

DRUM-MAJOR BUNNYKINS
FROM THE OOMPAH BAND
DB 90
© 1990 ROYAL DOULTON

DB90
DRUM-MAJOR BUNNYKINS™
Second Variation

Designer:	Harry Sales
Modeller:	David Lyttleton
Height:	3 ¾", 9.5 cm
Colour:	Blue and yellow
Issued:	1990 in a limited edition of 250
Varieties:	DB27, DB109
Series:	Bunnykins Oompah Band

Back Stamp	Price U.S. $	Can. $	U.K. £	Aust. $
BK-5	425.00	500.00	250.00	550.00

DB91
KING JOHN™
Second Variation

Designer:	Harry Sales
Modeller:	David Lyttleton
Height:	4", 10.1 cm
Colour:	Purple, yellow and white
Issued:	1990 in a limited edition of 250
Varieties:	DB45
Series:	Bunnykins Royal Family

Back Stamp	Price U.S. $	Can. $	U.K. £	Aust. $
BK-5 Special	450.00	550.00	250.00	600.00
Set DB91 - 95 (5 pcs.)	2,250.00	2,750.00	1,250.00	3,000.00

DB92
QUEEN SOPHIE™
Second Variation

Designer:	Harry Sales
Modeller:	David Lyttleton
Height:	4 ½", 11.9 cm
Colour:	Pink and purple
Issued:	1990 in a limited edition of 250
Varieties:	DB46
Series:	Bunnykins Royal Family

Back Stamp	Price U.S. $	Can. $	U.K. £	Aust. $
BK-5	450.00	550.00	250.00	600.00

DB93
PRINCESS BEATRICE™
Second Variation

Designer: Harry Sales
Modeller: David Lyttleton
Height: 3 ½", 8.9 cm
Colour: Yellow
Issued: 1990 in a limited edition of 250
Varieties: DB47
Series: Bunnykins Royal Family

Back Stamp	U.S. $	Price Can. $	U.K. £	Aust. $
BK-5a	450.00	550.00	250.00	600.00

DB94
PRINCE FREDERICK™
Second Variation

Designer: Harry Sales
Modeller: David Lyttleton
Height: 3 ½", 8.9 cm
Colour: Red, blue and yellow
Issued: 1990 in a limited edition of 250
Varieties: DB48
Series: Bunnykins Royal Family

Back Stamp	U.S. $	Price Can. $	U.K. £	Aust. $
BK-5a	450.00	550.00	250.00	600.00

DB95
HARRY THE HERALD™
Second Variation

Designer: Harry Sales
Modeller: David Lyttleton
Height: 3 ½", 8.9 cm
Colour: Blue, red, yellow and white
Issued: 1990 in a limited edition of 250
Varieties: DB49, DB115
Series: Bunnykins Royal Family

Back Stamp	U.S. $	Price Can. $	U.K. £	Aust. $
BK-5a	450.00	550.00	250.00	600.00

DB96
TOUCHDOWN BUNNYKINS™
Third Variation (Ohio State University)

Designer: Harry Sales
Modeller: David Lyttleton
Height: 3 ¼", 8.3 cm
Colour: Red, white and grey
Issued: 1990 in a limited edition of 200
Varieties: DB29A, DB29B, DB97, DB98, DB99, DB100

Back Stamp	Price U.S. $	Can. $	U.K. £	Aust. $
BK-5	575.00	700.00	325.00	800.00
Set DB96-100 (5 pcs.)	2,875.00	3,500.00	1,625.00	4,000.00

DB97
TOUCHDOWN BUNNYKINS™
Fourth Variation (University of Michigan)

Designer: Harry Sales
Modeller: David Lyttleton
Height: 3 ¼", 8.3 cm
Colour: Yellow, blue and white
Issued: 1990 in a limited edition of 200
Varieties: DB29A, DB29B, DB96, DB98, DB99, DB100

Back Stamp	Price U.S. $	Can. $	U.K. £	Aust. $
BK-5	575.00	700.00	325.00	800.00

DB98
TOUCHDOWN BUNNYKINS™
Fifth Variation (Cincinnati Bengals)

Designer: Harry Sales
Modeller: David Lyttleton
Height: 3 ½", 8.9 cm
Colour: Black, white and red
Issued: 1990 in a limited edition of 200
Varieties: DB29A, DB29B, DB96, DB97, DB99, DB100

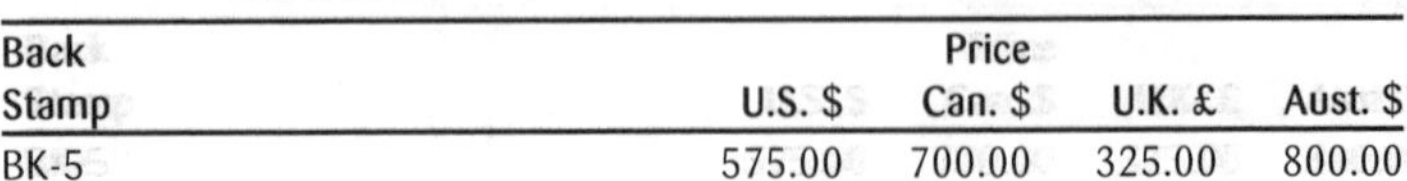

Back Stamp	Price U.S. $	Can. $	U.K. £	Aust. $
BK-5	575.00	700.00	325.00	800.00

DB99
TOUCHDOWN BUNNYKINS™
Sixth Variation (Notre Dame College)

Designer:	Harry Sales
Modeller:	David Lyttleton
Height:	3 ½", 8.9 cm
Colour:	Green, yellow and white
Issued:	1990 in a limited edition of 200
Varieties:	DB29A, DB29B, DB96, DB97, DB98, DB100

Back Stamp	U.S. $	Can. $	U.K. £	Aust. $
BK-5	575.00	700.00	325.00	800.00

DB100
TOUCHDOWN BUNNYKINS™
Seventh Variation (University of Indiana)

Designer:	Harry Sales
Modeller:	David Lyttleton
Height:	3 ½", 8.9 cm
Colour:	White and red
Issued:	1990 in a limited edition of 200
Varieties:	DB29A, DB29B, DB96, DB97, DB98, DB99

Back Stamp	U.S. $	Can. $	U.K. £	Aust. $
BK-5	575.00	700.00	325.00	800.00

DB101
BRIDE BUNNYKINS™

Designer:	Graham Tongue
Modeller:	Amanda Hughes-Lubeck
Height:	4", 10.1 cm
Colour:	Cream dress, grey, blue and white train
Issued:	1991 - 2001

Back Stamp	U.S. $	Can. $	U.K. £	Aust. $
BK-5	50.00	65.00	30.00	70.00

DB102
GROOM BUNNYKINS™

Designer:	Graham Tongue
Modeller:	Martyn Alcock
Height:	4 ½", 11.9 cm
Colour:	Grey and burgundy
Issued:	1991 - 2001

Back Stamp	U.S. $	Price Can. $	U.K. £	Aust. $
BK-5a	50.00	60.00	30.00	60.0

DB103
BEDTIME BUNNYKINS™
Fourth Variation

Designer:	Graham Tongue
Modeller:	David Lyttleton
Height:	3 ¼", 8.3 cm
Colour:	Yellow pyjamas, brown teddy bear
Issued:	1991 - 1991
Varieties:	DB55, DB63, DB79
Series:	Special Events Tour 1991

Back Stamp	Colour	U.S. $	Price Can. $	U.K. £	Aust. $
BK-5a Special	Pale yellow	200.00	250.00	120.00	275.00
BK-5a Special	Daffodil yellow	200.00	250.00	120.00	275.00

DB104
CAROL SINGER BUNNYKINS™

Designer:	Harry Sales
Modeller:	David Lyttleton
Height:	4", 10.1 cm
Colour:	Dark green, red, yellow and white
Issued:	1991 in a special edition of 1,000

Back Stamp	U.S. $	Price Can. $	U.K. £	Aust.
BK-5a, UK Backstamp - 700	275.00	325.00	160.00	350.0
BK-5a, USA Backstamp - 300	425.00	525.00	240.00	550.0

DB105
SOUSAPHONE BUNNYKINS™
Third Variation

Designer:	Harry Sales
Modeller:	David Lyttleton
Height:	4", 10.1 cm
Colour:	Dark green, red and yellow
Issued:	1991 in a special edition of 250
Varieties:	DB23, DB86
Series:	Bunnykins Oompah Band

Back Stamp	Price U.S. $	Can. $	U.K. £	Aust. $
BK-5	525.00	625.00	300.00	675.00
Set DB105 to 109 (5 pcs.)	2,975.00	3,600.00	1,700.00	3,900.00

DB106
TRUMPETER BUNNYKINS™
Third Variation

TRUMPETER BUNNYKINS
FROM THE OOMPAH BAND
DB 106
© 1991 ROYAL DOULTON

Designer:	Harry Sales
Modeller:	David Lyttleton
Height:	3 ¾", 9.5 cm
Colour:	Dark green, red and yellow
Issued:	1991 in a special edition of 250
Varieties:	DB24, DB87
Series:	Bunnykins Oompah Band

Back Stamp	Price U.S. $	Can. $	U.K. £	Aust. $
BK-5	525.00	625.00	300.00	675.00

DB107
CYMBALS BUNNYKINS™
Third Variation

Designer:	Harry Sales
Modeller:	David Lyttleton
Height:	4", 10.1 cm
Colour:	Dark green, red and yellow
Issued:	1991 in a special edition of 250
Varieties:	DB25, DB88
Series:	Bunnykins Oompah Band

Back Stamp	Price U.S. $	Can. $	U.K. £	Aust. $
BK-5	525.00	625.00	300.00	675.00

DB108
DRUMMER BUNNYKINS™
Style One, Fourth Variation

Designer:	Harry Sales
Modeller:	David Lyttleton
Height:	3 ½", 8.9 cm
Colour:	Dark green, red, yellow and white
Issued:	1991 in a special edition of 250
Varieties:	DB26B, DB89
Series:	Bunnykins Oompah Band

"DRUMMER BUNNYKINS"
FROM THE OOMPAH BAND
DB 108
SPECIAL COLOURWAY EDITION OF 250 SETS
EXCLUSIVE FOR UK FAIRS LTD.
© 1991 ROYAL DOULTON

Back Stamp	U.S. $	Price Can. $	U.K. £	Aust. $
BK-5 Special	525.00	625.00	300.00	675.00

DB109
DRUM-MAJOR BUNNYKINS™
Third Variation

Designer:	Harry Sales
Modeller:	David Lyttleton
Height:	3 ½", 8.9 cm
Colour:	Dark green, red and yellow
Issued:	1991 in a special edition of 250
Varieties:	DB27, DB90
Series:	Bunnykins Oompah Band

DRUM-MAJOR BUNNYKINS
FROM THE OOMPAH BAND
DB 109
© 1991 ROYAL DOULTON

Back Stamp	U.S. $	Price Can. $	U.K. £	Aust. $
BK-5	525.00	625.00	300.00	675.00

DB110 TO DB114 NOT ALLOCATED

DB115
HARRY THE HERALD™
Third Variation

Designer:	Harry Sales
Modeller:	David Lyttleton
Height:	3 ½", 8.9 cm
Colour:	Yellow and dark green
Issued:	1991 in a special edition of 300
Varieties:	DB49, DB95
Series:	Bunnykins Royal Family

Back Stamp	U.S. $	Price Can. $	U.K. £	Aust. $
BK-5a Special	875.00	1,100.00	500.00	1,200.00

DB116
GOALKEEPER BUNNYKINS™
First Variation

Designer:	Denise Andrews
Modeller:	Warren Platt
Height:	4 ½", 11.9 cm
Colour:	Green and black
Issued:	1991 in a special edition of 250
Varieties:	DB118, DB120, DB122
Series:	Footballers

GOALKEEPER BUNNYKINS
DB 116
© 1991 ROYAL DOULTON
EXCLUSIVELY PRODUCED FOR
U.K. INTERNATIONAL CERAMICS LTD.
SPECIAL EDITION OF 250 SETS

Back Stamp	U.S. $	Price Can. $	U.K. £	Aust. $
BK-5a Special	525.00	625.00	300.00	675.00

DB117
FOOTBALLER BUNNYKINS™
First Variation

Designer:	Denise Andrews
Modeller:	Warren Platt
Height:	4 ½", 11.9 cm
Colour:	Green and white
Issued:	1991 in a special edition of 250
Varieties:	DB119, DB121; also called Soccer Player, DB123
Series:	Footballers

FOOTBALLER BUNNYKINS
DB 117
© 1991 ROYAL DOULTON
EXCLUSIVELY PRODUCED FOR
U.K. INTERNATIONAL CERAMICS LTD.
SPECIAL EDITION OF 250 SETS

Back Stamp	U.S. $	Price Can. $	U.K. £	Aust. $
BK-5a Special	525.00	625.00	300.00	675.00

DB118
GOALKEEPER BUNNYKINS™
Second Variation

Designer:	Denise Andrews
Modeller:	Warren Platt
Height:	4 ½", 11.9 cm
Colour:	Red and black
Issued:	1991 in a special edition of 250
Varieties:	DB116, DB120, DB122
Series:	Footballers

GOALKEEPER BUNNYKINS
DB 118
© 1991 ROYAL DOULTON
EXCLUSIVELY PRODUCED FOR
U.K. INTERNATIONAL CERAMICS LTD
SPECIAL EDITION OF 250 SETS

Back Stamp	U.S. $	Price Can. $	U.K. £	Aust. $
BK-5a Special	525.00	625.00	300.00	675.00

DB119
FOOTBALLER BUNNYKINS™
Second Variation

Designer:	Denise Andrews
Modeller:	Warren Platt
Height:	4 ½", 11.9 cm
Colour:	Red
Issued:	1991 in a special edition of 250
Varieties:	DB117, DB121; also called Soccer Player, DB123
Series:	Footballers

FOOTBALLER BUNNYKINS
DB 119
© 1991 ROYAL DOULTON
EXCLUSIVELY PRODUCED FOR
U.K. INTERNATIONAL CERAMICS LTD
SPECIAL EDITION OF 250 SETS

Back Stamp	U.S. $	Price Can. $	U.K. £	Aust. $
BK-5a Special	525.00	625.00	300.00	675.00

DB120
GOALKEEPER BUNNYKINS™
Third Variation

Designer:	Denise Andrews
Modeller:	Warren Platt
Height:	4 ½", 11.9 cm
Colour:	Yellow and black
Issued:	1991 in a special edition of 250
Varieties:	DB116, DB118, DB122
Series:	Footballers

Back Stamp	U.S. $	Price Can. $	U.K. £	Aust. $
BK-5a Special	525.00	625.00	300.00	675.00

DB121
FOOTBALLER BUNNYKINS™
Third Variation

Designer:	Denise Andrews
Modeller:	Warren Platt
Height:	4 ½", 11.9 cm
Colour:	White and blue
Issued:	1991 in a special edition of 250
Varieties:	DB117, DB119; also called Soccer Player, DB123
Series:	Footballers

Back Stamp	U.S. $	Price Can. $	U.K. £	Aust. $
BK-5a Special	525.00	625.00	300.00	675.00

DB122
GOALKEEPER BUNNYKINS™
Fourth Variation

Designer: Denise Andrews
Modeller: Warren Platt
Height: 4 ½", 11.9 cm
Colour: Yellow and black
Issued: 1991 in a special edition of 250
Varieties: DB116, DB118, DB120
Series: Footballers

GOALKEEPER BUNNYKINS
DB 122
© 1991 ROYAL DOULTON
EXCLUSIVELY PRODUCED FOR
U.K. INTERNATIONAL CERAMICS LTD
SPECIAL EDITION OF 250 SETS

Back Stamp	U.S. $	Price Can. $	U.K. £	Aust. $
BK-5a Special	525.00	625.00	300.00	675.00

DB123
SOCCER PLAYER BUNNYKINS™

Designer: Denise Andrews
Modeller: Warren Platt
Height: 4 ½", 11.9 cm
Colour: Dark blue and white
Issued: 1991 in a special edition of 250
Varieties: Also called Footballer Bunnykins, DB117, DB119, DB121
Series: Footballers

SOCCER PLAYER BUNNYKINS
DB 123
© 1991 ROYAL DOULTON
EXCLUSIVELY PRODUCED FOR
U.K. INTERNATIONAL CERAMICS LTD.
SPECIAL EDITION OF 250 SETS

Back Stamp	U.S. $	Price Can. $	U.K. £	Aust. $
BK-5a Special	525.00	625.00	300.00	675.00

DB124
ROCK AND ROLL BUNNYKINS™

Designer: Harry Sales
Modeller: David Lyttleton
Height: 4 ½", 11.9 cm
Colour: White, blue and red
Issued: 1991 in a limited edition of 1,000
Varieties: Also called Mr. Bunnybeat Strumming, DB16

ROCK AND ROLL BUNNYKINS
PRODUCED EXCLUSIVELY
FOR ROYAL DOULTON USA
ROCK AND ROLL HALL OF FAME EDITION
LIMITED TO 1000
THIS IS No 251
© 1991 ROYAL DOULTON

Back Stamp	U.S. $	Price Can. $	U.K. £	Aust. $
BK-5a Special	425.00	500.00	250.00	550.00

MILKMAN BUNNYKINS
DB 125
© 1991 ROYAL DOULTON
EXCLUSIVELY PRODUCED FOR
U.K. INTERNATIONAL CERAMICS LTD
SPECIAL EDITION OF 1,000 PIECES

DB125
MILKMAN BUNNYKINS™

Designer: Graham Tongue
Modeller: Amanda Hughes-Lubeck
Height: 4 ½", 11.9 cm
Colour: White, green and grey
Issued: 1992 in a special edition of 1,000

Back Stamp	U.S. $	Price Can. $	U.K. £	Aust. $
BK-5a Special	475.00	575.00	275.00	600.00

DB126
MAGICIAN BUNNYKINS™
First Variation

Designer: Graham Tongue
Modeller: Warren Platt
Height: 4 ½", 11.9 cm
Colour: Black suit, yellow shirt, yellow table cloth with deeper yellow border
Issued: 1992 in a limited edition of 1,000
Varieties: DB159

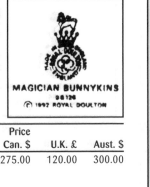

MAGICIAN BUNNYKINS
DB126
© 1992 ROYAL DOULTON

Back Stamp	U.S. $	Price Can. $	U.K. £	Aust. $
BK-5	225.00	275.00	120.00	300.00

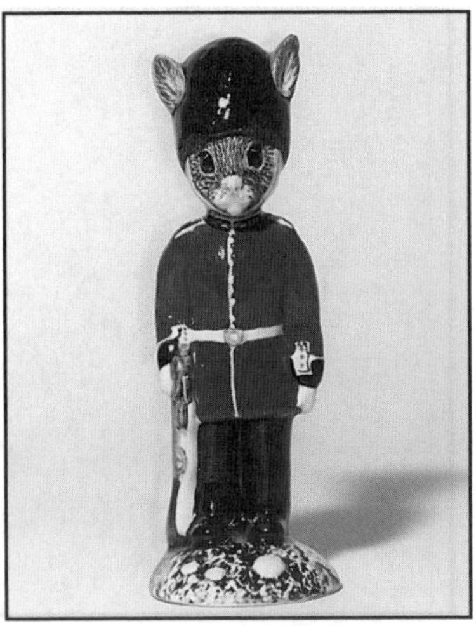

DB127
GUARDSMAN BUNNYKINS™

Designer: Denise Andrews
Modeller: Warren Platt
Height: 4 ½", 11.9 cm
Colour: Scarlet jacket, black trousers and bearskin hat
Issued: 1992 in a special edition of 1,000

GUARDSMAN BUNNYKINS
DB 127
PRODUCED EXCLUSIVELY
FOR U.K.I. CERAMICS LTD.
IN A SPECIAL EDITION OF 1,000
© 1992 ROYAL DOULTON

Back Stamp	U.S. $	Price Can. $	U.K. £	Aust. $
BK-5a Special	450.00	550.00	250.00	600.00

DB128
CLOWN BUNNYKINS™
First Variation

Designer: Denise Andrews
Modeller: Warren Platt
Height: 4 ¼", 10.8 cm
Colour: White costume with black stars and pompons, red square on trousers and red ruff at neck
Issued: 1992 in a special edition of 750
Varieties: DB129

CLOWN BUNNYKINS
DB 128
PRODUCED EXCLUSIVELY
FOR U.K.I. CERAMICS LTD
IN A SPECIAL EDITION OF 750
© 1992 ROYAL DOULTON

Back Stamp	U.S. $	Price Can. $	U.K. £	Aust. $
BK-5a Special	525.00	625.00	300.00	675.00

DB129
CLOWN BUNNYKINS™
Second Variation

Designer: Denise Andrews
Modeller: Warren Platt
Height: 4 ¼", 10.8 cm
Colour: White costume with red stars and black pompons, black square on trousers, black ruff around neck
Issued: 1992 in a special edition of 250
Varieties: DB128

CLOWN BUNNYKINS
DB 129
PRODUCED EXCLUSIVELY
FOR U.K.I. CERAMICS LTD
IN A SPECIAL EDITION OF 250
FOR THE LONDON DOULTON FAIR
© 1992 ROYAL DOULTON

Back Stamp	U.S. $	Price Can. $	U.K. £	Aust. $
BK-5a Special	1,000.00	1,250.00	575.00	1,350.00

DB130
SWEETHEART BUNNYKINS™
First Variation

Designer: Graham Tongue
Modeller: Warren Platt
Height: 3 ¾", 9.5 cm
Colour: Yellow sweater, blue trousers, red heart
Issued: 1992 - 1997
Varieties: DB174

SWEETHEART BUNNYKINS
DB130
© 1992 ROYAL DOULTON

Back Stamp	U.S. $	Price Can. $	U.K. £	Aust. $
BK-5	70.00	85.00	40.00	85.00

DB131
MASTER POTTER BUNNYKINS™

Designer:	Graham Tongue
Modeller:	Warren Platt
Height:	3 ¾", 9.5 cm
Colour:	Blue white, green and brown
Issued:	1992 - 1993
Series:	ICC Members Exclusive

Back Stamp	U.S. $	Price Can. $	U.K. £	Aust. $
BK-5 Special	220.00	275.00	125.00	300.00

DB132
HALLOWEEN BUNNYKINS™

Designer:	Graham Tongue
Modeller:	Martyn Alcock
Height:	3 ¼", 8.3 cm
Colour:	Orange and yellow pumpkin
Issued:	1993 - 1997

Back Stamp	U.S. $	Price Can. $	U.K. £	Aust. $
BK-5a	60.00	75.00	35.00	80.00

DB133
AUSSIE SURFER BUNNYKINS™

Designer:	Graham Tongue
Modeller:	Martyn Alcock
Height:	4", 10.1 cm
Colour:	Gold and green outfit, white surf board, blue base
Issued:	1994 - 1997

Back Stamp	U.S. $	Price Can. $	U.K. £	Aust. $
BK-5 Special	120.00	150.00	70.00	150.00

DB134
JOHN BULL BUNNYKINS™

Designer:	Denise Andrews
Modeller:	Amanda Hughes-Lubeck
Height:	4 ½", 11.9 cm
Colour:	Grey jacket and hat, yellow necktie and pantaloons, Union Jack waistcoat, black and brown boots
Issued:	1993 in a special edition of 1,000

JOHN BULL BUNNYKINS
DB 134
PRODUCED EXCLUSIVELY
FOR U.K.I CERAMICS LTD
N A SPECIAL EDITION OF 1,000
© 1993 ROYAL DOULTON

Back Stamp	U.S. $	Price Can. $	U.K. £	Aust. $
BK-5a Special	400.00	475.00	225.00	500.00

DB135
MOUNTIE BUNNYKINS™

Designer:	Graham Tongue
Modeller:	Warren Platt
Height:	4", 10.1 cm
Colour:	Red jacket, dark blue trousers and brown hat
Issued:	1993 in a special edition of 750
Varieties:	Also called Sergeant Mountie Bunnykins, DB136

Back Stamp	U.S. $	Price Can. $	U.K. £	Aust. $
Bk-5a Special	575.00	700.00	325.00	775.00

DB136
SERGEANT MOUNTIE BUNNYKINS™

Designer:	Graham Tongue
Modeller:	Warren Platt
Height:	4", 10.1 cm
Colour:	Red jacket, yellow stripes on sleeve, dark blue trousers, brown hat
Issued:	1993 in a special edition of 250
Varieties:	Also called Mountie Bunnykins, DB135

Back Stamp	U.S. $	Price Can. $	U.K. £	Aust. $
Bk-5a Special	1,000.00	1,200.00	575.00	1,350.00

DB137
60th ANNIVERSARY BUNNYKINS™

60th ANNIVERSARY BUNNYKINS
DB 137
© 1993 ROYAL DOULTON

Designer:	Graham Tongue
Modeller:	Martyn Alcock
Height:	4 ½", 11.9 cm
Colour:	Lemon-yellow dress, white collar and cake
Issued:	1994 - 1994

Back Stamp	U.S. $	Price Can. $	U.K. £	Aust. $
BK-5a	70.00	85.00	40.00	85.00

DB138 TO DB141 NOT ALLOCATED.

DB142
CHEERLEADER BUNNYKINS™
First Variation

CHEERLEADER BUNNYKINS
DB 142
PRODUCED EXCLUSIVELY
FOR U K I CERAMICS LTD
IN A SPECIAL EDITION OF 1,000
© 1994 ROYAL DOULTON
1994

Designer:	Denise Andrews
Modeller:	Warren Platt
Height:	4 ½", 11.9 cm
Colour:	Red, white, yellow and black
Issued:	1994 in a special edition of 1,000
Varieties:	DB143

Back Stamp	U.S. $	Price Can. $	U.K. £	Aust. $
BK-5a Special	250.00	300.00	150.00	350.00

DB143
CHEERLEADER BUNNYKINS™
Second Variation

CHEERLEADER BUNNYKINS
DB 143
PRODUCED EXCLUSIVELY
FOR U.K.I CERAMICS LTD
DOULTON FAIRS
SPECIAL EDITION OF 1,000
© 1994 ROYAL DOULTON
1994

Designer:	Denise Andrews
Modeller:	Warren Platt
Height:	4 ½", 11.9 cm
Colour:	Yellow, white and black
Issued:	1994 in a special edition of 1,000
Varieties:	DB142

Back Stamp	U.S. $	Price Can. $	U.K. £	Aust. $
BK-5a Special	250.00	300.00	150.00	350.00

BATSMAN BUNNYKINS
DB 144
PRODUCED EXCLUSIVELY
FOR U.K.I CERAMICS LTD
IN A SPECIAL EDITION OF 1,000
© 1994 ROYAL DOULTON
1994

DB144
BATSMAN BUNNYKINS™

Designer:	Denise Andrews
Modeller:	Amanda Hughes-Lubeck
Height:	4", 10.1 cm
Colour:	White, beige and black
Issued:	1994 in a special edition of 1,000
Series:	Cricket

Back Stamp	U.S. $	Price Can. $	U.K. £	Aust. $
BK-5a Special	350.00	425.00	200.00	475.00

DB145
BOWLER BUNNYKINS™

Designer:	Denise Andrews
Modeller:	Warren Platt
Height:	4", 10.1 cm
Colour:	White, beige and black
Issued:	1994 in a special edition of 1,000
Series:	Cricket

MADE IN ENGLAND
ROYAL DOULTON
ENGLAND
BOWLER BUNNYKINS
DB 145
PRODUCED EXCLUSIVELY
FOR U.K.I CERAMICS LTD
IN A SPECIAL EDITION OF 1,000
© 1994 ROYAL DOULTON
1994

Back Stamp	U.S. $	Price Can. $	U.K. £	Aust. $
BK-5a Special	350.00	425.00	200.00	475.00

DB146
CHRISTMAS SURPRISE BUNNYKINS™

Designer:	Graham Tongue
Modeller:	Warren Platt
Height:	3 ½", 8.9 cm
Colour:	Cream and red
Issued:	1994 - 2000
Varieties:	Also called Santa's Helper Bunnykins, DB192

Back Stamp	U.S. $	Price Can. $	U.K. £	Aust. $
BK-5 to BK-9	45.00	55.00	25.00	65.00

Note: A colourway variation exists see DB192 for details.

DB147
RAINY DAY BUNNYKINS™

Designer:	Graham Tongue
Modeller:	Warren Platt
Height:	4", 10.1 cm
Colour:	Yellow coat and hat, blue trousers, black boots
Issued:	1994 - 1997

RAINY DAY
BUNNYKINS
DB 147
© 1994 ROYAL DOULTON

Back Stamp	U.S. $	Price Can. $	U.K. £	Aust. $
BK-5a	45.00	55.00	25.00	60.00

DB148
BATHTIME BUNNYKINS™

Designer:	Graham Tongue
Modeller:	Warren Platt
Height:	4", 10.1 cm
Colour:	White bathrobe with grey trim, yellow towel and duck
Issued:	1994 - 1997

BATHTIME BUNNYKINS
DB 148
© 1994 ROYAL DOULTON

Back Stamp	U.S. $	Price Can. $	U.K. £	Aust. $
BK-5a	45.00	55.00	25.00	60.00

DB149
EASTER GREETINGS BUNNYKINS™

Designer:	Graham Tongue
Modeller:	Warren Platt
Height:	4 ½", 11.9 cm
Colour:	Yellow, white and green
Issued:	1995 - 1999
Varieties:	Also called Easter Surprise Bunnykins, DB225

Back Stamp	U.S. $	Price Can. $	U.K. £	Aust. $
BK-5 to BK-7	45.00	55.00	25.00	60.00

DB150
WICKETKEEPER BUNNYKINS™

Designer:	Denise Andrews
Modeller:	Amanda Hughes-Lubeck
Height:	3 ½", 8.9 cm
Colour:	White, beige and black
Issued:	1995 in a special edition of 1,000
Series:	Cricket

Back Stamp	U.S. $	Price Can. $	U.K. £	Aust. $
BK-5a Special	350.00	425.00	200.00	475.00

DB151
PARTNERS IN COLLECTING™

Designer:	Walter Hayward
Modeller:	Albert Hallam
Height:	3", 7.6 cm
Colour:	Red, white and blue
Issued:	1995 - 1995
Varieties:	Also called Storytime Bunnykins, DB9, DB59
Series:	ICC Members Exclusive (15th Anniversary of ICC)

Back Stamp	U.S. $	Price Can. $	U.K. £	Aust. $
BK-5 Special	100.00	125.00	60.00	150.00

DB152
BOY SKATER BUNNYKINS™
First Variation

Designer:	Graham Tongue
Modeller:	Martyn Alcock
Height:	4 ¼", 10.8 cm
Colour:	Green coat, brown pants, yellow hat, green boots and black skates
Issued:	1995 - 1998
Varieties:	DB187

Back Stamp	U.S. $	Price Can. $	U.K. £	Aust. $
BK-5 to BK-6	50.00	60.00	30.00	65.00

DB153
GIRL SKATER BUNNYKINS™

Designer:	Graham Tongue
Modeller:	Martyn Alcock
Height:	3 ½", 8.9 cm
Colour:	Green coat with white trim, pink dress, blue boots, yellow skates
Issued:	1995 - 1997

Back Stamp	U.S. $	Price Can. $	U.K. £	Aust. $
BK-5	50.00	60.00	30.00	65.00

DB154
FATHER BUNNYKINS™
Style One

Designer:	Martyn Alcock
Modeller:	Martyn Alcock
Height:	4", 10.1 cm
Colour:	Red and white striped blazer, creamy yellow trousers
Issued:	1996 - 1996
Series:	1. Bunnykins of the Year 2. Holiday Outing

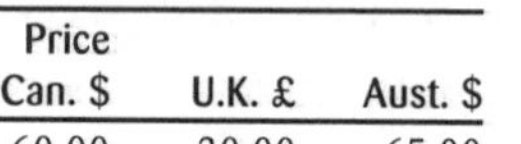

Back Stamp	U.S. $	Price Can. $	U.K. £	Aust. $
BK-5 Special	50.00	60.00	30.00	65.00

DB155
MOTHER'S DAY BUNNYKINS™

Designer:	Graham Tongue
Modeller:	Shane Ridge
Height:	3 ½", 8.9 cm
Colour:	Blue dungarees, orange carrot
Issued:	1995 - 2000

Back Stamp	U.S. $	Price Can. $	U.K. £	Aust. $
BK-5 to BK-9	50.00	60.00	30.00	65.00

DB156
GARDENER BUNNYKINS™

Designer: Warren Platt
Modeller: Warren Platt
Height: 4 ¼", 10.8 cm
Colour: Brown jacket, white shirt, grey trousers, light green wheelbarrow
Issued: 1996 - 1998

Back Stamp	U.S. $	Price Can. $	U.K. £	Aust. $
BK-5 to BK-6	50.00	60.00	30.00	65.00

DB157
GOODNIGHT BUNNYKINS™

Designer: Graham Tongue
Modeller: Shane Ridge
Height: 3 ¾", 9.5 cm
Colour: Pink nightgown, reddish brown teddy, blue and white base
Issued: 1995 - 1999

MADE IN ENGLAND
ROYAL DOULTON
GOODNIGHT BUNNYKINS
DB 157
© 1995 ROYAL DOULTON

Back Stamp	U.S. $	Price Can. $	U.K. £	Aust. $
BK-5 to BK-7	50.00	60.00	30.00	65.00

DB158
NEW BABY BUNNYKINS™

Designer: Graham Tongue
Modeller: Graham Tongue
Height: 3 ¾", 9.5 cm
Colour: Blue dress with white collar, pale blue cradle, pink pillow, yellow blanket
Issued: 1995 - 1999

MADE IN ENGLAND
ROYAL DOULTON
NEW BABY BUNNYKINS
DB 158
© 1995 ROYAL DOULTON

Back Stamp	U.S. $	Price Can. $	U.K. £	Aust. $
BK-5 to BK-7	50.00	60.00	30.00	65.00

DB159
MAGICIAN BUNNYKINS™
Second Variation

MADE IN ENGLAND ROYAL DOULTON ENGLAND
MAGICIAN BUNNYKINS
DB 159
© 1992 ROYAL DOULTON
NEW COLOURWAY 1998
SPECIAL EDITION OF 1,500 FOR SINCLAIRS

Designer:	Graham Tongue
Modeller:	Warren Platt
Height:	4 ½", 11.9 cm
Colour:	Black suit, yellow shirt, yellow table cloth with red border
Issued:	1998 in a special edition of 1,500
Varieties:	DB126

Back Stamp	U.S. $	Price Can. $	U.K. £	Aust. $
BK-5 Special	250.00	325.00	150.00	350.00

DB160
OUT FOR A DUCK BUNNYKINS™

MADE IN ENGLAND ROYAL DOULTON ENGLAND
OUT FOR A DUCK BUNNYKINS
DB 160
PRODUCED EXCLUSIVELY
FOR U.K.I. CERAMICS LTD.
IN A SPECIAL EDITION OF 1,250
© 1995 ROYAL DOULTON

Designer:	Denise Andrews
Modeller:	Amanda Hughes-Lubeck
Height:	4", 10.1 cm
Colour:	White, beige and green
Issued:	1995 in a special edition of 1,250
Series:	Cricket

Back Stamp	U.S. $	Price Can. $	U.K. £	Aust. $
BK-5 Special	350.00	425.00	200.00	475.00

DB161
JESTER BUNNYKINS™

Designer:	Denise Andrews
Modeller:	Shane Ridge
Height:	4 ½", 11.9 cm
Colour:	Red, green and yellow
Issued:	1995 in a special edition of 1,500

Back Stamp	U.S. $	Price Can. $	U.K. £	Aust. $
BK-5 Special	350.00	425.00	200.00	475.00

DB162
TRICK OR TREAT BUNNYKINS™

Designer: Denise Andrews
Modeller: Amanda Hughes-Lubeck
Height: 4 ½", 11.9 cm
Colour: Red dress, black hat, cloak and shoes, white moons and stars
Issued: 1995 in a special edition of 1,500

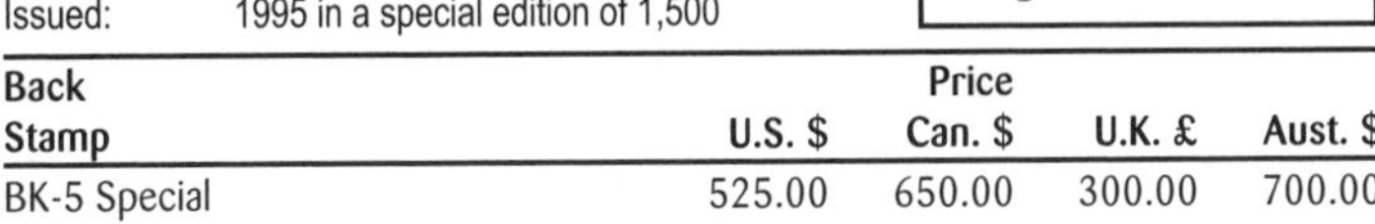

Back Stamp	U.S. $	Price Can. $	U.K. £	Aust. $
BK-5 Special	525.00	650.00	300.00	700.00

Note: A prototype colourway of Trick or Treat Bunnykins exists.

DB163
BEEFEATER BUNNYKINS™

Designer: Denise Andrews
Modeller: Amanda Hughes-Lubeck
Height: 4 ½", 11.9 cm
Colour: Red, gold, black and white livery, black hat with red, blue and white band
Issued: 1996 in a special edition of 1,500

Back Stamp	U.S. $	Price Can. $	U.K. £	Aust. $
BK-5a Special	300.00	375.00	175.00	400.00

DB164
JUGGLER BUNNYKINS™

Designer: Denise Andrews
Modeller: Warren Platt
Height: 4 ½", 11.9 cm
Colour: Blue suit, black pompons, white ruff
Issued: 1996 in a special edition of 1,500

Back Stamp	U.S. $	Price Can. $	U.K. £	Aust. $
BK-5 Special	250.00	300.00	150.00	325.00

DB165
RINGMASTER BUNNYKINS™

Designer:	Denise Andrews
Modeller:	Warren Platt
Height:	4 ½", 11.9 cm
Colour:	Black hat and trousers, red jacket, white waistcoat and shirt, black bowtie
Issued:	1996 in a special edition of 1,500

RINGMASTER BUNNYKINS
DB 165
PRODUCED EXCLUSIVELY
FOR U.K.I. CERAMICS LTD.
IN A SPECIAL EDITION OF 1,500
© 1996 ROYAL DOULTON

Back Stamp	U.S. $	Price Can. $	U.K. £	Aust. $
BK-5 Special	225.00	275.00	125.00	300.00

Note: A prototype colourway exists of Ringmaster Bunnykins.

DB166
SAILOR BUNNYKINS™
Style One

Designer:	Graham Tongue
Modeller:	Shane Ridge
Height:	2 ½", 6.4 cm
Colour:	White and blue
Issued:	1997 - 1997
Series:	1. Bunnykins of the Year 2. Holiday Outing

SAILOR BUNNYKINS
DB 166
BUNNYKINS OF THE YEAR 1997
© 1996 ROYAL DOULTON

Back Stamp	U.S. $	Price Can. $	U.K. £	Aust. $
BK-5a Special	50.00	60.00	30.00	65.00

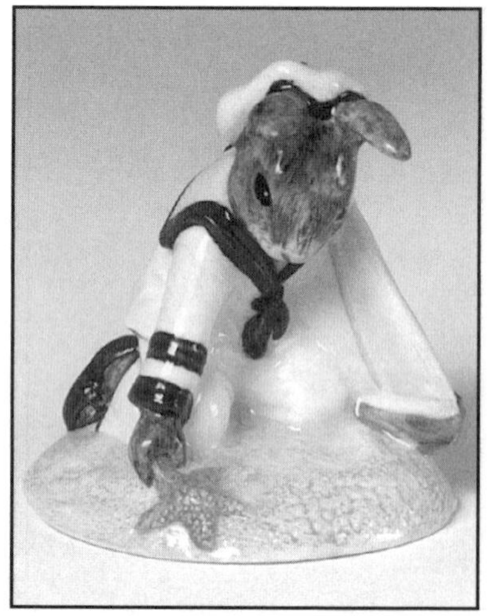

DB167
MOTHER AND BABY BUNNYKINS™
Style One

Designer:	Shane Ridge
Modeller:	Shane Ridge
Height:	4 ½", 11.9 cm
Colour:	Light pink dress, red shoes, yellow blanket
Issued:	1997 - 2001

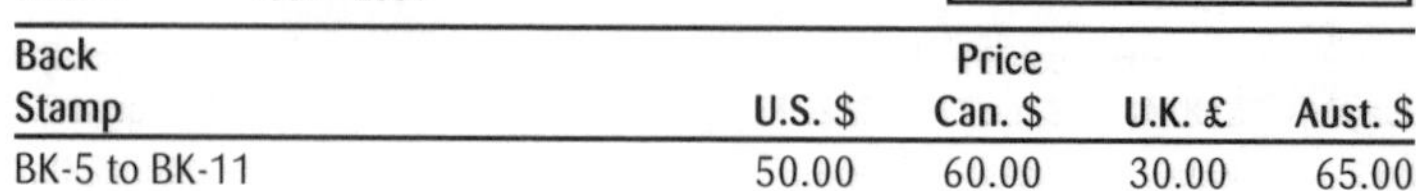

Back Stamp	U.S. $	Price Can. $	U.K. £	Aust. $
BK-5 to BK-11	50.00	60.00	30.00	65.00

DB168
WIZARD BUNNYKINS™

Designer: Denise Andrews
Modeller: Shane Ridge
Height: 5", 12.7 cm
Colour: Purple robe and cap
Issued: 1997 in a special edition of 2,000

Back Stamp	U.S. $	Price Can. $	U.K. £	Aust. $
BK-5 Special	350.00	425.00	200.00	450.00

DB169
JOCKEY BUNNYKINS™

Designer: Denise Andrews
Modeller: Martyn Alcock
Height: 4 ½", 11.9 cm
Colour: Yellow and green silks, white pants, black and brown boots
Issued: 1997 in a special edition of 2,000

Back Stamp	U.S. $	Price Can. $	U.K. £	Aust. $
BK-5a Special	225.00	275.00	125.00	300.00

DB170
FISHERMAN BUNNYKINS™
Style Two

Designer: Graham Tongue
Modeller: Shane Ridge
Height: 4", 10.1 cm
Colour: Blue hat and trousers, light yellow sweater, black wellingtons
Issued: 1997 - 2000

Back Stamp	U.S. $	Price Can. $	U.K. £	Aust. $
BK-5 to BK-9	50.00	60.00	30.00	65.00

DB171
JOKER BUNNYKINS™

MADE IN ENGLAND ROYAL DOULTON ENGLAND
JOKER BUNNYKINS
DB 171
PRODUCED EXCLUSIVELY
FOR U.K.I. CERAMICS LTD.
IN A SPECIAL EDITION OF 2,500
© 1997 ROYAL DOULTON
1109

Designer:	Denise Andrews
Modeller:	Martyn Alcock
Height:	5", 12.7 cm
Colour:	Yellow jacket, red and white striped trousers, black hat, blue bowtie and bucket
Issued:	1997 in a special edition of 2,500

Back Stamp	U.S. $	Price Can. $	U.K. £	Aust. $
BK-5 Special	125.00	150.00	70.00	170.00

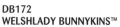

Note: Models exist with different coloured trousers.

DB172
WELSHLADY BUNNYKINS™

MADE IN ENGLAND ROYAL DOULTON ENGLAND
WELSHLADY BUNNYKINS
DB 172
PRODUCED EXCLUSIVELY
FOR U.K.I. CERAMICS LTD.
IN A SPECIAL EDITION OF 2,500
© 1997 ROYAL DOULTON
1930

Designer:	Denise Andrews
Modeller:	Warren Platt
Height:	5", 12.7 cm
Colour:	Light pink and yellow dress, black hat, maroon shawl
Issued:	1997 in a special edition of 2,500

Back Stamp	U.S. $	Price Can. $	U.K. £	Aust. $
BK-5 Special	225.00	275.00	125.00	300.00

Note: A colourway model exists with a white shawl and is 4" high.

DB173
BRIDESMAID BUNNYKINS™

Designer:	Graham Tongue
Modeller:	Amanda Hughes-Lubeck
Height:	3 ¾", 9.5 cm
Colour:	Yellow dress, darker yellow flowers
Issued:	1997 - 1999

Back Stamp	U.S. $	Price Can. $	U.K. £	Aust. $
BK-5a to BK-7a	50.00	60.00	30.00	65.00

DB174
SWEETHEART BUNNYKINS™
Second Variation - I Love Bunnykins

Designer: Graham Tongue
Modeller: Warren Platt
Height: 3 ¾", 9.5 cm
Colour: White and green; pink heart
Issued: 1997 in a special edition of 2,500
Varieties: DB130

Back Stamp	U.S. $	Price Can. $	U.K. £	Aust. $
BK-5 Special	150.00	175.00	80.00	185.00

DB175
UNCLE SAM BUNNYKINS™
Second Variation

Designer: Harry Sales
Modeller: David Lyttleton
Height: 4 ½", 11.9 cm
Colour: Red jacket, yellow waistcoat, blue and white striped trousers, red, white and blue hat, platinum bowtie
Issued: 1997 in a special edition of 1,500
Varieties: DB50
Series: American Heritage Collection

Back Stamp	U.S. $	Price Can. $	U.K. £	Aust. $
BK-5a Special	225.00	275.00	125.00	300.00

DB176
BALLERINA BUNNYKINS™

Designer: Graham Tongue
Modeller: Graham Tongue
Height: 3 ½", 8.9 cm
Colour: Pink dress, yellow footstool
Issued: 1998 - 2001

Back Stamp	U.S. $	Price Can. $	U.K. £	Aust. $
BK-6a to BK-9a	45.00	55.00	25.00	60.00

DB177
SEASIDE BUNNYKINS™

Designer:	Martyn Alcock
Modeller:	Martyn Alcock
Height:	3", 7.6 cm
Colour:	Blue bathing costume, white and blue bathing cap, yellow sandy base
Issued:	1998 - 1998
Series:	1. Bunnykins of the Year 2. Holiday Outing

Back Stamp	U.S. $	Price Can. $	U.K. £	Aust. $
BK-6 Special	70.00	85.00	40.00	85.00

DB178
IRISHMAN BUNNYKINS™

Designer:	Denise Andrews
Modeller:	Martyn Alcock
Height:	5", 12.7 cm
Colour:	Green waistcoat with shamrocks, white shirt, tan hat and trousers, white socks and black shoes
Issued:	1998 in a special edition of 2,500

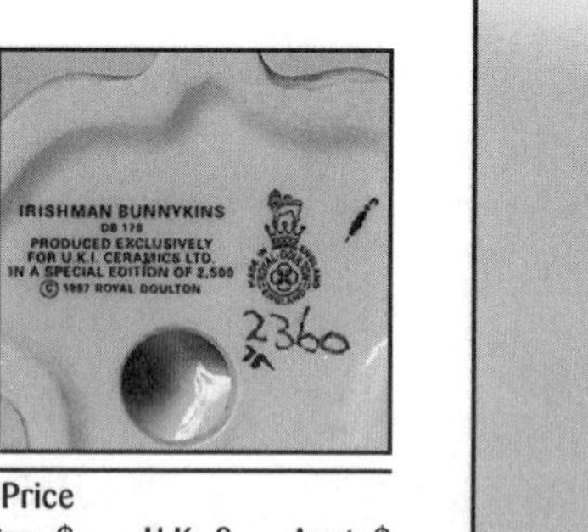

Back Stamp	U.S. $	Price Can. $	U.K. £	Aust. $
BK-6a Special	175.00	225.00	100.00	250.00

DB179
CAVALIER BUNNYKINS™

Designer:	Graham Tongue
Modeller:	Graham Tongue
Height:	4 ½", 11.9 cm
Colour:	Red tunic, white collar, black trousers and hat, yellow cape, light brown boots
Issued:	1998 in a special edition of 2,500

Back Stamp	U.S. $	Price Can. $	U.K. £	Aust. $
BK-6a Special	225.00	275.00	125.00	300.00

DB180
SCOTSMAN BUNNYKINS™

Designer:	Denise Andrews
Modeller:	Graham Tongue
Height:	5", 12.7 cm
Colour:	Dark blue jacket and hat, red-yellow kilt, white shirt, sporran and socks, black shoes
Issued:	1998 in a special edition of 2,500

Back Stamp	U.S. $	Price Can. $	U.K. £	Aust. $
BK-6a Special	140.00	175.00	80.00	200.00

DB181
DOCTOR BUNNYKINS™
Style One

Designer:	Martyn Alcock
Modeller:	Martyn Alcock
Height:	4 ¼", 10.8 cm
Colour:	White lab coat and shirt, dark blue trousers, black shoes, white and blue striped tie
Issued:	1998 - 2000

Back Stamp	U.S. $	Price Can. $	U.K. £	Aust. $
BK-6	55.00	65.00	30.00	70.00

DB182
BANJO PLAYER BUNNYKINS™

Designer:	Kimberley Curtis
Modeller:	Shane Ridge
Height:	5", 12.7 cm
Colour:	White and red striped blazer, black trousers, yellow straw hat
Issued:	1999 in a special edition of 2,500
Series:	Jazz Band Collection

Back Stamp	U.S. $	Price Can. $	U.K. £	Aust. $
BK-6a Special	140.00	175.00	80.00	200.00

DB183
FIREMAN BUNNYKINS™
Style One, Second Variation

Designer:	Graham Tongue
Modeller:	Martyn Alcock
Height:	4 ¼", 10.8 cm
Colour:	Red jacket and helmet, black trousers, yellow boots
Issued:	1998 in a special edition of 3,500
Varieties:	DB75; Also called American Firefighter Bunnykins, DB268

Back Stamp	U.S. $	Price Can. $	U.K. £	Aust. $
BK-6a Special	100.00	125.00	60.00	135.00

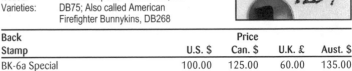

DB184
CLARINET PLAYER BUNNYKINS™

CLARINET PLAYER BUNNYKINS
FROM THE JAZZ BAND COLLECTION
DB 184
PRODUCED EXCLUSIVELY FOR U.K.I. CERAMICS LTD
IN A WORLDWIDE SPECIAL EDITION OF 2,500
© 1998 ROYAL DOULTON
2016

Designer:	Kimberley Curtis
Modeller:	Shane Ridge
Height:	5", 12.7 cm
Colour:	Blue and white striped jacket, grey trousers, yellow straw hat
Issued:	1999 in a special edition of 2,500
Series:	Jazz Band Collection

Back Stamp	U.S. $	Price Can. $	U.K. £	Aust. $
BK-6a Special	140.00	175.00	80.00	200.00

DB185
DOUBLE BASS PLAYER BUNNYKINS™

DOUBLE BASS PLAYER BUNNYKINS
FROM THE JAZZ BAND COLLECTION
DB 185
PRODUCED EXCLUSIVELY FOR U.K.I. CERAMICS LTD
IN A WORLDWIDE SPECIAL EDITION OF 2,500
© 1998 ROYAL DOULTON

Designer:	Kimberley Curtis
Modeller:	Shane Ridge
Height:	5", 12.7 cm
Colour:	Green and yellow striped jacket, green trousers, yellow straw hat
Issued:	1999 in a special edition of 2,500
Series:	Jazz Band Collection

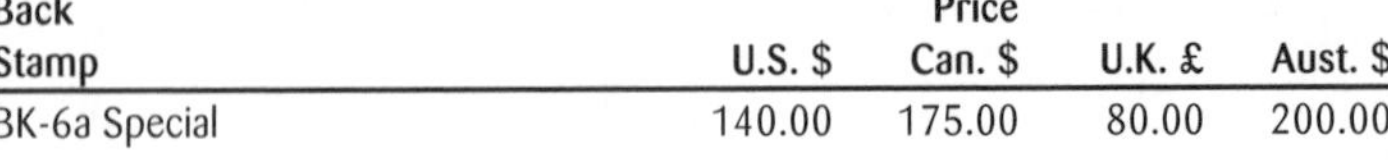

Back Stamp	U.S. $	Price Can. $	U.K. £	Aust. $
BK-6a Special	140.00	175.00	80.00	200.00

DB186
SAXOPHONE PLAYER BUNNYKINS™

Designer: Kimberley Curtis
Modeller: Shane Ridge
Height: 5", 12.7 cm
Colour: Navy and white striped shirt, navy vest, black trousers, yellow straw hat
Issued: 1999 in a special edition of 2,500
Series: Jazz Band Collection

Back Stamp	Price U.S. $	Can. $	U.K. £	Aust. $
BK-6 Special	140.00	175.00	80.00	200.00

DB187
BOY SKATER BUNNYKINS™
Second Variation

Designer: Graham Tongue
Modeller: Martyn Alcock
Height: 4 ¼", 10.8 cm
Colour: Blue jacket and cap, white trousers, red boots and skates
Issued: 1998 in a special edition of 2,500
Varieties: DB152

Back Stamp	Price U.S. $	Can. $	U.K. £	Aust. $
BK-6a Special	140.00	175.00	80.00	200.00

DB188
JUDGE BUNNYKINS™

Designer: Caroline Dadd
Modeller: Shane Ridge
Height: 4 ¼", 10.8 cm
Colour: Red and white
Issued: 1999 - 1999
Series: ICC Membership Gift

Back Stamp	Price U.S. $	Can. $	U.K. £	Aust. $
BK-6 Special	50.00	60.00	30.00	65.00

Note: White unfinished models exist on which the final red glaze was not applied.

DB189
MOTHER BUNNYKINS™

Designer: Caroline Dadd
Modeller: Martyn Alcock
Height: 4", 10.1 cm
Colour: Blue, white and red
Issued: 1999 - 1999
Series: 1. Bunnykins of the Year
2. Holiday Outing

Back Stamp	U.S. $	Price Can. $	U.K. £	Aust. $
BK-6 Special	45.00	55.00	25.00	55.00

DB190
TOURIST BUNNYKINS™

Designer: Caroline Dadd
Modeller: Martyn Alcock
Height: 5", 12.7 cm
Colour: Blue, yellow, ICC on hat
Issued: 1999 in a limited time offer.
Series: 1. Holiday Outing
2. ICC Members Exclusive

Back Stamp	U.S. $	Price Can. $	U.K. £	Aust. $
BK-7 Special	85.00	100.00	50.00	100.00

DB191
PIPER BUNNYKINS™

Designer: Martyn Alcock
Modeller: Martyn Alcock
Height: 4 ¼", 10.8 cm
Colour: Green, brown and black
Issued: 1999 in a special edition of 3,000

Back Stamp	U.S. $	Price Can. $	U.K. £	Aust. $
BK-6a Special	140.00	175.00	80.00	185.00

DB192
SANTA'S HELPER BUNNYKINS™

Designer:	Graham Tongue
Modeller:	Warren Platt
Height:	3 ½", 8.9 cm
Colour:	Brown, green, red and yellow
Issued:	1999 in a special edition of 2,500
Varieties:	Also called Christmas Surprise Bunnykins, DB146

Back Stamp	Price U.S. $	Can. $	U.K. £	Aust. $
BK-7a Special	100.00	125.00	60.00	135.00

Note: A colourway variation exists with a white box, suite and hat.

DB193
DETECTIVE BUNNYKINS™

Designer:	Kimberley Curtis
Modeller:	Warren Platt
Height:	4 ¾", 12.1 cm
Colour:	Brown, green, white and tan
Issued:	1999 in a special edition of 2,500

Back Stamp	Price U.S. $	Can. $	U.K. £	Aust. $
BK-7 Special	140.00	175.00	80.00	185.00

DB194
MERRY CHRISTMAS BUNNYKINS TABLEAU™

Designer:	Caroline Dadd
Modeller:	Shane Ridge
Height:	7 ¼" x 5 ½", 18.4 x 14.0 cm
Colour:	Brown, green, red, white and black
Issued:	1999 in a limited edition of 2,000
Series:	Tableau

Back Stamp	Price U.S. $	Can. $	U.K. £	Aust. $
BK-7 Special	350.00	425.00	200.00	450.00

DB195
SYDNEY BUNNYKINS™

Designer:	Dalglish, Bryant, Bartholomeucz
Modeller:	Amanda Hughes-Lubeck
Height:	5", 12.7 cm
Colour:	Blue shirt, white trousers, tan hat, black boots
Issued:	1999 in a special numbered edition of 2,500
Series:	Australian Heritage

Back Stamp	Price U.S. $	Can. $	U.K. £	Aust. $
BK-7a Special	140.00	175.00	80.00	185.00

DB196
ANGEL BUNNYKINS™

Designer:	Caroline Dadd
Modeller:	Martyn Alcock
Height:	4", 10.1 cm
Colour:	Yellow and white
Issued:	1999 - 2001

Back Stamp	Price U.S. $	Can. $	U.K. £	Aust. $
BK-7 to BK-9	45.00	55.00	25.00	60.00

DB197
MYSTIC BUNNYKINS™

Designer:	Martyn Alcock
Modeller:	Martyn Alcock
Height:	4 ¾", 12.1 cm
Colour:	Gold, green and purple robes and cap
Issued:	July to December 1999

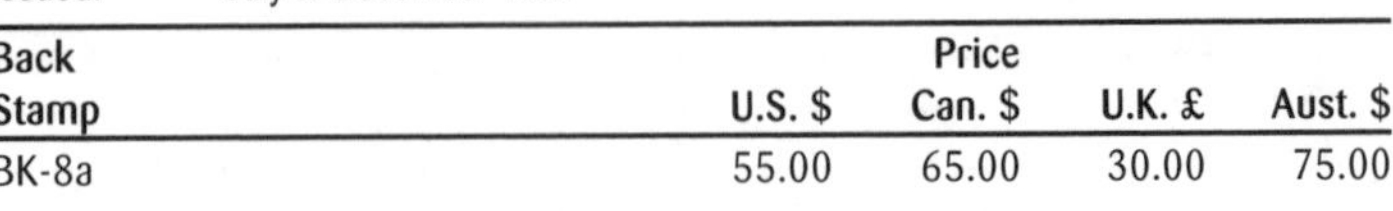

Back Stamp	Price U.S. $	Can. $	U.K. £	Aust. $
BK-8a	55.00	65.00	30.00	75.00

Note: This backstamp incorporates the Top Hat cypher of 1999 and the Millenium stamp.

DB198
STATUE OF LIBERTY BUNNYKINS™

Designer: Caroline Dadd
Modeller: Amanda Hughes-Lubeck
Height: 5", 12.7 cm
Colour: Red, white and blue
Issued: 1999 in a special edition of 3,000
Series: American Heritage

Back Stamp	U.S. $	Price Can. $	U.K. £	Aust. $
BK-7a Special	140.00	175.00	80.00	185.00

DB199
AIRMAN BUNNYKINS™

Designer: Caroline Dadd
Modeller: Shane Ridge
Height: 4 ¼", 10.8 cm
Colour: Maroon, yellow, blue and tan
Issued: 1999 in a numbered limited edition of 5,000

Back Stamp	U.S. $	Price Can. $	U.K. £	Aust. $
BK-7 Special	70.00	85.00	40.00	95.00

DB200
HAPPY MILLENNIUM BUNNYKINS™ TABLEAU

Backstamp not available at press time

Designer: Caroline Dadd
Modeller: Shane Ridge
Height: Unknown
Colour: Pink, yellow, blue, grey and red
Issued: 2000

Back Stamp	U.S. $	Price Can. $	U.K. £	Aust. $
BK- Not known		See below		

Note: Only two produced. One sold at the Bunnykins Millennium Exhibition Auction for £9,800.00, $15,000.00 U.S., with the proceeds going to charity. The other is held in the Royal Doulton Archives.

DB201
COWBOY BUNNYKINS™

Designer:	Kimberley Curtis
Modeller:	Martyn Alcock
Height:	4 ½", 11.9 cm
Colour:	Brown, red and cream
Issued:	1999 in a special edition of 2,500

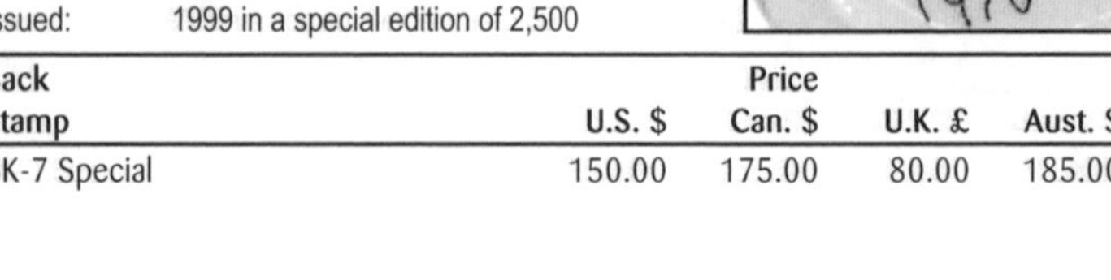

Back Stamp	U.S. $	Price Can. $	U.K. £	Aust. $
BK-7 Special	150.00	175.00	80.00	185.00

DB202
INDIAN BUNNYKINS™

Designer:	Kimberley Curtis
Modeller:	Martyn Alcock
Height:	4 ½", 11.9 cm
Colour:	Brown, cream, red, white and blue
Issued:	1999 in a special edition of 2,500

Back Stamp	U.S. $	Price Can. $	U.K. £	Aust. $
BK-7a Special	150.00	175.00	80.00	185.00

DB203
BUSINESSMAN BUNNYKINS™

Designer:	Caroline Dadd
Modeller:	Martyn Alcock
Height:	4 ¾", 12.1 cm
Colour:	Grey suit, black umbrella and bowler hat
Issued:	1999 in a numbered limited edition of 5,000

Back Stamp	U.S. $	Price Can. $	U.K. £	Aust. $
BK-7 Special	70.00	85.00	40.00	95.00

DB204
MORRIS DANCER BUNNYKINS™

Designer:	Caroline Dadd
Modeller:	Shane Ridge
Height:	4 ½", 11.9 cm
Colour:	Cream, black, red and green
Issued:	2000 - 2000
Series:	1. Dancers of the World 2. Special Events

Back Stamp	Price U.S. $	Can. $	U.K. £	Aust. $
BK-9a Special	70.00	85.00	40.00	95.00

DB205
RUNNER BUNNYKINS™

Designer:	Romanda Groom
Modeller:	Shane Ridge
Height:	4", 10.1 cm
Colour:	White, black, red and yellow
Issued:	1999 in a limited edition of 2,500
Series:	Bunnykins Games

Back Stamp	Price U.S. $	Can. $	U.K. £	Aust. $
BK-7 Special	90.00	110.00	50.00	120.00
DB205 - 209; 5 pce set	450.00	550.00	250.00	600.00

Note: The Bunnykins Games set was issued with a wooden display stand and certificate.

DB206
SWIMMER BUNNYKINS™

Designer:	Romanda Groom
Modeller:	Shane Ridge
Height:	3", 7.6 cm
Colour:	Green, yellow, blue and white
Issued:	1999 in a limited edition of 2,500
Series:	Bunnykins Games

Back Stamp	Price U.S. $	Can. $	U.K. £	Aust. $
BK-7a Special	90.00	110.00	50.00	120.00

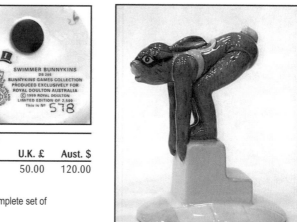

Note: There is only one individually numbered certificate for the complete set of Bunnykins Games.

DB207
GYMNAST BUNNYKINS™

Designer: Romanda Groom
Modeller: Shane Ridge
Height: 4", 10.1 cm
Colour: Yellow and red
Issued: 1999 in a limited edition of 2,500
Series: Bunnykins Games

Back Stamp	U.S. $	Price Can. $	U.K. £	Aust. $
BK-7 Special	90.00	110.00	50.00	120.00

DB208
BASKETBALL BUNNYKINS™
Style One

Designer: Romanda Groom
Modeller: Shane Ridge
Height: 5", 12.7 cm
Colour: Red, blue, white and brown
Issued: 1999 in a limited edition of 2,500
Series: Bunnykins Games

Back Stamp	U.S. $	Price Can. $	U.K. £	Aust. $
BK-7a Special	90.00	110.00	50.00	120.00

DB209
SOCCER BUNNYKINS™

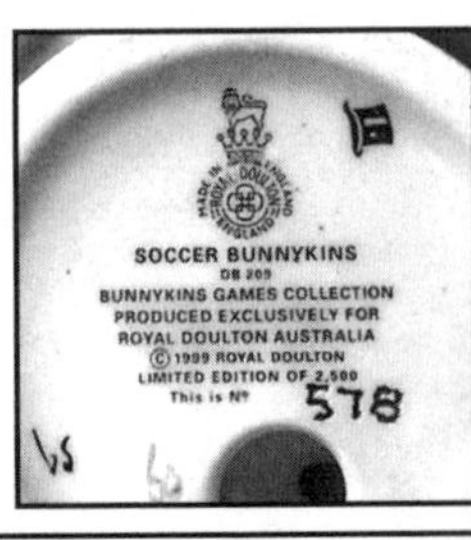

Designer: Romanda Groom
Modeller: Shane Ridge
Height: 4", 10.1 cm
Colour: Blue shirt, white shorts, white and black ball
Issued: 1999 in a limited edition of 2,500
Series: Bunnykins Games

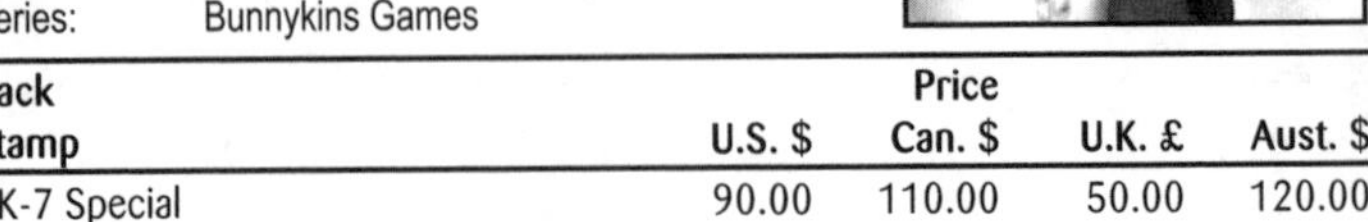

Back Stamp	U.S. $	Price Can. $	U.K. £	Aust. $
BK-7 Special	90.00	110.00	50.00	120.00

DB210
TRUMPET PLAYER BUNNYKINS™

Designer:	Kimberley Curtis
Modeller:	Shane Ridge
Height:	5", 12.7 cm
Colour:	Light blue and white striped jacket, black trousers, yellow straw hat
Issued:	2000 in a limited edition of 2,500
Series:	Jazz Band Collection

Back Stamp	U.S. $	Price Can. $	U.K. £	Aust. $
BK-8a to BK-9a Special	150.00	175.00	80.00	200.00

DB211
MINSTREL BUNNYKINS™

Designer:	Kimberley Curtis
Modeller:	Martyn Alcock
Height:	4 ½", 11.9 cm
Colour:	Red and yellow robes, green cap
Issued:	1999 in a numbered limited edition of 2,500

Back Stamp	U.S. $	Price Can. $	U.K. £	Aust. $
BK-7 Special	160.00	200.00	90.00	225.00

DB212
PILGRIM BUNNYKINS™

Designer:	Caroline Dadd
Modeller:	Amanda Hughes-Lubeck
Height:	4 ½", 11.9 cm
Colour:	Dark green, brown, white, black and pale blue
Issued:	1999 in a special numbered edition of 2,500
Series:	American Heritage

Back Stamp	U.S. $	Price Can. $	U.K. £	Aust. $
BK-7 Special	175.00	225.00	100.00	250.00

DB213
SUNDIAL BUNNYKINS™

Designer:	Martyn Alcock
Modeller:	Martyn Alcock
Height:	4 ½", 11.9 cm
Colour:	Pale blue, white and salmon
Issued:	2000 - 2000
Series:	1. Bunnykins of the Year 2. Time

Back Stamp	U.S. $	Price Can. $	U.K. £	Aust. $
BK-7 Special to BK-9 Special	50.00	60.00	30.00	65.00

DB214
LAWYER BUNNYKINS™

Designer:	Martyn Alcock
Modeller:	Martyn Alcock
Height:	4", 10.1 cm
Colour:	Black, grey and white
Issued:	2000 - 2000
Series:	ICC Membership Gift

Back Stamp	U.S. $	Price Can. $	U.K. £	Aust. $
BK-7 Special to BK-9 Special	50.00	60.00	30.00	65.00

DB215
SIGHTSEER BUNNYKINS™

Designer:	Caroline Dadd
Modeller:	Martyn Alcock
Height:	4 ½", 11.9 cm
Colour:	Pink dress, straw hat, brown shoulder bag
Issued:	From January to April, 2000
Series:	ICC Members Exclusive

Back Stamp	U.S. $	Price Can. $	U.K. £	Aust. $
BK-9 Special	70.00	85.00	40.00	85.00

DB216A
ENGLAND ATHLETE BUNNYKINS SYDNEY 2000™
First Variation (Union Jack)

Changed early in production to DB216B.

Designer:	Kimberley Curtis
Modeller:	Shane Ridge
Height:	5 ½", 14.0 cm
Colour:	White, blue and red
Issued:	2000 (quantity unknown)
Varieties:	DB216B

Back Stamp	Price U.S. $	Can. $	U.K. £	Aust. $
BK-9a Special	1,000.00	1,250.00	600.00	1,350.00

DB216B
ENGLAND ATHLETE BUNNYKINS SYDNEY 2000™
Second Variation (Sydney Flag)

Designer:	Kimberley Curtis
Modeller:	Shane Ridge
Height:	5 ½", 14.0 cm
Colour:	White, blue, red and cream
Issued:	2000 in a numbered limited edition of 2,500
Varieties:	DB216A

Back Stamp	Price U.S. $	Can. $	U.K. £	Aust. $
BK-9a Special	140.00	175.00	80.00	200.00

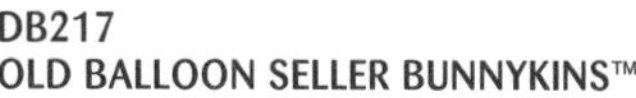

DB217
OLD BALLOON SELLER BUNNYKINS™

Designer:	From a design by Leslie Harradine
Modeller:	Amanda Hughes-Lubeck
Height:	4", 10.1 cm
Colour:	Dark green shawl and skirt, white apron, multicoloured balloons
Issued:	2000 in a special numbered edition of 2,000

Back Stamp	Price U.S. $	Can. $	U.K. £	Aust. $
BK-7a	200.00	250.00	120.00	275.00

DB218
FORTUNE TELLER BUNNYKINS™

Designer:	Warren Platt
Modeller:	Warren Platt
Height:	4 ½", 11.9 cm
Colour:	Pink, yellow and dark green
Issued:	April to September 2000

Back Stamp	U.S. $	Price Can. $	U.K. £	Aust. $
Bk-8a	50.00	60.00	30.00	65.00

DB219
BRITANNIA BUNNYKINS™

Designer:	Kimberley Curtis
Modeller:	Amanda Hughes-Lubeck
Height:	4 ¼", 10.8 cm
Colour:	White, yellow, red and blue
Issued:	2000 in a numbered limited edition of 2,500

Back Stamp	U.S. $	Price Can. $	U.K. £	Aust. $
BK-9 Special	125.00	150.00	70.00	175.00

DB220
LITTLE BO PEEP BUNNYKINS™

Designer:	Martyn Alcock
Modeller:	Martyn Alcock
Height:	4 ¼", 10.8 cm
Colour:	Yellow, red, pale blue and brown
Issued:	2000 - 2003
Series:	Nursery Rhyme Collection

Back Stamp	U.S. $	Price Can. $	U.K. £	Aust. $
BK-9a to BK-15a	60.00	75.00	35.00	80.00

DB221
LITTLE JACK HORNER BUNNYKINS™

Designer:	Martyn Alcock
Modeller:	Martyn Alcock
Height:	4 ¼", 10.8 cm
Colour:	Maroon suit and hat, black shoes, brown barrel
Issued:	2000 - 2003
Series:	Nursery Rhyme Collection

Back Stamp	U.S. $	Price Can. $	U.K. £	Aust. $
BK-9a to BK-14a	55.00	65.00	30.00	70.00

DB222
JACK AND JILL BUNNYKINS™

Designer:	Martyn Alcock
Modeller:	Martyn Alcock
Height:	4 ¼", 10.8 cm
Colour:	Jill: Yellow dress, white apron Jack: Cream shirt, light brown trousers, blue neckerchief
Issued:	2000 - 2003
Series:	Nursery Rhyme Collection

Back Stamp	U.S. $	Price Can. $	U.K. £	Aust. $
BK-9a to BK-14a	85.00	100.00	50.00	110.00

DB223
CHOIR SINGER BUNNYKINS™

Designer:	Martyn Alcock
Modeller:	Martyn Alcock
Height:	4", 10.5 cm
Colour:	White, red and black
Issued:	2001 - 2001
Series:	ICC Members Exclusive

Back Stamp	U.S. $	Price Can. $	U.K. £	Aust. $
BK-10a Special	55.00	65.00	30.00	70.00

DB224
FEDERATION BUNNYKINS™

Designer:	Brian Dalglish and Bill Bryant
Modeller:	Shane Ridge
Height:	5", 12.7 cm
Colour:	Blue, red and white
Issued:	2000 in a special edition of 2,500
Series:	Australian Heritage

Back Stamp	U.S. $	Price Can. $	U.K. £	Aust. $
BK-9a Special	160.00	200.00	90.00	225.00

DB225
EASTER SURPRISE BUNNYKINS™

Designer:	Graham Tongue
Modeller:	Warren Platt
Height:	4 ½", 11.9 cm
Colour:	Purple, pink and yellow
Issued:	2000 in a special edition of 2,500
Varieties:	Also called Easter Greetings Bunnykins, DB149

Back Stamp	U.S. $	Price Can. $	U.K. £	Aust. $
BK-9a Special	90.00	110.00	50.00	120.00

DB226
MOTHER AND BABY BUNNYKINS™
Style Two (Large Size)

Designer:	Amanda Hughes-Lubeck
Modeller:	Amanda Hughes-Lubeck
Height:	6 ¼", 15.9 cm
Colour:	Blue dress, white apron and collar, yellow blanket
Issued:	2000 in a limited edition of 2,000
Series:	The Bunnykins Family

Back Stamp	U.S. $	Price Can. $	U.K. £	Aust. $
BK-11 Special	70.00	85.00	40.00	95.00

Note: A colourway variation exists with a dark blue dress, pink and maroon apron, and dark yellow baby's shawl.

BUNNYKINS

DB198 – Statue of Liberty Bunnykins

DB199 – Airman Bunnykins

DB200 - Happy Millennium Bunnykins Tableau

DB201 - Cowboy Bunnykins

DB202 – Indian Bunnykins

DB203 – Businessman Bunnykins

DB204 – Morris Dancer Bunnykins

DB205 – Runner Bunnykins

DB206 – Swimmer Bunnykins

DB207 – Gymnast Bunnykins

DB208 – Basketball Bunnykins
Style One

BUNNYKINS

DB209 – Soccer Bunnykins

DB210 – Trumpet Player Bunnykins

DB211 – Minstrel Bunnykins

DB212 – Pilgrim Bunnykins

DB213 – Sundial Bunnykins

DB214 – Lawyer Bunnykins

DB215 – Sightseer Bunnykins

DB216A – England Athlete Bunnykins Sydney 2000, *First Variation*

DB216B – England Athlete Bunnykins Sydney 2000, *Second Variation*

DB217 – Old Balloon Seller Bunnykins

DB218 – Fortune Teller Bunnykins

DB219 – Britannia Bunnykins

DB220 – Little Bo Peep Bunnykins

DB221 – Little Jack Horner Bunnykins

DB222 – Jack and Jill Bunnykins

DB223 – Choir Singer Bunnykins

DB224 – Federation Bunnykins

DB225 – Easter Surprise Bunnykins

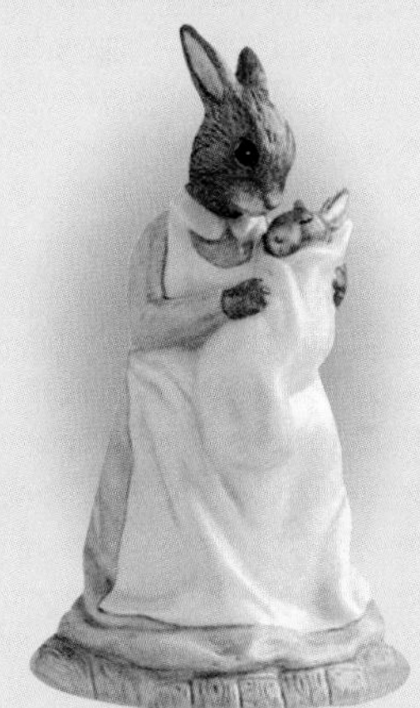
DB226 – Mother and Baby Bunnykins, *Style Two (Large Size)*

DB227 – Father Bunnykins *Style Two (Large Size)*

DB228 – Sandcastle Money Box

DB229 – Sands of Time Bunnykins

DB230 – Little Red Riding Hood Bunnykins

DB231 – Cinderella Bunnykins

DB233 – Shopper Bunnykins

DB234 – Mr. Punch Bunnykins

DB235 – Judy Bunnykins

DB236 – Waltzing Matilda Bunnykins

DB237 – Father Christmas Bunnykins

DB238 – On Line Bunnykins

DB239 – Little Boy Blue Bunnykins

DB240 – Little Miss Muffet Bunnykins

DB241 – Bath Night Bunnykins

Note: DB232 not issued.

DB242 Tyrolean Dancer Bunnykins

DB243 Little John Bunnykins
First Variation

DB244 – Robin Hood Bunnykins
First Variation

DB245 – Maid Marion Bunnykins
First Variation

DB246 – Friar Tuck Bunnykins
First Variation

DB247 – Mary Mary Quite Contrary Bunnykins

DB248 – Digger Bunnykins

DB249 – Dodgem Bunnykins

DB250 – Drummer Bunnykins
Style Two

DB251 – Captain Cook Bunnykins

DB252 – Mandarin Bunnykins

DB253 – Stop Watch Bunnykins

BUNNYKINS

DB254 – Vicar Bunnykins

DB255 – Golfer Bunnykins

DB256 – Flamenco Bunnykins

DB257 – Liberty Bell Bunnykins

DB258 – King Richard Bunnykins
First Variation

DB259 – Town Crier Bunnykins

DB260 – Day Trip Bunnykins

DB261 – Hornpiper Bunnykins

DB262 – Basketball Bunnykins
Style Two

DB263 – Mermaid Bunnykins

DB264 – Will Scarlett Bunnykins
First Variation

DB265 – Sheriff of Nottingham Bunnykins, *First Variation*

BUNNYKINS

DB266 – Prince John Bunnykins

DB267 – Chocs Away Bunnykins

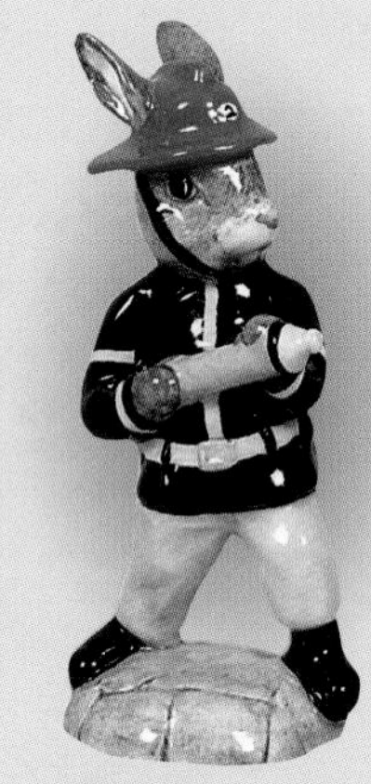
DB268 – American Firefighter

DB269 – With Love Bunnykins

DB270 – Wee Willie Winkle Bunnykins

DB271 – Caddie Bunnykins

DB272 – Test Century Bunnykins

DB273 – Deep Sea Diver Bunnykins

DB274 – Dutch Bunnykins

DB275 – Eskimo Bunnykins

DB276 – Sweet Dreams Baby Bunny

BUNNYKINS

DB277 – Strawberries Bunnykins

DB278 – Tennis Bunnykins

DB279 – Ship Ahoy Bunnykins

DB280 – Samurai Bunnykins

DB281 – Matador Bunnykins

DB282 – Ice Hockey Bunnykins

DB283 – Juliet Bunnykins

DB284 – Romeo Bunnykins

DB285 – Christmas Morning Bunnykins

DB286 – Graduation Day Bunnykins

DB287 – Wedding Day Bunnykins

DB227
FATHER BUNNYKINS™
Style Two (Large size)

Designer:	Amanda Hughes-Lubeck
Modeller:	Amanda Hughes-Lubeck
Height:	6 ¾", 17.1 cm
Colour:	Cream shirt, grey-green trousers, red braces, red and yellow striped tie
Issued:	2000 in a limited edition of 2,000
Series:	The Bunnykins Family

Back Stamp	U.S. $	Price Can. $	U.K. £	Aust. $
BK-11 Special	70.00	85.00	40.00	95.00

Note: A colourway variation exists with dark maroon braces, grey-blue shirt, maroon and yellow tie.

DB228
SANDCASTLE MONEY BOX™

Designer:	Warren Platt
Modeller:	Warren Platt
Height:	4 ¼", 10.8 cm
Colour:	Blue, green, pink, red, white and yellow
Issued:	2001-2002 in a limited edition of 2,002
Series:	Tableau

HAND MADE AND HAND DECORATED
Bunnykins
by ROYAL DOULTON
SANDCASTLE MONEY BOX
30th ANNIVERSARY OF
BUNNYKINS DB FIGURES
1972 - 2002
LIMITED TO THE YEAR 2002
DB 228
MADE IN ENGLAND © 2002 ROYAL DOULTON

Back Stamp	U.S. $	Price Can. $	U.K. £	Aust. $
BK-13a Special	175.00	225.00	100.00	250.00

DB229
SANDS OF TIME BUNNYKINS™

Designer:	Martyn Alcock
Modeller:	Martyn Alcock
Height:	3 ½", 9 cm
Colour:	Yellow robe with suns and moons
Issued:	2001 - 2001
Series:	1. Bunnykins of the Year 2. Time

Back Stamp	U.S. $	Price Can. $	U.K. £	Aust. $
BK-10a Special	55.00	70.00	30.00	75.00

DB230
LITTLE RED RIDING HOOD BUNNYKINS™

Designer:	Martyn Alcock
Modeller:	Martyn Alcock
Height:	4 ¼", 10.5 cm
Colour:	Red cloak, blue dress, white apron, brown basket
Issued:	2001 in a limited edition of 2000
Series:	1. Fairy Tales 2. Special Events

Back Stamp	U.S. $	Price Can. $	U.K. £	Aust. $
BK-12a Special	130.00	160.00	75.00	175.00

DB231
CINDERELLA BUNNYKINS™

Designer:	Unknown
Modeller:	Martyn Alcock
Height:	4 ¼",10.8 cm
Colour:	Pink and yellow
Issued:	2002 - 2002
Series:	1. Fairy Tales 2. ICC Members Exclusive

Back Stamp	U.S. $	Price Can. $	U.K. £	Aust. $
BK-13a Special	55.00	65.00	30.00	70.00

Note: DB232 assigned to May Queen but not issued.

DB233
SHOPPER BUNNYKINS™

Designer:	Warren Platt
Modeller:	Warren Platt
Height:	4 ½", 11.5 cm
Colour:	Light green dress, grey-blue coat and pink scarf
Issued:	2001 - 2003

Back Stamp	U.S. $	Price Can. $	U.K. £	Aust. $
BK-12 to BK-14	45.00	55.00	25.00	60.00

DB234
MR. PUNCH BUNNYKINS™

Designer:	Kimberley Curtis
Modeller:	Martyn Alcock
Height:	4 ¾", 12 cm
Colour:	Blue, yellow and red striped costume and cap
Issued:	2001 in a limited edition of 2,500
Series:	Punch and Judy Collection

Back Stamp	U.S. $	Price Can. $	U.K. £	Aust. $
BK-11a Special	125.00	150.00	70.00	175.00

DB235
JUDY BUNNYKINS™

Designer:	Kimberley Curtis
Modeller:	Martyn Alcock
Height:	4¼", 11 cm
Colour:	Blue and yellow
Issued:	2001 in a limited edition of 2,500
Series:	Punch and Judy Collection

Back Stamp	U.S. $	Price Can. $	U.K. £	Aust. $
BK-11a Special	125.00	150.00	70.00	175.00

DB236
WALTZING MATILDA BUNNYKINS™

Designer:	Wendy Boyce-Davies
Modeller:	Martyn Alcock
Height:	4", 10.1 cm
Colour:	Yellow shirt, red vest, blue trousers, brown hat and boots
Issued:	2001 in a limited edition of 2001
Series:	Australian Heritage

Back Stamp	U.S. $	Price Can. $	U.K. £	Aust. $
BK-11 Special	125.00	150.00	70.00	175.00

DB237
FATHER CHRISTMAS BUNNYKINS™

Designer: Warren Platt
Modeller: Warren Platt
Height: 5", 12.7 cm
Colour: Red, white, yellow, green and black
Issued: 2000 in a special edition of 2,500

Back Stamp	U.S. $	Price Can. $	U.K. £	Aust. $
BK-10 Special	85.00	100.00	50.00	110.00

DB238
ON LINE BUNNYKINS™

Designer: Shane Ridge
Modeller: Shane Ridge
Height: 2 ¾", 7.0 cm
Colour: Salmon pink pullover, blue and white shirt, blue trousers, cream computer
Issued: 2001 in a special edition of 2,500

Back Stamp	U.S. $	Price Can. $	U.K. £	Aust. $
BK-12 Special	150.00	175.00	80.00	200.00

DB239
LITTLE BOY BLUE BUNNYKINS™

Designer: Caroline Dadd
Modeller: Shane Ridge
Height: 3 ¾", 9.5 cm
Colour: Pale blue and white
Issued: 2002 - 2004
Series: Nursery Rhyme Collection

Back Stamp	U.S. $	Price Can. $	U.K. £	Aust. $
BK-11 to BK-14	55.00	65.00	30.00	70.00

DB240
LITTLE MISS MUFFET BUNNYKINS™

Designer:	Caroline Dadd
Modeller:	Warren Platt
Height:	3 ½", 8.9 cm
Colour:	Pale blue, white and green
Issued:	2002 - 2004
Series:	Nursery Rhyme Collection

Back Stamp	U.S. $	Price Can. $	U.K. £	Aust. $
BK-11 Special	60.00	75.00	35.00	80.00

DB241
BATH NIGHT BUNNYKINS™

Designer:	After a design by Barbara Vernon
Modeller:	Martyn Alcock
Height:	4 ¼", 10.8 cm
Colour:	Beige, blue, red and white
Issued:	2001 in a limited edition of 5,000
Series:	Tableau

Back Stamp	U.S. $	Price Can. $	U.K. £	Aust. $
BK-11 Special	125.00	150.00	70.00	165.00

DB242
TYROLEAN DANCER BUNNYKINS™

Designer:	Shane Ridge
Modeller:	Shane Ridge
Height:	4", 10.1 cm
Colour:	White, black and grey
Issued:	2001 - 2001
Series:	1. Dancers of the World 2. Special Events

Back Stamp	U.S. $	Price Can. $	U.K. £	Aust. $
BK-11 Special	60.00	75.00	35.00	80.00

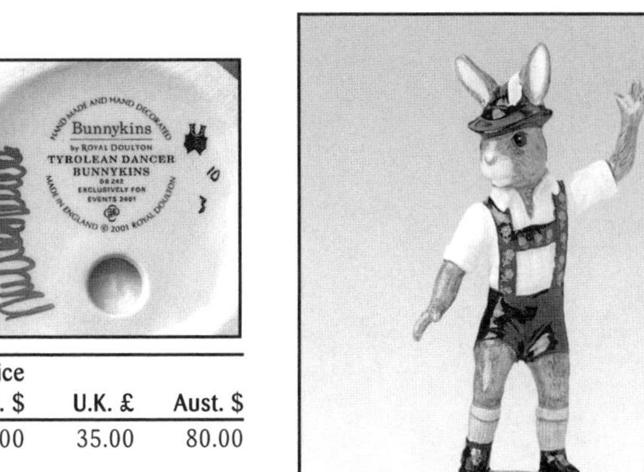

DB243
LITTLE JOHN BUNNYKINS™
First Variation

Designer:	Martyn Alcock
Modeller:	Martyn Alcock
Height:	5", 12.5 cm
Colour:	Brown cloak, maroon tunic
Issued:	2001 - 2003
Varieties:	DB355
Series:	Robin Hood Collection

Back Stamp	U.S. $	Price Can. $	U.K. £	Aust. $
BK-10a Special	45.00	55.00	25.00	60.00

Note: A castle-like stand is available for the eight Bunnykins of the Robin Hood Collection, see page 329.

DB244
ROBIN HOOD BUNNYKINS™
First Variation

Designer:	Martyn Alcock
Modeller:	Martyn Alcock
Height:	4 ½", 11.9 cm
Colour:	Green tunic, cloak and cap, brown boots
Issued:	2001 - 2003
Varieties:	DB357
Series:	Robin Hood Collection

Back Stamp	U.S. $	Price Can. $	U.K. £	Aust. $
BK-10a Special	45.00	55.00	25.00	60.00

DB245
MAID MARION BUNNYKINS™
First Variation

Designer:	Martyn Alcock
Modeller:	Martyn Alcock
Height:	4 ¼", 10.8 cm
Colour:	Pink, yellow, green and gold
Issued:	2001 - 2003
Varieties:	DB356
Series:	Robin Hood Collection

Back Stamp	U.S. $	Price Can. $	U.K. £	Aust. $
BK-10a Special	45.00	55.00	25.00	60.00

DB246
FRIAR TUCK BUNNYKINS™
First Variation

Designer: Martyn Alcock
Modeller: Martyn Alcock
Height: 4 ½", 11.9 cm
Colour: Brown, green, yellow and grey
Issued: 2001 - 2003
Varieties: DB354
Series: Robin Hood Collection

Back Stamp	U.S. $	Price Can. $	U.K. £	Aust. $
BK-11a Special	45.00	55.00	25.00	60.00

DB247
MARY MARY QUITE CONTRARY BUNNYKINS™

Designer: Caroline Dadd
Modeller: Shane Ridge
Height: 4 ¼", 10.8 cm
Colour: Pink and white
Issued: 2002 - 2003
Series: Nursery Rhyme Collection

Back Stamp	U.S. $	Price Can. $	U.K. £	Aust. $
BK-11a Special to BK-14a Special	60.00	75.00	35.00	80.00

DB248
DIGGER BUNNYKINS™

Designer: Dalglish, Bryant, Bartholmeucz
Modeller: Warren Platt
Height: 5 ½", 14 cm
Colour: Brown and yellow
Issued: 2001 in a special edition of 2,500
Series: Australian Heritage

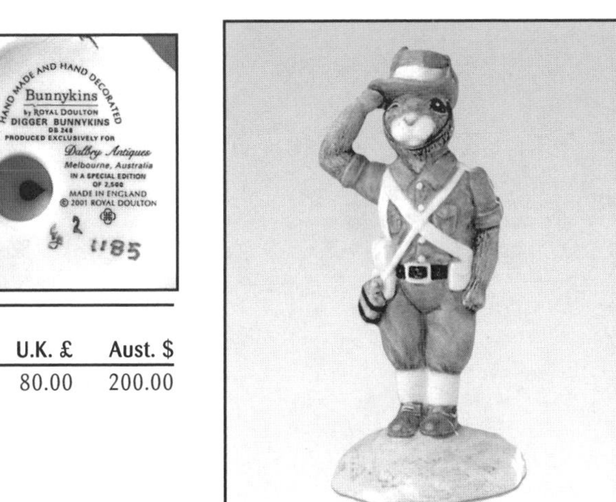

Back Stamp	U.S. $	Price Can. $	U.K. £	Aust. $
BK-11a Special	150.00	180.00	80.00	200.00

DB249
DODGEM BUNNYKINS™

Designer:	After a design by Barbara Vernon
Modeller:	Martyn Alcock
Height:	3" x 4", 7.6 x 10 cm
Colour:	Blue jacket, yellow cap, red Dodgem car
Issued:	2001 in a limited edition of 2,500
Series:	Travel Bunnykins

Back Stamp	U.S. $	Price Can. $	U.K. £	Aust. $
BK-11 Special	150.00	180.00	80.00	200.00

DB250
DRUMMER BUNNYKINS™
Style Two

Designer:	Kimberley Curtis
Modeller:	Shane Ridge
Height:	4 ¼", 10.8 cm
Colour:	Black, white, pink and blue
Issued:	2002 in a limited edition of 2,500
Series:	Jazz Band Collection

Back Stamp	U.S. $	Price Can. $	U.K. £	Aust. $
BK-11a Special	110.00	135.00	60.00	150.00

DB251
CAPTAIN COOK BUNNYKINS™

Designer:	Wendy Boyce-Davies
Modeller:	Warren Platt
Height:	4 ¼", 10.8 cm
Colour:	Blue jacket and hat with yellow trim, cream vest and pantaloons
Issued:	2002 in a limited edition of 2,500
Series:	Australian Heritage

Back Stamp	U.S. $	Price Can. $	U.K. £	Aust. $
BK-11a Special	110.00	135.00	60.00	150.00

DB252
MANDARIN BUNNYKINS™

Designer:	Caroline Dadd
Modeller:	Martyn Alcock
Height:	4 ¼", 10.8 cm
Colour:	Yellow robe with blue trim, grey dragon
Issued:	2001 in a limited edition of 2,500
Series:	Bunnykins of the World

Back Stamp	U.S. $	Price Can. $	U.K. £	Aust. $
BK-11 Special	125.00	150.00	70.00	160.00

DB253
STOP WATCH BUNNYKINS™

Designer:	Martyn Alcock
Modeller:	Martyn Alcock
Height:	4 ¼", 10.8 cm
Colour:	Green track suit and cap with yellow trim
Issued:	2002 - 2002
Series:	1. Bunnykins of the Year 2. Time

Back Stamp	U.S. $	Price Can. $	U.K. £	Aust. $
BK-11a Special	45.00	55.00	25.00	60.00

DB254
VICAR BUNNYKINS™

Designer:	Shane Ridge
Modeller:	Shane Ridge
Height:	4 ¼", 10.8 cm
Colour:	White and black robes
Issued:	2002 - 2002
Series:	ICC Membership Gift

Back Stamp	U.S. $	Price Can. $	U.K. £	Aust. $
BK-11a Special	65.00	80.00	35.00	90.00

DB255
GOLFER BUNNYKINS™

Designer: Shane Ridge
Modeller: Shane Ridge
Height: 5 ¼", 13.3 cm
Colour: Deep red and white
Issued: 2001 - 2002

Back Stamp	U.S. $	Price Can. $	U.K. £	Aust. $
BK-11	45.00	55.00	25.00	60.00

Note: Issued in the UK August 2001, in Australia March 2002 and Worldwide December 2002. Figure was exclusive to Royal Doulton outlets worldwide.

DB256
FLAMENCO BUNNYKINS™

Designer: Shane Ridge
Modeller: Shane Ridge
Height: 4 ½", 11.9 cm
Colour: Dark blue and yellow
Issued: 2002 - 2002
Series: 1. Dancers of the World
2. Special Events

Back Stamp	U.S. $	Price Can. $	U.K. £	Aust. $
BK-12 Special	55.00	65.00	30.00	70.00

DB257
LIBERTY BELL BUNNYKINS™

Designer: Shane Ridge
Modeller: Shane Ridge
Height: 5", 12.7 cm
Colour: Turquoise, white, grey, beige and black
Issued: 2001 in a limited edition of 2,000
Series: American Heritage

Back Stamp	U.S. $	Price Can. $	U.K. £	Aust. $
BK-11 Special	130.00	160.00	75.00	175.00

DB258
KING RICHARD BUNNYKINS™
First Variation

Designer:	Martyn Alcock
Modeller:	Martyn Alcock
Height:	4 ¼", 11.0 cm
Colour:	Blue, grey, white and red
Issued:	2002 - 2003
Varieties:	DB351
Series:	Robin Hood Collection

Back Stamp	Price U.S. $	Can. $	U.K. £	Aust. $
BK-12a Special to BK-14a Special	45.00	55.00	25.00	60.00

DB259
TOWN CRIER BUNNYKINS™

Designer:	Caroline Dadd
Modeller:	Martyn Alcock
Height:	4 ½", 11.9 cm
Colour:	Black, red, yellow and grey
Issued:	2002 in a limited edition of 2,500

Back Stamp	Price U.S. $	Can. $	U.K. £	Aust. $
BK-12 Special	100.00	125.00	60.00	135.00

DB260
DAY TRIP BUNNYKINS™

Designer:	Caroline Dadd
Modeller:	Martyn Alcock
Height:	3 ½", 9.0 cm
Colour:	Green, blue, red and yellow
Issued:	2002 in a limited edition of 2,500
Series:	Travel Bunnykins

Back Stamp	Price U.S. $	Can. $	U.K. £	Aust. $
BK-12a Special	140.00	175.00	80.00	200.00

DB261
HORNPIPER BUNNYKINS™

Modeller:	Warren Platt
Height:	4 ¼", 10.8 cm
Colour:	Dark and light blue, white, black and pink
Issued:	2003 - 2003
Series:	Special Events

Back Stamp	U.S. $	Price Can. $	U.K. £	Aust. $
BK-17 Modified	45.00	55.00	25.00	60.00

DB262
BASKETBALL BUNNYKINS™
Style Two

Modeller:	Shane Ridge
Height:	5", 12.7 cm
Colour:	Yellow, blue and brown
Issued:	2002 in a limited edition of 2,000

Back Stamp	U.S. $	Price Can. $	U.K. £	Aust. $
BK-12a Special	80.00	100.00	45.00	110.00

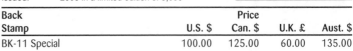

DB263
MERMAID BUNYKINS™

Modeller:	Shane Ridge
Height:	3 ¾", 9.5 cm
Colour:	Yellow, green, brown, grey, red and gold
Issued:	2003 in a limited edition of 3,000

Back Stamp	U.S. $	Price Can. $	U.K. £	Aust. $
BK-11 Special	100.00	125.00	60.00	135.00

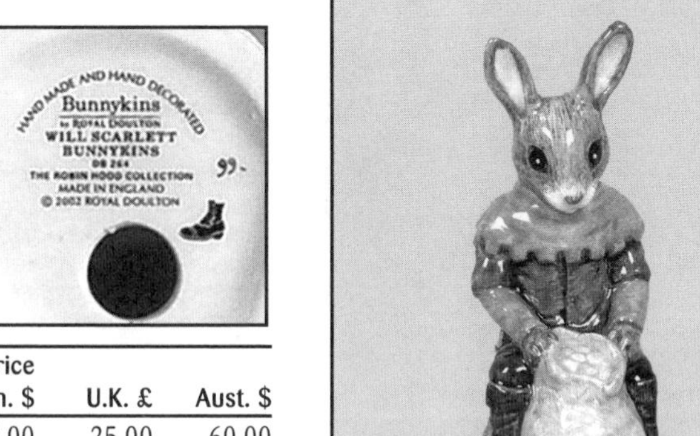

DB264
WILL SCARLETT BUNNYKINS™
First Variation

Modeller: Martyn Alcock
Height: 4", 10.1 cm
Colour: Scarlet, green, brown and tan
Issued: 2002 - 2003
Varieties: DB352
Series: Robin Hood Collection

Back Stamp	U.S. $	Price Can. $	U.K. £	Aust. $
BK-12a to BK-13a	45.00	55.00	25.00	60.00

DB265
SHERIFF OF NOTTINGHAM BUNNYKINS™
First Variation

Modeller: Martyn Alcock
Height: 4 ½", 11.5 cm
Colour: Black, grey and yellow
Issued: 2002 - 2003
Varieties: DB353
Series: Robin Hood Collection

Back Stamp	U.S. $	Price Can. $	U.K. £	Aust. $
BK-12a to BK-13a	45.00	55.00	25.00	60.00

DB266
PRINCE JOHN BUNNYKINS™
First Variation

Modeller: Martyn Alcock
Height: 4 ½", 11.5 cm
Colour: Pink tunic, green cloak, yellow crown
Issued: 2002 - 2003
Varieties: DB350
Series: Robin Hood Collection

Back Stamp	U.S. $	Price Can. $	U.K. £	Aust. $
BK-12a to BK-13a	45.00	55.00	25.00	60.00

DB267
CHOCS AWAY BUNNYKINS™

Modeller:	Martyn Alcock
Height:	4 ¼" x 5 ¼", 11.0 x 13.0 cm
Colour:	Yellow, red, blue, brown and black
Issued:	2003 in a limited edition of 2,000
Series:	Travel Bunnykins

Back Stamp	U.S. $	Price Can. $	U.K. £	Aust. $
BK-12a Special	175.00	225.00	100.00	250.00

DB268
AMERICAN FIREFIGHTER BUNNYKINS™

Designer:	Graham Tongue
Modeller:	Martyn Alcock
Height:	4 ¼", 10.5 cm
Colour:	Black jacket and boots, cream trousers, red helmet
Issued:	2002 in a limited edition of 2,001
Varieties:	Also called Fireman Bunnykins, DB75, DB183
Series:	American Heritage

Back Stamp	U.S. $	Price Can. $	U.K. £	Aust. $
BK-12a Special	90.00	110.00	50.00	125.00

DB269
WITH LOVE BUNNYKINS™

Modeller:	Shane Ridge
Height:	4", 10.1 cm
Colour:	Pale yellow dress, pink flowers and bow
Issued:	2002 - 2003

Back Stamp	U.S. $	Price Can. $	U.K. £	Aust. $
BK-12a Modified	60.00	75.00	35.00	85.00

Note: Issued with a brass plaque on the base for engraving.

DB270
WEE WILLIE WINKIE BUNNYKINS™

Modeller:	Shane Ridge
Height:	4 ½", 11.5 cm
Colour:	Pale blue and white
Issues:	2002 - 2003
Series:	Nursery Rhyme Collection

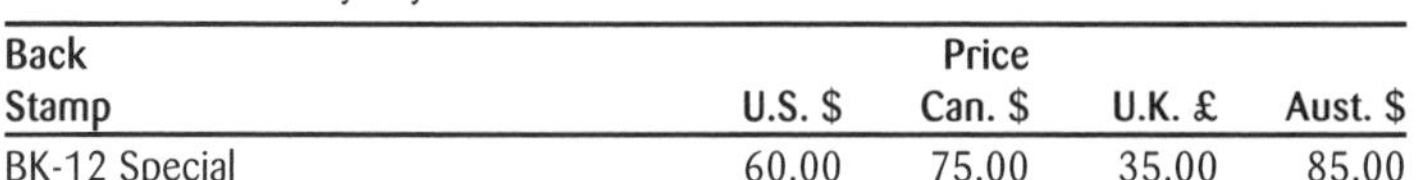

Back Stamp	U.S. $	Price Can. $	U.K. £	Aust. $
BK-12 Special	60.00	75.00	35.00	85.00

DB271
CADDIE BUNYKINS™

Modeller:	Shane Ridge
Height:	5", 12.7 cm
Colour:	Yellow jumper, tan trousers, red cap, green golf bag
Issued:	2002 - 2003

Back Stamp	U.S. $	Price Can. $	U.K. £	Aust. $
BK-12 Standard	70.00	85.00	40.00	95.00

DB272
TEST CENTURY BUNNYKINS™

Modeller:	Martyn Alcock
Height:	4 ½", 11.5 cm
Colour:	White, beige and green
Issued:	2003 in a limited edition of 2,000
Series:	Cricket

Backstamp not available at press time

Back Stamp	U.S. $	Price Can. $	U.K. £	Aust. $
BK-12a Special	130.00	160.00	75.00	175.00

DB273
DEEP SEA DIVER BUNNYKINS™

Modeller:	Shane Ridge
Height:	4 ¾", 12.0 cm
Colour:	White, yellow, black, grey and blue
Issued:	2003 in a limited edition of 3,000

Back Stamp	U.S. $	Price Can. $	U.K. £	Aust. $
BK-12a Special	115.00	150.00	65.00	165.00

DB274
DUTCH BUNNYKINS™

Modeller:	Martyn Alcock
Height:	4 ½", 11.5 cm
Colour:	Blue bodice, white sleeves, skirt and cap, yellow apron, brown baskets of red apples
Issued:	2003 in a limited edition of 2,000

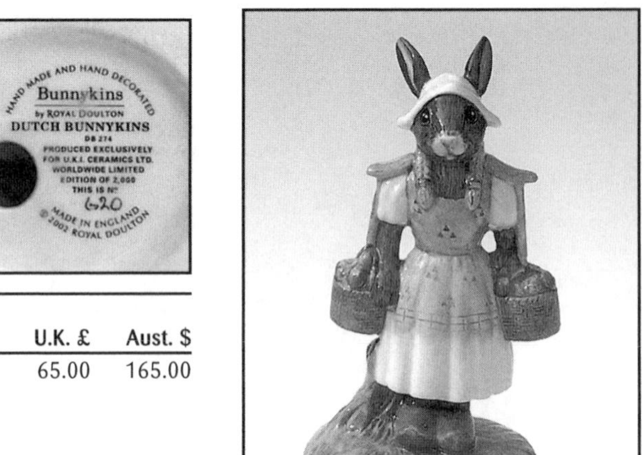

Back Stamp	U.S. $	Price Can. $	U.K. £	Aust. $
BK-12a Special	115.00	150.00	65.00	165.00

DB275
ESKIMO BUNNYKINS™

Modeller:	Shane Ridge
Height:	4 ¾", 12.1 cm
Colour:	Light brown, cream, red and black
Issued:	2003 - 2003
Series:	Bunnykins of the Year

Back Stamp	U.S. $	Price Can. $	U.K. £	Aust. $
BK-16 Standard	45.00	60.00	25.00	70.00

DB276
SWEET DREAMS BABY BUNNY™

Modeller: Martyn Alcock
Height: 3 ½", 8.9 cm
Colour: Green, pink, yellow and white
Issued: 2002 - 2003

Back Stamp	U.S. $	Price Can. $	U.K. £	Aust. $
BK-12 Standard	45.00	55.00	25.00	60.00

DB277
STRAWBERRIES BUNNYKINS™

Modeller: Warren Platt
Height: 3 ¼", 8.3 cm
Colour: Blue dress, pink romper suit, brown basket of strawberries
Issued: 2002 in a limited edition of 3,000

Back Stamp	U.S. $	Price Can. $	U.K. £	Aust. $
BK-12a Special	70.00	90.00	40.00	100.00

Note: Sold only as a pair with DB278

DB278
TENNIS BUNNYKINS™

Modeller: Warren Platt
Height: 3 ¾", 9.5 cm
Colour: Pink, white, tan and grey
Issued: 2002 in a limited edition of 3,000

Back Stamp	U.S. $	Price Can. $	U.K. £	Aust. $
BK-12a Special	70.00	90.00	40.00	100.00

Note: Sold only as a pair with DB277. U.K. price for the pair was £98.99.

DB279
SHIP AHOY BUNNYKINS™

Backstamp not available at press time

Modeller:	Shane Ridge
Height:	4 ¼", 11.0 cm
Colour:	Blue jacket trimmed with gold; white and blue cap; red and white tug boat
Issued:	2004 in a limited edition of 2,000
Series:	Travel Bunnykins

Back Stamp	U.S. $	Price Can. $	U.K. £	Aust. $
BK-14a Special	250.00	300.00	140.00	325.00

DB280
SAMURAI BUNNYKINS™

Modeller:	Shane Ridge
Height:	4 ¾", 12.0 cm
Colour:	Yellow and red robes, red cap, brown pot, green bush
Issued:	2003 in a limited edition of 2,000

Back Stamp	U.S. $	Price Can. $	U.K. £	Aust. $
BK-13a Special	125.00	150.00	70.00	175.00

DB281
MATADOR BUNNYKINS™

Modeller:	Shane Ridge
Height:	4 ½", 11.5 cm
Colour:	Green, red and black
Issued:	2003 in a limited edition of 2,000

Back Stamp	U.S. $	Price Can. $	U.K. £	Aust. $
BK-13a Special	125.00	150.00	70.00	175.00

DB282
ICE HOCKEY BUNNYKINS™

Modeller: Shane Ridge
Height: 4 ¾", 12.1 cm
Colour: Yellow, green and black
Issued: 2003 in a limited edition of 1,500
Series: Special Events

Back Stamp	U.S. $	Price Can. $	U.K. £	Aust. $
BK-13a Special	115.00	140.00	65.00	150.00

DB283
JULIET BUNNYKINS™

Modeller: Shane Ridge
Height: 4 ¼", 11.0 cm
Colour: Yellow and peach dress with red accents
Issued: 2003 - 2003
Series: I.C.C. Membership Gift

Back Stamp	U.S. $	Price Can. $	U.K. £	Aust. $
BK-17a Special	45.00	55.00	25.00	60.00

DB284
ROMEO BUNNYKINS™

Modeller: Martyn Alcock
Height: 3 ¾". 9.5 cm
Colour: Green and white tunic, pink pants, red cap, brown boots, black mask
Issued: 2003 - 2003
Series: I.C.C. Members Exclusive

Back Stamp	U.S. $	Price Can. $	U.K. £	Aust. $
BK-17a Special	45.00	55.00	25.00	60.00

DB285
CHRISTMAS MORNING BUNNYKINS™

Modeller: Shane Ridge
Height: 4 ¾", 12.1 cm
Colour: Pink dress, blue parcel with red ribbon, green tree
Issued: 2003 - 2005
Series: The Occasions Collection

Back Stamp	U.S. $	Price Can. $	U.K. £	Aust. $
BK-16 Standard	45.00	55.00	25.00	60.00

DB286
GRADUATION DAY BUNNYKINS™

Modeller: Shane Ridge
Height: 4 ¾", 12.1 cm
Colour: Black, white, grey, yellow and green
Issued: 2003 to the present
Series: The Occasions Collection

Back Stamp	U.S. $	Price Can. $	U.K. £	Aust. $
BK-16 Standard	43.00	85.00	25.00	80.00

DB287
WEDDING DAY BUNNYKINS™

Modeller: Martyn Alcock
Height: 4 ¾", 12.1 cm
Colour: White dress and veil, grey morning suit, pink and yellow flowers
Issued: 2003 to the present
Series: The Occasions Collection

Back Stamp	U.S. $	Price Can. $	U.K. £	Aust. $
BK-16 Standard	43.00	85.00	25.00	80.00

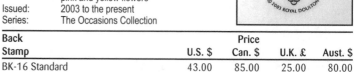

DB288
LOVE HEART BUNNYKINS™

Modeller:	Shane Ridge
Height:	4 ¾", 12.1 cm
Colour:	Blue dress, red heart, green base
Issued:	2003 - 2005
Series:	The Occasions Collection

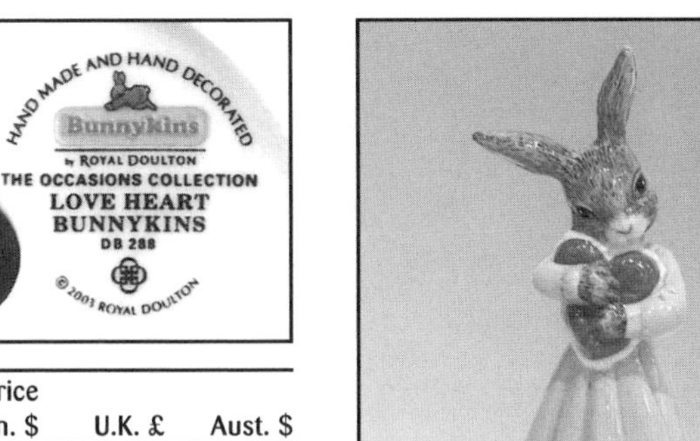

Back Stamp	U.S. $	Price Can. $	U.K. £	Aust. $
BK-16 Standard	45.00	55.00	25.00	60.00

DB289
EASTER TREAT BUNNYKINS™

Modeller:	Shane Ridge
Height:	3 ¾", 9.5 cm
Colour:	Blue, grey, coral, tan and yellow
Issued:	2003 - 2005
Series:	The Occasions Collection

Back Stamp	U.S. $	Price Can. $	U.K. £	Aust. $
BK-16 Standard	45.00	55.00	25.00	60.00

Note: A stand is available for the Occasions Collection, see page 329.

DB290
BIRTHDAY GIRL BUNNYKINS™

Modeller:	Shane Ridge
Height:	4 ¼", 11.0 cm
Colour:	Pink, yellow, green and beige
Issued:	2003 - 2005
Series:	The Occasions Collection

Back Stamp	U.S. $	Price Can. $	U.K. £	Aust. $
BK-16 Standard	45.00	55.00	25.00	60.00

DB291
CONGRATULATIONS BUNNYKINS™

Modeller:	Martyn Alcock
Height:	4 ¼", 11.0 cm
Colour:	Light blue, green, yellow, red, white, beige and black
Issued:	2003 to the present
Series:	The Occasions Collection

Back Stamp	U.S. $	Price Can. $	U.K. £	Aust. $
BK-17a Modified	43.00	85.00	25.00	80.00

DB292
EASTER PARADE BUNNYKINS™

Modeller:	Shane Ridge
Height:	4 ¼", 11.0 cm
Colour:	Yellow, blue, red, green and brown
Issued:	2003 - 2005
Series:	The Occasions Collection

Back Stamp	U.S. $	Price Can. $	U.K. £	Aust. $
BK-17a Modified	45.00	55.00	25.00	60.00

DB293
WITCHES CAULDRON BUNNYKINS™

Designer:	Caroline Dadd
Modeller:	Martyn Alcock
Height:	4 ¼", 11.0 cm
Colour:	Red, purple, dark green, brown, gold, green and black
Issued:	2004 in a limited edition of 1,500

Backstamp not available at press time

Back Stamp	U.S. $	Price Can. $	U.K. £	Aust. $
BK-14 Special	150.00	185.00	85.00	200.00

DB294
CENTURION BUNNYKINS™

Modeller: Martyn Alcock
Height: 4 ½", 11.5 cm
Colour: White, brown, peach, purple and yellow
Issued: 2004 to the present
Series: Roman Empire Collection

Backstamp not available at press time

Back Stamp	U.S. $	Price Can. $	U.K. £	Aust. $
BK-17 Standard	45.00	55.00	25.00	60.00

DB295
ANKHESENAMUN BUNNYKINS™

Modeller: Unknown
Height: 4 ½", 11.5 cm
Colour: Cream, orange, blue, green, brown and white
Issued: 2004 - 2004
Series: I.C.C. Membership Gift

Back Stamp	U.S. $	Price Can. $	U.K. £	Aust. $
BK-17a Modified	45.00	55.00	25.00	60.00

DB296
TUTANKHAMUN BUNNYKINS™

Modeller: Unknown
Height: 4 ½", 11.5 cm
Colour: Cream, blue, red, yellow, brown and green
Issued: 2004 - 2004
Series: I.C.C. Members Exclusive

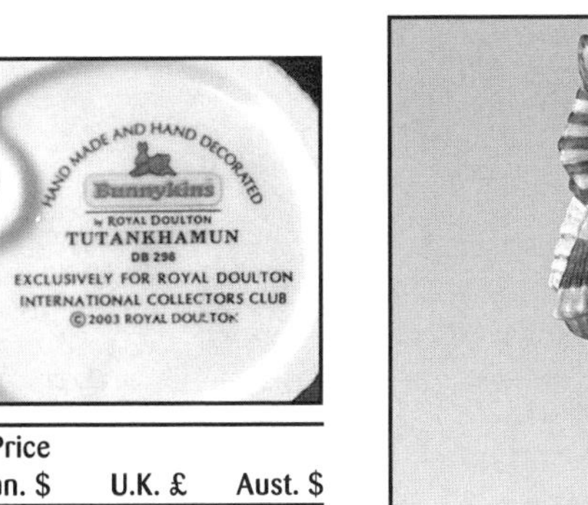

Back Stamp	U.S. $	Price Can. $	U.K. £	Aust. $
BK-17a Modified	45.00	55.00	25.00	60.00

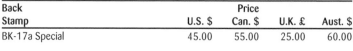

DB297
WINTER LAPLAND

Modeller:	Unknown
Height:	4 ½", 11.5 cm
Colour:	Blue, red, dark yellow, green, dark and light brown
Issued:	2004 - 2004
Series:	Bunnykins of the Year

Back Stamp	U.S. $	Price Can. $	U.K. £	Aust. $
BK-17a Special	45.00	55.00	25.00	60.00

DB298
SUMMER LAPLAND

Modeller:	Unknown
Height:	4 ½", 11.5 cm
Colour:	Red, white, blue, yellow, green and brown
Issued:	2004 - 2004
Series:	Special Events

HAND MADE AND HAND DECORATED
Bunnykins
by ROYAL DOULTON
EXCLUSIVELY FOR EVENTS
2004
SUMMER LAPLAND
DB 298
© 2003 ROYAL DOULTON

Back Stamp	U.S. $	Price Can. $	U.K. £	Aust. $
BK-17a Special	45.00	55.00	25.00	60.00

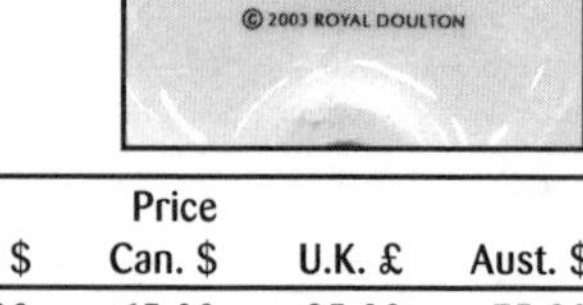

DB299
SIR GALAHAD

Designer:	Caroline Dadd
Modeller:	Unknown
Height:	4 ½", 11.5 cm
Colour:	Cream, red, white, purple, dark yellow, grey and brown
Issued:	2004 to the present
Series:	Athurian Legends Collection

Back Stamp	U.S. $	Price Can. $	U.K. £	Aust. $
BK-17a Modified	50.00	65.00	25.00	75.00

DB300
SIR GAWAIN

Designer: Caroline Dadd
Height: 3 ½", 9.0 cm
Colour: Yellow, maroon, red, green and brown
Issued: 2004 to the present
Series: Arthurian Legends Collection

Back Stamp	U.S. $	Price Can. $	U.K. £	Aust. $
BK-17a Modified	50.00	65.00	25.00	75.00

DB301
SIR LANCELOT

Designer: Caroline Dadd
Height: 5 ¾", 14.5 cm
Colour: Yellow, blue, red, light green, grey, orange, brown and dark green
Issued: 2004 to the present
Series: Arthurian Legends Collection

Back Stamp	U.S. $	Price Can. $	U.K. £	Aust. $
BK-17a Modified	70.00	90.00	35.00	100.00

DB302
QUEEN GUINEVERE

Designer: Caroline Dadd
Height: 4 ¼", 11.0 cm
Colour: Royal blue, red, yellow, cream and grey
Issued: 2004 to the present
Series: Arthurian Legends Collection

Back Stamp	U.S. $	Price Can. $	U.K. £	Aust. $
BK-17a Modified	43.00	55.00	25.00	60.00

DB303
MERLIN

Designer:	Caroline Dadd
Height:	4 ¾", 12.0 cm
Colour:	Dark green robe, purple cloak, yellow staff
Issued:	2004 to the present
Series:	Arthurian Legends Collection

HAND MADE AND HAND DECORATED
Bunnykins
by ROYAL DOULTON
THE ARTHURIAN LEGENDS COLLECTION
MERLIN
DB 303
© 2003 ROYAL DOULTON

Back Stamp	U.S. $	Price Can. $	U.K. £	Aust. $
BK-17a Modified	43.00	55.00	25.00	60.00

DB304
KING ARTHUR

Designer:	Caroline Dadd
Height:	4 ¾", 12.0 cm
Colour:	Royal blue, cream, red, grey and orange
Issued:	2004 to the present
Series:	Arthurian Legends Collection

HAND MADE AND HAND DECORATED
Bunnykins
by ROYAL DOULTON
THE ARTHURIAN LEGENDS COLLECTION
KING ARTHUR
DB 304
© 2003 ROYAL DOULTON

Back Stamp	U.S. $	Price Can. $	U.K. £	Aust. $
BK-17a Modified	43.00	55.00	25.00	60.00

DB305
HENRY VIII

Designer:	Caroline Dadd
Modeller:	Martyn Alcock
Height:	4", 10.1 cm
Colour:	Green, yellow, orange, red and brown
Issued:	2003 - 2005
Series:	Tudor Collection

HAND MADE AND HAND DECORATED
Bunnykins
by ROYAL DOULTON
THE TUDOR COLLECTION
HENRY VIII
DB 305
© 2003 ROYAL DOULTON

Back Stamp	U.S. $	Price Can. $	U.K. £	Aust. $
BK-17a Modified	45.00	55.00	25.00	60.00

Note: A scenic base is available for the seven Bunnykins of the Tudor Collection. The base is designed so collectors can chose how to arrange the queens, see page 330.

DB306
CATHERINE OF ARAGON

Designer:	Caroline Dadd
Modeller:	Martyn Alcock
Height:	4 ¼", 11.0 cm
Colour:	Red, coral, yellow, purple and gold
Issued:	2003 - 2005
Series:	Tudor Collection

Back Stamp	U.S. $	Price Can. $	U.K. £	Aust. $
BK-17a Modified	45.00	55.00	25.00	60.00

DB307
ANNE BOLEYN

Designer:	Caroline Dadd
Modeller:	Martyn Alcock
Height:	4 ¼", 11.0 cm
Colour:	Purple, yellow, gold and brown
Issued:	2003 - 2005
Series:	Tudor Collection

Back Stamp	U.S. $	Price Can. $	U.K. £	Aust. $
BK-17a Modified	45.00	55.00	25.00	60.00

DB308
JANE SEYMOUR

Designer:	Caroline Dadd
Modeller:	Martyn Alcock
Height:	4 ¼", 11.0 cm
Colour:	Red, light and dark green and gold
Issued:	2003 - 2005
Series:	Tudor Collection

Back Stamp	U.S. $	Price Can. $	U.K. £	Aust. $
BK-17a Modified	45.00	55.00	25.00	60.00

HAND MADE AND HAND DECORATED
Bunnykins
by ROYAL DOULTON
THE TUDOR COLLECTION
ANNE OF CLEVES
DB 309
© 2003 ROYAL DOULTON

DB309
ANNE OF CLEVES

Designer:	Caroline Dadd
Modeller:	Martyn Alcock
Height:	4 ¼", 11.0 cm
Colour:	Orange, black, yellow, red and gold
Issued:	2003 - 2005
Series:	Tudor Collection

Back		Price		
Stamp	U.S. $	Can. $	U.K. £	Aust. $
BK-17a Modified	45.00	55.00	25.00	60.00

DB310
KATHRYN HOWARD

Designer:	Caroline Dadd
Modeller:	Martyn Alcock
Height:	4 ¼", 11.0 cm
Colour:	Blue, black, yellow, red, white and gold
Issued:	2003 - 2005
Series:	Tudor Collection

Back		Price		
Stamp	U.S. $	Can. $	U.K. £	Aust. $
BK-17a Modified	45.00	55.00	25.00	60.00

HAND MADE AND HAND DECORATED
Bunnykins
by ROYAL DOULTON
THE TUDOR COLLECTION
KATHRYN HOWARD
DB 310
© 2003 ROYAL DOULTON

DB311
CATHERINE PARR

Designer:	Caroline Dadd
Modeller:	Martyn Alcock
Height:	4 ¼", 11.0 cm
Colour:	Green, orange, white and black
Issued:	2003 - 2005
Series:	Tudor Collection

Back		Price		
Stamp	U.S. $	Can. $	U.K. £	Aust. $
BK-17a Modified	45.00	55.00	25.00	60.00

DB312
EMPEROR BUNNYKINS™

Modeller:	Unknown
Height:	4 ¾", 12.0 cm
Colour:	Purple, grey, cream, gold, brown and red
Issued:	2004 to the present
Series:	Roman Empire Collection

Back Stamp	U.S. $	Price Can. $	U.K. £	Aust. $
BK- 17a Modified	45.00	85.00	25.00	95.00

DB313
BETSY ROSS BUNNYKINS™

Modeller:	Unknown
Height:	4 ¼", 10.5 cm
Colour:	Pale blue dress; white collar and cap, red, white and blue flag, brown basket
Issued:	2003 in a limited edition of 2,000
Series:	American Heritage Collection

Back Stamp	U.S. $	Price Can. $	U.K. £	Aust. $
BK-17a Special	75.00	90.00	40.00	100.00

DB314
EGYPTIAN BUNNYKINS™

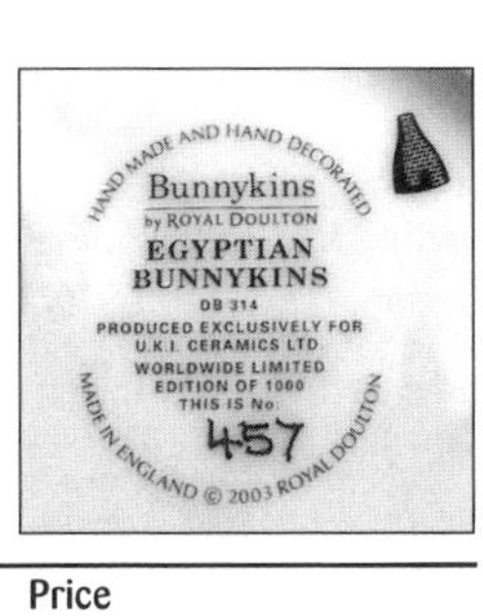

Designer:	Caroline Dadd
Modeller:	Shane Ridge
Height:	4 ½", 11.9 cm
Colour:	Blue, white, red, yellow and beige
Issued:	2004 in a limited edition of 1,000
Series:	Bunnykins of the World

Back Stamp	U.S. $	Price Can. $	U.K. £	Aust. $
BK-14a Special	175.00	225.00	100.00	250.00

DB315
ARABIAN NIGHTS BUNNYKINS™

Designer:	Caroline Dadd
Modeller:	Shane Ridge
Height:	5", 12.7 cm
Colour:	Maroon, brown, green and grey
Issued:	2005 in a limited edition of 1,000
Series:	Bunnykins of the World

Back Stamp	U.S. $	Price Can. $	U.K. £	Aust. $
BK-14a Special	175.00	225.00	100.00	250.00

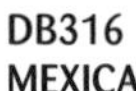

DB316
MEXICAN BUNNYKINS™

Designer:	Caroline Dadd
Modeller:	Shane Ridge
Height:	4 ½", 11.9 cm
Colour:	Blue poncho, maroon trousers, cream hat, green cactus
Issued:	2004 in a limited edition of 1,000
Series:	Bunnykins of the World

Back Stamp	U.S. $	Price Can. $	U.K. £	Aust. $
BK-14a Special	175.00	225.00	100.00	250.00

DB317
PARISIAN BUNNYKINS™

Designer:	Caroline Dadd
Modeller:	Shane Ridge
Height:	4 ½", 11.9 cm
Colour:	White and blue striped jersey, blue trousers, black beret
Issued:	2005 in a limited edition of 1,000
Series:	Bunnykins of the World

Back Stamp	Price U.S. $	Can. $	U.K. £	Aust. $
BK-14a Special	175.00	225.00	100.00	250.00

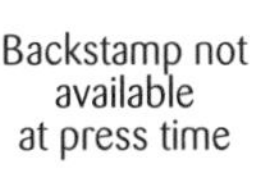

DB318
RUGBY PLAYER BUNNYKINS™

Height:	4 ¼", 10.8 cm
Colour:	Blue, white and black
Issued:	2004 in a limited edition of 1,000
Series:	Special Events

Back Stamp	Price U.S. $	Can. $	U.K. £	Aust. $
BK-14a Special	175.00	225.00	100.00	250.00

Note: Bunnykins Collectors Fair May 23/04.

DB319
CAPTAIN

THE SHIPMATES COLLECTION backstamp: HAND MADE AND HAND DECORATED / Bunnykins / by ROYAL DOULTON / THE SHIPMATES COLLECTION / CAPTAIN / DB 319 / © 2003 ROYAL DOULTON

Designer:	Caroline Dadd
Height:	5 ¼", 13.3 cm
Colour:	Royal blue jacket and hat trimmed with gold, yellow pantaloons, black cannon and balls
Issued:	2004 to the present
Series:	Shipmates Collection

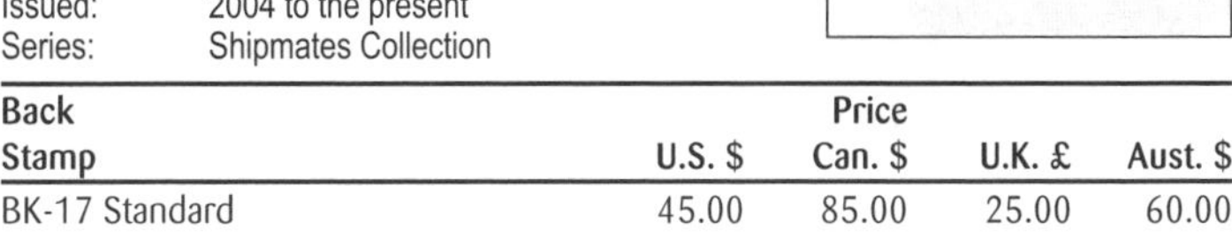

Back Stamp	Price U.S. $	Can. $	U.K. £	Aust. $
BK-17 Standard	45.00	85.00	25.00	60.00

DB320
CAPTAIN'S WIFE

Designer:	Caroline Dadd
Height:	4 ¾", 12.0 cm
Colour:	Orangey-yellow and red dress, white mobcap and apron
Issued:	2004 to the present
Series:	Shipmates Collection

Back Stamp	Price U.S. $	Can. $	U.K. £	Aust. $
BK-17 Standard	45.00	85.00	25.00	60.00

DB321
PIRATE

Designer:	Caroline Dadd
Height:	4 ¾", 12.0 cm
Colour:	Maroon and gold jacket, black cap and boots
Issued:	2004 to the present
Series:	Shipmates Collection

Back Stamp	U.S. $	Price Can. $	U.K. £	Aust. $
BK-17 Standard	45.00	85.00	25.00	95.00

DB322
SEAMAN

Designer:	Caroline Dadd
Height:	4 ¾", 12.0 cm
Colour:	Green jacket and cap, yellow waistcoat, white pants
Issued:	2004 to the present
Series:	Shipmates Collection

Back Stamp	U.S. $	Price Can. $	U.K. £	Aust. $
BK-17 Standard	45.00	85.00	25.00	95.00

DB323
BOATSWAIN

Designer:	Caroline Dadd
Height:	4 ¾", 12.0 cm
Colour:	Royal blue, white, yellow, black, brown and pale blue
Issued:	2004 to the present
Series:	Shipmates Collection

Back Stamp	U.S. $	Price Can. $	U.K. £	Aust. $
BK-17 Standarda	45.00	85.00	25.00	95.00

DB324
CABIN BOY

Designer: Caroline Dadd
Height: 4 ¾", 12.0 cm
Colour: Blue and white striped jersey, pale blue trousers, red kerchief, brown barrel, ginger cat
Issued: 2004 to the present
Series: Shipmates Collection

Back Stamp	U.S. $	Price Can. $	U.K. £	Aust. $
BK-17 Standard	45.00	85.00	25.00	95.00

DB325
SHIP'S COOK

Designer: Caroline Dadd
Height: 4 ¼", 10.8 cm
Colour: Cream and blue striped shirt, blue trousers, white cap and apron
Issued: 2004 to the present
Series: Shipmates Collection

Back Stamp	U.S. $	Price Can. $	U.K. £	Aust. $
BK-17 Standard	45.00	85.00	25.00	95.00

DB326
GLADIATOR

Modeller: Martyn Alcock
Height: 4 ¼", 10.8 cm
Colour: Beige, brown, blue, black, silver and yellow
Issued: 2004 - 2005
Series: Roman Empire Collection

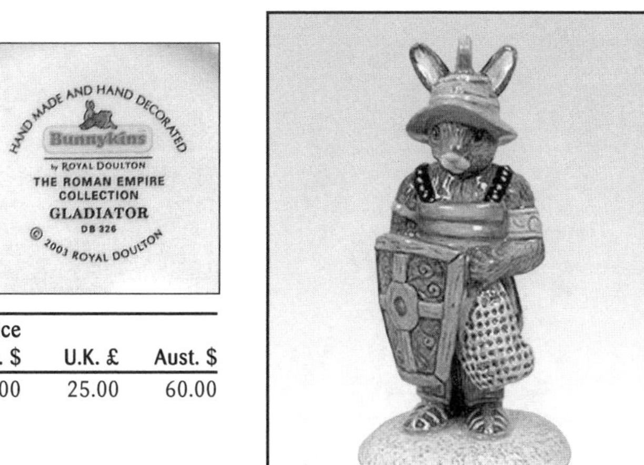

Back Stamp	U.S. $	Price Can. $	U.K. £	Aust. $
BK-17 Standard	45.00	55.00	25.00	60.00

HAND MADE AND HAND DECORATED
Bunnykins
by ROYAL DOULTON
THE OCCASIONS COLLECTION
CHRISTENING DAY GIRL
DB 327
© 2005 ROYAL DOULTON

DB327
CHRISTENING DAY GIRL

Modeller: Shane Ridge
Height: 4 ½", 11.9 cm
Colour: Pink, cream, yellow, brown, silver and black
Issued: 2005 to the present
Series: Occasions Collection

Back Stamp	U.S. $	Price Can. $	U.K. £	Aust. $
BK-17 Standard	43.00	85.00	25.00	95.00

HAND MADE AND HAND DECORATED
Bunnykins
by ROYAL DOULTON
THE OCCASIONS COLLECTION
CHRISTENING DAY BOY
DB 328
© 2005 ROYAL DOULTON

DB328
CHRISTENING DAY BOY

Modeller: Shane Ridge
Height: 3 ¾", 9.5 cm
Colour: Blue, red, yellow, silver and black
Issued: 2005 to the present
Series: Occasions Collection

Back Stamp	U.S. $	Price Can. $	U.K. £	Aust. $
BK-17 Standard	43.00	85.00	25.00	95.00

DB329
GRADUATION TIME

Modeller: Shane Ridge
Height: 4 ½", 11.9 cm
Colour: Black, red, pale yellow and white
Issued: 2005 to the present
Series: Occasions Collection

Back Stamp	U.S. $	Price Can. $	U.K. £	Aust. $
BK-17 Standard	43.00	85.00	25.00	95.00

DB330
RANDOLPH THE RINGMASTER

Modeller: Unknown
Height: 4 ½", 11.9 cm
Colour: Red, pale yellow, black, grey, blue and gold
Issued: 2005 - 2005
Series: Bunnykins of the Year

Back Stamp	U.S. $	Price Can. $	U.K. £	Aust. $
BK-17 Special	45.00	110.00	25.00	125.00

DB331
CLARRISA THE CLOWN

Modeller: Unknown
Height: 4 ½", 11.9 cm
Colour: Blue, red, yellow, pink and white
Issued: 2005 - 2005
Series: I.C.C. Membership Gift

Back Stamp	U.S. $	Price Can. $	U.K. £	Aust. $
BK-17 Special	50.00	65.00	30.00	75.00

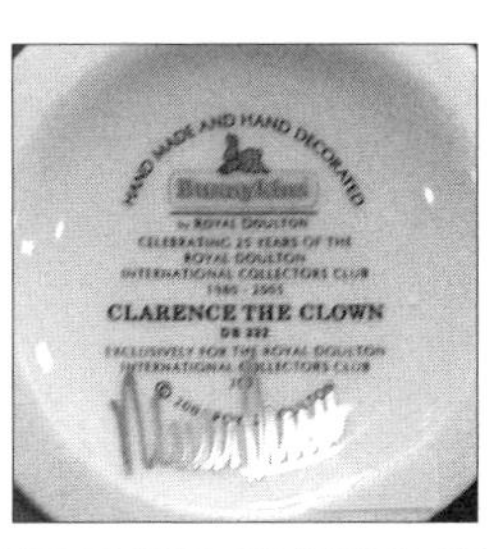

DB332
CLARENCE THE CLOWN

Modeller: Unknown
Height: 4 ½", 11.9 cm
Colour: Orange and green jacket, purple trousers with red and orange patches, blue and yellow striped shirt, red hat with blue band
Issued: 2005 - 2005
Series: I.C.C. Members Exclusive

Back Stamp	U.S. $	Price Can. $	U.K. £	Aust. $
BK-17 Special	50.00	65.00	30.00	75.00

DB333
TINO THE TRIXSTAR

Height:	4 ¾", 12.0 cm
Colour:	White shirt with pink trim, green pants, black sash and boots; white and black spotted dog
Issued:	2005 - 2005
Series:	Events Exclusive

Back Stamp	U.S. $	Price Can. $	U.K. £	Aust. $
BK-17 Standard	43.00	85.00	25.00	95.00

DB334
SISTER MARY BARBARA BUNNYKINS™

Height:	4 ¼", 10.8 cm
Colour:	Cream, black, tan, blue and red
Issued:	2005 to the present

Back Stamp	U.S. $	Price Can. $	U.K. £	Aust. $
BK-17 Special	43.00	65.00	25.00	75.00

DB335
MRS. COLLECTOR BUNNYKINS™

Height:	4", 10.1 cm
Colour:	Lilac blouse, blue skirt, coral chair, blue lamp
Issued:	2005 in a limited edition of 2,500
Series:	1. I.C.C. 25th Anniversary 2. RDICC Exclusive

Back Stamp	U.S. $	Price Can. $	U.K. £	Aust. $
BK-17a Special	75.00	110.00	40.00	110.00

DB 336 TO 341 NOT ISSUED.

DB342
CHRISTMAS ELF

Backstamp not available at press time

Height:	2 ¼", 5.7 cm
Colour:	Green suit and hat, red boots with yellow pompon at toes, blue and white toys
Issued:	2005 to the preset
Series:	Mini Christmas Set 1

Back Stamp		U.S. $	Price Can. $	U.K. £	Aust. $
BK-17 Standard	Price per set	50.00	60.00	30.00	50.00

Note: Sold as a set with DB343, DB346 and DB349.

DB343
FATHER CHRISTMAS

Backstamp not available at press time

Height:	2 ¼", 5.7 cm
Colour:	Red and white suit, black boots and belt with gold buckle, yellow sack of toys
Issued:	2005 to the present
Series:	Mini Christmas Set 1

Back Stamp		U.S. $	Price Can. $	U.K. £	Aust. $
BK-17 Standard	Price per set	50.00	60.00	30.00	50.00

Note: Sold as a set with DB342, DB346 and DB349.

DB344
MOTHER CHRISTMAS

Backstamp not available at press time

Height:	2 ¼", 5.7 cm
Colour:	Red and white coat, green and yellow skirt, yellow hat
Issued:	2005 to the present
Series:	Mini Christmas Set 2

Back Stamp		U.S. $	Price Can. $	U.K. £	Aust. $
BK-17 Standard	Price per set	50.00	60.00	30.00	50.00

Note: Sold as a set with DB345, DB347 and DB348.

DB345
CHRISTMAS ANGEL

Backstamp not available at press time

Height:	2 ¼", 5.7 cm
Colour:	White dress, beige wings, yellow, and black harp
Issued:	2005 to the present
Series:	Mini Christmas Set 2

Back Stamp		U.S. $	Price Can. $	U.K. £	Aust. $
BK-17 Standard	Price per set	50.00	60.00	30.00	50.00

Note: Sold as a set with DB344, DB347 and DB348.

DB346
CHRISTMAS EVE

Backstamp not available at press time

Height:	2 ¼", 5.7 cm
Colour:	Green Christmas tree, blue trousers, light blue and maroon jumper, red and yellow hat, cream boots
Issued:	2005 to the present
Series:	Mini Christmas Set 1

Back Stamp		U.S. $	Price Can. $	U.K. £	Aust. $
BK-17 Standard	Price per set	50.00	60.00	30.00	50.00

Note: Sold as a set with DB342, DB343 and DB349.

DB347
CHRISTMAS CRACKER

Backstamp not available at press time

Height:	2 ¼", 5.7 cm
Colour:	Pink dress with red and green flowers, yellow basket, blue shoes
Issued:	2005 to the present
Series:	Mini Christmas Set 2

Back Stamp		U.S. $	Price Can. $	U.K. £	Aust. $
BK-17 Standard	Price per set	50.00	60.00	30.00	50.00

Note: Sold as a set with DB344, DB345 and DB348.

DB348
CHRISTMAS CAROL SINGER

Backstamp not available at press time

Height:	2 ¼", 5.7 cm
Colour:	Light purple skirt and hat, green and brown coat with red bow, red and white book
Issued:	2005 to the present
Series:	Mini Christmas Set 2

Back Stamp		U.S. $	Price Can. $	U.K. £	Aust. $
BK-17 Standard	Price per set	50.00	60.00	30.00	50.00

Note: Sold as a set with DB344, DB345 and DB347.

DB349
CHRISTMAS BUSKER

Backstamp not available at press time

Height:	2 ¼", 5.7 cm
Colour:	Dark green coat, black trousers and hat, yellow shirt, yellow and white lantern, blue and red scarf, white song sheet
Issued:	2005 to the present
Series:	Mini Christmas Set 1

Back Stamp		U.S. $	Price Can. $	U.K. £	Aust. $
BK-17 Standard	Price per set	50.00	60.00	30.00	50.00

Note: Sold as a set with DB342, DB343 and DB346.

DB350
PRINCE JOHN BUNNYKINS™
Second Variation

Backstamp not available at press time

Modeller:	Martyn Alcock
Height:	4 ½", 11.9 cm
Colour:	Dark grey-green cloak, reddish tunic, yellow belt and cuffs, gold crown and cloak clasp
Issued:	2004 in a limited edition of 3,500
Varieties:	DB266
Series:	Robin Hood Collection, Gold Issue

Back Stamp	U.S. $	Price Can. $	U.K. £	Aust. $
BK-Unknown	100.00	175.00	40.00	200.00

DB351
KING RICHARD BUNNYKINS™
Second Variation

Designer:	Martyn Alcock
Modeller:	Martyn Alcock
Height:	4 ¼", 10.8 cm
Colour:	Blue, grey, white and red with gold cloak clasp and sword
Issued:	2004 in a limited edition of 3,500
Varieties:	DB258
Series:	Robin Hood Collection, Gold Issue

Backstamp not available at press time

Back Stamp	U.S. $	Price Can. $	U.K. £	Aust. $
BK-Unknown	100.00	175.00	40.00	200.00

DB352
WILL SCARLETT BUNNYKINS™
Second Variation

Designer:	Martyn Alcock
Modeller:	Martyn Alcock
Height:	4", 10.1 cm
Colour:	Forest green, scarlet, beige and black with gold highlights
Issued:	2004 in a limited edition of 3,500
Varieties:	DB264
Series:	Robin Hood Collection, Gold Issue

Backstamp not available at press time

Back Stamp	U.S. $	Price Can. $	U.K. £	Aust. $
BK-Unknown	100.00	175.00	40.00	200.00

DB353
SHERIFF OF NOTTINGHAM BUNNYKINS™
Second Variation

Designer:	Martyn Alcock
Modeller:	Martyn Alcock
Height:	4 ½", 11.9 cm
Colour:	Grey, white and black; gold highlights
Issued:	2004 in a limited edition of 3,500
Varieties:	DB265
Series:	Robin Hood Collection, Gold Issue

Backstamp not available at press time

Back Stamp	U.S. $	Price Can. $	U.K. £	Aust. $
BK-Unknown	100.00	175.00	40.00	200.00

DB354
FRIAR TUCK BUNNYKINS™
Second Variation

Backstamp not available at press time

Designer:	Martyn Alcock
Modeller:	Martyn Alcock
Height:	4 ½", 11.9 cm
Colour:	Brown with gold cross, chain, bible and belt
Issued:	2004 in a limited edition of 3,500
Variations:	DB246
Series:	Robin Hood Collection, Gold Issue

Back Stamp	U.S. $	Price Can. $	U.K. £	Aust. $
BK-Unknown	100.00	175.00	40.00	200.00

DB355
LITTLE JOHN BUNNYKINS™
Second Variation

Backstamp not available at press time

Designer:	Martyn Alcock
Modeller:	Martyn Alcock
Height:	5", 12.7 cm
Colour:	Brown cloak, maroon tunic, light brown pants, gold staff and belt
Issued:	2004 in a limited edition of 3,500
Variations:	DB243
Series:	Robin Hood Collection, Gold Issue

Back Stamp	U.S. $	Price Can. $	U.K. £	Aus.t $
BK-Unknown	100.00	175.00	40.00	200.00

DB356
MAID MARION BUNNYKINS™
Second Variation

Backstamp not available at press time

Designer:	Martyn Alcock
Modeller:	Martyn Alcock
Height:	4 ¼", 10.1 cm
Colour:	Purple, yellow and pale green with gold highlights
Issued:	2004 in a limited edition of 3,500
Variations:	DB245
Series:	Robin Hood Collection, Gold Issue

Back Stamp	U.S. $	Price Can. $	U.K. £	Aust. $
BK-Unknown	100.00	175.00	40.00	200.00

DB357
ROBIN HOOD BUNNYKINS™
Second Variation

Backstamp not available at press time

Designer:	Martyn Alcock
Modeller:	Martyn Alcock
Height:	4 ½", 11.9 cm
Colour:	Forest green, light green, brown and yellow with gold highlights
Issued:	2004 in a limited edition of 3,500
Variations:	DB244
Series:	Robin Hood Collection, Gold Issue

Back Stamp	U.S. $	Price Can. $	U.K. £	Aust. $
BK-Unknown	100.00	175.00	40.00	200.00

DB358 NOT ISSUED

DB359
SCARECROW BUNNYKINS™

Backstamp not available at press time

Designer:	Caroline Dadd
Modeller:	Shane Ridge
Height:	4 ¼", 10.8 cm
Colour:	Brown coat, blue trousers, yellow straw hat, brown straw, light brown fence
Issued:	2005 in a limited edition of 1,000

Back Stamp	U.S. $	Price Can. $	U.K. £	Aust. $
BK-Unknown	175.00	225.00	100.00	250.00

DB360
UMPIRE BUNNYKINS™

Backstamp not available at press time

Designer:	Caroline Dadd
Modeller:	Shane Ridge
Height:	4 ¾", 12.1 cm
Colour:	White jacket, cap and shoes, black trousers, green tie and hat band
Issued:	2005 in a limited edition of 1,000

Back Stamp	U.S. $	Price Can. $	U.K. £	Aust. $
BK-Unknown	175.00	225.00	100.00	250.00

DB361
JUST LIKE NEW

Size: 4 ¼" x 7", 10.8 x 17.8 cm
Colour: Blue, white, yellow, green and maroon
Issued: 2005 in a limited edition of 1,500
Series: 1. Bunnykins Mechanics
2. Special Events

Backstamp not available at press time

Back Stamp	U.S. $	Can. $	Price U.K. £	Aust. $
BK-Not known	175.00	225.00	100.00	250.00

DB362
ALL FUELLED UP

Size: 4 ¼" x 8 ¾", 10.8 x 22.2 cm
Colour: Red, blue, yellow, green and cream
Issued: 2005 in a limited edition of 1,500
Series: 1. Bunnykins Mechanics
2. Special Events

Backstamp not available at press time

Back Stamp	U.S. $	Can. $	Price U.K. £	Aust. $
BK-Not known	175.00	225.00	100.00	250.00

DB363
READY TO RIDE

Size: 4 ¼" x 6 ½", 10.8 x 16.5 cm
Colour: Blue, green, maroon and yellow
Issued: 2006 in a limited edition of 1,500
Series: Bunnykins Mechanics

Backstamp not available at press time

Back Stamp	U.S. $	Can. $	Price U.K. £	Aust. $
BK-Not known	175.00	225.00	100.00	250.00

Note: To be released in 2006.

DB364
BUNNYKINS CAMPING™

Backstamp not available at press time

Modeller:	Unknown
Height:	Unknown
Colour:	Orange, blue, green, red and yellow
Issued:	2005

Back Stamp	U.S. $	Price Can. $	U.K. £	Aust. $
BK-Not known	175.00	225.00	100.00	250.00

DB365
NELSON BUNNYKINS™

Backstamp not available at press time

Designer:	Caroline Dadd
Modeller:	Shane Ridge
Height:	4 ¼", 10.8 cm
Colour:	Navy, pale yellow, grey, gold and brown
Issued:	2005 in a limited edition of 750
Series:	Special Events

Back Stamp	U.S. $	Price Can. $	U.K. £	Aust. $
BK-Not known	Price not established at press time			

DB366
BALLOON MAN

Designer:	Caroline Dadd
Height:	4", 10.1 cm
Colour:	Black coat, grey trousers, pink waistcoat, brown hat, red cloth bag, multicoloured balloons
Issued:	2005 in a limited edition of 2,000

Back Stamp	U.S. $	Price Can. $	U.K. £	Aust. $
BK-Not known	85.00	110.00	50.00	125.00

DB367
GEORGE WASHINGTON

Designer:	Caroline Dadd
Height:	5", 12.7 cm
Colour:	Blue and yellow jacket, yellow waistcoat, white shirt and pantaloons, red cloak, black hat and boots, black and brown cannon, blue, red and yellow drum
Issued:	2005 in a limited edition of 2,000
Series:	American Heritage Collection

Back Stamp	U.S. $	Price Can. $	U.K. £	Aust. $
BK-Not known	85.00	110.00	50.00	125.00

DB368
SHEARER BUNNYKINS™

Backstamp not available at press time

Designer:	Wendy Boyce-Davies
Height:	4", 10.1 cm
Colour:	White shirt, blue jeans, tan shoes and belt
Issued:	2006 in a limited edition of 1,000
Series:	Australian Heritage

Back Stamp	U.S. $	Price Can. $	U.K. £	Aust. $
BK-Not known	–	–	–	99.00

DB369
PILOT BUNNYKINS™

Backstamp not available at press time

Height:	4 ¾", 12.1 cm
Colour:	Brown uniform, black shoes and goggles, dark brown and grey propeller, red parachute
Issued:	2005 to the present
Series:	World War II Collection

Back Stamp	U.S. $	Price Can. $	U.K. £	Aust. $
BK-Not known	45.00	65.00	25.00	50.00

DB370
SAILOR BUNNYKINS™
Style Two

Height: 4 ¾", 12.1 cm
Colour: Dark blue and white naval uniform, black shoes, red and white life saver, light grey base
Issued: 2005 to the present
Series: World War II Collection

Backstamp not available at press time

Back Stamp	U.S. $	Price Can. $	U.K. £	Aust. $
BK-Not known	45.00	65.00	25.00	50.00

DB371
HOMEGUARD BUNNYKINS™

Height: 4 ¼", 10.8 cm
Colour: Khaki uniform, dark brown shoes, gun and sacks, white cup, napkins and sandwich
Issued: 2005 to the present
Series: World War II Collection

Backstamp not available at press time

Back Stamp	U.S. $	Price Can. $	U.K. £	Aust. $
BK-Not known	45.00	65.00	25.00	50.00

DB372
LAND GIRL BUNNYKINS™

Height: 4 ¾", 12.1 cm
Colour: Cream dungarees, yellowy-brown jacket, grey and white shirt, brown sacks, pink and white hat
Issued: 2005 to the present
Series: World War II Collection

Backstamp not available at press time

Back Stamp	U.S. $	Price Can. $	U.K. £	Aust. $
BK-Not known	45.00	65.00	25.00	50.00

DB373
EVACUEES BUNNYKINS™

Height: 5", 12.7 cm
Colour: Boy: Blue coat, grey trousers, white socks, black shoes and hat
Girl: Maroon coat, blue and white striped skirt, white blouse and socks, black shoes, blue hat
Issued: 2005 to the present
Series: World War II Collection

Backstamp not available at press time

Back Stamp	U.S. $	Price Can. $	U.K. £	Aust. $
BK-Not known	65.00	75.00	40.00	70.00

DB374
BARRISTER BUNNYKINS™

Height: 4 ¾", 12.1 cm
Colour: Black robe, grey waistcoat, white shirt, grey and black striped trousers
Issued: 2005 to the present
Series: Professions Collection

Backstamp not available at press time

Back Stamp	U.S. $	Price Can. $	U.K. £	Aust. $
BK-Not known	45.00	65.00	25.00	50.00

DB375
NURSE BUNNYKINS™
Style Two

Height: 4 ¼", 10.8 cm
Colour: Nurse: Blue and white dress, white apron and cap, black cloak
Child: reddish-brown coat, green trousers, yellow shirt and socks, blue shoes
Issued: 2005 to the present
Series: Professions Collection

Backstamp not available at press time

Back Stamp	U.S. $	Price Can. $	U.K. £	Aust. $
BK-Not known	65.00	75.00	40.00	70.00

DB376
FIREMAN BUNNYKINS™
Style Two

Height:	4 ¾", 12.1 cm
Colour:	Dark blue uniform, black boots, yellow hat, grey pail, red fire hose and ginger cat
Issued:	2005 to the present
Series:	Professions Collection

Backstamp not available at press time

Back Stamp	U.S. $	Price Can. $	U.K. £	Aust. $
BK-Not known	45.00	65.00	25.00	50.00

DB377
POSTMAN BUNNYKINS™
Style Two

Height:	4 ¾", 12.1 cm
Colour:	Dark blue uniform with red trim, light brown postage bag, white letter, red, grey, black and brown bicycle
Issued:	2005 to the present
Series:	Professions Collection

Backstamp not available at press time

Back Stamp	U.S. $	Price Can. $	U.K. £	Aust. $
BK-Not known	55.00	70.00	30.00	70.00

DB378
PLUMBER BUNNYKINS™

Height:	4 ¾", 12.1 cm
Colour:	Blue dungarees, green and red checked shirt, red hat, black shoes, light blue tool box
Issued:	2005 to the present
Series:	Professions Collection

Backstamp not available at press time

Back Stamp	U.S. $	Price Can. $	U.K. £	Aust. $
BK-Not known	45.00	65.00	25.00	50.00

DB379
CHEF BUNNYKINS™

Height:	4 ¾", 12.1 cm
Colour:	White shirt, apron, hat and tea-towel, black and white checked trousers, red, brown and beige bowls
Issued:	2005 to the present
Series:	Professions Collection

Backstamp not available at press time

Back Stamp	U.S. $	Price Can. $	U.K. £	Aust. $
BK-Not known	45.00	65.00	25.00	50.00

DB380
TEACHER BUNNYKINS™

Height:	4 ¾", 12.1 cm
Colour:	Black robe with red and white trim at the neck, green trousers, black shoes and cap
Issued:	2005 to the present
Series:	Professions Collections

Backstamp not available at press time

Back Stamp	U.S. $	Price Can. $	U.K. £	Aust. $
BK-Not known	55.00	70.00	30.00	70.00

DB381
DOCTOR BUNNYKINS™
Style Two

Height:	4 ¾", 12.1 cm
Colour:	White lab coat, grey and blue pinstripe trousers, red and yellow tie, black shoes, brown desk
Issued:	2005 to the present
Series:	Professions Collection

Backstamp not available at press time

Back Stamp	U.S. $	Price Can. $	U.K. £	Aust. $
BK-Not known	55.00	70.00	30.00	50.00

DB382
AIR CONTROLLER BUNNYKINS™

Height: 4 ½", 11.9 cm
Colour: Dark grey uniform, black tie, shoes and stick, white, yellow and red radar map, brown wireless
Issued: 2005 to the present
Series: World War II Collection

Backstamp not available at press time

Back Stamp	Price U.S. $	Can. $	U.K. £	Aust. $
BK-Not known	45.00	65.00	25.00	50.00

BUNNYKINS FIGURINE BASES

ARTHURIAN LEGENDS COLLECTION CAMELOT BASE

Modeller: Unknown
Size: 4 ¾" x 13 ½" x 8 ¾", 12.0 x 34.0 x 22.0 cm
Colour: Green, grey and brown
Issued: 2004 - 2005

Description	U.S. $	Can. $	U.K. £	Aust. $
Camelot base	60.00	80.00	35.00	85.00

Note: This base accommodates the 6 figures in the Arthurian Legends Collection.

THE OCCASIONS COLLECTION SCENIC BASE

Modeller: Shane Ridge
Size: 3" x 15 ¼", 7.6 x 38.7 cm
Colour: Cream and red
Issued: 2003 to the present

Description	U.S. $	Can. $	U.K. £	Aust. $
Occasions base	60.00	110.00	35.00	125.00

Note: This base accommodates the 8 figures in the Occasions Collection.

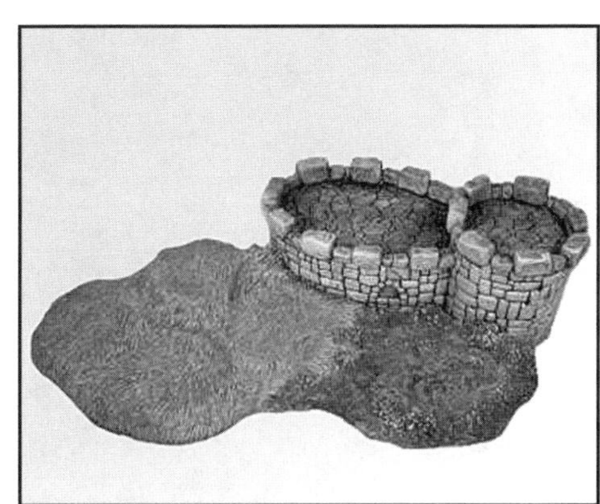

THE ROBIN HOOD COLLECTION BASE

Modeller: Martyn Alcock
Size: 3 ¼" x 14", 8.3 x 35.5 cm
Colour: Grey, green and brown
Issued: 2002 - 2003

Description	U.S. $	Can. $	U.K. £	Aust. $
Robin Hood base	60.00	80.00	35.00	85.00

Note: This base accommodates the 8 figures in the Robin Hood Collection.

THE SHIPMATES COLLECTION TALL SHIP BASE

Designer: Caroline Dadd
Size: 11 ¾" x 17 ¾", 29.8 x 45.0 cm
Colour: Brown, white, blue, orange-yellow, red and grey
Issued: 2004 to the present

Description	U.S. $	Can. $	U.K. £	Aust. $
Tall Ship base	70.00	110.00	40.00	125.00

Note: This base accommodates the 7 figures in the Shipmates Collection.

THE TUDOR COLLECTION SCENIC BASE

Modeller: Martyn Alcock
Size: 6 ¾" x 15 ¾", 17.2 x 40.0 cm
Colour: Red, brown and purple
Issued: 2003 - 2005

Description	U.S. $	Can. $	U.K. £	Aust. $
Tudor base, 7 figures	60.00	80.00	35.00	85.00

Note: This base accommodates the 7 figures in the Tudor Collection.

RESIN ISSUES

1996-1997

DBR1
HARRY BUNNYKINS
A LITTLE BUNNY AT PLAY™

Height: 1 ¾", 4.5 cm
Colour: Pale blue pyjamas, red and dark blue toys
Composition: Resin
Issued: 1996 - 1997

Doulton Number	U.S. $	Price Can. $	U.K. £	Aust. $
DBR1	25.00	30.00	15.00	35.00

DBR2
HARRY BUNNYKINS
PLAYTIME™

Height: 2", 5.0 cm
Colour: Pale blue pyjamas, yellow toys, pink, yellow and green pillow
Composition: Resin
Issued: 1996 - 1997

Doulton Number	U.S. $	Price Can. $	U.K. £	Aust. $
DBR2	25.00	30.00	15.00	35.00

DBR3
REGINALD RATLEY
UP TO NO GOOD™

Height: 2 ¼", 5.7 cm
Colour: Black jacket, hat and shoes, yellow shirt, red tie
Composition: Resin
Issued: 1996 - 1997

Doulton Number	U.S. $	Price Can. $	U.K. £	Aust. $
DBR3	45.00	55.00	25.00	60.00

DBR4
SUSAN BUNNYKINS
THE HELPER™

Photograph not available at press time

Height:	3", 7.6 cm
Colour:	White and blue dress
Composition:	Resin
Issued:	1996 - 1997

Doulton Number	U.S. $	Price Can. $	U.K. £	Aust. $
DBR4	35.00	45.00	20.00	50.00

DBR5
WILLIAM BUNNYKINS
ASLEEP IN THE SUN™

Height:	2 ¼", 5.7 cm
Colour:	White shirt, red jacket, brown trousers
Composition:	Resin
Issued:	1996 - 1997

Royal Doulton
William Bunnykins
Asleep in the sun
DBR5/-3626
© 1996 Royal Doulton
Made in China

Doulton Number	U.S. $	Price Can. $	U.K. £	Aust. $
DBR5	35.00	45.00	20.00	50.00

DBR6
LADY RATLEY
HER LADYSHIP EXPLAINS™

Height:	3 ¼", 8.3 cm
Colour:	Light and dark purple dress black shoes and handbag
Composition:	Resin
Issued:	1996 - 1997

Doulton Number	U.S. $	Price Can. $	U.K. £	Aust. $
DBR6	35.00	45.00	20.00	50.00

DBR7
MRS. BUNNYKINS
A BUSY MORNING SHOPPING™

Height: 3 ½", 8.9 cm
Colour: White dress with blue flowers, pale yellow apron and hat, brown basket
Composition: Resin
Issued: 1996 - 1997

Doulton Number	U.S. $	Price Can. $	U.K. £	Aust. $
DBR7	30.00	45.00	20.00	50.00

DBR8
FATHER BUNNYKINS
HOME FROM WORK™

Height: 3 ¾", 9.5 cm
Colour: Crean trousers, green jacket and black shoes
Composition: Resin
Issued: 1996 - 1997

Royal Doulton
Father Bunnykins
Home from work
DBR8/ 1036
© 1996 Royal Doulton
Made in China

Doulton Number	U.S. $	Price Can. $	U.K. £	Aust. $
DBR8	30.00	45.00	20.00	50.00

DBR9
WILLIAM BUNNYKINS
A BUNNY IN A HURRY™

Height: 2 ¼", 5.7 cm
Colour: Brown trousers, white shirt and red jacket
Composition: Resin
Issued: 1996 - 1997

Backstamp not available at press time

Doulton Number	U.S. $	Price Can. $	U.K. £	Aust. $
DBR9	30.00	45.00	20.00	50.00

Royal Doulton
Susan Bunnykins
Wildlife spotting
DBR10/ 3548
© 1996 Royal Doulton
Made in China

DBR10
SUSAN BUNNYKINS
WILDLIFE SPOTTING™

Height:	2 ¾", 7.0 cm
Colour:	White dress with blue flowers, brown basket
Composition:	Resin
Issued:	1996 - 1997

Doulton Number	U.S. $	Price Can. $	U.K. £	Aust. $
DBR10	30.00	45.00	20.00	50.00

DBR11
SUSAN AND HARRY BUNNYKINS
MINDING THE BABY BROTHER™

Height:	2 ½", 6.4 cm
Colour:	Susan - white dress with blue flowers Harry - pale blue pyjamas, multicoloured toys
Composition:	Resin
Issued:	1996 - 1997

Royal Doulton
Susan and Harry
Bunnykins
Minding the baby brother
DBR11/ 2850
© 1996 Royal Doulton
Made in China

Doulton Number	U.S. $	Price Can. $	U.K. £	Aust. $
DBR11	45.00	55.00	25.00	60.00

DBR12
FATHER BUNNYKINS AND HARRY
DECORATING THE TREE™

Height:	4", 10.1 cm
Colour:	Father - blue trousers, white shirt and red pullover Harry - white pyjamas, green tree
Composition:	Resin
Issued:	1996 - 1997

Doulton Number	U.S. $	Price Can. $	U.K. £	Aust. $
DBR12	50.00	65.00	30.00	70.00

DBR13
MRS. BUNNYKINS AND WILLIAM
THE BIRTHDAY CAKE™

Height: 3 ¼", 8.3 cm
Colour: Mrs. Bunnykins: White dress with blue flowers, light yellow apron
William: Red jacket, white shirt and brown trousers
Composition: Resin
Issued: 1996 - 1997

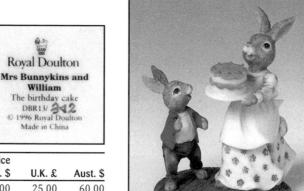

Royal Doulton
Mrs Bunnykins and William
The birthday cake
DBR13/ 342
© 1996 Royal Doulton
Made in China

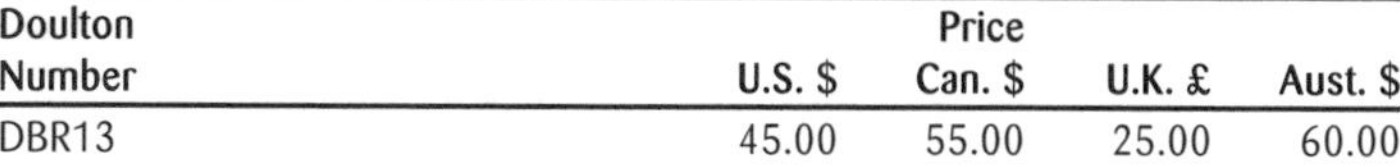

Doulton Number	U.S. $	Price Can. $	U.K. £	Aust. $
DBR13	45.00	55.00	25.00	60.00

DBR14
HAPPY CHRISTMAS FROM THE BUNNYKINS FAMILY™

Royal Doulton
Happy Christmas
from the Bunnykins family
DBR14/ 1018
© 1996 Royal Doulton
Made in China

Height: 6", 15.0 cm
Colour: Multi-coloured
Issued: 1996 - 1997
Composition: Resin
Series: Music Box

Doulton Number	U.S. $	Price Can. $	U.K. £	Aust. $
DBR14	130.00	160.00	75.00	175.00

DBR15
PICNIC TIME
WITH THE BUNNYKINS FAMILY™

Height: 5", 12.7 cm
Colour: Multi-coloured
Issued: 1996 - 1997
Composition: Resin
Series: Music Box

Doulton Number	U.S. $	Price Can. $	U.K. £	Aust. $
DBR15	130.00	160.00	75.00	175.00

DBR16
BIRTHDAY GIRL™

Royal Doulton
Bunnykins
Birthday Girl
DBR16/874
©1996 Royal Doulton
Made in China

Height: 1 ½", 4 cm
Colour: Pink and white dress
Composition: Resin
Issued: 1997 - 1997

Doulton Number	U.S.$	Can. $	Price U.K. £	Aust. $
DBR16	25.00	30.00	15.00	35.00

DBR17
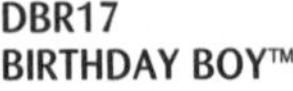

BIRTHDAY BOY™

Height: 1 ½", 4 cm
Colour: Blue pyjamas, white bib
Composition: Resin
Issued: 1997 - 1997

Doulton Number	U.S.$	Price Can. $	U.K. £	Aust. $
DBR17	25.00	30.00	15.00	35.00

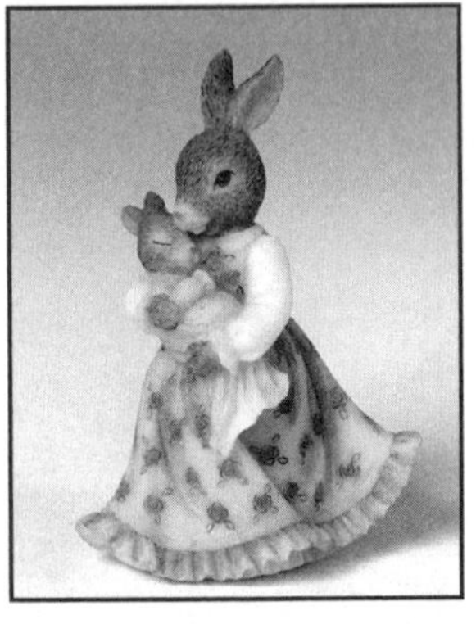

DBR18
THE NEW BABY™

Royal Doulton
Bunnykins
The New Baby
DBR18/101
©1996 Royal Doulton
Made in China

Height: 3 ½", 8.9 cm
Colour: Mother - white, lilac and rose
Baby - light blue
Composition: Resin
Issued: 1997 - 1997

Doulton Number	U.S. $	Price Can. $	U.K. £	Aust. $
DBR18	30.00	45.00	20.00	50.00

DBR19

THE ROCKING HORSE™

Height: 2 ¾", 7.0 cm
Colour: Brown bunny, red and white dress, white rocking horse
Composition: Resin
Issued: 1997 - 1997

Doulton Number	U.S. $	Price Can. $	U.K. £	Aust. $
DBR19	30.00	45.00	20.00	45.00

SECTION TWO

STORYBOOK AND CARTOON CHARACTERS

Alice in Wonderland	338
Brambly Hedge	340
Frosty Family	363
Harry Potter	364
Noddy	368
Nursery Rhyme Collection	369
Old Bear and Friends	370
Paddington Bear	373
Rupert Bear	377
St. Tiggywinkles	381
Snowman Gift Collection	386
Thelwell	397
Wind in the Willows	399
Wizard of Oz	402

ALICE IN WONDERLAND

RESIN SERIES 1997-1997

ALICE™
Style One

Designer: Adrian Hughes
Height: 4", 10.1 cm
Colour: Pale blue and white dress, red and white toadstool, green base
Composition: Resin
Issued: 1997 - 1997

Doulton Number	Price U.S. $	Can. $	U.K. £	Aust. $
–	25.00	30.00	15.00	35.00
Complete Set (6 pcs.)	150.00	180.00	90.00	210.00

CHESHIRE CAT™
Style One

Designer: Adrian Hughes
Height: 4", 10.1 cm
Colour: Ginger striped cat, blue butterfly, red ladybird, brown tree stump, green base
Composition: Resin
Issued: 1997 - 1997

Doulton Number	Price U.S. $	Can. $	U.K. £	Aust. $
–	25.00	30.00	15.00	35.00

DODO™

Designer: Adrian Hughes
Height: 4", 10.1 cm
Colour: White bird with blue wing tips, yellow head and black beak
Composition: Resin
Issued: 1997 - 1997

Doulton Number	Price U.S. $	Can. $	U.K. £	Aust. $
–	25.00	30.00	15.00	35.00

Note: The *Alice In Wonderland* resin series does not carry a backstamp. It was sold as a set through Lawleys By Post.

MAD HATTER™
Style One

Designer: Adrian Hughes
Height: 4", 10.1 cm
Colour: Brown trousers and top hat, green jacket, blue waistcoat, green base
Composition: Resin
Issued: 1997 - 1997

Doulton Number	Price U.S. $	Can. $	U.K. £	Aust. $
—	25.00	30.00	15.00	35.00

QUEEN OF HEARTS™

Designer: Adrian Hughes
Height: 4", 10.1 cm
Colour: Red coat trimmed with ermine, white dress with red and black design, black and red crown
Composition: Resin
Issued: 1997 - 1997

Doulton Number	Price U.S. $	Can. $	U.K. £	Aust. $
—	25.00	30.00	15.00	35.00

WHITE RABBIT™
Style One

Designer: Adrian Hughes
Height: 4", 10.1 cm
Colour: White rabbit with brown jacket and green waistcoat, green base
Composition: Resin
Issued: 1997 in a limited edition of 2,500

Doulton Number	Price U.S. $	Can. $	U.K. £	Aust. $
—	25.00	30.00	15.00	35.00

BRAMBLY HEDGE

DBH 1
POPPY EYEBRIGHT™
Style One

Designer:	Harry Sales
Modeller:	David Lyttleton
Height:	3 ¼", 8.3 cm
Colour:	Grey-white and pink dress, white apron trimmed with blue flowers
Issued:	1983 - 1997

Doulton Number	U.S. $	Price Can. $	U.K. £	Aust. $
DBH 1	55.00	65.00	30.00	75.00

DBH 2
MR. APPLE™
Style One

Designer:	Harry Sales
Modeller:	David Lyttleton
Height:	3 ¼", 8.3 cm
Colour:	Black trousers, white and blue striped shirt, white apron
Issued:	1983 - 1997

Doulton Number	U.S. $	Price Can. $	U.K. £	Aust. $
DBH 2	55.00	65.00	30.00	75.00

DBH 3
MRS. APPLE™
Style One

Designer:	Harry Sales
Modeller:	David Lyttleton
Height:	3 ¼", 8.3 cm
Colour:	White and blue striped dress, white apron
Issued:	1983 - 1997

Doulton Number	U.S. $	Price Can. $	U.K. £	Aust. $
DBH 3	55.00	65.00	30.00	75.00

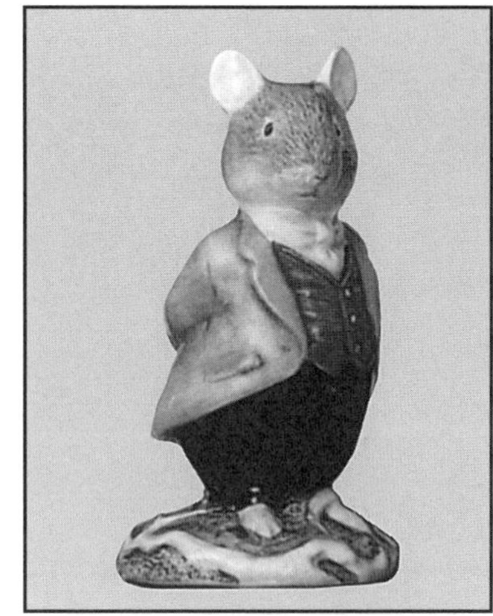

DBH 4
LORD WOODMOUSE™
Style One

Designer: Harry Sales
Modeller: David Lyttleton
Height: 3 ¼", 8.3 cm
Colour: Green trousers, brown coat and burgundy waistcoat
Issued: 1983 - 1997

Doulton Number	U.S. $	Price Can. $	U.K. £	Aust. $
DBH 4	55.00	65.00	30.00	75.00

DBH 5
LADY WOODMOUSE™
Style One

Designer: Harry Sales
Modeller: David Lyttleton
Height: 3 ¼", 8.3 cm
Colour: Red and white striped dress, white apron
Issued: 1983 - 1997

Doulton Number	U.S. $	Price Can. $	U.K. £	Aust. $
DBH 5	55.00	65.00	30.00	75.00

DBH 6
DUSTY DOGWOOD™
Style One

Designer: Harry Sales
Modeller: David Lyttleton
Height: 3 ¼", 8.3 cm
Colour: Dark grey suit, rose-pink waistcoat
Issued: 1984 - 1995

Doulton Number	U.S. $	Price Can. $	U.K. £	Aust. $
DBH 6	60.00	75.00	35.00	85.00

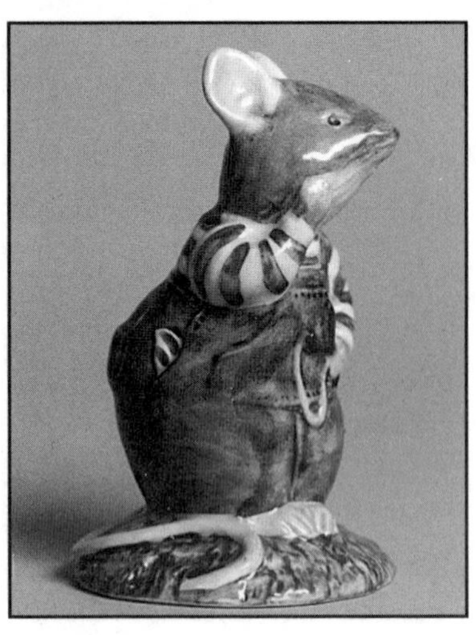

Royal Doulton
WILFRED TOADFLAX
D BH 7
FROM THE BRAMBLY HEDGE
GIFT COLLECTION
© JILL BARKLEM 1982

DBH 7
WILFRED TOADFLAX™
Style One

Designer:	Harry Sales
Modeller:	David Lyttleton
Height:	3 ¼", 8.3 cm
Colour:	Grey overalls, red and white striped shirt
Issued:	1983 - 1997

Doulton Number	U.S. $	Price Can. $	U.K. £	Aust. $
DBH 7	70.00	90.00	40.00	100.00

Royal Doulton
PRIMROSE WOODMOUSE
D BH 8
FROM THE BRAMBLY HEDGE
GIFT COLLECTION
© JILL BARKLEM 1982

DBH 8
PRIMROSE WOODMOUSE™

Designer:	Harry Sales
Modeller:	David Lyttleton
Height:	3 ¼", 8.3 cm
Colour:	Yellow dress with white apron
Issued:	1983 - 1997

Doulton Number	U.S. $	Price Can. $	U.K. £	Aust. $
DBH 8	70.00	90.00	40.00	100.00

DBH 9
OLD MRS. EYEBRIGHT™
Style One

Designer:	Harry Sales
Modeller:	David Lyttleton
Height:	3 ¼", 8.3 cm
Colour:	Mauve skirt, white and pink striped shawl, white apron
Issued:	1984 - 1995

Doulton Number	U.S. $	Price Can. $	U.K. £	Aust. $
DBH 9	100.00	125.00	60.00	135.00

DBH 10A
MR. TOADFLAX™
Style One, First Version (Tail at front, with cushion)

Designer: Harry Sales
Modeller: David Lyttleton
Height: 3 ¼", 8.3 cm
Colour: Blue and white striped shirt, pink trousers, burgundy braces, multicoloured patchwork quilt
Issued: 1984 - 1984

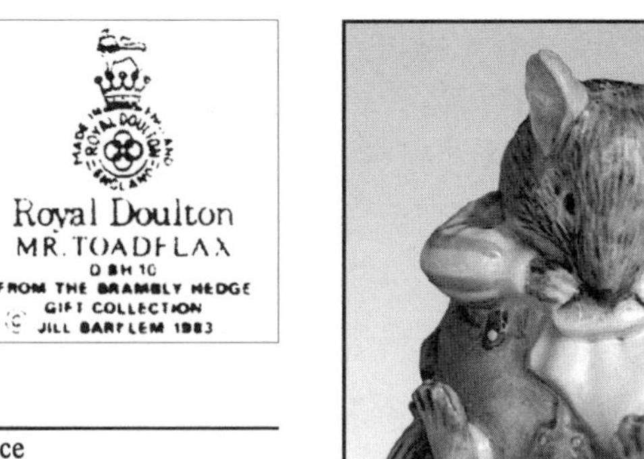

Doulton Number	U.S. $	Price Can. $	U.K. £	Aust. $
DBH 10A	1,400.00	1,700.00	775.00	1,800.00

DBH 10B
MR. TOADFLAX™
Style One, Second Version (Tail at back, without cushion)

Designer: Harry Sales
Modeller: David Lyttleton
Height: 3 ¼", 8.3 cm
Colour: Blue and white striped shirt, pink trousers, burgundy braces
Issued: 1984 - 1985

Doulton Number	U.S. $	Price Can. $	U.K. £	Aust. $
DBH 10B	400.00	475.00	225.00	500.00

DBH 10C
MR. TOADFLAX™
Style One, Third Version (Tail at back, with cushion)

Designer: Harry Sales
Modeller: David Lyttleton
Height: 3 ¼", 8.3 cm
Colour: Blue and white striped shirt, lilac trousers, burgundy braces, multicoloured patchwork cushion
Issued: 1985 - 1997

Doulton Number	U.S. $	Price Can. $	U.K. £	Aust. $
DBH 10C	65.00	80.00	35.00	90.00

DBH 11
MRS. TOADFLAX™

Designer:	Harry Sales
Modeller:	David Lyttleton
Height:	3 ¼", 8.3 cm
Colour:	Green and white striped dress, white apron
Issued:	1985 - 1995

Doulton Number	U.S. $	Price Can. $	U.K. £	Aust. $
DBH 11	90.00	110.00	50.00	120.00

Note: The contents of the bowl may vary in colour.

DBH 12
CATKIN™

Designer:	Harry Sales
Modeller:	David Lyttleton
Height:	3 ¼", 8.3 cm
Colour:	Yellow dress and white apron
Issued:	1985 - 1994

Doulton Number	U.S. $	Price Can. $	U.K. £	Aust. $
DBH 12	140.00	170.00	80.00	180.00

DBH 13
OLD VOLE™

Designer:	Harry Sales
Modeller:	David Lyttleton
Height:	3 ¼", 8.3 cm
Colour:	Green jacket, blue trousers, yellow waistcoat
Issued:	1985 - 1992

Doulton Number	U.S. $	Price Can. $	U.K. £	Aust. $
DBH 13	330.00	400.00	190.00	450.00

DBH 14
BASIL™
Style One

Designer:	Harry Sales
Modeller:	David Lyttleton
Height:	3 ¼", 8.3 cm
Colour:	Brown waistcoat, green and white striped trousers
Issued:	1985 - 1992

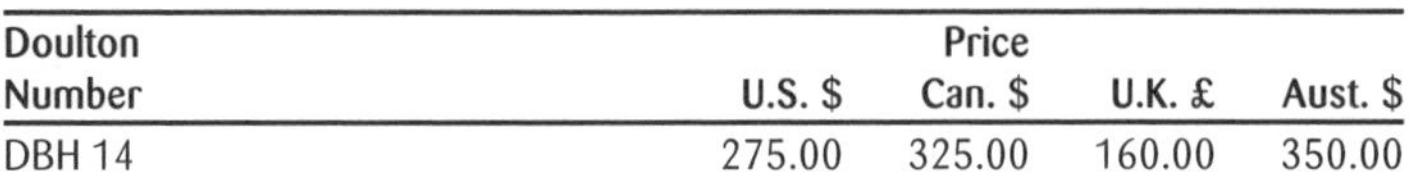

Doulton Number	U.S. $	Price Can. $	U.K. £	Aust. $
DBH 14	275.00	325.00	160.00	350.00

DBH 15
MRS. CRUSTYBREAD™

Designer:	Graham Tongue
Modeller:	Ted Chawner
Height:	3 ¼", 8.3 cm
Colour:	Yellow dress, white apron and cap
Issued:	1987 - 1994

Doulton Number	U.S. $	Price Can. $	U.K. £	Aust. $
DBH 15	275.00	325.00	160.00	350.00

DBH 16
CLOVER™

Designer:	Graham Tongue
Modeller:	Graham Tongue
Height:	3 ¼", 8.3 cm
Colour:	Burgundy dress, white apron
Issued:	1987 - 1997

Doulton Number	U.S. $	Price Can. $	U.K. £	Aust. $
DBH 16	55.00	65.00	30.00	75.00

DBH 17
TEASEL™

Designer:	Graham Tongue
Modeller:	Ted Chawner
Height:	3 ¼", 8.3 cm
Colour:	Blue-grey dungarees, blue and white striped shirt
Issued:	1987 - 1992

Doulton Number	U.S. $	Price Can. $	U.K. £	Aust. $
DBH 17	330.00	400.00	190.00	450.00

DBH 18
STORE STUMP MONEY BOX™

Designer:	Martyn Alcock
Height:	3 ¼", 8.3 cm
Colour:	Browns
Issued:	1987 - 1989

Doulton Number	U.S. $	Price Can. $	U.K. £	Aust. $
DBH 18	265.00	320.00	150.00	350.00

DBH 19
LILY WEAVER™
Style One

Designer:	Graham Tongue
Modeller:	Ted Chawner
Height:	3 ¼", 8.3 cm
Colour:	White dress with green and mauve, white cap
Issued:	1988 - 1993

Doulton Number	U.S. $	Price Can. $	U.K. £	Aust. $
DBH 19	250.00	300.00	140.00	350.00

DBH 20
FLAX WEAVER™
Style One

Designer:	Graham Tongue
Modeller:	Ted Chawner
Height:	3 ¼", 8.3 cm
Colour:	Grey trousers, grey and white striped shirt
Issued:	1988 - 1993

Doulton Number	Price U.S. $	Can. $	U.K. £	Aust. $
DBH 20	275.00	325.00	160.00	350.00

DBH 21
CONKER™

Designer:	Graham Tongue
Modeller:	Ted Chawner
Height:	3 ¼", 8.3 cm
Colour:	Green jacket, yellow waistcoat, green striped trousers
Issued:	1988 - 1994

Doulton Number	Price U.S. $	Can. $	U.K. £	Aust. $
DBH 21	275.00	325.00	160.00	350.00

DBH 22
PRIMROSE ENTERTAINS™

Designer:	Graham Tongue
Modeller:	Alan Maslankowski
Height:	3 ¼", 8.3 cm
Colour:	Green and yellow dress
Issued:	1990 - 1995

Doulton Number	Price U.S. $	Can. $	U.K. £	Aust. $
DBH 22	150.00	175.00	80.00	200.00

DBH 23
WILFRED ENTERTAINS™

Designer:	Graham Tongue
Modeller:	Alan Maslankowski
Height:	3 ¼", 8.3 cm
Colour:	Burgundy and yellow outfit, black hat
Issued:	1990 - 1995

Doulton Number	U.S. $	Price Can. $	U.K. £	Aust $
DBH 23	175.00	225.00	100.00	250.00

DBH 24
MR. SALTAPPLE™
Style One

Designer:	Graham Tongue
Modeller:	Warren Platt
Height:	3 ¼", 8.3 cm
Colour:	Blue and white striped outfit, beige base
Issued:	1993 - 1997

Doulton Number	U.S. $	Price Can. $	U.K. £	Aust. $
DBH 24	70.00	90.00	40.00	100.00

DBH 25
MRS. SALTAPPLE™
Style One

Designer:	Graham Tongue
Modeller:	Warren Platt
Height:	3 ¼", 8.3 cm
Colour:	Rose and cream dress, beige hat and base
Issued:	1993 - 1997

Doulton Number	U.S. $	Price Can. $	U.K. £	Aust. $
DBH 25	70.00	90.00	40.00	100.00

DBH 26
DUSTY AND BABY™

Designer:	Graham Tongue
Modeller:	Martyn Alcock
Height:	3 ¾", 9.5 cm
Colour:	Dusty: Blue striped shirt with beige dungarees Baby: White gown
Issued:	1995 - 1997

Doulton Number	U.S. $	Price Can. $	U.K. £	Aust. $
DBH 26	70.00	90.00	40.00	100.00

DBH 30
THE ICE BALL™

Designer:	Shane Ridge
Modeller:	Shane Ridge
Height:	4 ¼", 10.8 cm
Colour:	Green, yellow, pink and white
Issued:	2000 in a limited edition of 3,000 (C of A)
Series:	Tableau

Doulton Number	U.S. $	Price Can. $	U.K. £	Aust. $
DBH 30	150.00	175.00	80.00	200.00

DBH 31
LORD WOODMOUSE™
Style Two

Designer:	Shane Ridge
Modeller:	Shane Ridge
Height:	4 ¼", 10.8 cm
Colour:	Brown, salmon, black, red and yellow
Issued:	2000 - 2002

Doulton Number	U.S. $	Price Can. $	U.K. £	Aust. $
DBH 31	55.00	65.00	30.00	75.00

DBH 32
LADY WOODMOUSE™
Style Two

Designer:	Warren Platt
Modeller:	Warren Platt
Height:	4 ¼", 10.8 cm
Colour:	White, pale blue, red and yellow
Issued:	2000 - 2002

Doulton Number	U.S. $	Price Can. $	U.K. £	Aust. $
DBH 32	55.00	65.00	30.00	75.00

DBH 33
PRIMROSE PICKING BERRIES™

Designer:	Shane Ridge
Modeller:	Shane Ridge
Height:	3 ½", 8.9 cm
Colour:	Yellow, white and purple
Issued:	2000 - 2002

Doulton Number	U.S. $	Price Can. $	U.K. £	Aust. $
DBH 33	45.00	55.00	25.00	65.00

DBH 34
WILFRED CARRIES THE PICNIC™

Designer:	Shane Ridge
Modeller:	Shane Ridge
Height:	3 ½", 8.9 cm
Colour:	Blue, brown and red
Issued:	2000 - 2002

Doulton Number	U.S. $	Price Can. $	U.K. £	Aust. $
DBH 34	45.00	55.00	25.00	65.00

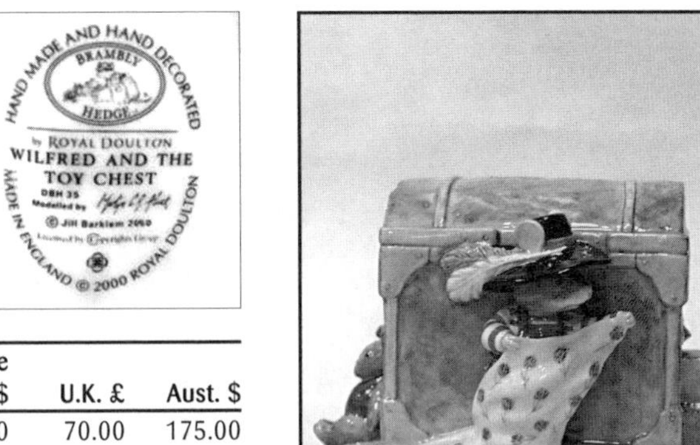

DBH 35
WILFRED AND THE TOY CHEST (Money Box)™

Designer:	Martyn Alcock
Modeller:	Martyn Alcock
Height:	3 ¾", 9.5 cm
Colour:	Green, yellow, red and black
Issued:	2000 - 2002

Doulton Number	U.S. $	Price Can. $	U.K. £	Aust. $
DBH 35	125.00	150.00	70.00	175.00

DBH 36
POPPY EYEBRIGHT™
Style Two

Designer:	Warren Platt
Modeller:	Warren Platt
Height:	4", 10.1 cm
Colour:	White skirt with red polka-dots; blue blouse; white apron
Issued:	2001 - 2002

Doulton Number	U.S. $	Price Can. $	U.K. £	Aust. $
DBH 36	60.00	75.00	35.00	85.00

DBH 37
DUSTY DOGWOOD™
Style Two

Designer:	Martyn Alcock
Modeller:	Martyn Alcock
Height:	4", 10.1 cm
Colour:	Blue and white striped shirt; white, yellow and orange pants; white apron and neckerchief; tan sack
Issued:	2001 - 2002

Doulton Number	U.S. $	Price Can. $	U.K. £	Aust. $
DBH 37	60.00	75.00	35.00	85.00

DBH 38
BASIL™
Style Two

Designer:	Shane Ridge
Modeller:	Shane Ridge
Height:	3 ½", 8.9 cm
Colour:	Red waistcoat, green and white striped trousers
Issued:	2001 - 2002

Doulton Number	U.S. $	Price Can. $	U.K. £	Aust. $
DBH 38	55.00	65.00	30.00	75.00

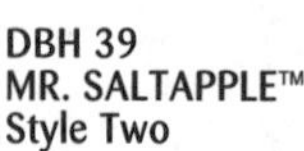

DBH 39
MR. SALTAPPLE™
Style Two

Designer:	Shane Ridge
Modeller:	Shane Ridge
Height:	4", 10.0 cm
Colour:	Blue shirt, brown overalls and basket, green neckerchief
Issued:	2001 - 2002
Series:	Sea Story

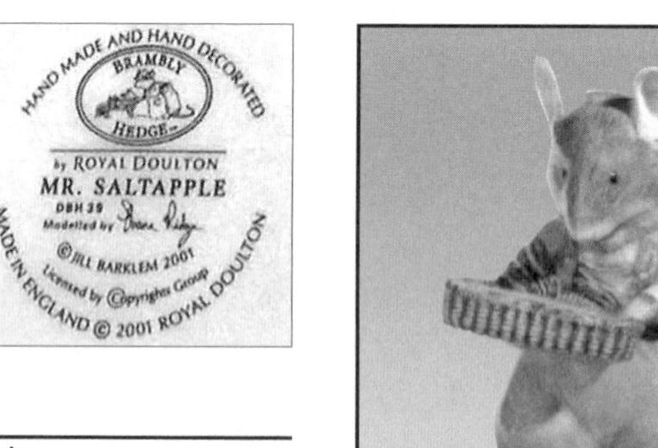

Doulton Number	U.S. $	Price Can. $	U.K. £	Aust. $
DBH 39	55.00	65.00	30.00	75.00

DBH 40
MRS. SALTAPPLE™
Style Two

Designer:	Martyn Alcock
Modeller:	Martyn Alcock
Height:	3 ½", 8.9 cm
Colour:	Lilac and white dress; pale yellow bonnet with purple ribbon; brown basket
Issued:	2001 - 2002
Series:	Sea Story

Doulton Number	U.S. $	Price Can. $	U.K. £	Aust. $
DBH 40	55.00	65.00	30.00	75.00

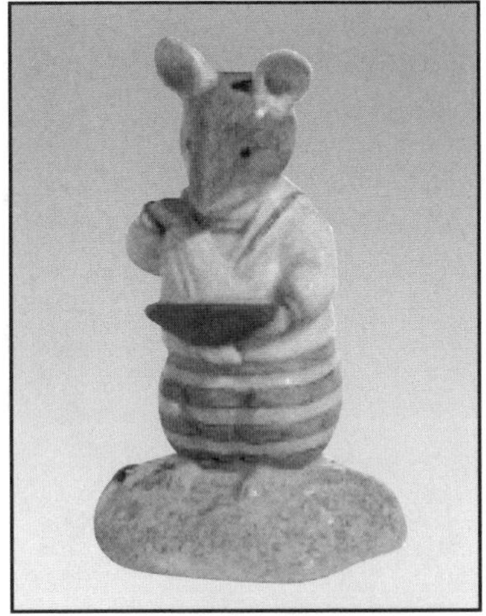

DBH 41
PEBBLE™

Designer: Martyn Alcock
Modeller: Martyn Alcock
Height: 3 ¼", 8.3 cm
Colour: Blue and white striped sailor suit; red boat
Issued: 2001 - 2002
Series: Sea Story

Doulton Number	U.S. $	Price Can. $	U.K. £	Aust. $
DBH 41	55.00	65.00	30.00	75.00

DBH 42
SHELL™

Designer: Warren Platt
Modeller: Warren Platt
Height: 3 ½", 8.9 cm
Colour: Pink and white dress; pale yellow bonnet
Issued: 2001 - 2002
Series: Sea Story

Doulton Number	U.S. $	Price Can. $	U.K. £	Aust. $
DBH 42	55.00	65.00	30.00	75.00

DBH 43
SHRIMP™

Designer: Warren Platt
Modeller: Warren Platt
Height: 3", 7.6 cm
Colour: White dress and hat, pink ribbons
Issued: 2001 - 2002
Series: Sea Story

Doulton Number	U.S. $	Price Can. $	U.K. £	Aust. $
DBH 43	55.00	65.00	30.00	75.00

DBH 44
THE BRIDE AND GROOM™

Designer:	Martyn Alcock
Modeller:	Martyn Alcock
Height:	4 ¼", 10.8 cm
Colour:	Bride: (Poppy Eyebright) White skirt, pink and white striped sleeves, white apron trimmed with flowers; multicoloured bouquet Groom: (Dusty Dogwood) Dary grey suit, lavender waistcoat
Issued:	2001 - 2002

Doulton Number	Price U.S. $	Can. $	U.K. £	Aust. $
DBH 44	100.00	125.00	60.00	150.00

DBH 45
HAPPY BIRTHDAY WILFRED™

Designer:	Martyn Alcock
Modeller:	Martyn Alcock
Height:	3", 7.6 cm
Colour:	Multicoloured quilt, brown bed; brown mouse wearing red and white striped sweater; pink and white table cloth
Issued:	2001 in a limited edition of 3,000 (C of A)
Series:	Tableau

Doulton Number	Price U.S. $	Can. $	U.K. £	Aust. $
DBH 45	175.00	225.00	100.00	250.00

DBH 46
MR. TOADFLAX™
Style Two

Designer:	Warren Platt
Modeller:	Warren Platt
Height:	3 ¼", 8.3 cm
Colour:	Mauve trousers, blue and white striped shirt; red braces
Issued:	2002 - 2002

Doulton Number	Price U.S. $	Can. $	U.K. £	Aust. $
DBH 46	55.00	65.00	30.00	75.00

DBH 47
MRS. APPLE™
Style Two

Designer:	Martyn Alcock
Modeller:	Martyn Alcock
Height:	4", 10.1 cm
Colour:	Blue and white striped dress; white apron; green tea set
Issued:	2002 - 2002

Doulton Number	U.S. $	Price Can. $	U.K. £	Aust. $
DBH 47	55.00	65.00	40.00	75.00

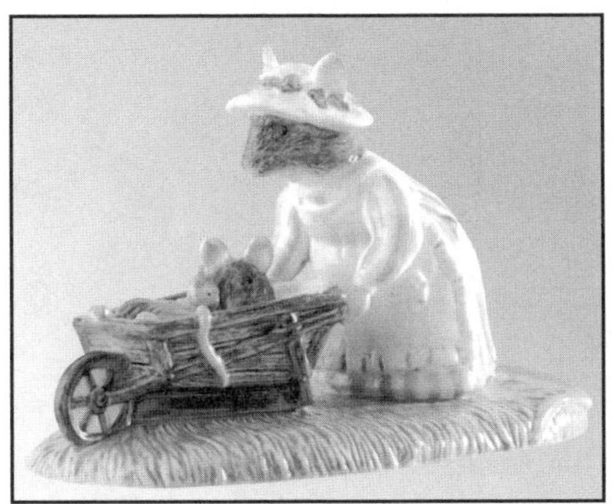

DBH 48
HEADING HOME™

Designer:	Martyn Alcock
Modeller:	Martyn Alcock
Height:	3 ½", 8.9 cm
Colour:	Blue and white striped dress; white apron; yellow straw hat; brown wheel barrow
Issued:	2003 - 2005
Series:	Spring Story

Doulton Number	U.S. $	Can. $	Price U.K. £	Aust. $
DBH 48	55.00	65.00	30.00	75.00

DBH 49
WILFRED'S BIRTHDAY CAKE™

Designer:	Warren Platt
Modeller:	Warren Platt
Height:	3 ¼", 8.3 cm
Colour:	Red and white striped shirt; blue overalls; pink and white cake
Issued:	2003 - 2005
Series:	Spring Story

Doulton Number	U.S. $	Price Can. $	U.K. £	Aust. $
DBH 49	45.00	55.00	25.00	65.00

DBH 50
WHERE ARE BASIL'S TROUSERS?™

Height: 3 ¼", 8.3 cm
Colour: Multicoloured quilt and cushion; pink sofa; brown table
Issued: 2003 - 2005
Series: Spring Story

Doulton Number	U.S. $	Price Can. $	U.K. £	Aust. $
DBH 50	55.00	65.00	30.00	75.00

DBH 51
DUSTY'S BUNS™

Height: 3 ½", 8.9 cm
Colour: Blue and white striped shirt; yellow trousers, white apron and neckerchief
Issued: 2003 - 2005
Series: Spring Story

Doulton Number	U.S. $	Price Can. $	U.K. £	Aust. $
DBH 51	45.00	55.00	25.00	65.00

DBH 52
MRS. TOADFLAX DECORATES CAKE™

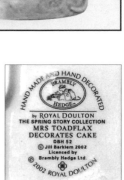

Height: 3 ¾", 9.5 cm
Colour: Cream dress with orange and yellow stars; cream apron; pink and white cake; tan table
Issued: 2003 - 2005
Series: Spring Story

Doulton Number	U.S. $	Price Can. $	U.K. £	Aust. $
DBH 52	60.00	75.00	35.00	85.00

DBH 53
MR. APPLE™
Style Two

Height: 3 ½", 8.9 cm
Colour: Black trousers and waistcoat; blue and white striped shirt; red neckerchief; brown jacket; yellow knapsack
Issued: 2003 - 2005
Series: High Hills Collection

HAND MADE AND HAND DECORATED
BRAMBLY HEDGE
by ROYAL DOULTON
THE HIGH HILLS COLLECTION
MR APPLE
DBH 53
© Jill Barklem 2002
Licenced by
Brambly Hedge Ltd.
© 2002 ROYAL DOULTON

Doulton Number	U.S. $	Price Can. $	U.K. £	Aust. $
DBH 53	45.00	55.00	25.00	65.00

DBH 54
LILY WEAVER™
Style Two

Height: 3 ¾", 9.5 cm
Colour: Brown coat, yellow dress and knapsack, straw hat, brown basket
Issued: 2003 - 2005
Series: High Hills Collection

Doulton Number	U.S. $	Price Can. $	U.K. £	Aust. $
DBH 54	45.00	55.00	25.00	65.00

DBH 55
FLAX WEAVER™
Style Two

Height: 4 ¼", 10.8 cm
Colour: Blue jacket and trousers; orange and red striped shirt; red neckerchief
Issued: 2003 - 2005
Series: High Hills Collection

Doulton Number	U.S. $	Price Can. $	U.K. £	Aust. $
DBH 55	45.00	55.00	25.00	65.00

DBH 56
WILFRED TOADFLAX™
Style Two

Height:	2 ½", 6.4 cm
Colour:	Blue overalls, red and white striped shirt and hat; purple coat; yellow knapsack
Issued:	2003 - 2005
Series:	High Hills Collection

Doulton Number	U.S. $	Price Can. $	U.K. £	Aust. $
DBH 56	45.00	55.00	25.00	65.00

DBH 57
ON THE EDGE™

Height:	4 ¾", 12.1 cm
Colour:	Wilfred: Purple coat, blue overalls; red and white striped shirt and hat Mr. Apple: Tan coat, black trousers and waistcoat; blue and white striped shirt; red neckerchief
Issued:	2003 - 2005
Series:	High Hills Collection

Doulton Number	U.S. $	Price Can. $	U.K. £	Aust. $
DBH 57	60.00	75.00	35.00	85.00

DBH 58
LILY WEAVER SPINNING™

Height:	4 ¼", 10.8 cm
Colour:	Mustard skirt, brown top, pink, yellow and white striped sleeves; white apron, cap and neckerchief; brown spinning wheel
Issued:	2003 - 2005
Series:	High Hills Collection

Doulton Number	U.S. $	Price Can. $	U.K. £	Aust. $
DBH 58	60.00	75.00	35.00	85.00

DBH 59
TEA AT HORNBEAM TREE™

Height:	4", 10.1 cm
Colour:	White skirt with yellow and orange design, green blouse with grey dots, white apron, white bonnet with yellow ribbon, tray with blue and white striped crockery
Issued:	2003 - 2005
Series:	High Hills Collection

Doulton Number	U.S. $	Price Can. $	U.K. £	Aust. $
DBH 59	45.00	55.00	25.00	65.00

DBH 60
A CHEERFUL BLAZE™

Height:	3 ½", 8.9 cm
Colour:	Browns, green, red and blue
Issued:	2003 - 2005
Series:	High Hills Collection

Doulton Number	U.S. $	Price Can. $	U.K. £	Aust. $
DBH 60	80.00	100.00	45.00	110.00

DBH 61
SHOOTING THE RAPIDS™

Height:	3 ¾", 9.5 cm
Colour:	Browns, purple, blues and white
Issued:	2003 in a limited edition of 2,000
Series"	High Hills Collection

Doulton Number	U.S. $	Price Can. $	U.K. £	Aust. $
DBH 61	100.00	125.00	55.00	135.00

DBH 62
OLD MRS. EYEBRIGHT™
Style Two

Height: 3 ¾", 9.5 cm
Colour: Pink, purple and brown
Issued: 2004 - 2005
Series: Autumn Collection

Doulton Number	U.S. $	Price Can. $	U.K. £	Aust. $
DBH 62	65.00	75.00	35.00	85.00

DBH 63
YOU'RE SAFE™

Height: 4", 10.1 cm
Colour: Green, pink and grey
Issued: 2004 - 2005
Series: Autumn Collection

Doulton Number	U.S. $	Price Can. $	U.K. £	Aust. $
DBH 63	55.00	65.00	30.00	75.00

DBH 64
IN THE WOODS™

Height: 4", 10.1 cm
Colour: Pink, blue and brown
Issued: 2004 - 2005
Series: Autumn Collection

Doulton Number	U.S. $	Price Can. $	U.K. £	Aust. $
DBH 64	45.00	55.00	25.00	65.00

DBH 65
IN THE BRAMBLES™

Height: 3 ½", 8.9 cm
Colour: Yellow, brown, red and green
Issued: 2004 - 2005
Series: Autumn Collection

Doulton Number	U.S. $	Price Can. $	U.K. £	Aust. $
DBH 65	55.00	65.00	30.00	75.00

DBH 66
OFF TO PICK MUSHROOMS™

Height: 4 ¼", 10.8 cm
Colour: Pink, brown, red and green
Issued: 2004 - 2005
Series: Autumn Collection

Doulton Number	U.S. $	Price Can. $	U.K. £	Aust. $
DBH 66	60.00	75.00	35.00	85.00

DBH 67
LET'S MAKE A SNOWMOUSE™

Height: 3 ½", 8.9 cm
Colour: Grey, red and brown
Issued: 2004 - 2005
Series: Winter Story

Doulton Number	U.S. $	Price Can. $	U.K. £	Aust. $
DBH 67	45.00	55.00	25.00	65.00

DBH 68
HOT BUTTERED TOAST FOR BREAKFAST™

Height: 7", 17.8 cm
Colour: Pink, white, brown, grey, yellow and red
Issued: 2004 - 2005
Series: Winter Story

Doulton Number	U.S. $	Price Can. $	U.K. £	Aust. $
DBH 68	65.00	75.00	35.00	85.00

DBH 69
HOME FOR SUPPER™

Height: 4 ¼", 10.8 cm
Colour: Browns, grey, dark purple and red
Issued: 2004 - 2005
Series: Winter Story

Doulton Number	U.S. $	Price Can. $	U.K. £	Aust. $
DBH 69	55.00	65.00	30.00	75.00

FROSTY FAMILY

FF 1
MR. FROSTY'S SPECIAL GIFT

Designer: Caroline Dadd
Height: 5 ¼", 13.3 cm
Colour: White, red, green, yellow and blue
Issued: 2004 - 2005

U.S. $45.00
Can. $55.00
U.K. £25.00
Aust. $65.00

FF 2
MRS. FROSTY'S FINISHING TOUCH

Designer: Caroline Dadd
Height: 4 ½", 11.4 cm
Colour: White, blue, green, orange and red
Issued: 2004 - 2005

U.S. $45.00
Can. $55.00
U.K. £25.00
Aust. $65.00

FF 3
SNOWFLAKE ON ICE

Designer: Caroline Dadd
Height: 4 ¼", 10.8 cm
Colour: White, purple, pink and yellow
Issued: 2004 - 2005

U.S. $45.00
Can. $55.00
U.K. £25.00
Aust. $65.00

FF 4
SLUSHY BUILDS A SNOWMAN

Designer: Caroline Dadd
Height: 4", 10.1 cm
Colour: White, green, yellow and red
Issued: 2004 - 2005

U.S. $45.00
Can. $55.00
U.K. £25.00
Aust. $65.00

FF 5
SNOWDRIFT'S CHRISTMAS SURPRISE

Designer: Caroline Dadd
Height: 3 ¾", 9.5 cm
Colour: Red, yellow, blue, pink and white
Issued: 2004 - 2005

U.S. $45.00
Can. $55.00
U.K. £25.00
Aust. $65.00

FF 6
SNOWDRIFT LEADS THE WAY

Designer: Caroline Dadd
Height: 3 ½" x 5", 8.9 x 12.7 cm
Colour: White, green, pink, purple, brown and red
Issued: 2004 - 2005

U.S. $ 70.00
Can. $ 90.00
U.K. £ 40.00
Aust. $100.00

FF 7
THE FROSTY FAMILY TREE

Designer: Caroline Dadd
Height: 5 ½", 14.0 cm
Colour: Green, white, red, yellow and purple
Issued: 2004 - 2005

U.S. $45.00
Can. $55.00
U.K. £25.00
Aust. $65.00

HARRY POTTER

HP 1
THE REMEMBRALL RECOVERY™

Height:	4", 10.1 cm
Colour:	Black, blue and brown
Issued:	2001 - 2003
U.S.	$55.00
Can.	$65.00
U.K.	£30.00
Aust.	$75.00

HP 2
HARRY CASTS A MAGICAL SPELL™

Height:	4 ½", 11.9 cm
Colour:	Black, blue, red beige and brown
Issued:	2001 - 2003
U.S.	$55.00
Can.	$65.00
U.K.	£30.00
Aust.	$75.00

HP 3
HERMIONE STUDIES FOR POTIONS CLASS™

Height:	5", 12.7 cm
Colour:	Black, blue, pink, green, brown and gold
Issued:	2001 - 2003
U.S.	$55.00
Can.	$65.00
U.K.	£30.00
Aust.	$75.00

HP 4
RON FOLLOWS THE WEASLEY FAMILY TRADITION™

Height:	5 ¼", 13.3 cm
Colour:	Black, blue and purple
Issued:	2001 - 2002
U.S.	$55.00
Can.	$65.00
U.K.	£30.00
Aust.	$75.00

HP 5
PROFESSOR SEVERUS SNAPE™

Height:	6 ¼" 15.9 cm
Colour:	Black
Issued:	2001 - 2002
U.S.	$55.00
Can.	$65.00
U.K.	£30.00
Aust.	$75.00

HP 6
HEADMASTER ALBUS DUMBLEDORE™

Height:	6 ½", 16.5 cm
Colour:	Purple, green, white and brown
Issued:	2001 - 2003
U.S.	$55.00
Can.	$65.00
U.K.	£30.00
Aust.	$75.00

HP 7
WIZARD-IN-TRAINING™

Height:	5 ¼", 13.3 cm
Colour:	Black, blue, red, white, brown and gold
Issued:	2001 - 2003
U.S.	$55.00
Can.	$65.00
U.K.	£30.00
Aust.	$75.00

HP 8
THE FRIENDSHIP BEGINS™

Height:	5 ¼", 13.3 cm
Colour:	Blue, red, white, purple, green and brown
Issued:	2001 in a limited edition of 5,000
U.S.	$100.00
Can.	$125.00
U.K.	£ 60.00
Aust.	$135.00

HP 9
HARRY'S 11TH BIRTHDAY™

Height:	6 ¼", 15.9 cm
Colour:	Brown, white, red, blue, olive green and pink
Issued:	2001 in a limited edition of 5,000
U.S.	$150.00
Can.	$175.00
U.K.	£ 80.00
Aust.	$185.00

HP 10
STRUGGLING THROUGH POTIONS CLASS™

Height:	3 ¾", 9.5 cm
Colour:	Black, green, red and tan
Issued:	2002 -2003
U.S.	$110.00
Can.	$135.00
U.K.	£ 60.00
Aust.	$150.00

HP 11
SLYTHERIN OR GRYFFINDOR™

Height:	4 ¾", 12.1 cm
Colour:	Black, blue, red and beige
Issued:	2002 - 2003
U.S.	$55.00
Can.	$65.00
U.K.	£30.00
Aust.	$75.00

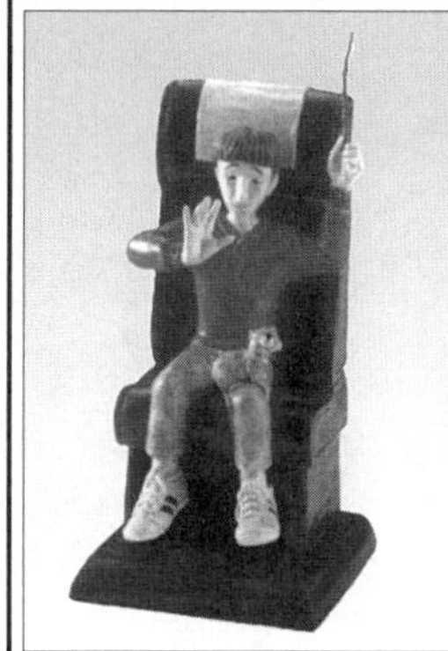

HP 12
RON AND SCRABBERS™

Height:	4 ½", 11.9 cm
Colour:	Purple, blue and green
Issued:	2002 - 2003
U.S.	$55.00
Can.	$65.00
U.K.	£30.00
Aust.	$75.00

HP 13
HERMIONE LEARNS TO LEVITATE™

Height:	4 ½", 11.9 cm
Colour:	Black, pink, blue and brown
Issued:	2002 - 2003
U.S.	$55.00
Can.	$65.00
U.K.	£30.00
Aust.	$75.00

HP 14
PROFESSOR McGONAGALL™

Height:	5 ¼", 13.3 cm
Colour:	Dark green
Issued:	2002 - 2003
U.S.	$55.00
Can.	$65.00
U.K.	£30.00
Aust.	$75.00

HP 15
PROFESSOR QUIRRELL™

Height:	5", 12.7 cm
Colour:	Dark blue and purple
Issued:	2002 - 2003
U.S.	$55.00
Can.	$65.00
U.K.	£30.00
Aust.	$75.00

HP 16
HEDWIG™

Height:	3 ½", 8.9 cm
Colour:	White, yellow and beige
Issued:	2002 - 2003
U.S.	$ 90.00
Can.	$110.00
U.K.	£ 50.00
Aust.	$125.00

HP 17
THE BIRTH OF NORBERT™

Height:	4 ¼", 10.8 cm
Colour	Green, grey, purple and brown
Issued:	2002 - 2003
U.S.	$ 70.00
Can.	$ 90.00
U.K.	£ 40.00
Aust.	$100.00

HP 18
THE MIRROR HOLDS THE ANSWER™

Height:	10", 25.4 cm
Colour:	Gold, black, blue, yellow and grey
Issued:	2002 in a limited edition of 5,000
U.S.	$160.00
Can.	$200.00
U.K.	£ 90.00
Aust.	$225.00

HP 19
THE JOURNEY TO HOGWARTS™

Height:	3 ½", 8.9 cm
Colour:	Black, brown and blue
Issued:	2002 in a limited edition of 5,000
U.S.	$150.00
Can.	$175.00
U.K.	£ 80.00
Aust.	$200.00

HP 20
MADAME HOOCH™

Height:	5 ¼", 13.3 cm
Colour:	Black and white
Issued:	2002 - 2003
U.S.	$55.00
Can.	$65.00
U.K.	£30.00
Aust.	$75.00

HP 21
PROFESSOR SPROUT™

Height:	5", 12.7 cm
Colour:	Olive green and orange
Issued:	2002 - 2003
U.S.	$ 90.00
Can.	$110.00
U.K.	£ 50.00
Aust.	$125.00

HP 22
HARRY POTTER™ PLAYING QUIDDITCH

Height:	4 ¾", 12.1 cm
Colour:	Red, teal blue, black and brown
Issued:	2002 - 2003
U.S.	$130.00
Can.	$160.00
U.K.	£ 75.00
Aust.	$175.00

HP 23
DOBBY™

Height:	2 ¼", 5.7 cm
Colour:	Blue and lilac
Issued:	2002 - 2003
U.S.	$130.00
Can.	$160.00
U.K.	£ 75.00
Aust.	$175.00

HP 24
DURSLEY FAMILY™

Height:	6", 15.0 cm
Colour:	Black, blue, red, green, white, yellow and brown
Issued:	2002 in a limited edition of 1,000
U.S.	$175.00
Can.	$225.00
U.K.	£100.00
Aust.	$250.00

HP 25
WHOMPING WILLOW™

Height:	9 ½", 24.0 cm
Colour:	Brown, green and turquoise
Issued:	2002 in a limited edition of 1,000
U.S.	$600.00
Can.	$725.00
U.K.	£350.00
Aust.	$800.00

HP 26
RESCUE IN THE FORBIDDEN FOREST™

Height:	7 ¼", 18.4 cm
Colour:	Cream, brown, black and blue
Issued:	2002 in a limited edition of 5,000
U.S.	$175.00
Can.	$225.00
U.K.	£100.00
Aust.	$250.00

NODDY

3676
BIG EARS™

Designer:	Enid Blyton
Modeller:	Andy Moss
Height:	5", 12.7 cm
Colour:	Red, white, dark blue, yellow and red
Issued:	1997 in a special edition of 1,500
U.S.	$175.00
Can.	$225.00
U.K.	£100.00
Aust.	$250.00

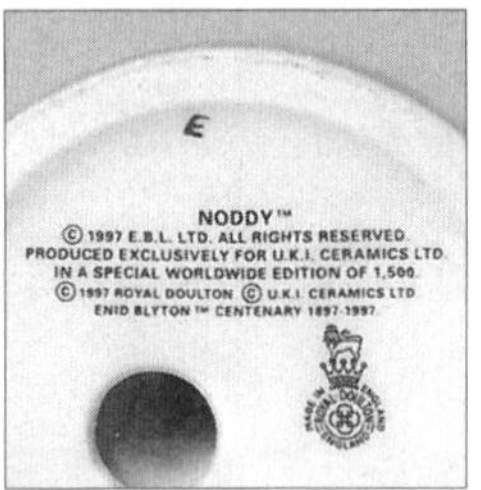

3678
NODDY™

Designer:	Enid Blyton
Modeller	Andy Moss
Height:	5", 12.7 cm
Colour:	Red, light blue, dark blue and light brown
Issued:	1997 in a special edition of 1,500
U.S.	$175.00
Can.	$225.00
U.K.	£100.00
Aust.	$250.00

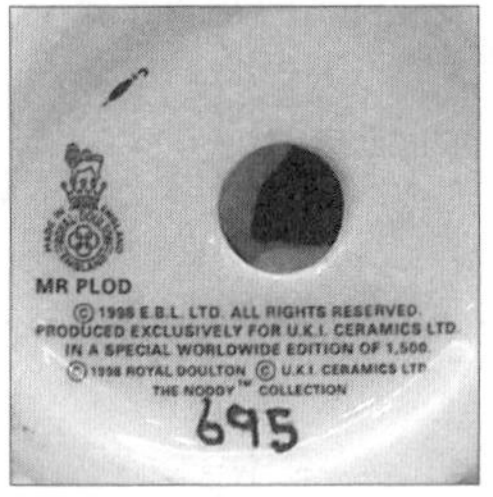

3679
MR. PLOD™

Designer:	Enid Blyton
Modeller:	Andy Moss
Height:	5", 12.7 cm
Colour:	Navy, yellow and white
Issued:	1998 in a special edition of 1,500
U.S.	$175.00
Can.	$225.00
U.K.	£100.00
Aust.	$250.00

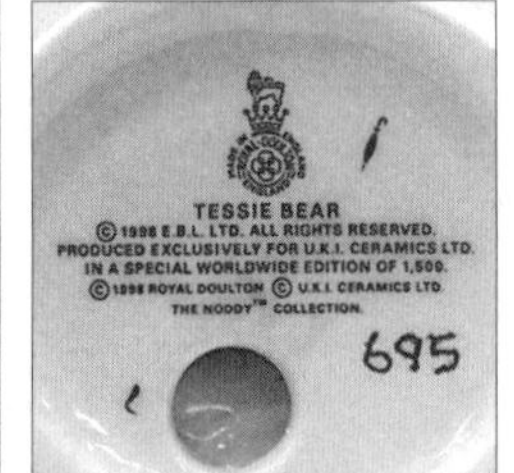

3770
TESSIE BEAR™

Designer:	Enid Blyton
Modeller:	Andy Moss
Height:	5", 12.7 cm
Colour:	Yellow, pink, green and white
Issued:	1998 in a special edition of 1,500
U.S.	$175.00
Can.	$225.00
U.K.	£100.00
Aust.	$250.00

NODDY AND BIG EARS™

Designer:	Enid Blyton
Modeller:	Andy Moss
Height:	3 ½", 8.9 cm
Colour:	Red, yellow, blue, brown and black
Issued:	2002 in a special edition of 750 (C of A)

Doulton Number	Price U.S. $	Can. $	U.K. £	Aust. $
–	275.00	325.00	160.00	350.00

NURSERY RHYME COLLECTION

HUMPTY DUMPTY
FROM THE NURSERY RHYME COLLECTION
PRODUCED EXCLUSIVELY FOR UK FAIRS LTD
IN A WORLDWIDE SPECIAL EDITION OF 1,500
© 1998 ROYAL DOULTON © UK FAIRS LTD
1246

DNR 1
HUMPTY DUMPTY™

Designer:	Andy Moss
Height:	5 ½", 14.0 cm
Colour:	Red, pink, orange and black
Issued:	1998 in a special edition of 1,500
U.S.	$ 85.00
Can.	$100.00
U.K.	£ 50.00
Aust.	$110.00

LITTLE MISS MUFFET
DNR 2
FROM THE NURSERY RHYME COLLECTION.
PRODUCED EXCLUSIVELY FOR UKI CERAMICS LTD.
IN A WORLDWIDE SPECIAL EDITION OF 1,500.
© 1999 ROYAL DOULTON © UKI CERAMICS LTD
151

DNR 2
LITTLE MISS MUFFET™

Designer:	Andy Moss
Height:	6", 15.0 cm
Colour:	Pink dress and hair ribbon, white apron and collar, red shoes, black spider
Issued:	1998 in a special edition of 1,500
U.S.	$ 85.00
Can.	$100.00
U.K.	£ 50.00
Aust.	$110.00

OLD MOTHER HUBBARD
DNR 3
FROM THE NURSERY RHYME COLLECTION.
PRODUCED EXCLUSIVELY FOR UKI CERAMICS LTD.
IN A WORLDWIDE SPECIAL EDITION OF 1,500.
© 1999 ROYAL DOULTON. © UKI CERAMICS LTD.

DNR 3
OLD MOTHER HUBBARD™

Designer:	Andy Moss
Height:	7 ½", 19.1 cm
Colour:	Red and green dress, blue and white apron and cap, black dog
Issued:	1999 in a special edition of 1,500
U.S.	$ 85.00
Can.	$100.00
U.K.	£ 50.00
Aust.	$110.00

THE CAT AND THE FIDDLE
DNR 4
FROM THE NURSERY RHYME COLLECTION
PRODUCED EXCLUSIVELY FOR UKI CERAMICS LTD
IN A WORLDWIDE SPECIAL EDITION OF 1,500
© 1999 ROYAL DOULTON © UKI CERAMICS LTD

DNR 4
THE CAT AND THE FIDDLE™

Designer:	Andy Moss
Height:	6", 15.0 cm
Colour:	Black jacket and shoes, white waistcoat with red dots, grey trousers
Issued:	1999 in a special edition of 1,500
U.S.	$ 85.00
Can.	$100.00
U.K.	£ 50.00
Aust.	$110.00

DNR 5
OLD KING COLE™

Designer:	Andy Moss
Height:	7", 17.8 cm
Colour:	Red, white, yellow and brown
Issued:	2000 in a special edition of 1,500

OLD KING COLE
DNR 5
FROM THE NURSERY RHYME COLLECTION
PRODUCED EXCLUSIVELY FOR UKI CERAMICS LTD
IN A WORLDWIDE SPECIAL EDITION OF 1,500
© 2000 ROYAL DOULTON © UKI CERAMICS LTD
46

Doulton Number	Price U.S. $	Can. $	U.K. £	Aust. $
DNR 5	100.00	125.00	60.00	150.00

OLD BEAR AND FRIENDS

OB4601
OLD BEAR™

Designer:	Jane Hissey
Modeller:	Paul Gurney
Height:	4", 10.1 cm
Colour:	Light brown bear
Composition:	Resin
Issued:	1997 - 2001
U.S.	$ 70.00
Can.	$ 90.00
U.K.	£ 40.00
Aust.	$100.00

OB4602
TIME FOR BED™

Designer:	Jane Hissey
Modeller:	Paul Gurney
Height:	4", 10.1 cm
Colour:	Golden brown, light brown, blue white and yellow
Composition:	Resin
Issued:	1997 - 1999
U.S.	$60.00
Can.	$75.00
U.K.	£35.00
Aust.	$85.00

OB4603
BRAMWELL BROWN HAS A GOOD IDEA™

Designer:	Jane Hissey
Modeller:	Paul Gurney
Height:	4", 10.1 cm
Colour:	Brown, beige, red, green and white
Composition:	Resin
Issued:	1997 - 1998
U.S.	$60.00
Can.	$75.00
U.K.	£35.00
Aust.	$85.00

OB4604
DON'T WORRY RABBIT™

Designer:	Jane Hissey
Modeller:	Paul Gurney
Height:	4", 10.1 cm
Colour:	Light brown, beige, yellow, red and green
Composition:	Resin
Issued:	1997 - 2000
U.S.	$60.00
Can.	$75.00
U.K.	£35.00
Aust.	$85.00

OB4605
THE LONG RED SCARF™

Designer:	Jane Hissey
Modeller:	Paul Gurney
Height:	4", 10.1 cm
Colour:	Golden brown giraffe wearing long red scarf, dark brown bear
Composition:	Resin
Issued:	1997 - 1999
U.S.	$ 90.00
Can.	$110.00
U.K.	£ 50.00
Aust.	$125.00

OB4606
WAITING FOR SNOW™

Designer:	Jane Hissey
Modeller:	Paul Gurney
Height:	4", 10.1 cm
Colour:	Golden brown, light brown, white and brown
Composition:	Resin
Issued:	1997 - 1999
U.S.	$ 80.00
Can.	$100.00
U.K.	£ 45.00
Aust.	$110.00

OB4607
THE SNOWFLAKE BISCUITS™

Designer:	Jane Hissey
Modeller:	Paul Gurney
Height:	4", 10.1 cm
Colour:	Golden brown, red, light brown, white, black and brown
Composition:	Resin
Issued:	1997 - 2001
U.S.	$110.00
Can.	$130.00
U.K.	£ 65.00
Aust.	$150.00

OB4608
WELCOME HOME, OLD BEAR™

Designer:	Jane Hissey
Modeller:	Paul Gurney
Height:	4", 10.1 cm
Colour:	Brown bear with two light brown bears and a white duck
Composition:	Resin
Issued:	1997 - 2001
U.S.	$60.00
Can.	$75.00
U.K.	£35.00
Aust.	$85.00

OB4609
RUFF'S PRIZE™

Designer:	Jane Hissey
Modeller:	Paul Gurney
Height:	2 ½", 6.5 cm
Colour:	Light brown, dark brown and red
Composition:	Resin
Issued:	1997 - 1999
U.S.	$60.00
Can.	$75.00
U.K.	£35.00
Aust.	$85.00

OB4610
TIME FOR A CUDDLE, HUG ME TIGHT™

Designer:	Jane Hissey
Modeller:	Paul Gurney
Height:	3 ½", 8.9 cm
Colour:	Golden brown, light brown, blue and white
Composition:	Resin
Issued:	1997 - 2000
U.S.	$60.00
Can.	$75.00
U.K.	£35.00
Aust.	$85.00

OB4611
DON'T FORGET OLD BEAR™

Designer:	Jane Hissey
Modeller:	Paul Gurney
Height:	3", 7.6 cm
Colour:	Brown bear in brown box, red book covers
Composition:	Resin
Issued:	1998 - 2001
U.S.	$60.00
Can.	$75.00
U.K.	£35.00
Aust.	$85.00

OB4612
HOLD ON TIGHT™

Designer:	Jane Hissey
Modeller:	Paul Gurney
Height:	3", 7.6 cm
Colour:	White, blue and light brown
Composition:	Resin
Issued:	1998 - 2001
U.S.	$60.00
Can.	$75.00
U.K.	£35.00
Aust.	$85.00

OB4613
RESTING WITH CAT™

Designer:	Jane Hissey
Modeller:	Paul Gurney
Height:	2 ½", 6.4 cm
Colour:	Black, red and light brown
Composition:	Resin
Issued:	1998 - 2001
U.S.	$ 90.00
Can.	$110.00
U.K.	£ 50.00
Aust.	$125.00

OB4614
LOOKING FOR A SAILOR™

Designer:	Jane Hissey
Modeller:	Paul Gurney
Height:	5", 12.7 cm
Colour:	Red and blue horse, light brown bear
Composition:	Resin
Issued:	1998 - 2001
U.S.	$ 90.00
Can.	$110.00
U.K.	£ 50.00
Aust.	$125.00

OB4615
TOO MUCH FOOD™

Designer:	Jane Hissey
Modeller:	Paul Gurney
Height:	4", 10.1 cm
Colour:	Golden brown, brown, light brown and red
Composition:	resin
Issued:	1998 - 2001
U.S.	$ 90.00
Can.	$110.00
U.K.	£ 50.00
Aust.	$125.00

OB4616
NEST OF SOCKS™

Designer:	Jane Hissey
Modeller:	Paul Gurney
Height:	2 ¾", 7.0 cm
Colour:	Pale brown, blue, green, white yellow and red
Composition:	Resin
Issued:	2000 - 2001
U.S.	$ 90.00
Can.	$110.00
U.K.	£ 50.00
Aust.	$125.00

OB4617
SNOW DECORATIONS™

Designer:	Jane Hissey
Modeller:	Paul Gurney
Height:	3 ½", 8.9 cm
Colour:	Brown bear
Composition:	Resin
Issued:	2000 - 2001
U.S.	$60.00
Can.	$75.00
U.K.	£35.00
Aust.	$85.00

OB4618
STORYTIME™

Designer:	Jane Hissey
Modeller:	Paul Gurney
Height:	2 ½", 6.4 cm
Colour:	Black, beige, red, light blue, and white
Composition:	Resin
Issued:	2000 - 2001
U.S.	$ 80.00
Can.	$100.00
U.K.	£ 45.00
Aust.	$110.00

OB4619
DUCK™

Designer:	Jane Hissey
Modeller:	Paul Gurney
Height:	3", 7.6 cm
Colour:	White, brown and yellow duck, multicoloured quilt
Composition:	Resin
Issued:	2000 - 2001
U.S.	$ 90.00
Can.	$110.00
U.K.	£ 50.00
Aust.	$120.00

OB4620
UP, UP AND AWAY™

Designer:	Jane Hissey
Modeller:	Paul Gurney
Height:	3 ½", 8.9 cm
Colour:	White, red, brown, blue and silver
Composition:	Resin
Issued:	2000 - 2001
U.S.	$ 90.00
Can.	$110.00
U.K.	£ 50.00
Aust.	$125.00

PADDINGTON BEAR

Royal Doulton
Paddington ™
"At the Station"
PB1
© Paddington & Co. Ltd. 1996
Licensed by ©OPYRIGHTS

PB1
PADDINGTON™ "AT THE STATION"
Style One

Designer: Zoe Annand
Height: 4 ¼", 10.8 cm
Colour: Brown, blue and, yellow
Composition: Resin
Issued: 1996 - 1998

Doulton Number	Price U.S. $	Price Can. $	Price U.K. £	Price Aust. $
PB1	35.00	45.00	20.00	50.00

PB2
PADDINGTON™ "BAKES A CAKE"

Designer: Zoe Annand
Height: 4 ¼", 10.8 cm
Colour: Red jacket, black hat, multicoloured cake, blue and white striped bowl
Composition: Resin
Issued: 1996 - 1998

Doulton Number	Price U.S. $	Price Can. $	Price U.K. £	Price Aust. $
PB2	35.00	45.00	20.00	50.00

Royal Doulton
Paddington ™
"Decorating"
PB3
© Paddington & Co. Ltd. 1996
Licensed by ©OPYRIGHTS

PB3
PADDINGTON™ "DECORATING"

Designer: Zoe Annand
Height: 4 ¾", 12.0 cm
Colour: Blue coat, red hat, silver bucket, cream paint
Composition: Resin
Issued: 1996 - 1998

Doulton Number	Price U.S. $	Price Can. $	Price U.K. £	Price Aust. $
PB3	35.00	45.00	20.00	50.00

Royal Doulton
Paddington ™
"Surfing"
PB4
© Paddington & Co. Ltd. 1996
Licensed by ©OPYRIGHTS

PB4
PADDINGTON™ "SURFING"

Designer: Zoe Annand
Height: 4", 10.1 cm
Colour: Blue, yellow, red and brown
Composition: Resin
Issued: 1996 - 1998

Doulton Number	U.S. $	Price Can. $	U.K. £	Aust. $
PB4	35.00	45.00	20.00	50.00

Royal Doulton
Paddington ™
"Gardening"
PB5
© Paddington & Co. Ltd. 1996
Licensed by ©OPYRIGHTS

PB5
PADDINGTON™ "GARDENING"

Designer: Zoe Annand
Height: 4", 10.1 cm
Colour: Blue, red, green and yellow
Composition: Resin
Issued: 1996 - 1998

Doulton Number	U.S. $	Price Can. $	U.K. £	Aust. $
PB5	35.00	45.00	20.00	50.00

Royal Doulton
Paddington ™
"Bathtime"
PB6
© Paddington & Co. Ltd. 1996
Licensed by ©OPYRIGHTS

PB6
PADDINGTON™ "BATHTIME"

Designer: Zoe Annand
Height: 3 ¼", 8.5 cm
Colour: Blue, yellow, brown and pink
Composition: Resin
Issued: 1996 - 1998

Doulton Number	U.S. $	Price Can. $	U.K. £	Aust. $
PB6	35.00	45.00	20.00	50.00

BUNNYKINS

DB288 – Love Heart Bunnykins

DB289 – Easter Treat Bunnykins

DB290 –Birthday Girl Bunnykins

DB291 - Congratulations Bunnykins

DB292 – Easter Parade Bunnykins

DB293 – Witches Cauldron Bunnykins

DB294 – Centurion Bunnykins

DB295 – Ankhesenamun Bunnykins

DB296 – Tutankhamun Bunnykins

DB297 – Winter Lapland

DB298 – Summer Lapland

DB299 – Sir Galahad

BUNNYKINS

DB300 – Sir Gawain

DB301 – Sir Lancelot

DB302 – Queen Guinevere

DB303 – Merlin

DB304 – King Arthur

DB305 – Henry VIII

DB306 – Catherine of Aragon

DB307 – Anne Boleyn

DB308 – Jane Seymour

DB309 – Anne of Cleves

DB310 – Kathryn Howard

BUNNYKINS

DB311 – Catherine Parr

DB312 – Emperor Bunnykins

DB313 – Betsy Ross Bunnykins

DB314 – Egyptian Bunnykins

DB315 – Arabian Nights Bunnykins

DB316 – Mexican Bunnykins

DB317 – Parisian Bunnykins

DB318 – Rugby Player Bunnykins

DB319 – Captain

DB320 – Captain's Wife

DB321 – Pirate

BUNNYKINS

DB322 – Seaman

DB323 – Boatswain

DB324 – Cabin Boy

DB325 – Ship's Cook

DB326 – Gladiator

DB327 – Christening Day Girl

DB328 – Christening Day Boy

DB329 – Graduation Time

DB330 – Randolph The Ringmaster

DB331 – Clarissa The Clown

DB332 – Clarence The Clown

DB333 – Tino The Trixstar

DB334 – Sister Mary Barbara Bunnykins

DB335 – Mrs. Collector Bunnykins

DB342 – Christmas Elf

DB343 – Father Christmas

DB344 – Mother Christmas

DB345 – Christmas Angel

DB346 – Christmas Eve

DB347 – Christmas Cracker

DB348 – Christmas Carol Singer

DB349 – Christmas Busker

DB350 – Prince John Bunnykins
Second Variation

DB351 – King Richard Bunnykins
Second Variation

DB352 – Will Scarlett Bunnykins
Second Variation

DB353 – Sheriff of Nottingham Bunnykins, *Second Variation*

DB354 – Friar Tuck Bunnykins
Second Variation

DB355 – Little John Bunnykins
Second Variation

DB356 – Maid Marion Bunnykins
Second Variation

DB357 – Robin Hood Bunnykins
Second Variation

DB359 – Scarecrow Bunnykins

DB360 – Umpire Bunnykins

DB361 – Just Like New

DB362 – All Fuelled Up

BUNNYKINS

DB363 – Ready To Ride

DB364 – Bunnykins Camping

DB365 – Nelson Bunnykins

DB366 – Balloon Man

DB367 – George Washington

DB368 – Shearer Bunnykins

DB369 – Pilot Bunnykins

DB370 – Sailor Bunnykins

DB371 – Homeguard Bunnykins

DB372 – Land Girl Bunnykins

DB373 – Evacuees Bunnykins

DB374 – Barrister Bunnykins

DB375 – Nurse Bunnykins, *Style Two*

DB376 – Fireman Bunnykins
Style Two

DB377 – Postman Bunnykins
Style Two

DB378 – Plumber Bunnykins

DB379 – Chef Bunnykins

DB380 – Teacher Bunnykins

DB381 – Doctor Bunnykins
Style Two

DB382 – Air Controller Bunnykins

PB7
PADDINGTON™ "THE GOLFER"

Designer: Zoe Annand
Height: 3 ¾", 9.5 cm
Colour: White, red, yellow and green
Composition: Resin
Issued: 1996 - 1998

Doulton Number	U.S. $	Price Can. $	U.K. £	Aust. $
PB7	35.00	45.00	20.00	50.00

PB8
PADDINGTON™ "THE MUSICIAN"

Designer: Zoe Annand
Height: 3 ¾", 9.5 cm
Colour: Black, red, brown and brass
Composition: Resin
Issued: 1996 - 1998

Royal Doulton
Paddington ™
"The Musician"
PB8
© Paddington & Co. Ltd. 1996
Licensed by ©OPYRIGHTS

Doulton Number	U.S. $	Price Can. $	U.K. £	Aust. $
PB8	35.00	45.00	20.00	50.00

PB9
PADDINGTON™ "AT CHRISTMAS TIME"

Designer: Zoe Annand
Height: 3 ½", 8.9 cm
Colour: Red coat, blue boots, yellow sleigh
Composition: Resin
Issued: 1996 - 1998

Doulton Number	U.S. $	Price Can. $	U.K. £	Aust. $
PB9	35.00	45.00	20.00	50.00

PB10
PADDINGTON™ "MARMALADE SANDWICH"

Royal Doulton
Paddington™
"Marmalade Sandwich"
PB10
© Paddington & Co. Ltd. 1996
Licensed by ©OPYRIGHTS

Designer:	Zoe Annand
Height:	3 ½", 8.9 cm
Colour:	Dark blue coat, yellow hat, green book, orange and white sandwiches
Composition:	Resin
Issued:	1997 - 1998

Doulton Number	U.S. $	Price Can. $	U.K. £	Aust. $
PB10	35.00	45.00	20.00	50.00

PB11
PADDINGTON™ "GOING TO BED"

Royal Doulton
Paddington™
"Going to Bed"
PB11
© Paddington & Co. Ltd. 1996
Licensed by ©OPYRIGHTS

Designer:	Zoe Annand
Height:	3 ¾", 9.5 cm
Colour:	Turquoise, red and yellow pyjamas, red hat
Composition:	Resin
Issued:	1997 - 1998

Doulton Number	U.S. $	Price Can. $	U.K. £	Aust. $
PB11	35.00	45.00	20.00	50.00

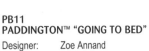

PB12
PADDINGTON™ "THE FISHERMAN"

Royal Doulton
Paddington™
"The Fisherman"
PB12
© Paddington & Co. Ltd. 1996
Licensed by ©OPYRIGHTS

Designer:	Zoe Annand
Height:	3 ½", 8.9 cm
Colour:	Red jacket with yellow buttons, dark blue hat and wellingtons,
Composition:	Resin
Issued:	1997 - 1998

oulton Number	U.S. $	Price Can. $	U.K. £	Aust. $
PB12	35.00	45.00	20.00	50.00

RUPERT BEAR

RB 1
RUPERT'S TOY RAILWAY

Height: 4 ¼", 10.8 cm
Colour: Red, blues, turquoise, gold, yellow and black
Issued: 2004 in a limited edition of 2,500

Doulton Number	Price U.S. $	Can. $	U.K. £	Aust. $
RB1	175.00	225.00	95.00	250.00

RB 2
PRETENDING TO BE AN OUTLAW
(Edward Trunk)

Height: 5 ¼", 13.3 cm
Colour: Blue coat, red waistcoat, yellow check trousers
Issued: 2004 - 2005

Doulton Number	Price U.S.	Can.	U.K. £	Aust. $
RB 2	50.00	60.00	£30.00	70.00

RB 3
LEADING THE WAY
(Ping Pong)

Height: 5 ¼", 13.3 cm
Colour: Black top with blue details, brown trousers
Issued: 2004 - 2005

Doulton Number	Price U.S. $	Can. $	U.K. £	Aust. $
RB 3	50.00	60.00	30.00	70.00

RB 4
RUPERT RIDES HOME

Height:	6", 15.0 cm
Colour:	Red, yellow, green, pink and blue
Issued:	2004 in a limited edition of 2,500
U.S.	$140.00
Can.	$165.00
U.K.	£ 80.00
Aust.	$175.00

RB 5
TEMPTED TO TRESPASS

Height:	5 ¼", 13.3 cm
Colour:	Red, yellow, blue, purple and brown
Issued:	2004 in a limited edition of 2,500
U.S.	$100.00
Can.	$125.00
U.K.	£ 60.00
Aust.	$135.00

RB 6
LOOKING LIKE ROBIN HOOD (Algy Pug)

Height:	5 ¼", 13.3 cm
Colour:	Blue coat, yellow waistcoat, red trousers
Issued:	2004 - 2005
U.S.	$50.00
Can.	$60.00
U.K.	£30.00
Aust.	$70.00

RB 7
FINISHING ARROWS AND STRINGING HIS BOW (Rupert)

Height:	5", 12.7 cm
Colour:	Red sweater, yellow checked trousers and scarf
Issued:	2004 to the present
U.S.	–
Can.	–
U.K.	£30.00
Aust.	–

RB 8
RUPERT'S SILVER TRUMPET

Height:	5", 12.7 cm
Colour:	Red sweater, yellow checked trousers and scarf
Issued:	2004 to the present
U.S.	–
Can.	–
U.K.	£30.00
Aust.	–

RB 9
PODGY LANDS WITH A BUMP

Height:	3 ¼", 8.3 cm
Colour:	White, light brown, yellow, red, black and green
Issued:	2004 - 2005
U.S.	$50.00
Can.	$60.00
U.K.	£30.00
Aust.	$70.00

RB 10
BINGO'S HUGE FIREWORK

Height:	4 ¾", 12.1 cm
Colour:	White, blue-grey, brown, pink, black and yellow
Issued:	2004 - 2005
U.S.	$50.00
Can.	$60.00
U.K.	£30.00
Aust.	$70.00

RB 11
RUPERT, BILL AND THE MYSTERIOUS CAR

Height: 4 ½", 11.9 cm
Colour: Light green car; Rupert wears a red sweater and yellow and black checked scarf, Bill wears a blue jacket
Issued: 2004 in a limited edition of 2,500

U.S.	$150.00
Can.	$175.00
U.K.	£ 80.00
Aust.	$200.00

RB 12
REGGIE AND REX

Height: 4 ¾", 12.0 cm
Colour: Yellow, red, white, blue and black
Issued: 2005 to the present

U.S.	–
Can.	–
U.K.	£40.00
Aust.	–

RB 13
SOMETHING TO DRAW

Height: 3 ¾", 9.5 cm
Colour: Yellow, red, black, pale blue, white and green
Issued: 2005 to the present

U.S.	–
Can.	–
U.K.	£30.00
Aust.	–

RB 14
OUT FOR THE DAY

Height: 4 ½", 11.4 cm
Colour: White, red, yellow, black and brown
Issued: 2005 to the present

U.S.	–
Can.	–
U.K.	£30.00
Aust.	–

RB 15
THE IMP OF SPRING

Height: 3 ¼" x 4 ½", 8.3 cm x 11.9 cm
Colour: White, red, yellow, light brown, blue and black
Issued: 2005 in a limited edition of 2,500

U.S.	$150.00
Can.	$175.00
U.K.	£ 75.00
Aust.	$200.00

RB 16
WE MEANT TO PUT THEM BACK!

Height: 4 ½", 11.4 cm
Colour: White, red, yellow, brown, green, orange and black
Issued: 2005 to the present

U.S.	–
Can.	–
U.K.	£35.00
Aust.	–

RB 17
BANGING ON HIS DRUM

Height: 5 ½", 14.0 cm
Colour: White, blue, yellow, orange, red and black
Issued: 2005 to the present

U.S.	–
Can.	–
U.K.	£30.00
Aust.	–

RB 18
GOING OUT LATE

Height: 4 ½", 12.0 cm
Colour: Purple, white, red, yellow, pale blue, and light brown
Issued: 2005 to the present

U.S.	–
Can.	–
U.K.	£45.00
Aust.	–

RB 20
RUPERT TAKES A SKI-ING LESSON

Height: 4 ½", 10.8 cm
Colour: Red sweater, yellow trousers with black check, brown ski's and black ski poles
Issued: 2005 to the present

U.S.	–
Can.	–
U.K.	£35.00
Aust.	–

RB 21
RUPERT AND THE KING

Height: 4 ¾", 12.0 cm
Colour: Red, yellow, black, white, pink, purple and light brown
Issued: 2005 in a limited edition of 2,000

U.S.	$150.00
Can.	$175.00
U.K.	£ 80.00
Aust.	$200.00

Note: Issued to celebrate the 85th birthday of Rupert Bear who first appeared in the Daily Express on November 8, 1920.

RB 26
RUPERT TAKES A FLYING LESSON

Height: 5 ¼" X 8", 13.3 X 20.3 cm
Colour: Orange, blue, red, green and yellow
Issued: 2005 in a limited edition of 550

U.S.	$175.00
Can.	$225.00
U.K.	£100.00
Aust.	$250.00

ST. TIGGYWINKLES

Royal Doulton
St. Tiggywinkles
Henry Hedgehog
TW1/1999
© St.Tiggywinkles 1996
Made in Thailand

TW1
HENRY HEDGEHOG™

Modeller:	Amanda Hughes-Lubeck
Height:	3 ½", 8.5 cm
Colour:	Light and dark brown hedgehog wearing a purple sweater
Issued:	1997 - 1999
Composition:	Resin
Series:	Wildlife Hospital Trust

Doulton Number	U.S. $	Price Can. $	U.K. £	Aust. $
TW1	25.00	30.00	15.00	35.00

Royal Doulton
St. Tiggywinkles
Harry Hedgehog
TW2/1269
© St.Tiggywinkles 1996
Made in Thailand

TW2
HARRY HEDGEHOG™

Modeller:	Amanda Hughes-Lubeck
Height:	3 ½", 8.9 cm
Colour:	Light and dark brown hedgehog wearing a purple sweater and red cap
Issued:	1997 - 1999
Composition:	Resin
Series:	Wildlife Hospital Trust

Doulton Number	U.S. $	Price Can. $	U.K. £	Aust. $
TW2	25.00	30.00	15.00	35.00

TW3
FRED FOX™

Modeller:	Warren Platt
Height:	4", 10.1 cm
Colour:	Light brown fox wearing light blue overalls, pink shirt, white bandage around his head and tail
Issued:	1997 - 1998
Composition:	Resin
Series:	Wildlife Hospital Trust

Doulton Number	U.S. $	Price Can. $	U.K. £	Aust. $
TW3	25.00	30.00	15.00	35.00

TW4
BOB BADGER™

Modeller:	Amanda Hughes-Lubeck
Height:	3 ¾", 9.5 cm
Colour:	Brown, black and white badger wearing a yellow jumper and brown scarf; beige crutch
Issued:	1997 - 1999
Composition:	Resin
Series:	Wildlife Hospital Trust

Royal Doulton
St. Tiggywinkles
Bob Badger
TW4/ 1698
© St.Tiggywinkles 1996
Made in Thailand

Doulton Number	U.S. $	Price Can. $	U.K. £	Aust. $
TW4	25.00	30.00	15.00	35.00

TW5
ROSIE RABBIT™

Modeller:	Amanda Hughes-Lubeck
Height:	3 ½", 8.9 cm
Colour:	Grey rabbit wearing a light blue dress and rose pinafore
Issued:	1997 - 1999
Composition:	Resin
Series:	Wildlife Hospital Trust

Royal Doulton
St. Tiggywinkles
Rosie Rabbit
TW5/ 1456
© St.Tiggywinkles 1996
Made in Thailand

Doulton Number	U.S. $	Price Can. $	U.K. £	Aust. $
TW5	25.00	30.00	15.00	35.00

TW6
SARAH SQUIRREL™

Modeller: Amanda Hughes-Lubeck
Height: 3 ¼", 8.3 cm
Colour: Brown squirrel wearing a pink and white dress
Issued: 1997 - 1998
Composition: Resin
Series: Wildlife Hospital Trust

Doulton Number	U.S. $	Price Can. $	U.K. £	Aust. $
TW6	25.00	30.00	15.00	35.00

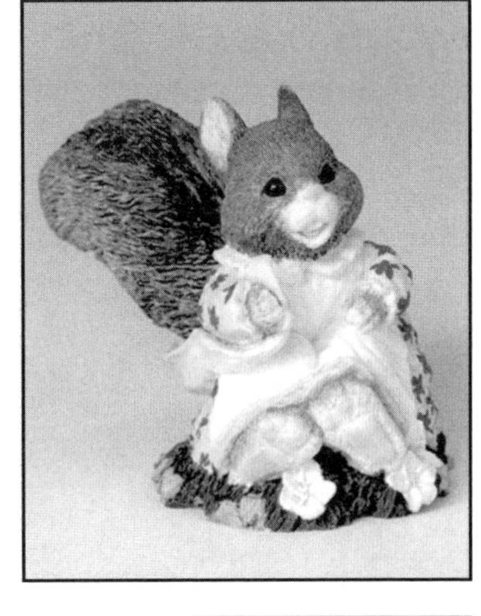

TW7
DANIEL DUCK™

Modeller: Shane Ridge
Height: 3 ½", 8.5 cm
Colour: Yellow duck, white and red bandage, brown satchel
Issued: 1997 - 1999
Composition: Resin
Series: Wildlife Hospital Trust

Royal Doulton
St. Tiggywinkles
Daniel Duck
TW7/ 1925
© St.Tiggywinkles 1996
Made in Thailand

Doulton Number	U.S. $	Price Can. $	U.K. £	Aust. $
TW7	25.00	30.00	15.00	35.00

TW8
OLIVER OWL™

Modeller: Warren Platt
Height: 4", 10.1 cm
Colour: Dark and light brown owl, white arm sling, red book
Issued: 1997 - 1999
Composition: Resin
Series: Wildlife Hospital Trust

Doulton Number	U.S. $	Price Can. $	U.K. £	Aust. $
TW8	25.00	30.00	15.00	35.00

Royal Doulton
St. Tiggywinkles®
Friends
TW9/ 1430
© St.Tiggywinkles 1996
Made in Thailand

TW9
FRIENDS™

Modeller:	Amanda Hughes-Lubeck
Height:	4", 10.1 cm
Colour:	Light and dark brown hedgehog, green and yellow jacket, maroon hat, yellow ducklings, white bandages
Issued:	1997 - 1999
Composition:	Resin
Series:	Wildlife Hospital Trust

Doulton Number	U.S. $	Price Can. $	U.K. £	Aust. $
TW9	25.00	30.00	15.00	35.00

TW10
A HELPING HAND™

Modeller:	Amanda Hughes-Lubeck
Height:	4", 10.1 cm
Colour:	Light and dark brown hedgehog, white and grey rabbits, blue, yellow, pink and red clothing
Issued:	1997 - 1999
Composition:	Resin
Series:	Wildlife Hospital Trust

Royal Doulton
St. Tiggywinkles®
A Helping Hand
TW10/ 0303
© St.Tiggywinkles 1996
Made in Thailand

Doulton Number	U.S. $	Price Can. $	U.K. £	Aust. $
TW10	35.00	40.00	20.00	50.00

TW11
DEBORAH DORMOUSE™

Modeller:	Rob Simpson
Height:	3 ¼", 8.3 cm
Colour:	Brown dormouse wearing a pink dress, white apron, carrying a brown basket
Issued:	1998 - 1999
Composition:	Resin
Series:	Wildlife Hospital Trust

Doulton Number	U.S. $	Price Can. $	U.K. £	Aust. $
TW11	25.00	30.00	15.00	35.00

TW12
MONTY MOLE™

Modeller: Rob Simpson
Height: 3 ½", 8.5 cm
Colour: Dark brown mole wearing a blue jacket, yellow hat, white arm sling
Issued: 1998 - 1999
Composition: Resin
Series: Wildlife Hospital Trust

Doulton Number	Price U.S. $	Can. $	U.K. £	Aust. $
TW12	25.00	30.00	15.00	35.00

TW13
FRANCHESCA FAWN™

Modeller: Rob Simpson
Height: 3", 7.6 cm
Colour: Pale brown fawn, white bandages
Issued: 1998 - 1999
Composition: Resin
Series: Wildlife Hospital Trust

Royal Doulton
St. Tiggywinkles.
Franchesca Fawn
TW13/48
© St.Tiggywinkles 1998
Made in Thailand

Doulton Number	Price U.S. $	Can. $	U.K. £	Aust. $
TW13	25.00	30.00	15.00	35.00

THE SNOWMAN GIFT COLLECTION

DS 1
JAMES™
Style One

Royal Doulton®
THE SNOWMAN™
GIFT COLLECTION
JAMES
DS 1
© 1985 ROYAL DOULTON (UK)
© S ENT 1985

Designer:	Harry Sales
Modeller:	David Lyttleton
Height:	3 ¾", 9.5 cm
Colour:	Brown dressing gown, blue and white striped pyjamas
Issued:	1985 - 1993

Doulton Number	Price U.S. $	Can. $	U.K. £	Aust. $
DS 1	130.00	150.00	75.00	160.00

DS 2
THE SNOWMAN™
Style One

Royal Doulton®
THE SNOWMAN™
GIFT COLLECTION
THE SNOWMAN
DS 2
© 1985 ROYAL DOULTON (UK)
© S ENT 1985

Designer:	Harry Sales
Modeller:	David Lyttleton
Height:	5", 12.7 cm
Colour:	White snowman wearing a green hat and scarf
Issued:	1985 - 1994

Doulton Number	Price U.S. $	Can. $	U.K. £	Aust. $
DS 2	100.00	125.00	60.00	135.00

DS 3
STYLISH SNOWMAN™

Designer: Harry Sales
Modeller: David Lyttleton
Height: 5", 12.7 cm
Colour: White snowman wearing blue trousers, lilac braces, grey hat, yellow tie with red stripes
Issued: 1985 - 1993

Doulton Number	U.S. $	Price Can. $	U.K. £	Aust. $
DS 3	130.00	150.00	75.00	160.00

DS 4
THANK YOU SNOWMAN™

Designer: Harry Sales
Modeller: David Lyttleton
Height: 5", 12.7 cm
Colour: Snowman - Green hat and scarf
James - Brown dressing gown
Issued: 1985 - 1994

Royal Doulton®
THE SNOWMAN™
GIFT COLLECTION
THANK YOU SNOWMAN
DS 4
© 1985 ROYAL DOULTON (UK)
© S. ENT 1985

Doulton Number	U.S. $	Price Can. $	U.K. £	Aust. $
DS 4	100.00	125.00	60.00	135.00

DS 5
SNOWMAN MAGIC MUSIC BOX™

Designer: Harry Sales
Modeller: David Lyttleton
Height: 8", 20.3 cm
Colour: White snowman wearing a green hat and scarf, cream music box with blue, green and pink balloon design
Issued: 1985 - 1994
Tune: 'Walking in the Air'

Backstamp not available at press time

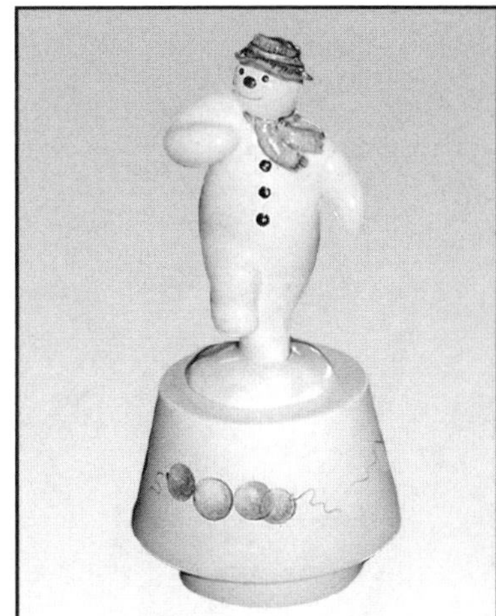

Doulton Number	U.S. $	Price Can. $	U.K. £	Aust. $
DS 5	225.00	275.00	125.00	300.00

DS 6
COWBOY SNOWMAN™

Royal Doulton®
THE SNOWMAN™
GIFT COLLECTION
COWBOY SNOWMAN
DS 6
© 1985 ROYAL DOULTON (UK)
© S ENT 1985

Designer:	Harry Sales
Modeller:	David Lyttleton
Height:	5", 12.7 cm
Colour:	White snowman wearing a brown hat and holster belt
Issued:	1986 - 1992

Doulton Number	Price U.S. $	Can. $	U.K. £	Aust. $
DS 6	225.00	275.00	125.00	300.00

DS 7
HIGHLAND SNOWMAN™

Royal Doulton®
THE SNOWMAN™
GIFT COLLECTION
HIGHLAND SNOWMAN
DS 7
© 1985 ROYAL DOULTON (UK)
© S ENT 1985

Designer:	Harry Sales
Modeller:	David Lyttleton
Height:	5 ¼", 13.3 cm
Colour:	White snowman wearing a red, blue and white kilt
Issued:	1987 - 1993

Doulton Number	Price U.S. $	Can. $	U.K. £	Aust. $
DS 7	225.00	275.00	125.00	300.00

DS 8
LADY SNOWMAN™

Designer:	Harry Sales
Modeller:	David Lyttleton
Height:	5", 12.7 cm
Colour:	White snowman wearing a pink apron and blue hat
Issued:	1987 - 1992

Doulton Number	Price U.S. $	Can. $	U.K. £	Aust. $
DS 8	450.00	550.00	250.00	600.00

DS 9
BASS DRUMMER SNOWMAN™

Designer: Graham Tongue
Modeller: Warren Platt
Height: 5 ¼", 13.3 cm
Colour: White snowman with pale blue hat, pink and yellow drum, pale brown straps
Issued: 1987 - 1993

Doulton Number	Price U.S. $	Can. $	U.K. £	Aust. $
DS 9	250.00	300.00	150.00	325.00

DS 10
FLAUTIST SNOWMAN™

Designer: Graham Tongue
Modeller: Warren Platt
Height: 5 ½", 14.0 cm
Colour: White snowman wearing a yellow and red hat and a brown tie
Issued: 1987 - 1993

Royal Doulton®
THE SNOWMAN™
GIFT COLLECTION
FLAUTIST SNOWMAN
DS 10
© 1987 ROYAL DOULTON
© S. ENT 1987

Doulton Number	Price U.S. $	Can. $	U.K. £	Aust. $
DS 10	200.00	250.00	110.00	275.00

DS 11
VIOLINIST SNOWMAN™

Designer: Graham Tongue
Modeller: Warren Platt
Height: 5 ¼", 13.3 cm
Colour: White snowman wearing a green waistcoat with yellow collar, blue bowtie, brown cap, playing a violin
Issued: 1987 - 1994

Doulton Number	Price U.S. $	Can. $	U.K. £	Aust. $
DS 11	160.00	200.00	90.00	225.00

Royal Doulton®
THE SNOWMAN™
GIFT COLLECTION
PIANIST SNOWMAN
DS 12
© 1987 ROYAL DOULTON
© S ENT 1987

DS 12
PIANIST SNOWMAN™

Designer:	Graham Tongue
Modeller:	Warren Platt
Height:	5", 12.7 cm
Colour:	White snowman wearing a blue crown and orange tie
Issued:	1987 - 1994

Doulton Number	U.S. $	Price Can. $	U.K. £	Aust. $
DS 12	100.00	125.00	60.00	135.00

DS 13
SNOWMAN'S PIANO™

Designer:	Graham Tongue
Modeller:	Warren Platt
Height:	5 ¼", 13.3 cm
Colour:	White piano
Issued:	1987 - 1994

Royal Doulton®
THE SNOWMAN™
GIFT COLLECTION
SNOWMAN'S PIANO
DS 13
© 1987 ROYAL DOULTON
© S. ENT 1987

Doulton Number	U.S. $	Price Can. $	U.K. £	Aust. $
DS 13	70.00	90.00	40.00	100.00

DS 14
CYMBAL PLAYER SNOWMAN™

Designer:	Graham Tongue
Modeller:	Warren Platt
Height:	5 ¼", 13.3 cm
Colour:	White snowman wearing a brown waistcoat, green hat and bowtie, playing yellow cymbals
Issued:	1988 - 1993

Doulton Number	U.S. $	Price Can. $	U.K. £	Aust. $
DS 14	400.00	475.00	225.00	500.00

DS 15
DRUMMER SNOWMAN™

Designer: Graham Tongue
Modeller: Warren Platt
Height: 5 ¾", 14.6 cm
Colour: White snowman wearing a red and black hat, purple bowtie, playing pink and yellow drum
Issued: 1988 - 1994

Doulton Number	Price U.S. $	Can. $	U.K. £	Aust. $
DS 15	130.00	160.00	75.00	175.00

DS 16
TRUMPETER SNOWMAN™

Designer: Graham Tongue
Modeller: Warren Platt
Height: 5", 12.7 cm
Colour: White snowman wearing a pink hat playing a yellow trumpet
Issued: 1988 - 1993

Doulton Number	Price U.S. $	Can. $	U.K. £	Aust. $
DS 16	450.00	550.00	250.00	600.00

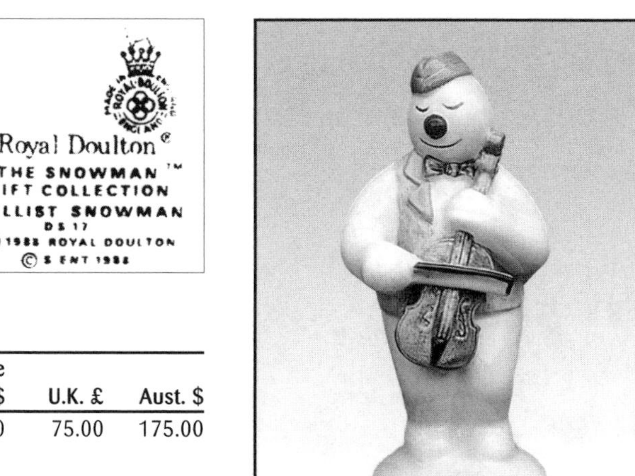

DS 17
CELLIST SNOWMAN™

Designer: Graham Tongue
Modeller: Warren Platt
Height: 5 ¼", 13.3 cm
Colour: White snowman wearing a green waistcoat with yellow collar, blue bowtie, playing a brown cello
Issued: 1988 - 1993

Doulton Number	Price U.S. $	Can. $	U.K. £	Aust. $
DS 17	130.00	160.00	75.00	175.00

DS 18
SNOWMAN MUSICAL BOX™

Height:	8", 22.5 cm
Colour:	White snowman wearing a red, blue and white kilt, green and cream music box with pink and blue balloon design
Issued:	1988 - 1990
Tune:	'Blue Bells of Scotland'

Backstamp not available at press time

Doulton Numbers	U.S. $	Price Can. $	U.K. £	Aust. $
DS 18	450.00	550.00	250.00	600.00

DS 19
THE SNOWMAN MONEY BOX™

Designer:	Graham Tongue
Modeller:	Warren Platt
Height:	8 ½", 21.6 cm
Colour:	White snowman wearing a green hat with grey band and green scarf
Issued:	1990 - 1994

Doulton Number	U.S. $	Price Can. $	U.K. £	Aust. $
DS 19	175.00	225.00	100.00	250.00

DS 20
THE SNOWMAN TOBOGGANING™

Designer:	Graham Tongue
Modeller:	Warren Platt
Height:	5", 12.7 cm
Colour:	White snowman wearing a green hat and scarf, rose-pink toboggan
Issued:	1990 - 1994

Doulton Number	U.S. $	Price Can. $	U.K. £	Aust. $
DS 20	175.00	225.00	100.00	250.00

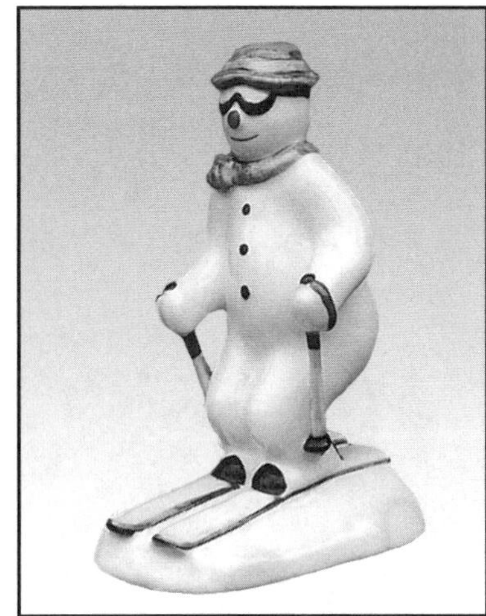

DS 21
THE SNOWMAN SKIING™

Designer:	Graham Tongue
Modeller:	Warren Platt
Height:	5", 12.7 cm
Colour:	White snowman wearing a green hat and scarf, yellow and black goggles
Issued:	1990 - 1992

Doulton Number	U.S. $	Price Can. $	U.K. £	Aust. $
DS 21	775.00	950.00	450.00	1,000.00

DS 22
THE SNOWMAN SNOWBALLING™

Designer:	Graham Tongue
Modeller:	Warren Platt
Height:	5", 12.7 cm
Colour:	White snowman wearing a green hat and scarf, brown tree stump
Issued:	1990 - 1994

Doulton Number	U.S. $	Price Can. $	U.K. £	Aust. $
DS 22	225.00	275.00	125.00	300.00

DS 23
BUILDING THE SNOWMAN™

Designer:	Graham Tongue
Modeller:	Warren Platt
Height:	4", 10.1 cm
Colour:	White snowman wearing a green hat and scarf
Issued:	1990 - 1994

Doulton Number	U.S. $	Price Can. $	U.K. £	Aust. $
DS 23	225.00	275.00	125.00	300.00

DANCING IN THE SNOW™

Designer: Shane Ridge
Modeller: Shane Ridge
Height: 5 ¾", 14.6 cm
Colour: Snowman: White, black buttons, yellow scarf
James: Brown dressing gown, blue and white striped pyjamas
Issued: 1999 in a limited edition of 2,500
Series: Tableau

Doulton Number	U.S. $	Price Can. $	U.K. £	Aust. $
–	350.00	425.00	200.00	450.00

Note: Issued to commemorate the 21st Anniversary of Raymond Briggs' Tale.

JAMES™
Style Two

Designer: Shane Ridge
Modeller: Shane Ridge
Height: 4 ¼", 10.8 cm
Colour: Brown dressing gown, white and blue striped pyjamas
Issued: 1999 in a limited edition of 2,500

Doulton Number	U.S. $	Price Can. $	U.K. £	Aust. $
–	135.00	165.00	75.00	185.00

Note: Issued as a pair with The Snowman (Style Two).

THE SNOWMAN™
Style Two

Designer: Shane Ridge
Modeller: Shane Ridge
Height: 5 ¾", 14.6 cm
Colour: White snowman, green hat and scarf
Issued: 1999 in a limited edition of 2,500

Doulton Number	U.S. $	Price Can. $	U.K. £	Aust. $
–	135.00	165.00	75.00	185.00

Note: Issued as a pair with James (Style Two).

JAMES™
Style Three
(James Builds a Snowman)

Designer:	Shane Ridge
Height:	4", 10.1 cm
Colour:	Maroon sweater, blue trousers, black wellingtons
Issued:	2000 in a limited edition of 2,500

Doulton Number	Price U.S. $	Can. $	U.K. £	Aust. $
—	135.00	165.00	75.00	185.00

Note: Issued, numbered and sold as a pair with The Snowman (Style Three).

THE SNOWMAN™
Style Three
(James Builds a Snowman)

Designer:	Shane Ridge
Height:	6", 15.0 cm
Colour:	White snowman wearing a green hat and scarf
Issued:	2000 in a limited edition of 2,500

Doulton Number	Price U.S. $	Can. $	U.K. £	Aust. $
—	135.00	165.00	75.00	185.00

Note: Issued, numbered and sold as a pair with James (Style Three).

SNOWMAN AND JAMES THE ADVENTURE BEGINS™

Designer:	Shane Ridge
Height:	6", 15.0 cm
Colour:	Snowman: White snowman wearing a green hat and scarf James: Brown dressing gown, blue and white striped pyjamas
Issued:	2000 in a limited edition of 2,500
Series:	Tableau

Doulton Number	Price U.S. $	Can. $	U.K. £	Aust. $
—	350.00	425.00	200.00	475.00

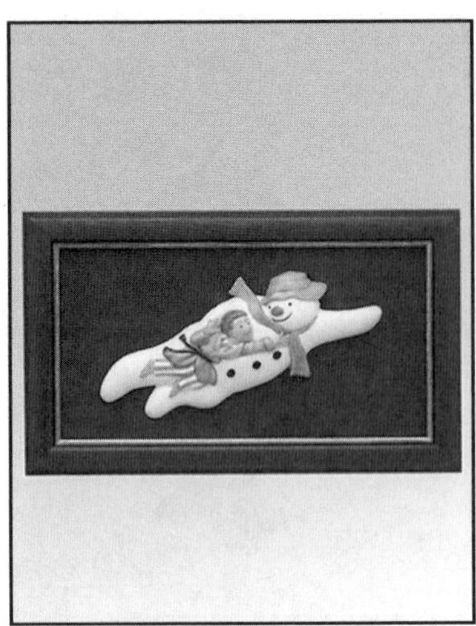

WALKING IN THE AIR™
Wall Plaque

Designer: Shane Ridge
Modeller: Shane Ridge
Height: 8" x 13 ½", 20.3 x 34.3 cm
Colour: Blue, white, tan, brown and green
Issued: 2001 in a limited edition of 2,500

Doulton Number	U.S. $	Price Can. $	U.K. £	Aust. $
–	175.00	225.00	100.00	250.00

DRESSING THE SNOWMAN™

Designer: Shane Ridge
Modeller: Shane Ridge
Height: 6", 15.0 cm
Colour: White, green, red, blue and black
Issued: 2002 in a limited edition of 2,500

Doulton Number	U.S. $	Price Can. $	U.K. £	Aust. $
–	450.00	550.00	250.00	600.00

THE JOURNEY ENDS™

Designer: Shane Ridge
Modeller: Shane Ridge
Height: 4", 10.0 cm
Colour: Blue, white, tan, brown and green
Issued: 2002 in a limited edition of 2,500

Doulton Number	U.S. $	Price Can. $	U.K. £	Aust. $
–	600.00	725.00	350.00	775.00

THELWELL

NT 1
LOSING HURTS™

Designer: A. Hughes-Lubeck
Height: 5", 12.7 cm
Colour: Palomino horse, rider wears navy jacket and hat, yellow jodhpurs
Issued: 2001 in a limited edition of 1,000

U.S.	$450.00
Can.	$550.00
U.K.	£250.00
Aust.	$600.00

NT 2
POWERFUL HINDQUARTERS ARE A DISTINCT ADVANTAGE™

Designer: A. Hughes-Lubeck
Height: 5 ¼", 13.3 cm
Colour: Grey horse; rider has blonde hair and wears a black cap
Issued: 2001 in a limited edition of 1,000

U.S.	$275.00
Can.	$325.00
U.K.	£150.00
Aust.	$350.00

NT 3
EXHAUSTED™

Designer: A. Hughes-Lubeck
Height: 4 ¼", 10.8 cm
Colour: Brown horse; rider wears red jacket, yellow jodhpurs, black hat and shoes
Issued: 2001 in a limited edition of 1,000

U.S.	$275.00
Can.	$325.00
U.K.	£150.00
Aust.	$350.00

NT 4
CHOOSING GOOD FEET™

Designer: A. Hughes-Lubeck
Height: 4 ¼", 10.8 cm
Colour: Chestnut horse; rider wears a burgundy jacket, white jodhpurs, black hat and shoes
Issued: 2001 in a limited edition of 1,000

U.S.	$275.00
Can.	$325.00
U.K.	£150.00
Aust.	$350.00

NT 5
EXCESSIVE PRAISE™

Designer: A. Hughes-Lubeck
Height: 5 ¼", 13.3 cm
Colour: Brown horse; rider wears blue jersey and pale yellow jodhpurs
Issued: 2001 in a limited edition of 1,000

U.S. $225.00
Can. $275.00
U.K. £125.00
Aust. $300.00

NT 6
SUPPLING EXERCISES™

Designer: A. Hughes-Lubeck
Height: 4 ¾", 12.1 cm
Colour: Black horse; rider wears red jersey, yellow jodhpurs; blonde hair
Issued: 2001 in a limited edition of 1,000

U.S. $275.00
Can. $325.00
U.K. £150.00
Aust. $350.00

NT 7
BODY BRUSH™

Designer: Shane Ridge
Height: 5 ¼", 13.3 cm
Colour: Grey horse; rider wears black jacket and yellow jodhpurs
Issued: 2003 - 2005

U.S. $60.00
Can. $75.00
U.K. £35.00
Aust. $80.00

NT 8
DETECTING AILMENTS™

Designer: Warren Platt
Height: 5 ¼", 13.3 cm
Colour: Chestnut horse; doctor wears white medical coat, blue tie, grey trousers
Issued: 2003 - 2005

U.S. $60.00
Can. $75.00
U.K. £35.00
Aust. $80.00

NT 9
ICE CREAM TREAT™

Designer: Martyn Alcock
Height: 5", 12.7 cm
Colour: Dun horse; rider wears black jacket and cap, white jodhpurs
Issued: 2003 - 2005

U.S. $60.00
Can. $75.00
U.K. £35.00
Aust. $80.00

NT 10
IDEAL PONY FOR A NERVOUS CHILD™

Designer: Martyn Alcock
Height: 5 ¼", 13.3 cm
Colour: Brown horse; rider wears black hat and yellow jodhpurs
Issued: 2003 - 2005

U.S. $60.00
Can. $75.00
U.K. £35.00
Aust. $80.00

NT 11
SO TREAT HIM LIKE A FRIEND™

Designer: Shane Ridge
Height: 5", 12.7 cm
Colour: Horse: Browns
Rider: Dark and light browns, red and yellow
Issued: 2003 - 2005

U.S. $60.00
Can. $75.00
U.K. £35.00
Aust. $80.00

NT 12
HE'LL FIND YOU™

Designer: Shane Ridge
Height: 4 ¼", 10.8 cm
Colour: Grey horse; rider wears black jacket and hat, yellow jodhpurs
Issued: 2003 - 2005

U.S. $60.00
Can. $75.00
U.K. £35.00
Aust. $80.00

WIND IN THE WILLOWS

WW 1
THE DELIGHT OF SPRING™

Designer:	Caroline Dadd
Height:	4", 10.1 cm
Colour:	Brown, white, yellow, red and pink
Issued:	2004 - 2005
U.S.	$45.00
Can.	$55.00
U.K.	£25.00
Aust.	$65.00

WW 2
THE OPEN ROAD, THE DUSTY HIGHWAY™

Designer:	Caroline Dadd
Height:	4 ½", 11.9 cm
Colour:	Green jacket, yellow checked trousers and waistcoat, brown hat and shoes
Issued:	2004 - 2005
U.S.	$55.00
Can.	$65.00
U.K.	£30.00
Aust.	$75.00

WW 3
NO AMOUNT OF SHAKING™

Designer:	Caroline Dadd
Length:	6 ¼", 15.9 cm
Colour:	Mole: Yellow waistcoat, mauve trousers Ratty: Yellow striped suit Blanket: multicoloured
Issued:	2004 - 2005
U.S.	$ 80.00
Can.	$ 95.00
U.K.	£ 45.00
Aust.	$100.00

WW 4
PERSUADING RATTY™

Designer: Caroline Dadd
Height: 4 ¾", 12.1 cm
Colour: Yellow, tan, green, blue, pink and mauve
Issued: 2004 in a limited edition of 1,000

U.S.	$135.00
Can.	$160.00
U.K.	£ 75.00
Aust.	$175.00

WW 5
SPRAWLING BY THE RIVERBANK™

Designer: Caroline Dadd
Height: 2 ¾" x 6 ¼", 7.0 x 15.9 cm
Colour: White shirt, yellow striped trousers, pink cushion, brown picnic hamper, white and blue blanket
Issued: 2004 - 2005

U.S.	$55.00
Can.	$65.00
U.K.	£30.00
Aust.	$75.00

WW 6
WHO IS IT THIS TIME?™

Designer: Caroline Dadd
Height: 5 ¼", 13.3 cm
Colour: Maroon dressing gown, blue and white striped pyjamas
Issued: 2004 - 2005

U.S.	$55.00
Can.	$65.00
U.K.	£30.00
Aust.	$75.00

WW 7
AS GOOD AS NEW!™

Designer: Caroline Dadd
Height: 4 ½", 11.4 cm
Colour: Green, yellow, maroon, white and blue
Issued: 2005 in a limited edition of 1,000

U.S.	$135.00
Can.	$160.00
U.K.	£ 75.00
Aust.	$175.00

WW 8
BADGER'S WINTER STORE™

Designer: Caroline Dadd
Height: 5 ½", 14.0 cm
Colour: White, black, pink, brown, yellow, blue and red
Issued: 2005 to the present

U.S.	–
Can.	–
U.K.	£30.00
Aust.	–

WW 9
EVERY HOLE POSSESSED A FACE™

Designer: Caroline Dadd
Height: 4", 10.1 cm
Colour: Black, yellow, purple, grey, brown, red, blue and green
Issued: 2005 to the present

U.S.	–
Can.	–
U.K.	£30.00
Aust.	–

WW 10
RATTY! IS THAT REALLY YOU?™

Designer: Caroline Dadd
Height: 4", 10.1 cm
Colour: Black, brown, green, red, blue, grey and pale yellow
Issued: 2005 to the present

U.S.	–
Can.	–
U.K.	£40.00
Aust.	–

WW 11
SHORT WINTER DAYS™

Designer: Caroline Dadd
Height: 3 ¾", 9.5 cm
Colour: Brown, yellow, blue, white, black and pink
Issued: 2005 to the present

U.S.	–
Can.	–
U.K.	£30.00
Aust.	–

THE WIZARD OF OZ

3709
SCARECROW™

Designer:	Andy Moss
Height:	6 ½", 16.5 cm
Colour:	Black hat and shirt, brown pants and shoes
Issued:	1998 in a special edition of 1,500
Series:	The Wizard of Oz
U.S.	$130.00
Can.	$150.00
U.K.	£ 75.00
Aust.	$165.00

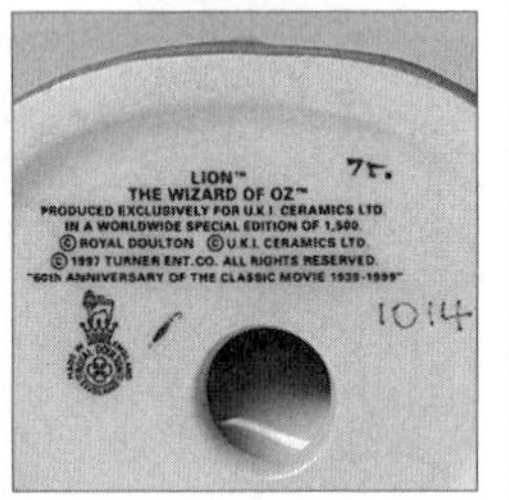

3731
LION™

Designer:	Andy Moss
Height:	6", 15.0 cm
Colour:	Light and dark brown
Issued:	1998 in a special edition of 1,500
Series:	The Wizard of Oz
U.S.	$130.00
Can.	$150.00
U.K.	£ 75.00
Aust.	$165.00

3732
DOROTHY™

Designer:	Andy Moss
Height:	5", 12.7 cm
Colour:	Blue and white dress, red shoes, black dog
Issued:	1998 in a special edition of 1,500
Series:	The Wizard of Oz
U.S.	$175.00
Can.	$225.00
U.K.	£100.00
Aust.	$250.00

3738
TINMAN™

Designer:	Andy Moss
Height:	7", 17.8 cm
Colour:	Grey
Issued:	1998 in a special edition of 1,500
Series:	The Wizard of Oz
U.S.	$130.00
Can.	$150.00
U.K.	£ 75.00
Aust.	$165.00

SECTION THREE

DISNEY CHARACTERS

101 DALMATIANS 404
CINDERELLA 408
DISNEY PRINCESS COLLECTION 411
DISNEY SHOWCASE COLLECTION 415
DISNEY VILLAINS COLLECTION 425
FANTASIA 2000 427
FILM CLASSICS COLLECTION 429
MICKEY MOUSE COLLECTION 432
SLEEPING BEAUTY 434
SNOW WHITE AND THE SEVEN DWARFS 437
WINNIE THE POOH 445

101 DALMATIANS

DM 1
CRUELLA DE VIL™
Style One

Hand made and hand decorated
Royal Doulton®
DISNEY'S
101 DALMATIANS
CRUELLA DE VIL
DM 1
© Disney

Designer:	Martyn Alcock
Modeller:	Martyn Alcock
Height:	6 ¼", 15.9 cm
Colour:	Black dress, pale yellow coat with red lining and red gloves
Issued:	1997 - 2001
Series:	101 Dalmatians Collection

Doulton		Price		
Number	U.S. $	Can. $	U.K. £	Aust. $
DM 1	130.00	150.00	75.00	165.00

DM 2
PENNY™

Hand made and hand decorated
Royal Doulton®
DISNEY'S
101 DALMATIANS
PENNY
DM 2
© Disney

Designer:	Shane Ridge
Modeller:	Shane Ridge
Height:	2 ¾", 7.0 cm
Colour:	White and black dalmatian, red collar
Issued:	1997 - 2001
Series:	101 Dalmatians Collection

Doulton		Price		
Number	U.S. $	Can. $	U.K. £	Aust. $
DM 2	35.00	40.00	20.00	45.00

DM 3
PENNY™ AND FRECKLES™

Hand made and hand decorated
Royal Doulton®
DISNEY'S
101 DALMATIANS
PENNY AND FRECKLES
DM 3
© Disney

Designer:	Martyn Alcock
Modeller:	Martyn Alcock
Height:	2 ¼", 5.5 cm
Colour:	Two white and black Dalmatians with red collars
Issued:	1997 - 2001
Series:	101 Dalmatians Collection

Doulton Number	U.S. $	Price Can. $	U.K. £	Aust. $
DM 3	45.00	55.00	25.00	60.00

DM 4
ROLLY™

Designer:	Shane Ridge
Modeller:	Shane Ridge
Height:	2 ¾", 7.0 cm
Colour:	White and black Dalmatian, red collar, black base
Issued:	1997 - 1999
Series:	101 Dalmatians Collection

Doulton Number	U.S. $	Price Can. $	U.K. £	Aust. $
DM 4	35.00	40.00	20.00	45.00

DM 5
PATCH™, ROLLY™ AND FRECKLES™

Designer:	Shane Ridge
Modeller:	Shane Ridge
Height:	3 ¾", 9.5 cm
Length:	7 ½", 19.0 cm
Colour:	Three white and black Dalmatians wearing red collars
Issued:	1997 in a limited edition of 3,500
Series:	1. 101 Dalmatians Collection 2. Tableau

Doulton Number	U.S. $	Price Can. $	U.K. £	Aust. $
DM 5	175.00	225.00	100.00	250.00

DM 6
PONGO™

Hand made and hand decorated
Royal Doulton®
DISNEY'S
101 DALMATIANS
PONGO
DM 6
© Disney

Designer:	Martyn Alcock
Modeller:	Martyn Alcock
Height:	4 ½", 11.9 cm
Colour:	White and black Dalmatian, red collar
Issued:	1997 - 1998
Series:	101 Dalmatians Collection

Doulton		Price		
Number	U.S. $	Can. $	U.K. £	Aust. $
DM 6	55.00	65.00	30.00	75.00

DM 7
PERDITA™

Designer:	Martyn Alcock
Modeller:	Martyn Alcock
Height:	2 ½", 6.4 cm
Colour:	White and black Dalmatian, dark turquoise collar and blanket
Issued:	1997 - 2001
Series:	101 Dalmatians Collection

Doulton		Price		
Number	U.S. $	Can. $	U.K. £	Aust. $
DM 7	55.00	65.00	30.00	75.00

DM 8
LUCKY™

Designer:	Martyn Alcock
Modeller:	Martyn Alcock
Height:	2 ¾", 7.0 cm
Colour:	White and black Dalmatian, red collar
Issued:	1997 - 2001
Series:	101 Dalmatians Collection

Doulton		Price		
Number	U.S. $	Can. $	U.K. £	Aust. $
DM 8	45.00	55.00	25.00	60.00

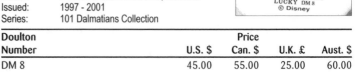

DM 9
PATCH™ IN BASKET

Designer:	Graham Tongue
Modeller:	Graham Tongue
Height:	2 ¼", 5.7 cm
Colour:	White and black Dalmatian, beige basket
Issued:	1998 - 2001
Series:	101 Dalmatians Collection

Doulton Number	U.S. $	Price Can. $	U.K. £	Aust. $
DM 9	55.00	65.00	30.00	75.00

DM 10
LUCKY™ AND FRECKLES™ ON ICE

Designer:	Warren Platt
Modeller:	Warren Platt
Height:	2 ½", 6.4 cm
Colour:	White and black Dalmatians
Issued:	1998 - 1999
Series:	101 Dalmatians Collection

Doulton Number	U.S. $	Price Can. $	U.K. £	Aust. $
DM 10	90.00	110.00	50.00	125.00

DM 11
PUPS IN THE CHAIR™

Designer:	Martyn Alcock
Modeller:	Martyn Alcock
Height:	4", 10.1 cm
Colour:	White and black Dalmatians, yellow chair
Issued:	February 1st to May 12th, 1999 (101 days)
Series:	101 Dalmatians Collection

Doulton Number	U.S. $	Price Can. $	U.K. £	Aust. $
DM 11	130.00	150.00	75.00	165.00

CINDERELLA

CN1
CINDERELLA™ THE DRESS OF DREAMS

Designer: Shane Ridge
Modeller: Shane Ridge
Height: 6 ¾", 17.2 cm
Colour: Pink and white dress
Issued: 2000 in a limited edition of 2,000
Series: Film Classics Collection

Doulton Number	Price U.S. $	Can. $	U.K. £	Aust. $
CN1	125.00	150.00	75.00	175.00

CN2
JAQ™

Height: 3", 7.6 cm
Colour: Brown, reddish-brown, white, blue, dark brown, purple and red
Issued: 2005 to the present
Series: Showcase Collection

Doulton Number	Price U.S. $	Can. $	U.K. £	Aust. $
CN2	–	–	25.00	–

CN3
LUCIFER™

Height: 3 ½", 8.9 cm
Colour: Black cat with brown paws and brown on tip of tail; light brown mouse; blue jar, green water dish and brown base
Issued: 2005 to the present
Series: Showcase Collection

Doulton Number	U.S. $	Price Can. $	U.K. £	Aust. $
CN3	–	–	25.00	–

CN4
WITH A WAVE OF HER MAGIC WAND™

Height: 5", 12.7 cm
Colour: Purple and pink cloak and skirt, white blouse, red bow; brown base
Issued: 2005 to the present
Series: Showcase Collection

Doulton Number	U.S. $	Price Can. $	U.K. £	Aust. $
CN4	–	–	30.00	–

CN5
THEY CAN'T STOP ME FROM DREAMING™

Height: 3 ½", 8.9 cm
Colour: Brown dress with blue sleeves; cream apron and hair band, brown and black pail
Issued: 2005 to the present
Series: Showcase Collection

Doulton Number	U.S. $	Price Can. $	U.K. £	Aust. $
CN5	–	–	35.00	–

CN6
GUS™

Height: 3 ¼", 8.2 cm
Colour: Brown mouse, with green shirt and blue hat; blue and purple buttons
Issued: 2005 to the present
Series: Showcase Collection

Doulton Number	U.S. $	Price Can. $	U.K. £	Aust. $
CN6	–	–	25.00	–

CN7
IT'S A PERFECT FIT™

Height: 4 ¾", 12.1 cm
Colour: Brown, blue, white, red, light brown, blue-grey and black
Issued: 2005 in a limited edition of 1,500
Series: Showcase Collection

Doulton Number	U.S. $	Price Can. $	U.K. £	Aust. $
CN7	–	–	90.00	–

CN8
OFF TO THE BALL™

Size: 6 ½" x 6" x 17 ¼", 16.5 x 15.0 x 44.0 cm
Colour: Blue-grey, green and yellow coach; white horses with yellow harness and pink plumes; blue dress and headband
Issued: 2005 in a limited edition of 1,000
Series: Showcase Collection

Doulton Number	U.S. $	Price Can. $	U.K. £	Aust. $
CN8	–	–	275.00	–

THE DISNEY PRINCESS COLLECTION

SERIES ONE 1995-1996

HN 3677
CINDERELLA™
Style One

Designer:	Pauline Parsons
Height:	8", 20.3 cm
Colour:	Blue and white dress, yellow hair
Issued:	1995 in a limited edition of 2,000
Series:	The Disney Princess Collection, Series One

Doulton Number	U.S. $	Price Can. $	U.K. £	Aust. $
HN 3677	475.00	575.00	275.00	625.00

HN 3678
SNOW WHITE™
Style One

Designer:	Pauline Parsons
Height:	8 ¼", 21.0 cm
Colour:	Yellow, blue and white dress, royal blue and red cape, black hair
Issued:	1995 in a limited edition of 2,000
Series:	The Disney Princess Collection, Series One

Doulton Number	U.S. $	Price Can. $	U.K. £	Aust. $
HN 3678	475.00	575.00	275.00	625.00

HN 3830
BELLE™
Style One

Designer:	Pauline Parsons
Height:	8", 20.3 cm
Colour:	Yellow dress and gloves, brown hair
Issued:	1996 in a limited edition of 2,000
Series:	The Disney Princess Collection, Series One

Doulton Number	U.S. $	Price Can. $	U.K. £	Aust. $
HN 3830	425.00	500.00	250.00	550.00

HN 3831
ARIEL™
Style One

Designer:	Pauline Parsons
Height:	8 ¼", 21.0 cm
Colour:	White dress and veil, red hair
Issued:	1996 in a limited edition of 2,000
Series:	The Disney Princess Collection, Series One

Doulton Number	U.S. $	Price Can. $	U.K. £	Aust. $
HN 3831	425.00	500.00	250.00	550.00

HN 3832
JASMINE™
Style One

Designer:	Pauline Parsons
Height:	7 ½", 19.1 cm
Colour:	Lilac dress
Issued:	1996 in a limited edition of 2,000
Series:	The Disney Princess Collection, Series One

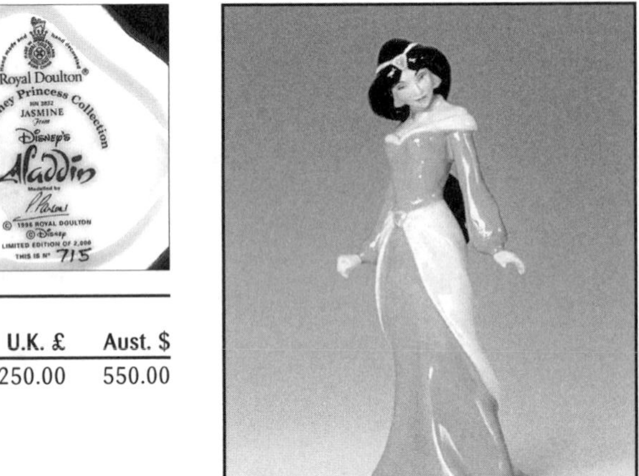

Doulton Number	U.S. $	Price Can. $	U.K. £	Aust. $
HN 3832	425.00	500.00	250.00	550.00

HN 3833
AURORA™

Designer:	Pauline Parsons
Height:	7 ½", 19.1 cm
Colour:	Light and dark blue dress with white trim
Issued:	1996 in a limited edition of 2,000
Series:	The Disney Princess Collection, Series One

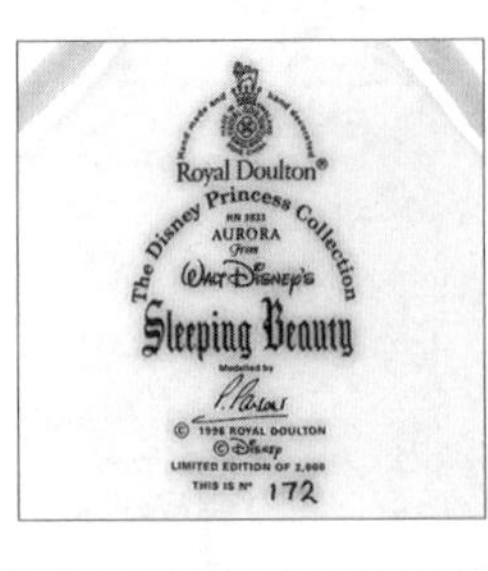

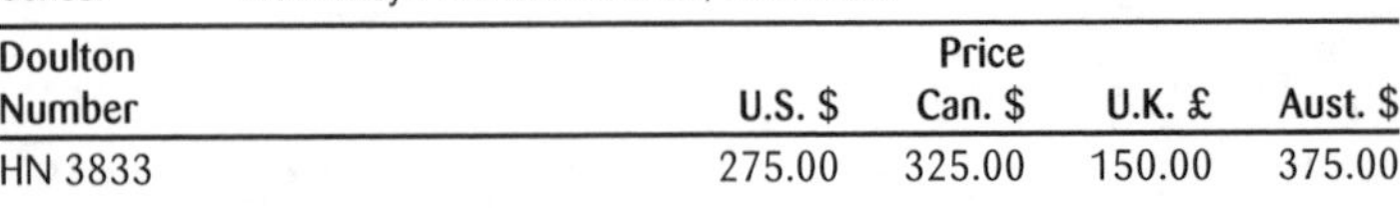

Doulton Number	U.S. $	Price Can. $	U.K. £	Aust. $
HN 3833	275.00	325.00	150.00	375.00

THE DISNEY PRINCESS COLLECTION

SERIES TWO – 2005 TO THE PRESENT

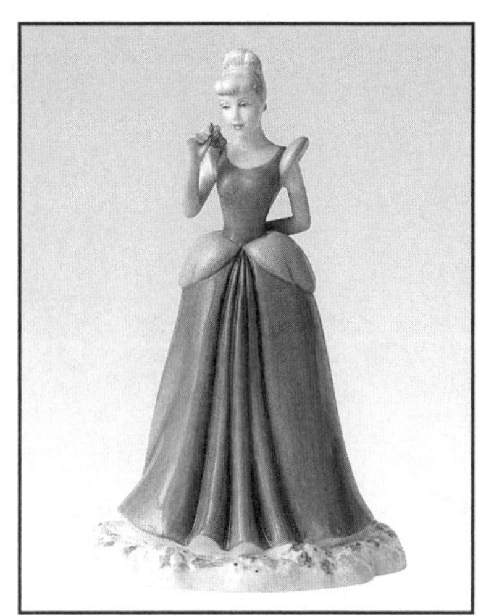

DP1
CINDERELLA™
Style Two

Height: 6 ¾", 17.1 cm
Colour: Blue and pale blue dress, pale blue gloves and hair band, deep red rose, yellow hair
Issued: 2005 to the present
Series: The Disney Princess Collection, Series Two

Doulton Number	U.S. $	Can. $	Price U.K. £	Aust. $
DP1	–	–	60.00	–

DP2
SLEEPING BEAUTY™

Height: 6 ¾", 17.1 cm
Colour: Deep rose pink and pink dress, yellow hair, deep red rose
Issued: 2005 to the present
Series: The Disney Princess Collection, Series Two

Doulton Number	U.S. $	Can. $	Price U.K. £	Aust. $
DP2	–	–	60.00	–

DP3
BELLE™
Style Two

Height: 6 ¾", 17.1 cm
Colour: Yellow dress, deep red rose, dark brown hair, white base with pink and purple flowers
Issued: 2005 to the present
Series: The Disney Princess Collection, Series Two

Doulton Number	U.S. $	Can. $	Price U.K. £	Aust. $
DP3	–	–	60.00	–

DP4
ARIEL™
Style Three

Height: 6 ¾", 17.1 cm
Colour: White and pink dress, white veil, deep red rose, red hair
Issued: 2005 to the present
Series: The Disney Princess Collection, Series Two

Doulton Number	U.S. $	Price Can. $	U.K. £	Aust. $
DP4	–	–	60.00	–

DP5
SNOW WHITE™
Style Three

Height: 6 ¾", 17.1 cm
Colour: Yellow skirt, blue bodice, white sleeves with red dots; red rose and head band; yellow basket
Issued: 2005 to the present
Series: The Disney Princess Collection, Series Two

Doulton Number	U.S. $	Price Can. $	U.K. £	Aust. $
DP5	–	–	60.00	–

DP6
JASMINE™
Style Two

Height: 7 ½", 19.1 cm
Colour: Pale aqua dress, white scarf, black hair, deep red rose
Issued: 2005 to the present
Series: The Disney Princess Collection, Series Two

Doulton Number	U.S. $	Price Can. $	U.K. £	Aust. $
DP6	–	–	60.00	–

DISNEY SHOWCASE COLLECTION

ALICE IN WONDERLAND

AW1
ALICE™
Style Two

Designer: Shane Ridge
Modeller: Shane Ridge
Height: 4 ¾", 12.1 cm
Colour: Blue dress, white apron; red with white polka-dot mushroom
Issued: 2001 in a limited edition of 2,000
Series: Alice In Wonderland

Doulton Number	Price U.S. $	Can. $	U.K. £	Aust. $
AW1	80.00	95.00	45.00	110.00

AW2
MAD HATTER™
Style Two

Designer: Martyn Alcock
Modeller: Martyn Alcock
Height: 4 ¾", 12.1 cm
Colour: Yellow coat, black shirt and shoes, green trousers and bowtie, and green top hat with black band
Issued: 2001 in a limited edition of 2,000
Series: Alice In Wonderland

Doulton Number	Price U.S. $	Can. $	U.K. £	Aust. $
AW2	110.00	130.00	60.00	150.00

AW3
MARCH HARE™

Designer:	Martyn C. R. Alcock
Modeller:	Martyn C. R. Alcock
Height:	2 ½", 6.4 cm
Colour:	Yellow rabbit; red coat, black leggings, white and red tea pot and cup
Issued:	2001 in a limited edition of 2,000
Series:	Alice In Wonderland

Doulton Number	U.S. $	Price Can. $	U.K. £	Aust. $
AW3	80.00	95.00	45.00	110.00

AW4
WHITE RABBIT™
Style Two

Designer:	Shane Ridge
Modeller:	Shane Ridge
Height:	2 ¾", 7.0 cm
Colour:	Red coat, yellow shirt, black bowtie, grey trousers; yellow and white clock
Issued:	2001 in a limited edition of 2,000
Series:	Alice In Wonderland

Doulton Number	U.S. $	Price Can. $	U.K. £	Aust. $
AW4	100.00	125.00	55.00	150.00

AW5
CHESHIRE CAT™
Style Two

Designer:	Shane Ridge
Modeller:	Shane Ridge
Height:	2 ¾", 7.0 cm
Colour:	Pink and white striped cat
Issued:	2001 in a limited edition of 2,000
Series:	Alice In Wonderland

Doulton Number	U.S. $	Price Can. $	U.K. £	Aust. $
AW5	100.00	125.00	55.00	150.00

DISNEY SHOWCASE COLLECTION

THE JUNGLE BOOK

HAND MADE AND HAND DECORATED
DISNEY SHOWCASE COLLECTION
by ROYAL DOULTON
THE JUNGLE BOOK
MOWGLI
JB 1
MADE IN ENGLAND © 2000 DISNEY

JB 1
MOWGLI™

Designer:	Shane Ridge
Modeller:	Shane Ridge
Height:	2 ½", 6.4 cm
Colour:	Fleshtones, black and red
Issued:	2000 - 2001
Series:	Jungle Book

Doulton Number	Price U.S. $	Can. $	U.K. £	Aust. $
JB 1	100.00	125.00	60.00	150.00

HAND MADE AND HAND DECORATED
DISNEY SHOWCASE COLLECTION
by ROYAL DOULTON
THE JUNGLE BOOK
BABY ELEPHANT
JB 2
MADE IN ENGLAND © 2000 DISNEY

JB 2
BABY ELEPHANT™

Designer:	Martyn Alcock
Modeller:	Martyn Alcock
Height:	3 ¼", 8.3 cm
Colour:	Tan
Issued:	2000 - 2001
Series:	Jungle Book

Doulton Number	Price U.S. $	Can. $	U.K. £	Aust. $
JB 2	70.00	90.00	40.00	110.00

JB 3
BALOO™

Designer:	Shane Ridge
Modeller:	Shane Ridge
Height:	5 ¼", 13.3 cm
Colour:	Grey and white
Issued:	2000 - 2001
Series:	Jungle Book

Doulton Number	U.S. $	Price Can. $	U.K. £	Aust. $
JB 3	100.00	125.00	60.00	150.00

JB 4
BAGHEERA™

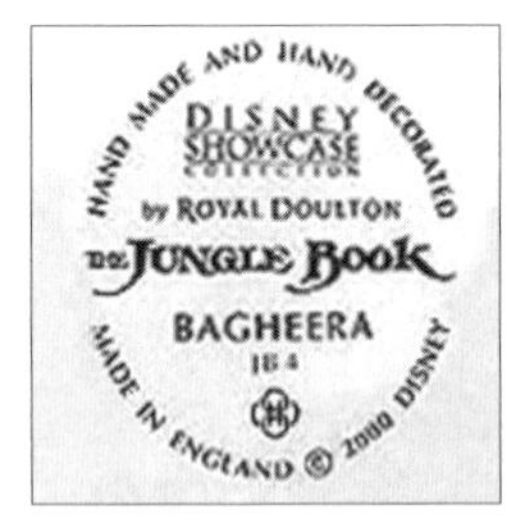

Designer:	Shane Ridge
Modeller:	Shane Ridge
Height:	4 ¾", 12.1 cm
Colour:	Black
Issued:	2000 - 2001
Series:	Jungle Book

Doulton Number	U.S. $	Price Can. $	U.K. £	Aust. $
JB 4	80.00	95.00	45.00	110.00

JB 5
SHERE KHAN™

Designer:	Martyn Alcock
Modeller:	Martyn Alcock
Height:	3 ¼", 8.3 cm
Colour:	Yellow with dark brown stripes
Issued:	2000 - 2001
Series:	Jungle Book

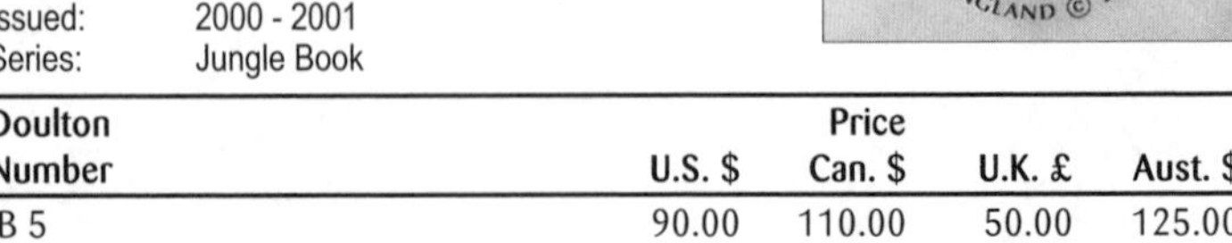

Doulton Number	U.S. $	Price Can. $	U.K. £	Aust. $
JB 5	90.00	110.00	50.00	125.00

JB 6
FLOATING ALONG™

Designer: Martyn Alcock
Modeller: Martyn Alcock
Height: 2 ¾", 7.0 cm
Colour: White and grey bear; fleshtones, black and red
Issued: 2001 in a limited edition of 3,500
Series: 1. Jungle Book
2. Tableau

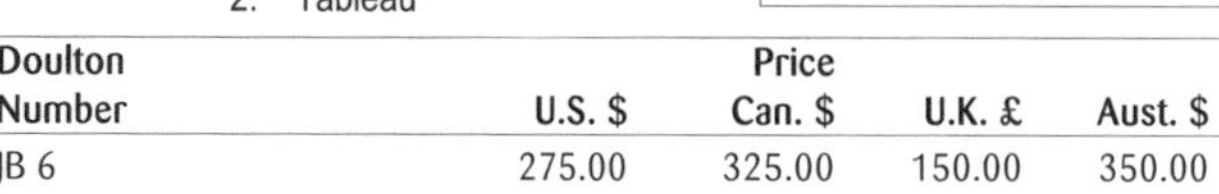

Doulton Number	U.S. $	Price Can. $	U.K. £	Aust. $
JB 6	275.00	325.00	150.00	350.00

JB 7
KING LOUIE™

Designer: Warren Platt
Modeller: Warren Platt
Height: 4", 10.1 cm
Colour: Orange
Issued: 2001 - 2003
Series: Jungle Book

Doulton Number	U.S. $	Price Can. $	U.K. £	Aust. $
JB 7	600.00	725.00	350.00	800.00

DISNEY SHOWCASE COLLECTION

THE LITTLE MERMAID

LM 1
ARIEL™
Style Two

Height:	4 ½", 11.9 cm
Colour:	Green, purple, red and yellow
Issued:	2002 - 2003
Series:	The Little Mermaid

Doulton Number	U.S. $	Price Can. $	U.K. £	Aust. $
LM 1	65.00	80.00	35.00	90.00

LM 2
FLOUNDER™

Height:	2 ½", 6.4 cm
Colour:	Yellow fish with blue striped fins
Issued:	2002 - 2003
Series:	The Little Mermaid

Doulton Number	U.S. $	Price Can. $	U.K. £	Aust. $
LM 2	45.00	55.00	25.00	65.00

LM 3
SEBASTIAN™

Height: 2 ¼", 5.5 cm
Colour: Yellow, red and coral
Issued: 2002 - 2003
Series: The Little Mermaid

Doulton Number	U.S. $	Price Can. $	U.K. £	Aust. $
LM 3	45.00	55.00	25.00	65.00

LM 4
URSULA™

Height: 4 ¼", 10.8 cm
Colour: Purple, black and green
Issued: 2002 - 2003
Series: The Little Mermaid

Doulton Number	U.S. $	Price Can. $	U.K. £	Aust. $
LM 4	70.00	90.00	40.00	100.00

LM 5
SCUTTLE™

Height: 3", 7.6 cm
Colour: White, purple, black and orange
Issued: 2002 - 2003
Series: The Little Mermaid

Doulton Number	U.S. $	Price Can. $	U.K. £	Aust. $
LM 5	45.00	55.00	25.00	65.00

DISNEY SHOWCASE COLLECTION

PETER PAN

HAND MADE AND HAND DECORATED
DISNEY
SHOWCASE
COLLECTION
by ROYAL DOULTON
PETER PAN
PETER PAN
PAN 1
MADE IN THAILAND © 2002 DISNEY

PAN 1
PETER PAN™

Height:	5 ½", 14.0 cm
Colour:	Light green tunic, darker green tights and cap, brown shoes
Issued:	2002 to the present
Series:	Peter Pan

Doulton Number	U.S. $	Price Can. $	U.K. £	Aust. $
PAN 1	70.00	95.00	40.00	100.00

HAND MADE AND HAND DECORATED
DISNEY
SHOWCASE
COLLECTION
by ROYAL DOULTON
PETER PAN
TINKER BELL
PAN 2
MADE IN THAILAND © 2002 DISNEY

PAN 2
TINKER BELL™

Height:	6", 15.0 cm
Colour:	Green dress and slippers, lilac and white wings
Issued:	2002 to the present
Series:	Peter Pan

Doulton Number	U.S. $	Price Can. $	U.K. £	Aust. $
PAN 2	70.00	95.00	40.00	100.00

PAN 3
THE DUEL™

Height:	6 ¼", 15.9 cm
Colour:	Peter Pan: Green tunic and cap, darker green tights; brown belt Captain: Red and gold coat, pink and lilac hat, white neckerchief and stockings, black shoes
Issued:	2002 in a limited edition of 3,000
Series:	Peter Pan

Doulton Number	U.S. $	Price Can. $	U.K. £	Aust. $
PAN 3	125.00	150.00	70.00	175.00

PAN 4
CAPTAIN HOOK™

Height:	7", 17.8 cm
Colour:	Red and gold coat, pink and lilac hat, white neckerchief and stockings, black shoes
Issued:	2002 to the present
Series:	Peter Pan

Doulton Number	U.S. $	Price Can. $	U.K. £	Aust. $
PAN 4	80.00	100.00	45.00	110.00

PAN 5
WENDY™

Height:	5", 12.7 cm
Colour:	Blue dress, blonde hair, yellow block
Issued:	2002 to the present
Series:	Peter Pan

Doulton Number	U.S. $	Price Can. $	U.K. £	Aust. $
PAN 5	65.00	85.00	35.00	90.00

HAND MADE AND HAND DECORATED
DISNEY
SHOWCASE
COLLECTION
by ROYAL DOULTON
PETER PAN
TIC TOC
CROCODILE
PAN 6
MADE IN THAILAND © 2002 DISNEY

PAN 6
TIC TOC CROCODILE™

Height:	5 ½", 14.0 cm
Colour:	Green, grey, red, blue and white
Issued:	2002 to the present
Series:	Peter Pan

Doulton Number	U.S. $	Price Can. $	U.K. £	Aust. $
PAN 6	70.00	95.00	40.00	100.00

PAN 7
HEADING FOR SKULL ROCK

Height:	6", 15.0 cm
Colour:	Captain Hook: Red and gold coat; pink and lilac hat Princess Tiger Lily: Brown, red and orange dress Smee: Blue and white striped shirt, blue shorts, red cap
Issued:	2002 in a limited edition of 3,000
Series:	Peter Pan

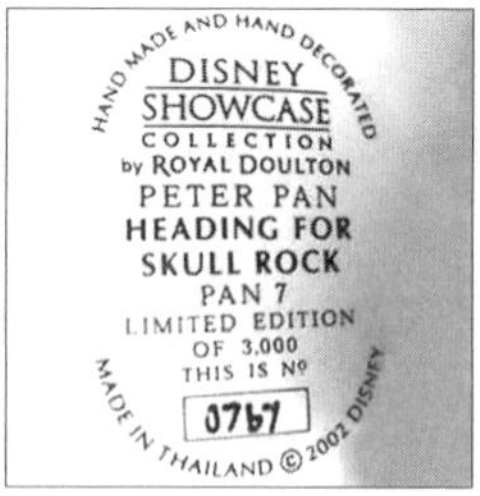
HAND MADE AND HAND DECORATED
DISNEY
SHOWCASE
COLLECTION
by ROYAL DOULTON
PETER PAN
HEADING FOR
SKULL ROCK
PAN 7
LIMITED EDITION
OF 3,000
THIS IS Nº
0767
MADE IN THAILAND © 2002 DISNEY

Doulton Number	U.S. $	Price Can. $	U.K. £	Aust. $
PAN 7	125.00	150.00	70.00	175.00

DISNEY VILLAINS COLLECTION

HN 3839
CRUELLA DE VIL™
Style Two

Designer:	Pauline Parsons
Height:	8", 20.3 cm
Colour:	Black dress, white fur coat, red gloves
Issued:	1997 in a limited edition of 2,000
Series:	The Disney Villains Collection

Doulton Number	U.S. $	Price Can. $	U.K. £	Aust. $
HN 3839	425.00	500.00	250.00	550.00

HN 3840
MALEFICENT™

Designer:	Pauline Parsons
Height:	8", 20.3 cm
Colour:	Black and purple
Issued:	1997 in a limited edition of 2,000
Series:	The Disney Villains Collection

Doulton Number	U.S. $	Price Can. $	U.K. £	Aust. $
HN 3840	425.00	500.00	250.00	550.00

HN 3847
THE QUEEN™

Designer:	Pauline Parson
Height:	8 ¾", 22.2 cm
Colour:	Black, white, purple, red and yellow
Issued:	1998 in a limited edition of 2,000
Series:	The Disney Villains Collection

Doulton Number	U.S. $	Price Can. $	U.K. £	Aust. $
HN 3847	425.00	500.00	250.00	550.00

HN 3848
THE WITCH™

Designer:	Pauline Parsons
Height:	7", 17.8 cm
Colour:	Black robes, red apple
Issued:	1998 in a limited edition of 2,000
Series:	The Disney Villains Collection

Doulton Number	U.S. $	Price Can. $	U.K. £	Aust. $
HN 3848	425.00	500.00	250.00	550.00

FANTASIA 2000

FAN 1
BUCKETS OF MISCHIEF™

Designer:	Shane Ridge
Modeller:	Shane Ridge
Height:	4 ½", 11.9 cm
Colour:	Brown broom and buckets, blue water
Issued:	2000 in a limited edition of 2,000
Series:	Fantasia 2000

Back Stamp	Doulton Number	U.S. $	Price Can. $	U.K. £	Aust. $
FAN 1	8226	95.00	115.00	55.00	125.00

FAN 2
FOLLOW ME™

Designer:	Shane Ridge
Modeller:	Shane Ridge
Height:	5 ¼", 13.3 cm
Colour:	Red, purple, black and white
Issued:	2000 in a limited edition of 2,000
Series:	Fantasia 2000

Back Stamp	Doulton Number	U.S. $	Price Can. $	U.K. £	Aust. $
FAN 2	8227	125.00	150.00	70.00	175.00

FAN 3
NOAH'S™ HELPER

Designer: Shane Ridge
Modeller: Shane Ridge
Height: 4", 10.1 cm
Colour: Brown, white and yellow
Issued: 2000 in a limited edition of 2,000
Series: Fantasia 2000

Back Stamp	Doulton Number	U.S. $	Price Can. $	U.K. £	Aust. $
FAN 3	8228	100.00	125.00	60.00	135.00

FAN 4
HEART ON A STRING™
(Pomp and Circumstance)

Designer: Shane Ridge
Modeller: Shane Ridge
Height: 4 ¼", 10.8 cm
Colour: Blue, yellow and white
Issued: 2000 in a limited edition of 2,000
Series: Fantasia 2000

Back Stamp	Doulton Number	U.S. $	Price Can. $	U.K. £	Aust. $
FAN 4	8325	125.00	150.00	70.00	175.00

FAN 5
A FLOWER AND HIS HEART™
(Shostakovich's Piano Concerto No. 2)

Designer: Shane Ridge
Modeller: Shane Ridge
Height: 6 ½", 16.5 cm
Colour: Red, white and pink
Issued: 2000 in a limited edition of 2,000
Series: 1. Fantasia 2000
2. Tableau

Back Stamp	Doulton Number	U.S. $	Price Can. $	U.K. £	Aust. $
FAN 5	8225	250.00	300.00	150.00	350.00

FILM CLASSICS COLLECTION

FC 1
BAMBI™

Designer: Martyn Alcock
Modeller: Martyn Alcock
Height: 4", 10.1 cm
Colour: Brown deer, yellow spots, black nose and tip on top of ears
Issued: 1999 in a limited edition of 1,500
Series: Film Classics Collection

Back Stamp	Doulton Number	U.S. $	Price Can. $	U.K. £	Aust. $
FC 1	4440	100.00	125.00	60.00	135.00

FC 2
THUMPER™

Designer: Martyn Alcock
Modeller: Martyn Alcock
Height: 3 ¼", 8.3 cm
Colour: Grey, white and cream rabbit, pink nose
Issued: 1999 in a limited edition on 1,500
Series: Film Classics Collection

Back Stamp	Doulton Number	U.S. $	Price Can. $	U.K. £	Aust. $
FC 2	4432	115.00	135.00	65.00	150.00

FC 3
DUMBO™

Modeller:	Shane Ridge
Height:	4 ½", 11.9 cm
Colour:	Grey elephant, pink inner ears
Issued:	1999 in a limited edition of 1,500
Series:	Film Classics Collection

Back Stamp	Doulton Number	U.S. $	Price Can. $	U.K. £	Aust. $
FC 3	4427	130.00	160.00	75.00	175.00

FC 4
PINOCCHIO™

Designer:	Shane Ridge
Modeller:	Shane Ridge
Height:	5 ½", 14.0 cm
Colour:	Yellow shirt and hat, red trousers and shoes, blue bowtie and book
Issued:	1999 in a limited edition of 1,500
Series:	Film Classics Collection

Back Stamp	Doulton Number	U.S. $	Price Can. $	U.K. £	Aust. $
FC 4	4431	130.00	160.00	75.00	175.00

FC 5
JIMINY CRICKET™

Designer:	Warren Platt
Modeller:	Warren Platt
Height:	4 ¼", 10.8 cm
Colour:	Dark blue jacket and shoes, tan trousers, orange waistcoat, blue hat with orange band, red umbrella
Issued:	2000 in a limited edition of 1,500
Series:	Film Classics Collection

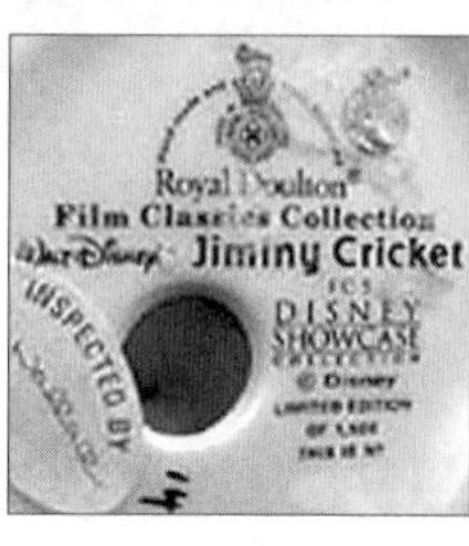

Back Stamp	Doulton Number	U.S. $	Price Can. $	U.K. £	Aust. $
FC 5	3149	100.00	125.00	60.00	135.00

FC 6
TIMOTHY MOUSE™

Designer: Amanda Hughes-Lubeck
Modeller: Amanda Hughes-Lubeck
Height: 3 ¼", 8.3 cm
Colour: Red and yellow suit and hat
Issued: 2000 in a limited edition of 1,500
Series: Film Classics Collection

Back Stamp	Doulton Number	U.S. $	Price Can. $	U.K. £	Aust. $
FC 6	–	90.00	110.00	50.00	125.00

HAND MADE AND HAND DECORATED
DISNEY
SHOWCASE
COLLECTION
by ROYAL DOULTON
Film Classics Collection
LADY
FC 7
LIMITED EDITION OF 1,500
THIS IS Nº
MADE IN ENGLAND © 2001 DISNEY

FC 7
LADY™

Designer: Shane Ridge
Modeller: Shane Ridge
Height: 3 ¼", 8.3 cm
Colour: Tan and brown dog, blue collar
Issued: 2001 in a limited edition of 1,500
Series: Film Classics Collection

Back Stamp	Doulton Number	U.S. $	Price Can. $	U.K. £	Aust. $
FC 7	–	100.00	125.00	60.00	135.00

FC 8
TRAMP™

Designer: Shane Ridge
Modeller: Shane Ridge
Height: 4", 10.1 cm
Colour: Grey and white dog, red collar, gold dog tag
Issued: 2001 in a limited edition of 1,500
Series: Film Classics Collection

Back Stamp	Doulton Number	U.S. $	Price Can. $	U.K. £	Aust. $
FC 8	–	90.00	110.00	50.00	125.00

MICKEY MOUSE COLLECTION

MM 1/MM 7
MICKEY MOUSE™

Designer:	Warren Platt
Modeller:	Warren Platt
Height:	4 ¾", 12.1 cm
Colour:	Black, red and light brown
Issued:	1. 1998 - 1998 2. 1999 - 2000
Series:	Mickey Mouse Collection

Doulton Number	U.S. $	Price Can. $	U.K. £	Aust. $
MM 1, 70th Anniv.	90.00	110.00	50.00	125.00
MM 7	90.00	110.00	50.00	125.00

MM 2/MM 8
MINNIE MOUSE™

Designer:	Warren Platt
Modeller:	Warren Platt
Height:	5 ½", 14.0 cm
Colour:	Black, blue and red
Issued:	1. 1998 - 1998 2. 1999 - 2000
Series:	Mickey Mouse Collection

Doulton Number	U.S. $	Price Can. $	U.K. £	Aust. $
MM 2, 70th Anniv.	90.00	110.00	50.00	125.00
MM 8	90.00	110.00	50.00	125.00

MM 3/MM 9
DONALD DUCK™

Designer:	Warren Platt
Modeller:	Shane Ridge
Height:	4 ¾", 12.1 cm
Colour:	Blue, white and red
Issued:	1. 1998 - 1998 2. 1999 - 2000
Series:	Mickey Mouse Collection

Doulton Number	U.S. $	Price Can. $	U.K. £	Aust. $
MM 3, 70th Anniv.	90.00	110.00	50.00	125.00
MM 9	90.00	110.00	50.00	125.00

MM 4/MM 10
DAISY DUCK™

Designer:	Shane Ridge
Modeller:	Shane Ridge
Height:	5 ½", 14.0 cm
Colour:	Blue, white and pink
Issued:	1. 1998 - 1998 2. 1999 - 2000
Series:	Mickey Mouse Collection

Doulton Number	U.S. $	Price Can. $	U.K. £	Aust. $
MM 4, 70th Anniv.	90.00	110.00	50.00	125.00
MM 10	90.00	110.00	50.00	125.00

MM 5/MM 11
GOOFY™

Designer:	Shane Ridge
Modeller:	Graham Tongue
Height:	5", 12.7 cm
Colour:	Red, blue and black
Issued:	1. 1998 - 1998 2. 1999 - 2000
Series:	Mickey Mouse Collection

Doulton Number	U.S. $	Price Can. $	U.K. £	Aust. $
MM 5, 70th Anniv.	90.00	110.00	50.00	125.00
MM11	90.00	110.00	50.00	125.00

MM 6/MM 12
PLUTO™

Designer:	Graham Tongue
Modeller:	Graham Tongue
Height:	4 ½", 12.1 cm
Colour:	Light brown
Issued:	1. 1998 - 1998 2. 1999 - 2000
Series:	Mickey Mouse Collection

Doulton Number	U.S. $	Price Can. $	U.K. £	Aust. $
MM 6, 70th Anniv.	90.00	110.00	50.00	125.00
MM 12	90.00	110.00	50.00	125.00

SLEEPING BEAUTY

SB 1
BRIAR ROSE™
Singing of Loves Dreams

Height:	5 ½", 14.0 cm
Colour:	Pink and purple
Issued:	2004 to the present

Doulton Number	U.S. $	Price Can. $	U.K. £	Aust. $
SB 1	–	–	35.00	–

SB 2
FLORA™
Nurturing Fairy

Height:	4 ¼", 10.8 cm
Colour:	Light purple and pink
Issued:	2004 to the present

Doulton Number	U.S. $	Price Can. $	U.K. £	Aust. $
SB 2	–	–	30.00	–

SB 3
FAUNA™
Thoughtful Fairy

Height: 4 ¼", 10.8 cm
Colour: Dark and light green and black
Issued: 2004 to the present

Doulton Number	Price U.S. $	Can. $	U.K. £	Aust. $
SB 3	–	–	30.00	–

SB 4
MERRYWEATHER™
Feisty Fairy

Height: 4 ¼", 10.8 cm
Colour: Light and dark blue
Issued: 2004 to the present

Doulton Number	Price U.S. $	Can. $	U.K. £	Aust. $
SB 4	–	–	30.00	–

Backstamp not available at press time

SB 5
MALEFICENT™
"Stand Back You Fools"

Height: 6 ¼", 15.9 cm
Colour: Black, pink and mauve
Issued: 2004 to the present

Doulton Number	Price U.S. $	Can. $	U.K. £	Aust. $
SB 5	–	–	40.00	–

SB 6
WOODLAND WALTZ™

Height: 5 ¾", 14.6 cm
Colour: Red, lilac, yellow, green and black
Issued: 2004 in a limited edition of 1,500

Doulton Number	U.S. $	Price Can. $	U.K. £	Aust. $
SB 6	150.00	180.00	80.00	200.00

SB 7
LOVES FIRST KISS™

Height: 4 ¼", 10.8 cm
Colour: Red, pink, yellow and blue
Issued: 2004 in a limited edition of 1,500

Doulton Number	U.S. $	Price Can. $	U.K. £	Aust. $
SB 7	150.00	180.00	80.00	200.00

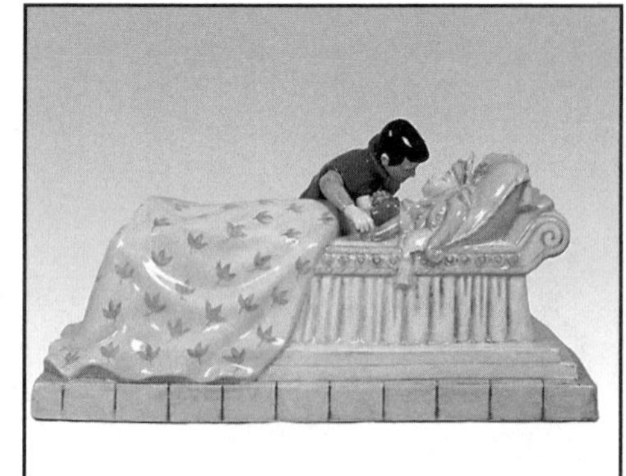

SNOW WHITE AND THE SEVEN DWARFS

SW 1 / SW 9
SNOW WHITE™
Style Two

Designer: Amanda Hughes-Lubeck
Height: 5 ¾", 14.6 cm
Colour: Yellow and blue dress, red cape, white collar
Issued: SW 1 1997 in a limited edition of 2,000
SW 9 1998 - 2002

Doulton Number	U.S. $	Price Can. $	U.K. £	Aust. $
SW 1, 60th Anniv.	225.00	275.00	125.00	300.00
SW 9	135.00	165.00	75.00	175.00

SW 2 / SW 10
DOC™

Designer: Amanda Hughes-Lubeck
Height: 3 ¼", 8.3 cm
Colour: Red tunic, brown trousers, yellow hat, green book
Issued: SW 2 1997 in a limited edition of 2,000
SW 10 1998 - 2002

Doulton Number	U.S. $	Price Can. $	U.K. £	Aust. $
SW 2, 60th Anniv.	70.00	85.00	40.00	90.00
SW 10	55.00	65.00	30.00	70.00

SW3 / SW11
GRUMPY™

Designer: Shane Ridge
Height: 3 ½", 8.9 cm
Colour: Dark rust tunic and trousers, brown hat, light brown basket
Issued: SW 3 1997 in a limited edition of 2,000
SW 11 1998 - 2002

Doulton Number	U.S. $	Price Can. $	U.K. £	Aust. $
SW 3, 60th Anniv.	70.00	85.00	40.00	90.00
SW 11	55.00	65.00	30.00	70.00

SW 4 / SW 12
HAPPY™

Designer:	Amanda Hughes-Lubeck
Height:	3 ½", 8.9 cm
Colour:	Brown and orange tunic, light blue trousers with black belt and a yellow hat
Issued:	SW 4 1997 in a limited edition of 2,000 SW 12 1998 - 2002

Doulton Number	U.S. $	Price Can. $	U.K. £	Aust. $
SW 4, 60th Anniv.	70.00	85.00	40.00	90.00
SW 12	55.00	65.00	30.00	70.00

SW 5 / SW 13
DOPEY™

Designer:	Shane Ridge
Height:	3 ½", 8.9 cm
Colour:	Yellow coat and trousers, purple hat, black belt
Issued:	SW 5 1997 in a limited edition of 2,000 SW 13 1998 - 2002

Doulton Number		U.S. $	Price Can. $	U.K. £	Aust. $
SW 5, Anniv.	70.00	85.00	40.00	90.00	
SW 13	SW 13	55.00	65.00	30.00	70.00

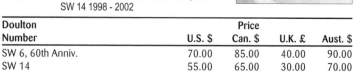

SW 6 / SW 14
SNEEZY™

Designer:	Warren Platt
Height:	3 ½", 8.9 cm
Colour:	Light brown tunic, dark brown trousers, black belt
Issued:	SW 6 1997 in a limited edition of 2,000 SW 14 1998 - 2002

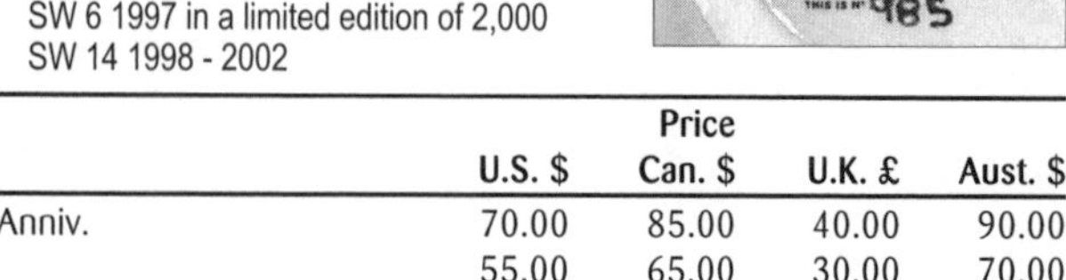

Doulton Number	U.S. $	Price Can. $	U.K. £	Aust. $
SW 6, 60th Anniv.	70.00	85.00	40.00	90.00
SW 14	55.00	65.00	30.00	70.00

SW 7 / SW 15
SLEEPY™

Designer:	Warren Platt
Height:	3 ½", 8.9 cm
Colour:	Beige tunic, dark brown trousers, green hat and a yellow bottle
Issued:	SW 7 1997 in a limited edition of 2,000 SW 15 1998 - 2002

Doulton Number	U.S. $	Price Can. $	U.K. £	Aust. $
SW 7, 60th Anniv.	70.00	85.00	40.00	90.00
SW 15	55.00	65.00	30.00	70.00

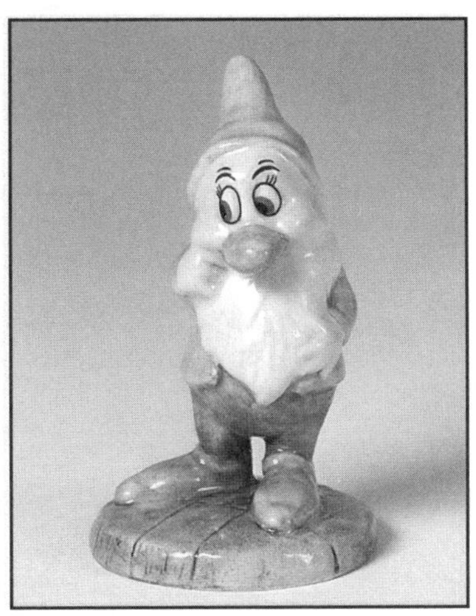

SW 8 / SW 16
BASHFUL™

Designer:	Amanda Hughes-Lubeck
Height:	3 ½", 8.9 cm
Colour:	Dark yellow tunic, light brown trousers, green hat
Issued:	SW 8 1997 in a limited edition of 2,000 SW 16 1998 - 2002

Doulton Number	U.S. $	Price Can. $	U.K. £	Aust. $
SW 8, 60th Anniv.	70.00	85.00	40.00	90.00
SW 16	55.00	65.00	30.00	70.00

SW 17
DOPEY™ BY CANDLELIGHT

Designer:	Shane Ridge
Height:	3 ½", 8.9 cm
Colour:	Green
Issued:	1998 - 2002

Doulton Number	U.S. $	Price Can. $	U.K. £	Aust. $
SW 17	55.00	65.00	30.00	70.00

SW 18
BASHFUL'S™ MELODY

Designer: Graham Tongue
Modeller: Graham Tongue
Height: 3 ½", 8.9 cm
Colour: Blue
Issued: 1998 - 2002

Doulton Number	U.S. $	Price Can. $	U.K. £	Aust. $
SW 18	55.00	65.00	30.00	70.00

SW 19
DOC™ WITH LANTERN

Designer: Warren Platt
Modeller: Warren Platt
Height: 3 ½", 8.9 cm
Colour: Red and yellow
Issued: 1999 - 2002

Doulton Number	U.S. $	Price Can. $	U.K. £	Aust. $
SW 19	55.00	65.00	30.00	70.00

SW 20
GRUMPY'S™ BATHTIME

Designer: Shane Ridge
Modeller: Shane Ridge
Height: 3 ½", 8.9 cm
Colour: White, brown, red and yellow
Issued: 1999 - 1999

Doulton Number	U.S. $	Price Can. $	U.K. £	Aust. $
SW 20	140.00	170.00	80.00	185.00

Note: Serial numbered

SW 21
DOPEY'S™ FIRST KISS

Designer:	Disney
Modeller:	Shane Ridge
Height:	5 ¼", 13.3 cm
Colour:	Yellow, blue, red and green
Issued:	2000 in a limited edition of 2,000
Series:	1. Disney Classics 2. Tableau

Doulton Number	U.S. $	Price Can. $	U.K. £	Aust. $
SW 21	175.00	225.00	100.00	250.00

SW 22
SNOW WHITE™ (Fairest Of Them All)

Height:	5 ¼", 13.3 cm
Colour:	Blue, yellow, pink, black, white and green
Issued:	2004 to the present

Doulton Number	U.S. $	Price Can. $	U.K. £	Aust. $
SW 22	–	–	45.00	–

SW 23
AW SHUCKS

Height:	4", 10.1 cm
Colour:	Yellow, brown, white and blue
Issued:	2004 to the present

Doulton Number	U.S. $	Price Can. $	U.K. £	Aust. $
SW 23	–	–	25.00	–

SW 24
IRRESISTIBLY LOVEABLE

Height: 3 ½", 8.9 cm
Colour: Yellow, pink, purple and grey
Issued: 2004 to the present

Doulton Number	U.S. $	Price Can. $	U.K. £	Aust. $
SW 24	–	–	25.00	–

SW 25
DEAR OLD DOC™

Height: 4", 10.1 cm
Colour: Brown, tan, beige, yellow and grey
Issued: 2004 to the present

Doulton Number	U.S. $	Price Can. $	U.K. £	Aust. $
SW 25	–	–	25.00	–

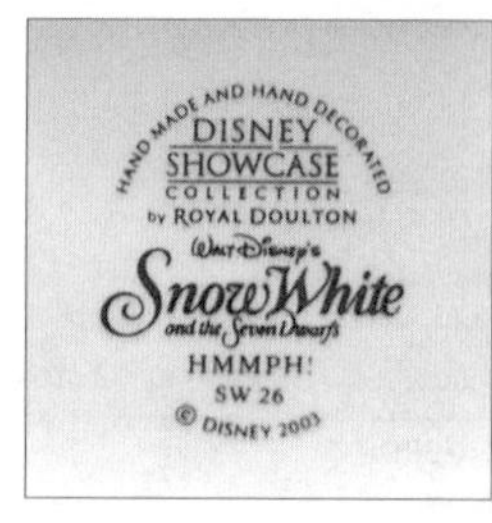

SW 26
HMMPH!

Height: 3 ½", 8.9 cm
Colour: Red, brown, beige and grey
Issued: 2004 to the present

Doulton Number	U.S. $	Price Can. $	U.K. £	Aust. $
SW 26	–	–	25.00	–

SW 27
HAPPY, THAT'S ME!

Height: 3 ½", 8.9 cm
Colour: Blue, browns, yellow and beige
Issued: 2004 to the present

Doulton Number	U.S. $	Can. $	U.K. £	Aust. $
SW 27	–	–	25.00	–

SW 28
ZZZZZZ

Height: 2", 5.0 cm
Colour: White, pink, beige, light brown and green
Issued: 2004 to the present

Doulton Number	U.S. $	Can. $	U.K. £	Aust. $
SW 28	–	–	25.00	–

SW 29
"AH, AH, AACHOO!"

Height: 3 ½", 8.9 cm
Colour: Light and dark brown, yellow, white and red
Issued: 2004 to the present

Doulton Number	U.S. $	Can. $	U.K. £	Aust. $
SW 29	–	–	25.00	–

SW 30
TAKE THE APPLE, DEARIE

Height: 6", 15.0 cm
Colour: Black, grey, white and red
Issued: 2004 to the present

Doulton Number	U.S. $	Price Can. $	U.K. £	Aust. $
SW 30	–	–	35.00	–

SW 31
HEIGH HO™

Length: 5 ¼", 13.3 cm
Colour: Browns, yellows, blue, red, green, pink and grey
Issued: 2004 in a limited edition of 1,500

Doulton Number	U.S. $	Price Can. $	U.K. £	Aust. $
SW 31	–	–	245.00	–

WINNIE THE POOH COLLECTION

WP 1
WINNIE THE POOH™ AND THE HONEYPOT

Designer: Warren Platt
Height: 2 ½", 6.5 cm
Colour: Yellow bear, red jersey, red-brown honeypot
Issued: 1996 - 1999
Series: Winnie the Pooh and Friends from the Hundred Acre Wood

Doulton Number	U.S. $	Price Can. $	U.K. £	Aust. $
WP 1, 70th Anniv.	60.00	75.00	35.00	85.00
WP 1	45.00	55.00	25.00	65.00

WP 2
POOH™ AND PIGLET™—THE WINDY DAY

Designer: Martyn Alcock
Height: 3 ¼", 8.3 cm
Colour: Yellow bear, pink piglet with green suit, light brown base
Issued: 1996 - 2002
Series: Winnie the Pooh and Friends from the Hundred Acre Wood

Doulton Number	U.S. $	Price Can. $	U.K. £	Aust. $
WP 2, 70th Anniv.	60.00	75.00	35.00	85.00
WP 2	45.00	55.00	25.00	65.00

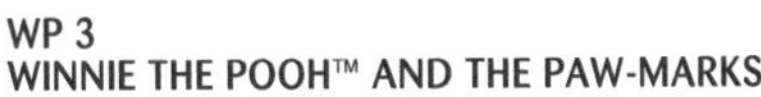

WP 3
WINNIE THE POOH™ AND THE PAW-MARKS

Designer: Warren Platt
Height: 2 ¾", 7.0 cm
Colour: Yellow bear, red jersey
Issued: 1996 - 1997
Series: Winnie the Pooh and Friends from the Hundred Acre Wood

Doulton Number	U.S. $	Price Can. $	U.K. £	Aust. $
WP 3, 70th Anniv.	70.00	90.00	40.00	100.00
WP 3	60.00	75.00	35.00	85.00

WP 4
WINNIE THE POOH™ IN THE ARMCHAIR

Designer:	Shane Ridge
Height:	3 ¼", 8.3 cm
Colour:	Yellow bear, pink armchair
Issued:	1996 - 1998
Series:	Winnie the Pooh and Friends from the Hundred Acre Wood

Doulton Number	U.S. $	Price Can. $	U.K. £	Aust. $
WP 4, 70th Anniv.	60.00	75.00	35.00	85.00
WP 4	45.00	55.00	25.00	65.00

WP 5
PIGLET™ AND THE BALLOON

Designer:	Warren Platt
Height:	2 ¾", 7.0 cm
Colour:	Pink piglet, green suit, blue balloon, light brown base
Issued:	1996 - 1998
Series:	Winnie the Pooh and Friends from the Hundred Acre Wood

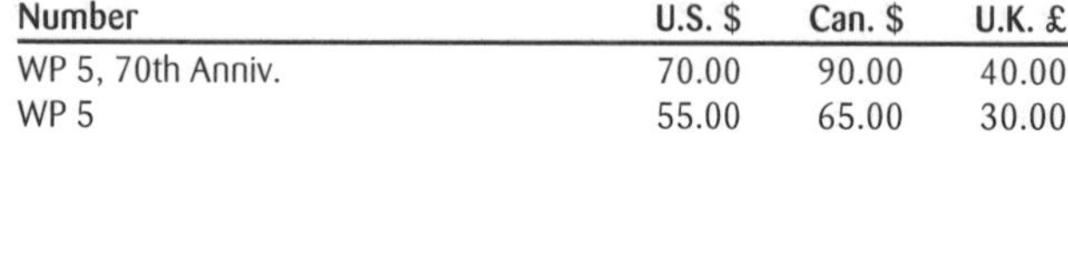

Doulton Number	U.S. $	Price Can. $	U.K. £	Aust. $
WP 5, 70th Anniv.	70.00	90.00	40.00	100.00
WP 5	55.00	65.00	30.00	75.00

WP 6
TIGGER™ SIGNS THE RISSOLUTION

Designer:	Martyn Alcock
Height:	1 ¾", 4.5 cm
Colour:	Yellow and black
Issued:	1996 - 2000
Series:	Winnie the Pooh and Friends from the Hundred Acre Wood

Doulton Number	U.S. $	Price Can. $	U.K. £	Aust. $
WP 6, 70th Anniv.	55.00	65.00	30.00	75.00
WP 6	45.00	55.00	25.00	65.00

WP 7
EEYORE'S™ TAIL

Designer: Shane Ridge
Height: 3 ½", 8.9 cm
Colour: Grey donkey with black markings, pink bow
Issued: 1996 - 1999
Series: Winnie the Pooh and Friends from the Hundred Acre Wood

Doulton Number	U.S. $	Price Can. $	U.K. £	Aust. $
WP 7, 70th Anniv.	60.00	75.00	35.00	85.00
WP 7	45.00	55.00	25.00	65.00

WP 8
KANGA™ AND ROO™

Designer: Martyn Alcock
Height: 3 ½", 8.9 cm
Colour: Dark and light brown kangaroos
Issued: 1996 - 1998
Series: Winnie the Pooh and Friends from the Hundred Acre Wood

Doulton Number	U.S. $	Price Can. $	U.K. £	Aust. $
WP 8, 70th ANniv.	80.00	100.00	45.00	110.00
WP 8	45.00	55.00	25.00	65.00

WP 9
CHRISTOPHER ROBIN™

Designer: Shane Ridge
Height: 5 ½", 14.0 cm
Colour: White and blue checked shirt, blue shorts, black wellingtons, red-brown hair
Issued: 1996 - 2001
Series: Winnie the Pooh and Friends from the Hundred Acre Wood

Doulton Number	U.S. $	Price Can. $	U.K. £	Aust. $
WP 9, 70th Anniv.	90.00	110.00	50.00	125.00
WP 9	55.00	65.00	30.00	75.00

WP 10
CHRISTOPHER ROBIN™ AND POOH™

Designer:	Shane Ridge
Height:	3 ¼", 8.5 cm
Colour:	Light blue shirt and shorts, black boots, reddish brown hair, yellow bear
Issued:	1996 - 1997
Series:	Winnie the Pooh and Friends from the Hundred Acre Wood

Doulton Number	U.S. $	Price Can. $	U.K. £	Aust. $
WP 10, 70th Anniv.	110.00	135.00	60.00	150.00
WP 10	70.00	90.00	40.00	100.00

WP 11
POOH™ LIGHTS THE CANDLE

Designer:	Graham Tongue
Height:	3 ½", 8.9 cm
Colour:	Yellow bear with white candle and hat
Issued:	1997 - 1998
Series:	Winnie the Pooh and Friends from the Hundred Acre Wood

Doulton Number	U.S. $	Price Can. $	U.K. £	Aust. $
WP 11	45.00	55.00	25.00	65.00

WP 12
POOH™ COUNTING THE HONEYPOTS

Designer:	Martyn Alcock
Height:	3 ½", 8.9 cm
Colour:	Yellow bear, brown honeypots
Issued:	1997 - 1999
Series:	Winnie the Pooh and Friends from the Hundred Acre Wood

Doulton Number	U.S. $	Price Can. $	U.K. £	Aust. $
WP 12	45.00	55.00	25.00	65.00

WP 13
PIGLET™ PICKING THE VIOLETS

Designer:	Graham Tongue
Height:	2 ½", 6.4 cm
Colour:	Pink, light and dark greens
Issued:	1997 - 2000
Series:	Winnie the Pooh and Friends from the Hundred Acre Wood

Doulton Number	U.S. $	Price Can. $	U.K. £	Aust. $
WP 13	45.00	55.00	25.00	65.00

WP 14
EEYORE'S™ BIRTHDAY

Designer:	Martyn Alcock
Height:	2 ¾", 7.0 cm
Colour:	Grey and black
Issued:	1997 - 2002
Series:	Winnie the Pooh and Friends from the Hundred Acre Wood

Doulton Number	U.S. $	Price Can. $	U.K. £	Aust. $
WP 14	45.00	55.00	25.00	65.00

WP 15
EEYORE™ LOSES A TAIL

Designer:	Martyn Alcock
Height:	4", 10.1 cm
Colour:	Pink, yellow, grey, green and brown
Issued:	1997 in a limited edition of 5,000
Series:	1. Tableau 2. Winnie the Pooh and Friends from the Hundred Acre Wood

Doulton Number	U.S. $	Price Can. $	U.K. £	Aust. $
WP 15	225.00	275.00	125.00	300.00

WP 16
POOH'S™ BLUE BALLOON (MONEY BOX)

Royal Doulton®
THE
WINNIE THE POOH
COLLECTION
POOH'S BLUE BALLOON
WP 16
© Disney

Designer:	Shane Ridge
Height:	4 ¼", 10.8 cm
Colour:	Yellow bear, pink pig wearing green suit, white balloon with dark blue rope
Issued:	1997 - 1998
Series:	Winnie the Pooh and Friends from the Hundred Acre Wood

Doulton Number	U.S. $	Price Can. $	U.K. £	Aust. $
WP 16	70.00	90.00	40.00	100.00

WP 17
WOL™ SIGNS THE RISSOLUTION

Designer:	Martyn Alcock
Height:	3 ¾", 9.5 cm
Colour:	Grey and black
Issued:	1998 in a special edition of 2,500
Series:	Winnie the Pooh and Friends from the Hundred Acre Wood

Doulton Number	U.S. $	Price Can. $	U.K. £	Aust. $
WP 17	300.00	375.00	165.00	425.00

WP 18
WINNIE THE POOH™ AND THE PRESENT

Designer:	Graham Tongue
Height:	3 ¾", 9.5 cm
Colour:	Yellow and brown
Issued:	1999 - 2002
Series:	Winnie the Pooh and Friends from the Hundred Acre Wood

Doulton Number	U.S. $	Price Can. $	U.K. £	Aust. $
WP 18	45.00	55.00	25.00	65.00

WP 19
WINNIE THE POOH™ AND THE FAIR-SIZED BASKET

Designer:	Graham Tongue
Height:	2 ¾", 7.0 cm
Colour:	Yellow bear, brown basket
Issued:	1999 - 2002
Series:	Winnie the Pooh and Friends from the Hundred Acre Wood

Doulton Number	U.S. $	Price Can. $	U.K. £	Aust. $
WP 19	45.00	55.00	25.00	65.00

WP 20
THE MORE IT SNOWS, TIDDELY POM™

Designer:	Shane Ridge
Height:	3 ¼", 8.3 cm
Colour:	Yellow, red, pink and green
Issued:	1999 - 2002
Series:	Winnie the Pooh and Friends from the Hundred Acre Wood

Doulton Number	U.S. $	Price Can. $	U.K. £	Aust. $
WP 20	55.00	65.00	30.00	75.00

WP 21
SUMMER'S DAY PICNIC™

Designer:	Warren Platt
Length:	2 ½", 5.7 cm
Colour:	Blue, yellow and green
Issued:	1998 in a limited edition of 5,000
Series:	1. Tableau 2. Winnie the Pooh and Friends from the Hundred Acre Wood

Doulton Number	U.S. $	Price Can. $	U.K. £	Aust. $
WP 21	150.00	175.00	80.00	200.00

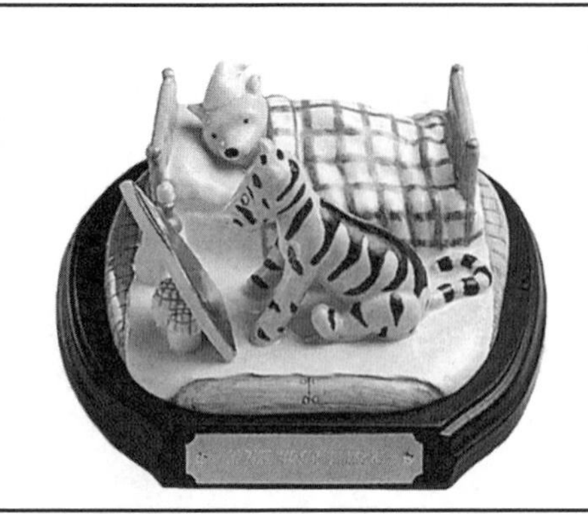

WP 22
I'VE FOUND SOMEBODY JUST LIKE ME™

Designer:	Martyn Alcock
Length:	5 ¼", 13.3 cm
Colour:	Yellow, black, blue and white
Issued:	1999 in a limited edition of 5,000
Series:	1. Tableau 2. Winnie the Pooh and Friends from the Hundred Acre Wood

Doulton Number	U.S. $	Can. $	Price U.K. £	Aust. $
WP 22	175.00	225.00	100.00	250.00

WP 23
RABBIT™ READS THE PLAN

Designer:	Martyn Alcock
Height:	4 ½", 11.9 cm
Colour:	Grey rabbit, pink inner ears
Issued:	1999 - 1999
Series:	Classic Pooh

Doulton Number	U.S. $	Price Can. $	U.K. £	Aust. $
WP 23	55.00	65.00	30.00	75.00

WP 24
HOW SWEET TO BE A CLOUD™ (CLOCK)

Designer:	Warren Platt
Height:	4 ½", 11.9 cm
Colour:	Blue, white, yellow and red
Issued:	2000 - 2000
Series:	Classic Pooh

Doulton Number	U.S. $	Price Can. $	U.K. £	Aust. $
WP 24	100.00	125.00	60.00	150.00

WP 25
EEYORE™ NOSE TO THE GROUND

Designer: Martyn Alcock
Height: 3 ¾", 9.5 cm
Size: Large
Colour: Grey and black
Issued: 2000 in a limited edition of 2,000
Series: Large Size

Doulton Number	U.S. $	Price Can. $	U.K. £	Aust. $
WP 25	110.00	130.00	60.00	150.00

WP 26
PIGLET™ PLANTING A HAYCORN

Designer: Martyn Alcock
Height: 3 ¾", 9.5 cm
Size: Large
Colour: Pink, green and brown
Issued: 2000 in a limited edition of 2,000
Series: Large Size

Doulton Number	U.S. $	Price Can. $	U.K. £	Aust. $
WP 26	80.00	100.00	45.00	110.00

WP 27
TIGGER™ LOVES TIGGER LILIES

Designer: Martyn Alcock
Height: 4 ¼", 10.8 cm
Size: Large
Colour: Brown, black and red
Issued: 2000 in a limited edition of 2,000
Series: Large Size

Doulton Number	U.S. $	Price Can. $	U.K. £	Aust. $
WP 27	90.00	110.00	50.00	125.00

WP 28
POOH BEGAN TO EAT™

Designer: Shane Ridge
Height: 3 ¾", 9.5 cm
Size: Large
Colour: Yellow and green
Issued: 2000 in a limited edition of 2,000
Series: Large Size

Doulton Number	U.S. $	Price Can. $	U.K. £	Aust. $
WP 28	150.00	180.00	85.00	200.00

WP 29
PIGLET AND THE HONEYPOT™

Designer: Amanda Hughes-Lubeck
Height: 2 ½", 6.4 cm
Colour: Pink, green, grey and yellow
Issued: 2000 - 2002
Series: Classic Pooh

Doulton Number	U.S. $	Price Can. $	U.K. £	Aust. $
WP 29	45.00	55.00	25.00	65.00

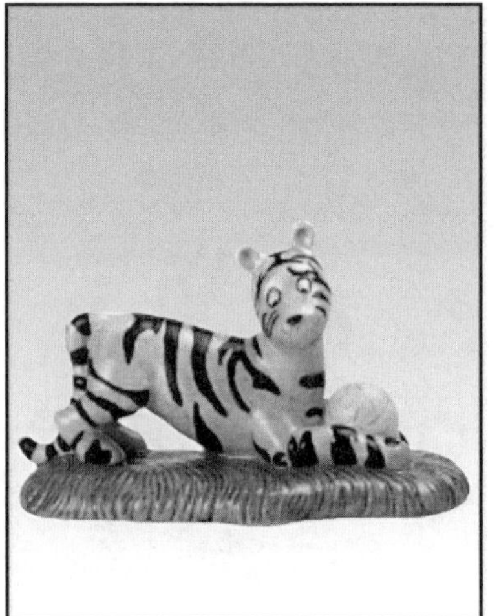

WP 30
TIGGER PLAYS BALL™

Designer: Warren Platt
Height: 3", 7.6 cm
Colour: Brown, black and yellow
Issued: 2000 - 2002
Series: Classic Pooh

Doulton Number	U.S. $	Price Can. $	U.K. £	Aust. $
WP 30	90.00	110.00	50.00	125.00

WP 31
THE BRAIN OF POOH™

Designer: Amanda Hughes-Lubeck
Height: 4", 10.1 cm
Colour: Black, grey, yellow and green
Issued: 2000 in a limited edition of 5,000
Series: Classic Pooh

Doulton Number	Price U.S. $	Can. $	U.K. £	Aust. $
WP 31	250.00	300.00	140.00	325.00

WP 32
CHRISTOPHER READS TO POOH™

Designer: Shane Ridge
Height: 3 ½", 8.9 cm
Colour: Yellow, red, white and black
Issued: 2001 (time limited)
Series: Classic Pooh

Doulton Number	Price U.S. $	Can. $	U.K. £	Aust. $
WP 32	125.00	150.00	70.00	175.00

WP 33
POOH™ AND THE PARTY HAT

Designer: Amander Hughes-Lubeck
Height: 2 ¾", 7.0 cm
Colour: Yellow bear, red hat, pale blue ribbon
Issued: 2001 - 2002
Series: Classic Pooh

Doulton Number	Price U.S. $	Can. $	U.K. £	Aust. $
WP 33	55.00	65.00	30.00	75.00

WP 34
GOING SLEDGING™

Designer:	Shane Ridge
Height:	4", 10.1 cm
Colour:	Blue, yellow, red, brown, green and grey
Issued:	2001 in a limited edition of 5,000
Series:	Classic Pooh

Doulton Number	U.S. $	Price Can. $	U.K. £	Aust. $
WP 34	175.00	225.00	100.00	250.00

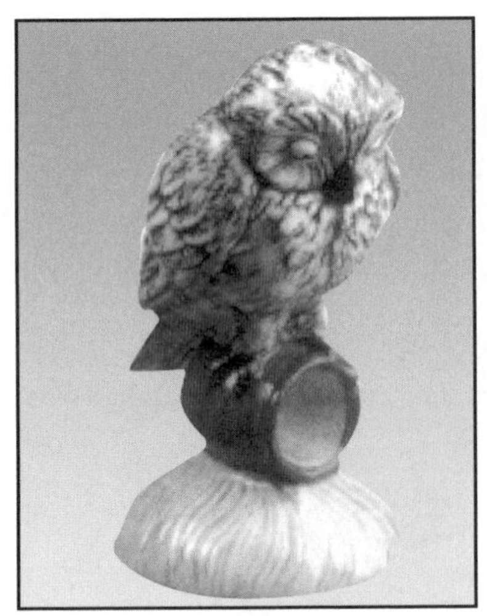

WP 35
WOL™ AND THE HONEYPOT

Designer:	Warren Platt
Height:	3 ¼", 8.3 cm
Colour:	Grey, white, brown and tan
Issued:	2001 - 2002
Series:	Classic Pooh

Doulton Number	U.S. $	Price Can. $	U.K. £	Aust. $
WP 35	55.00	65.00	30.00	75.00

WP 36
UNDER THE NAME 'MR. SANDERS'™

Height:	3", 7.6 cm
Colour:	Yellow bear, brown log
Issued:	2001 - 2002
Series:	Classic Pooh

Doulton Number	U.S. $	Price Can. $	U.K. £	Aust. $
WP 36	55.00	65.00	30.00	75.00

WP 37
ALL THE FLOWERS ARE WAKING UP (Spring)™

Designer: Warren Platt
Height: 3", 7.6 cm
Colour: Yellow bear, grey pot with pink flowers
Issued: 2002 - 2005
Series: 1. Classic Pooh
2. Four Seasons

Doulton Number	Price U.S. $	Can. $	U.K. £	Aust. $
WP 37	35.00	45.00	20.00	55.00

WP 38
SUMMER IS FULL OF FLUTTERY SURPRISES (Summer)™

Designer: Warren Platt
Height: 2 ½", 6.4 cm
Colour: Pink, green and lilac
Issued: 2002 - 2005
Series: Four Seasons

Doulton Number	Price U.S. $	Can. $	U.K. £	Aust. $
WP 38	35.00	45.00	20.00	55.00

WP 39
LOVE MAKES ALL YOUR BOTHERS DISAPPEAR™

Designer: Shane Ridge
Height: 2 ¼", 5.7 cm
Colour: Yellow, red, white and green
Issued: 2002 to the present
Series: Love and Friendship

Doulton Number	Price U.S. $	Can. $	U.K. £	Aust. $
WP 39	–	–	25.00	–

HAND MADE AND HAND DECORATED
CLASSIC POOH
by ROYAL DOULTON
WINNIE THE POOH BIRTHDAY COLLECTION
A PRESENT FOR ME? HOW GRAND!
2001
WP 40
©Disney
Based on the "Winnie the Pooh" works by A.A.Milne and E.H.Shepard
MADE IN THAILAND

WP 40
A PRESENT FOR ME? HOW GRAND!™

Designer:	Shane Ridge
Height:	3 ¼", 8.3 cm
Colour:	Yellow bear, red gift box, purple ribbon
Issued:	2002 - 2002
Series:	Birthday Collection

Doulton Number	Price U.S. $	Can. $	U.K. £	Aust. $
WP 40	45.00	55.00	25.00	65.00

HAND MADE AND HAND DECORATED
CLASSIC POOH
by ROYAL DOULTON
WINNIE THE POOH
CHRISTMAS COLLECTION
A LITTLE TREE
TRIMMING IS IN ORDER
WP 41
© DISNEY
Based on the "Winnie the Pooh" works by A.A.Milne and E.H.Shepard. 2002
MADE IN THAILAND

WP 41
A LITTLE TREE TRIMMING IS IN ORDER™

Designer:	Martyn Alcock
Height:	3 ¾", 9.6 cm
Colour:	Yellow bear, blue nightshirt and cap, red tree ornament
Issued:	2002 - 2002
Series:	Christmas Collection

Doulton Number	Price U.S. $	Can. $	U.K. £	Aust. $
WP 41	45.00	55.00	25.00	65.00

Note: Set with The Most Perfect Tree in all the Wood (WP 42) and Christopher Dresses the Tree (WP 57).

HAND MADE AND HAND DECORATED
CLASSIC POOH
by ROYAL DOULTON
WINNIE THE POOH
CHRISTMAS COLLECTION
THE MOST PERFECT TREE
IN ALL THE WOOD
WP 42
© DISNEY
Based on the "Winnie the Pooh" works by A.A.Milne and E.H.Shepard 2002
MADE IN THAILAND

WP 42
THE MOST PERFECT TREE IN ALL THE WOOD™

Designer:	Martyn Alcock
Height:	4 ¾", 12.1 cm
Colour:	Green tree, red and purple decorations
Issued:	2002 - 2002
Series:	Christmas Collection

Doulton Number	Price U.S. $	Can. $	U.K. £	Aust. $
WP 42	45.00	55.00	25.00	65.00

Note: Set with A Little Tree Trimming is in Order (WP 41) and Christopher Dresses the Tree (WP 57).

WP 43
SOMETIMES AUTUMN TICKLES YOUR NOSE™ (Autumn)

Designer: Shane Ridge
Height: 3", 7.6 cm
Colour: Tan, black, pink, green and brown
Issued: 2002 - 2003
Series: Four Seasons

Doulton Number	U.S. $	Price Can. $	U.K. £	Aust. $
WP 43	45.00	55.00	25.00	65.00

WP 44
EEYORE™ MADE A WINTERY WISH (Winter)

Designer: Shane Ridge
Height: 3 ¼", 8.3 cm
Colour: Grey, white and pink
Issued: 2002 - 2003
Series: Four Seasons

Doulton Number	U.S. $	Price Can. $	U.K. £	Aust. $
WP 44	45.00	55.00	25.00	65.00

WP 45
WHO'S CAKE? POOH'S™ CAKE?

Designer: E. H. Shephard
Height: 3 ¼", 8.3 cm
Colour: Pink piglet wearing a green suit; pink, white and yellow cake
Issued: 2003 - 2003
Series: Birthday Collection

Doulton Number	U.S. $	Price Can. $	U.K. £	Aust. $
WP 45	45.00	55.00	25.00	65.00

HAND MADE AND HAND DECORATED
CLASSIC POOH
by ROYAL DOULTON
WINNIE THE POOH
LOVE & FRIENDSHIP COLLECTION
I LOVE YOU SO MUCH BEAR
WP46
© DISNEY
Based on the "Winnie the Pooh" works,
by A.A.Milne and E.H.Shepard 2003

WP 46
I LOVE YOU SO MUCH BEAR™

Designer: E. H. Shephard
Height: 4", 10.1 cm
Colour: Yellow, pink and green
Issued: 2003 to the present
Series: Love and Friendship

Doulton Number	U.S. $	Price Can. $	U.K. £	Aust. $
WP 46	–	–	35.00	–

WP 47
TOOT TOOT WENT THE WHISTLE™

Designer: E. H. Shephard
Height: 3 ¼", 8.3 cm
Colour: Yellow bear, black train, red and black train station, grey train tracks
Issued: 2003 to the present

Doulton Number	U.S. $	Price Can. $	U.K. £	Aust. $
WP 47	–	–	30.00	–

HAND MADE AND HAND DECORATED
CLASSIC POOH
by ROYAL DOULTON
WINNIE THE POOH
COLLECTION
ANY HUNNY LEFT
FOR ME ?
WP48
© DISNEY

WP 48
ANY HUNNY LEFT FOR ME?™

Designer: E. H. Shephard
Height: 4", 10.1 cm
Colour: Yellow bear, blue and brown honey pots
Issued: 2003 to the present

Doulton Number	U.S. $	Price Can. $	U.K. £	Aust. $
WP 48	–	–	30.00	–

HAND MADE AND HAND DECORATED
CLASSIC POOH
by ROYAL DOULTON
WINNIE THE POOH
BATHTIME COLLECTION
A CLEAN BEAR IS A
HAPPY BEAR
WP49
© DISNEY
Based on the "Winnie the Pooh" works
by A.A. Milne and E.H. Shepard 2003

WP 49
A CLEAN BEAR IS A HAPPY BEAR™

Designer: E. H. Shephard
Height: 3 ¼", 8.3 cm
Colour: Yellow bear and ducks, brown washtub, blue and white bubbles, green towel
Issued: 2003 - 2005
Series: Bathtime Collection

Doulton Number	U.S. $	Price Can. $	U.K. £	Aust. $
WP 49	45.00	55.00	25.00	65.00

WP 50
PRESENTS AND PARTIES™

Designer: E. H. Shephard
Height: 4 ¼", 10.8 cm
Colour: Yellow bear, blue hat, green gift box with pink ribbon, white cake
Issued: 2003 to the present
Series: Birthday Collection

HAND MADE AND HAND DECORATED
CLASSIC POOH
by ROYAL DOULTON
WINNIE THE POOH
COLLECTION
PRESENTS AND PARTIES
WP50
© DISNEY
Based on the "Winnie the Pooh" works
by A.A. Milne and E.H. Shepard 2003

Doulton Number	U.S. $	Price Can. $	U.K. £	Aust. $
WP 50	—	—	30.00	—

HAND MADE AND HAND DECORATED
CLASSIC POOH
by ROYAL DOULTON
WINNIE THE POOH
BATHTIME COLLECTION
A LITTLE SPONGE FOR
A LITTLE PIGLET
WP51
© DISNEY
Based on the "Winnie the Pooh" works
by A.A. Milne and E.H. Shepard 2003

WP 51
A LITTLE SPONGE FOR A LITTLE PIGLET™

Designer: E. H. Shephard
Height: 3 ¼", 8.3 cm
Colour: Pink piglet wearing green suit, brown washtub, blue and white bubbles, grey bucket
Issued: 2003 - 2005
Series: Bathtime Collection

Doulton Number	U.S. $	Price Can. $	U.K. £	Aust. $
WP 51	35.00	45.00	20.00	55.00

WP 52
BOUNCY BOUNCY BOO-TO-YOU!™

Designer:	E. H. Shephard
Height:	3 ¼", 8.3 cm
Colour:	Orange and black tiger, green, yellow and blue toy box
Issued:	2003 to the present

Doulton Number	U.S. $	Price Can. $	U.K. £	Aust. $
WP 52	–	–	30.00	–

WP 53
A SLEEPY DAY IN THE HUNDRED ACRE WOOD™

Designer:	E. H. Shephard
Height:	4 ¾", 12.1 cm
Colour:	Grey and black donkey, yellow bear, brown and black tiger, pink piglet wearing a green suit
Issued:	2003 to the present

Doulton Number	U.S. $	Price Can. $	U.K. £	Aust. $
WP 53	–	–	70.00	–

WP 54
A CLEAN LITTLE ROO™ IS BEST!

Designer:	E. H. Shephard
Height:	4 ¾", 12.1 cm
Colour:	Brown kangaroos, brown washtub, blue and white bubbles
Issued:	2003 - 2005
Series:	Bathtime Collection

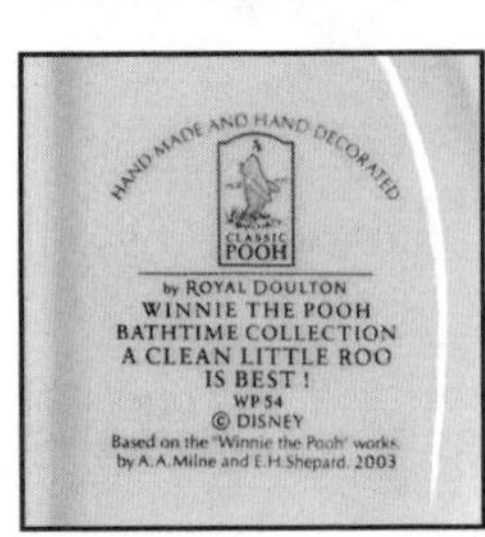

Doulton Number	U.S. $	Price Can. $	U.K. £	Aust. $
WP 54	45.00	55.00	25.00	65.00

WP 55/56
PUSH...PULL! COME ON POOH™ (Bookends)

Designer:	E. H. Shephard
Height:	4 ¾". 12.1 cm
Colour:	Left: Grey rabbit, brown, blue, pink and yellow honey pots Right: Grey donkey, brown and black tiger, pink piglet
Issued:	2003 in a limited edition of 2,000 pairs

Doulton Number	U.S. $	Price Can. $	U.K. £	Aust. $
WP 55/56	115.00	140.00	65.00	160.00

WP 57
CHRISTOPHER™ DRESSES THE TREE

Designer:	E. H. Shephard
Height:	4 ¾", 12.1 cm
Colour:	Green sweater, blue trousers, red scarf, red and white hat, black boots
Issued:	2003 to the present
Series:	Christmas Collection

Doulton Number	U.S. $	Price Can. $	U.K. £	Aust. $
WP 57	–	–	25.00	–

Note: Set with A Little Tree Trimming (WP 41) and The Most Perfect Tree in all the Wood (WP 42).

WP 58
TIGGER'S™ SPLASH TIME

Designer:	E. H. Shephard
Height:	4", 10.1 cm
Colour:	Orange and black striped tiger, brown washtub
Issued:	2003 - 2005
Series:	Bathtime Collection

Doulton Number	U.S. $	Price Can. $	U.K. £	Aust. $
WP 58	45.00	55.00	25.00	65.00

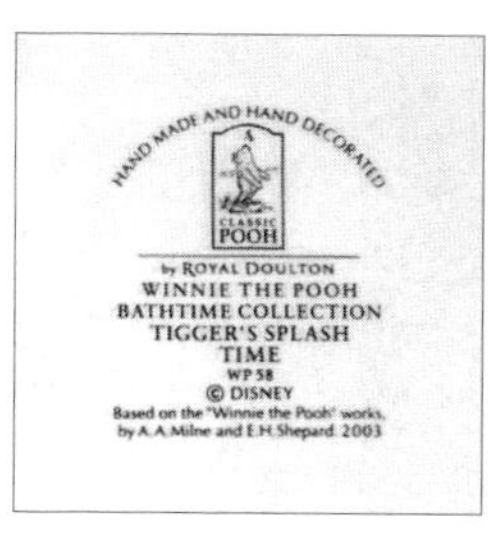

WP 59
OH DEAR! BATH TIME'S HERE!™

Designer: E. H. Shepard
Height: 2 ¾", 7.0 cm
Colour: Grey and black donkey, brown basket
Issued: 2003 - 2005
Series: Bathtime Collection

Doulton Number	U.S. $	Price Can. $	U.K. £	Aust. $
WP 59	45.00	55.00	25.00	65.00

WP 60
ISN'T IT FUNNY HOW A BEAR LIKES HONEY™

Designer: E. H. Shepard
Height: 4 ¼", 10.8 cm
Colour: Yellow bear, blue and purple honey pots
Issued: 2003 to the present

Doulton Number	U.S. $	Price Can. $	U.K. £	Aust. $
WP 60	–	–	25.00	–

WP 61
IT'S HONEY ALL THE WAY DOWN™

Designer: E. H. Shepard
Height: 4 ¼", 10.8 cm
Colour: Yellow bear, brown tree trunk
Issued: 2003 to the present

Doulton Number	U.S. $	Price Can. $	U.K. £	Aust. $
WP 61	–	–	25.00	–

HAND MADE AND HAND DECORATED
CLASSIC POOH
by ROYAL DOULTON
WINNIE THE POOH
WHERE DOES THE
WIND COME FROM?
WP 62
© DISNEY
Based on the "Winnie the Pooh" works,
by A.A. Milne and E.H. Shepard 2003

WP 62
WHERE DOES THE WIND COME FROM?™

Designer:	E. H. Shephard
Height:	3 ¼", 8.3 cm
Colour:	Yellow bear, red and blue kite
Issued:	2003 - 2005

Doulton Number	U.S. $	Price Can. $	U.K. £	Aust. $
WP 62	35.00	45.00	20.00	55.00

HAND MADE AND HAND DECORATED
CLASSIC POOH
by ROYAL DOULTON
WINNIE THE POOH
RUM-TUM-TUM-
WINNIE ON HIS DRUM
WP 63
© DISNEY
Based on the "Winnie the Pooh" works,
by A.A. Milne and E.H. Shepard. 2003

WP 63
RUM-TUM-TUM WINNIE™ ON HIS DRUM

Designer:	E. H. Shephard
Height:	3 ¼", 8.3 cm
Colour:	Yellow bear, green, red and blue drum
Issued:	2003 to the present

Doulton Number	U.S. $	Price Can. $	U.K. £	Aust. $
WP 63	–	–	25.00	–

WP 64
A BIG NOISE FOR A LITTLE PIGLET™

Designer:	E. H. Shephard
Height:	3", 7.6 cm
Colour:	Pink piglet, green suit and yellow cymbals
Issued:	2003 to the present

Doulton Number	U.S. $	Price Can. $	U.K. £	Aust. $
WP 64	–	–	25.00	–

WP 65
TIGGER'S BIRTHDAY SURPRISE™

Height: 4 ¼", 10.8 cm
Colour: Orange and black tiger; yellow balloon, blue and green hat
Issued: 2004 - 2004
Series: Birthday

Doulton Number	U.S. $	Price Can. $	U.K. £	Aust. $
WP 65	45.00	55.00	25.00	65.00

Note: This was a time limited piece for 2004.

WP 66
WITH LOVE™

Height: 3 ¼", 8.3 cm
Colour: Pink piglet; green outfit, red scarf with gold fringe, beige heart
Issued: 2004 to the present
Series: Love and Friendship

Doulton Number	U.S. $	Price Can. $	U.K. £	Aust. $
WP 66	–	–	25.00	–

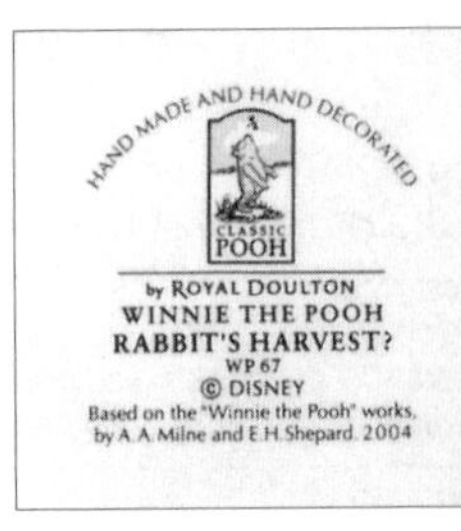

WP 67
RABBIT'S HARVEST?™

Height: 4 ¼", 10.8 cm
Colour: Grey rabbit; orange and green vegetables, green and brown baskets
Issued: 2004 - 2005

Doulton Number	U.S. $	Price Can. $	U.K. £	Aust. $
WP 67	35.00	45.00	20.00	55.00

WP 69
PREPARATIONS FOR CARROT HONEY PIE™

Height: 3 ¾", 9.5 cm
Colour: Yellow bear; maroon hat, brown basket, orange and green vegetables
Issued: 2004 to the present

Doulton Number	U.S. $	Price Can. $	U.K. £	Aust. $
WP 69	–	–	25.00	–

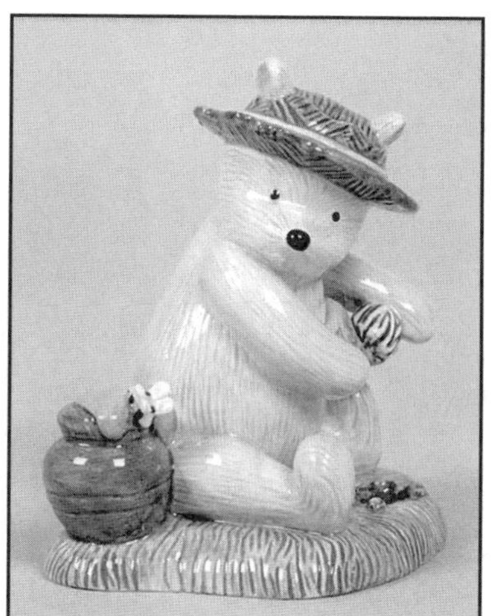

WP 70
THE PERFECT HAT FOR GARDENING™

Height: 3 ¼", 8.3 cm
Colour: Yellow bear; maroon hat, blue honey pot
Issued: 2004 to the present

Doulton Number	U.S. $	Price Can. $	U.K. £	Aust. $
WP 70	–	–	25.00	–

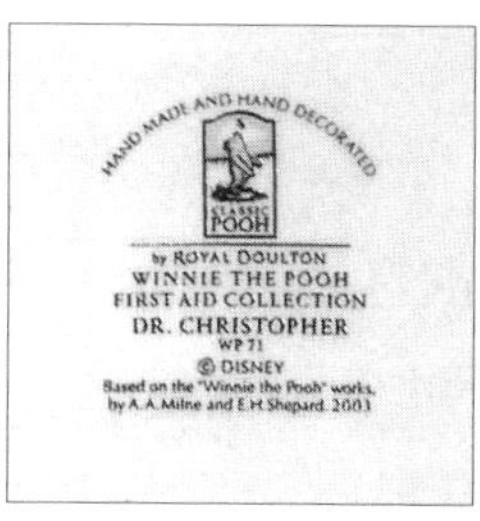

WP 71
DR. CHRISTOPHER™

Height: 3 ¾", 9.5 cm
Colour: White, blue and brown
Issued: 2005 to the present
Series: First Aid Collection

Doulton Number	U.S. $	Price Can. $	U.K. £	Aust. $
WP 71	–	–	25.00	–

HAND MADE AND HAND DECORATED
CLASSIC POOH
by ROYAL DOULTON
WINNIE THE POOH
FIRST AID COLLECTION
FIRST AID FRIENDS
WP 72
© DISNEY
Based on the "Winnie the Pooh" works, by A.A. Milne and E.H. Shepard 2003

WP 72
FIRST AID FRIENDS™

Height:	3", 7.6 cm
Colour:	Grey and black donkey, red and white bandages; pink piglet wearing green outfit
Issued:	2005 to the present
Series:	First Aid Collection

Doulton Number	U.S. $	Price Can. $	U.K. £	Aust. $
WP 72	–	–	35.00	–

WP 73
NURSE TIGGER™

Height:	4 ¼", 10.8 cm
Colour:	Orange, black, white, green and red
Issued:	2005 to the present
Series:	First Aid Collection

Doulton Number	U.S. $	Price Can. $	U.K. £	Aust. $
WP 73	–	–	25.00	–

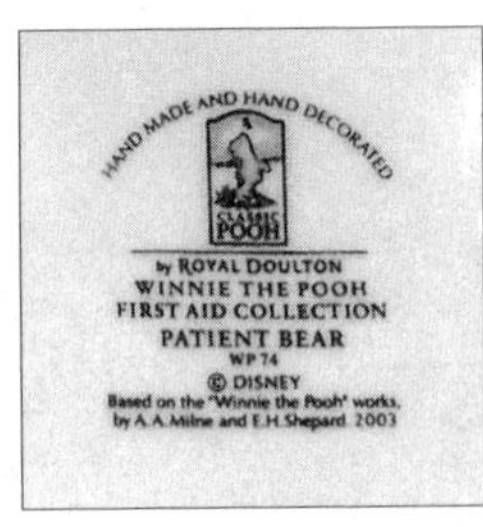

WP 74
PATIENT BEAR™

Height:	3 ¾", 9.5 cm
Colour:	Yellow, white and red
Issued:	2005 to the present
Series:	First Aid Collection

Doulton Number	U.S. $	Price Can. $	U.K. £	Aust. $
WP 74	–	–	25.00	–

WP 75
HONEY AND TEA IS A VERY GRAND THING™

Height: 4", 10.1 cm
Colour: Yellow bear; brown tree trunk, blue and white cup and saucer, red and white napkin
Issued: 2004 to the present
Series: Tea Time Collection

Doulton Number	U.S. $	Can. $	Price U.K. £	Aust. $
WP 75	—	—	75.00 Set price	—

Note: Sold as a set with WP 77 and 78.

WP 76
CHRISTMAS PIGLET™

Height: 2 ½", 6.4 cm
Colour: Pink piglet; green outfit, yellow parcel, red ribbon and dark green holly
Issued: 2004 to the present
Series: Christmas Collection

Doulton Number	U.S. $	Can. $	Price U.K. £	Aust. $
WP 76	—	—	25.00	—

WP 77
TEA FOR TWO™

Height: 2 ¼", 5.7 cm
Colour: Brown tree trunk, red and white table cloth, blue and white tea set
Issued: 2004 to the present
Series: Tea Time Collection

Doulton Number	U.S. $	Can. $	Price U.K. £	Aust. $
WP 77	—	—	75.00 Set price	—

Note: Sold as a set with WP 75 and 78.

WP 78
PIGLET'S TEA TIME™

Height: 3 ¼", 8.3 cm
Colour: Pink piglet; green outfit, blue and white cup and saucer, red and white napkin, brown tree trunk
Issued: 2004 to the present
Series: Tea Time Collection

Doulton Number	U.S. $	Price Can. $	U.K. £	Aust. $
WP 78	–	–	75.00 Set Price	–

Note: Sold as a set with WP 75 and 77.

WP 79
CHRISTOPHER ROBIN STRUMS A MELODY™

Height: 4 ¾", 12.1 cm
Colour: Red, tan, blue, black and beige
Issued: 2005 to the present
Series: Music Collection

Doulton Number	U.S. $	Price Can. $	U.K. £	Aust. $
WP 79	–	–	30.00	–

WP 80
EEYORE ON PERCUSSION™

Height: 2 ¾", 7.0 cm
Colour: Grey, black, red, yellow and cream
Issued: 2005 to the present
Series: Music Collection

Doulton Number	U.S. $	Price Can. $	U.K. £	Aust. $
WP 80	–	–	30.00	–

WP 81
TIGGER'S BOUNCY BEAT™

Height: 4 ¼", 10.8 cm
Colour: Orange, black and gold
Issued: 2005 to the present
Series: Music Collection

Doulton Number	U.S. $	Can. $	U.K. £	Aust. $
WP 81	–	–	25.00	–

WP 82
TIGGER'S LOVEHEART™

Height: 4 ", 10.1 cm
Colour: Orange, black and white
Issued: 2005 to the present
Series: Love and Friendship

Doulton Number	U.S. $	Can. $	U.K. £	Aust. $
WP 82	–	–	25.00	–

WP 83
MANY HAPPY RETURNS OF THE DAY™

Height: 2 ¾", 7.0 cm
Colour: Grey, black, yellow, pink, green and red
Issued: 2005 - 2005
Series: BIrthday

Doulton Number	U.S. $	Can. $	U.K. £	Aust. $
WP 83	–	–	30.00	–

WP 84
POOH STICKS™

Designer:	E. H. Shepard
Size:	6 ¼" x 6 ¾", 15.9 x 17.2 cm
Colour:	Yellow, pink, grey, green, brown and blue
Issued:	2005 in a limited edition of 1,500

Doulton Number	U.S. $	Price Can. $	U.K. £	Aust. $
WP 84	135.00	165.00	75.00	175.00

WP 87
HAPPY CHRISTMAS TIGGER™

Height:	4 ¼", 10.8 cm
Colour:	Orange, black, grey and red
Issued:	2005 to the present
Series:	Christmas Collection

Doulton Number	U.S. $	Price Can. $	U.K. £	Aust. $
WP 87	–	–	25.00	–

WP 88
BIG CHIEF POOH™ (Winnie the Pooh)

Height:	4 ¼", 10.8 cm
Colour:	Yellow, white, red, black, blue, brown and green
Issued:	2005 to the present
Series:	Wild West Collection

Doulton Number	U.S. $	Price Can. $	U.K. £	Aust. $
WP 88	–	–	25.00	–

WP 89
HOWDY SHERIFF (Piglet)™

Height:	3 ½", 8.9 cm
Colour:	Pink, green, yellow, brown and white
Issued:	2005 to the present
Series:	Wild West Collection

Doulton		Price		
Number	U.S. $	Can. $	U.K. £	Aust. $
WP 89	–	–	25.00	–

WP 90
YEE HAH! (Tigger)™

Height:	4 ¾", 12.1 cm
Colour:	Dark orange, black, red, blue, brown and yellow
Issued:	2005 to the present
Series:	Wild West Collection

Doulton		Price		
Number	U.S. $	Can. $	U.K. £	Aust. $
WP 90	–	–	30.00	–

WP 91
DEPUTY EEYORE™

Height:	4 ¼", 10.8 cm
Colour:	Grey, red, white, brown and black
Issued:	2005 to the present
Series:	Wild West Collection

Doulton		Price		
Number	U.S. $	Can. $	U.K. £	Aust. $
WP 91	–	–	30.00	–

WP 92
CHRISTOPHER TO THE RESCUE™

Height: 4", 10.1 cm
Colour: Dark brown, white, blue, brown and red
Issued: 2005 to the present
Series: Wild West Collection

Doulton Number	U.S. $	Price Can. $	U.K. £	Aust. $
WP 92	–	–	30.00	–

WP 93
LITTLE INDIANS (Kanga and Roo)™

Height: 4 ¼", 10.8 cm
Colour: Light brown, yellow, pale green, brown, red and blue
Issued: 2005 to the present
Series: Wild West Collection

Doulton Number	U.S. $	Price Can. $	U.K. £	Aust. $
WP 93	–	–	30.00	–

SECTION FOUR

ADVERTISING CHARACTERS

AC 1
GOLLY™

Modeller:	William K. Harper
Height:	5 ¾", 14.6 cm
Colour:	Blue, red, orange and white
Issued:	1999 in a limited edition of 2,000
Slogan:	Golly it's Good!
U.S.	$275.00
Can.	$325.00
U.K.	£160.00
Aust.	$350.00

AC 2
FATHER WILLIAM™

Modeller:	William K. Harper
Height:	6 ¼", 15.9 cm
Colour:	Black, yellow, red and grey
Issued:	1999 in a limited edition of 2,000
Slogan:	Get YOUNGER every day
U.S.	$175.00
Can.	$225.00
U.K.	£100.00
Aust.	$250.00

AC 3
SIR KREEMY KNUT™
(Sharps Toffee-Trebor Bassett Ltd)

Modeller:	William K. Harper
Height:	6 ¼", 15.9 cm
Colour:	Blue, white, red black and brown
Issued:	1999 in a limited edition of 2,000
Slogan:	Sharps the word for Toffee!
U.S.	$175.00
Can.	$225.00
U.K.	£100.00
Aust.	$250.00

AC 4
FOX'S POLAR BEAR™
(Fox's Glacier Mints - Nestlé)

Modeller:	William K. Harper
Height:	4", 10.1 cm
Colour:	White
Issued:	1999 in a limited edition of 2,000
Slogan:	FOX
U.S.	$275.00
Can.	$350.00
U.K.	£150.00
Aust.	$400.00

AC 5
PLAYER'S 'HERO' SAILOR™
(John Player & Sons Ltd - Imperial Tobacco Ltd)

Modeller:	William K. Harper
Height:	6", 15.0 cm
Colour:	Navy and white
Issued:	1999 in a limited edition of 2,000
Slogan:	Player's / Please
U.S.	$175.00
Can.	$225.00
U.K.	£100.00
Aust.	$250.00

AC 6
JOHN GINGER™
(Huntley & Palmers - Jacobs Bakery Ltd)

Modeller:	William K. Harper
Height:	6", 15.0 cm
Colour:	Dark green, white
Issued:	2000 ltd. ed. 2,000
Slogan:	There are no ifs, nor ands, not buts, they are the finest Ginger Nuts!
U.S.	$175.00
Can.	$225.00
U.K.	£100.00
Aust.	$250.00

AC 7
THE MILKY BAR KID™
(Nestlé)

Modeller:	William K. Harper David Biggs
Height:	5 ¾", 14.6 cm
Colour:	Blue, red, brown
Issued:	2000 ltd. ed. 2,000
Slogan:	The Milkybars are on me!
U.S.	$175.00
Can.	$225.00
U.K.	£100.00
Aust.	$250.00

AC 8
GUINNESS TOUCAN™
(©Guinness Ltd)

Modeller:	William K. Harper
Height:	5", 12.7 cm
Colour:	Black, white, blue and orange
Issued:	2000 in a limited edition of 2,000
Slogan:	Lovely day for a / GUINNESS
U.S.	$ 975.00
Can.	$1,175.00
U.K.	£ 550.00
Aust.	$1,275.00

MCL 1
PENFOLD GOLFER™

Modeller:	David Biggs
Height:	5 ¾", 14.6 cm
Colour:	Grey, white, tan, black and green
Issued:	2001 ltd. ed. 2,000
Slogan:	He Played A Penfold
U.S.	$150.00
Can.	$180.00
U.K.	£ 80.00
Aust.	$200.00

MCL 2
DUNLOP CADDIE™

Modeller:	David Biggs
Height:	5 ¼", 13.3 cm
Colour:	Blue, red, white, black and green
Issued:	2001 ltd. ed. 2,000
Slogan:	We Plan Dunlop 65
U.S.	$150.00
Can.	$180.00
U.K.	£ 80.00
Aust.	$200.00

MCL 3
BIG CHIEF TOUCAN™

Modeller:	Shane Ridge
Height:	6", 15.0 cm
Colour:	Black, white, yellow, red and blue
Issued:	2001 ltd. ed. 2,000
Slogan:	Guinness – Him Strong
U.S.	$300.00
Can.	$350.00
U.K.	£175.00
Aust.	$375.00

MCL 4
BISTO KIDS™

Modeller:	Rob Donaldson
Height:	4 ½", 11.9 cm
Colour:	Black, red, green, blue, brown,yellow
Issued:	2002 in a limited edition of 1,000
U.S.	$350.00
Can.	$425.00
U.K.	£200.00
Aust.	$475.00

MCL 5
P..P..P..PICK UP A..PENGUIN™

Modeller:	Martyn Alcock
Height:	4 ½", 11.9 cm
Colour:	Black, white, yellow
Issued:	2002 in a limited edition of 1,500
Slogan:	P... P... P... PICK UP A ...PENGUIN
U.S.	$150.00
Can.	$180.00
U.K.	£ 80.00
Aust.	$200.00

MCL 6
CHRISTMAS TOUCAN™

Modeller:	Shane Ridge
Height:	5 ¾", 14.6 cm
Colour:	Black, white, red, orange, green, blue
Issued:	2002 in a limited edition of 2,000
Slogan:	GUINNESS / is good for yule
U.S.	$275.00
Can.	$325.00
U.K.	£150.00
Aust.	$425.00

MCL 7
SEASIDE TOUCAN™

Modeller:	Martyn Alcock
Height:	6", 15.0 cm
Colour:	Black, white, yellow, red and beige
Issued:	2003 in a limited edition of 2,000
Slogan:	GUINNESS / Goodness-on-sea
U.S.	$275.00
Can.	$325.00
U.K.	£150.00
Aust.	$425.00

MCL 8
TONY THE TIGER™

Modeller:	Martyn Alcock
Height:	5 ½", 14.0 cm
Colour:	Orange and black
Issued:	2003 in a limited edition of 1,500
Slogan:	"THEY'RE GR-R-REAT!"
U.S.	$150.00
Can.	$180.00
U.K.	£ 80.00
Aust.	$200.00

MCL 9
BIBENDUM THE MICHELIN MAN

Designer:	Martyn Alcock
Height:	5 ½", 14.0 cm
Colour:	White, dark red and black
Issued:	2003 in a limited edition of 2,000
Slogan:	Switch to Michelin
U.S.	$160.00
Can.	$200.00
U.K.	£ 90.00
Aust.	$225.00

MCL 10
MINER TOUCAN

Modeller:	Martyn Alcock
Height:	5 ¼", 13.3 cm
Colour:	Black, white, yellow and blue
Issued:	2004 in a limited edition of 2,000
Slogan:	Mine's a GUINNESS
U.S.	$160.00
Can.	$200.00
U.K.	£ 90.00
Aust.	$225.00

MCL 11
NEWSVENDOR NAMESTAND

Height:	3", 7.6 cm
Colour:	Black, yellow and blue
Issued:	2004 in a limited edition of 2,000
Slogan:	Royal Doulton Guinness Toucans 2000-2004
U.S.	$ 70.00
Can.	$ 90.00
U.K.	£ 40.00
Aust.	$100.00

MCL 13
QUALITY STREET FIGURE

Designer:	Alan Maslankowski
Height:	7 ¼", 18.5 cm
Colour:	Pink, blue, red, white, black, yellow and tan
Issued:	2004 in a limited edition of 950
U.S.	$250.00
Can.	$300.00
U.K.	£145.00
Aust.	$325.00

MCL 14
COCA-COLA BATHING BELLE

Designer:	A, Maslankowski
Height:	6 ¾", 17.2 cm
Colour:	Greens, brown, red, pink, black and white
Issued:	2005 in a limited edition of 1,250
Slogan:	Drink Coca-Cola
U.S.	–
Can.	–
U.K.	£105.00
Aust.	–

MCL 15
WHISKAS CATS

Height:	5", 12.7 cm
Colour:	1. Ginger 2. Silver tabby
Issued:	2005 in a limited edition of 750 each
Slogan:	"8 out of 10 owners said their cats preferred it"
U.S.	–
Can.	–
U.K.	£78.00
Aust.	–

HIS MASTER'S VOICE 'NIPPER'™

Modeller:	David Biggs
Size:	6 ¼" x 12", 15.9 X 30.5 CM
Colour:	White dog with brown ears; brown and copper phonograph
Issued:	2000 in a limited edition of 2,000
U.S.	$600.00
Can.	$725.00
U.K.	£350.00
Aust.	$800.00

Note:
1. Issued to commemorate the 100th anniversary of the use of the dog "Nipper" in the advertising of EMI's products (EMI Records Ltd.)
2. Only 1,000 pieces were produced due to breakages in shipping.

INDICES

ALPHABETICAL INDEX TO BUNNYKINS TABLEWARE

A

	Page No.
A Scene (CT96)	13
ABC Scene (CT95)	13
ABCDEF Scene (CT94)	13
Aerobics/Jogging	14
Aeroplane	14
Afternoon Tea (HW116)	15
Airmail Delivery (LFa)	16
Apple Picking (SF25)	17
Art Class (LF107)	17
Artist (HW1)	18
Asleep in a Sleeping Bag (36)	41
Asleep in the Open Air (HW10)	19

B

Baby in a Crib with Father Looking On (CT76)	37
Baby in Crib (CT78)	37
Baking (SF19)	22
Baking Cakes with Mother (7)	23
Bath Night (LF7)	24
Bathtime	
Style One (SF18)	25
Style Two, First Variation (CT21)	26
Style Two, Second Variation (CT24)	26
Style Three (22)	28
Beating Carpet (20)	157
Bedtime in Bunks	
Style One (SF3)	29
Style Two (13)	30
Bedtime Story (SF130)	29
Bedtime with Dollies (EC125)	31
Beware of the Bull (LF108)	31
Birthday Inscription (CT61)	89
Blowing and Bursting Bubbles (23)	28
Blowing Bubbles and Sailing Boats (24)	28
Bonfire (LF128)	32
Breakfast Time	32
Broken Umbrella (HW27R)	176
Bugler with Toy Donkey (HW26R)	59
Building a Snowman (59)	154
Building Sand Castles (HW138)	33
Bunnies in the Bath	
First Version (CT25)	26
Second Version (CT34)	27
Bunny on Rocking Horse (CT29)	116
Bunny on Swing (54)	127
Bunny on Trike (CT23)	147
Bunny with Bag (27)	145
Bunny with Cake Plate (CT88)	21
Bunny with Mirror (CT35)	117
Bunnykins Build a Snowman (PN198)	34
Bunnykins Celebrate Australia's Bicentenary 1788-1988	189
Bunnykins Celebrate Their Golden Jubilee	
Birthday Cake (SF140)	188
Chicken Pulling a Cart (SF141)	188
Bunnykins Celebrate your Christening	
Style One, First Version (SF139)	35
Style One, Second Version (HW142)	35
Style Two, First Variation (CT38)	36
Style Two, Second Variation (CT41)	36
Bunnykins Help Santa (PN175)	38
Bunnykins 60th Anniversary Inscription (CT93)	190
Bunnykins Teaching Clock	
Classroom Scene, Style One	39
Classroom Scene, Style Two	39
Four Individual Scenes	40

C

	Page No.
Cake Stall (CT12)	120
Camp Site (SF113)	40
Campfire (35)	41
Camping (34)	41
Carol Singer Bunnykins (CT70)	42
Carrying Letter (30)	129
Carrying Net (6)	75
Carrying Plates (45)	55
Carving the Chicken (LFc)	42
Chicken Pulling a Cart (SF8)	43, 188
Christening Inscription	
(CT42)	36
(CT65)	36
(CT77)	37
(CT79)	37
(HW142R)	33
Christmas 1991 (CT69)	143
Christmas 1992 (CT71)	42
Christmas 1994 (CT81)	165
Christmas Inscription (CT44)	109
Christmas Morn	44
Christmas Ornaments	
1991 Santa Bunnykins (CT68)	143
1992 Carol Singer Bunnykins (CT70)	42
1994 Trimming the Tree	165
1995 Fun in the Snow	80
1996 Christmas Morn	44
Christmas Party (LF9)	44
Christmas Tree (LF16)	45
Classroom Scene	
Style One (SF138)	39
Style Two, First Version (CT36)	39, 46
Style Two, Second Version (CT16)	46
Cleaning Bike (48)	51
Coconut Shy (32)	66
Commemorate Leaf Border (CT85)	20
Conducting the Orchestra (LF5)	47
Convalescing (SF5)	47
Cook and Bunny (CT31)	146
Counting Motif (CT8)	135
Cowboy on Rocking Horse (HW140R)	47
Cowboys and Indians (HW140)	47
Cricket Game (LF12)	49
Cricketer (HW22R)	174
Cuddling Under a Mushroom (HW4)	49
Cycling (HW15R)	50
Cycle Ride (46)	51

D

Daisy Chains (HW25)	52
Dancing in the Moonlight	
First Version (LFb)	53
Second Version, First Variation (CT91)	190
Second Version, Second Variation (CT92)	53
Dancing Round the Barrel Organ (HW139)	54
Dancing with Doll (HW115R)	126
Decorating the Cake (9)	23
Disturbing Sleeping Father (HW118)	56
Dodgem Cars (LF4)	57
Dog Carriage (LFe)	57
Doll's House, The (HW120)	58
Dress Making (HW26)	59
Dressing Up	
First Version (SF22)	60
Second Version	60

D (cont.) Page No.

Drummer (EC2) 61
Drummer and Bugler (EC126) 61
Duet, The (LF13) 62
Dunce (HW1R) 63
Dusting (19) 157

E

Eating Apples (3) 150
Embracing at a Window (HW5) 64
Engine Pulling a Carriage (HW17) 65

F

Family at Breakfast (HW12) 67
Family Christmas Scene
    First Version (CT72) 110
    Second Version (CT74) 110
Family Cycling (LF11) 68
Family Going out on Washing Day (HW8) 69
Family Group with Father Kneeing (CT98) 114
Family Group with Father Standing (CT97) 114
Family in the Garden (SF135) 70
Family Photograph (LF15) 70
Family with Pram
    Style One (HW15) 71
    Style Two (CT14) 72
Family with Pram/Raising Hat 71
Father Asleep (CT90) 21
Father Bunnykins with Fishing Rod (CT27) 97
Feeding the Baby (HW13) 73
Fishing at the Pond (4) 75
Fishing in the Goldfish Bowl (HW3R) 76
Fishing on the Pier (LF3) 76
Fixing Braces (HW3) 77
Flying Kites (SF133) 77
Footballer (HW13R) 78
Frightening Spider (SF4) 79
Fun in the Snow (CT80) 80

G

Game of Golf (SF11) 80
Gardener with Wheelbarrow (HW9R) 82
Gardening
    Style One (HW9) 83
    Style Two (55) 84
Geography Lesson (LF17) 85
Getting Dressed (LF2) 85
Going Shopping (SF10) 86
Golfer (HW4R) 87
Greetings (HW7) 87

H

Happy Birthday from Bunnykins
    Style One (SF136) 88
    Style Two, First Version (CT37) 89
    Style Two, Second Version (CT60) 89
Happy Birthday from Bunnykins Inscription (CT64) 89
Happy Birthday Inscription (CT61) 89
Happy Birthday Inscription 88
Happy Easter from Bunnykins
    First Version (CT40) 90
    Second Version (CT62) 90
Happy Easter Inscription (CT63) 90
Happy Easter Inscription (CT67) 90
Hat Shop (HW28) 91
Haymaking (HW29) 92
Hiker Resting with Ice Cream (HW23R) 99

H (cont.) Page No.

Hikers (EC124) 93
Hobby Horse
    Style One (HW24R) 140
    Style Two (EC121) 94
Holding Hat and Coat (EC4) 95
Home Decorating (SF131) 96
Home from Fishing
    First Variation (CT18) 96
    Second Variation (CT26) 97
Hoopla (LF129) 97

I

Ice Cream on the Beach (HW136R) 134
Ice Cream Seller
    First Variation (CT5) 98
    Second Variation (CT11) 98
Ice Cream Vendor (HW23) 99
Ice Skating (SF24) 100

J

Jack and Jill (CT9) 101
Jack and Jill Nursery Rhyme (CT10) 101
Jogging 14
Juggling (LF127) 101

K

Kissing Under the Mistletoe (HW11R) 102

L

Lambeth Walk (HW16)
    First Version 103
    Second Version 104
Lasso Games (HW117) 105
Lassoing (HW117R) 105
Leapfrog (HW12R) 105
Letter Box (29) 129
Letterbox (SF13) 106
Lunch Break (HW29R) 92

M

Maths Lesson (25) 145
Medicine Time (SF1) 107
Member of Bunnykins Club 38
Merry Christmas from Bunnykins
    Style One (SF137) 108
    Style Two, First Variation (CT39) 109
    Style Two, Second Variation (CT43) 109
    Style Three, First Version (CT72) 110
    Style Three, Second Version (CT74) 110
Merry Christmas from Bunnykins Inscription
    (CT44) 109
    (CT66) 109
    (CT73) 110
    (CT75) 110
    (SF137) 108
Mr. Piggly's Stores (SF14) 111
Mrs. Moppet's Tea Room (LF6) 112

N

Netting a Cricket (HW6) 113
New Arrival Inscription (CT99) 114
Nipped by a Crab (HW21R) 142
Nursery
    First Version (CT19) 116
    Second Version (CT28) 116

O

Page No.

Orange Vendor (SF12) 118

P

Pea Shooter (HW118R) 56
Petrol in the Sports Car (37) 81
Picking Daisies (CT4) 120
Picnic
  Style One, First Version 119
  Style One, Second Version (LF10) 119
  Style Two (16) 121
Picnic and Cake Stall (CT2) 120
Picnic Scene (CT87) 21
Picnic Scene with Hamper (CT89) 21
Picnic with Kangaroo and Koala
  First Variation (CT84) 20
  Second Variation (CT86) 20
Pillow Fight
  Style One (SF7) 122
  Style Two (14) 30
Playing and Reading (15) 30
Playing Badminton (17) 121
Playing in Tree House (56) 84
Playing on the River (SF16) 123
Playing with Ball (42) 115
Playing with Balloons (33) 66
Playing with Cup and Spoon (EC6) 124
Playing with Doll and Pram (EC123) 125
Playing with Doll and Teddy (HW120R) 58
Playing with Dolls and Prams (HW115) 126
Portrait Painter (SF20) 128
Posting Letters (28) 129
Postman Delivering Letters (HW19) 130
Preparing Dinner (43) 55
Pressing Trousers (HW14) 131
Proposal (HW11) 132
Pulling on Trousers (HW2) 133
Pumping Tyre (38) 81
Pumping Water (11) 74
Punch and Judy Show (HW136) 134
Pushing Pram (41) 115
Pushing Swing (53) 127
Pushing the Wheelbarrow (CT3) 175

Q

Queen of the May
  First Variation (CT7) 135
  Second Variation (CT13) 135

R

Raft (SF111) 136
Raising Hat
  Style One (HW16R) 137
  Style Two (EC7) 138
Reading (EC122) 138
Reading the Times (HW2R) 139
Resting
  Style One (18) 121
  Style Two (21) 157
  Style Three (47) 51
Resting by Pond (5) 75
Resting in Wheelbarrow (57) 84
Ring-a-Ring o'Roses (SF21) 139
Rocking Horse (HW24) 140
Roller Skating Arm in Arm (HW137R) 141
Roller Skating Race (HW137) 141
Row Boat (HW21) 142

S

Page No.

Sailing Boats (HW138R) 33
Santa Bunnykins (CT68) 143
Santa Claus (SF9) 144
School Dinner
  First Variation (CT17) 146
  Second Variation (CT30) 146
School Gates
  First Variation (CT20) 147
  Second Variation (CT22) 147
See-saw
  Style One (SF17) 148
  Style Two (52) 127
Serving Dinner (44) 55
Serving Tea (HW116R) 15
Sheltering Under an Umbrella (EC3) 149
Shopping (1) 150
Showing Baby at Window (40) 115
Sitting on Oil Drum (39) 81
Sitting on Suitcase (51) 164
Skipping (HW20R) 159
Skipping Game (HW139R) 54
Sledging
  Style One (HW141) 151
  Style Two (60) 154
Sleeping in a Rocking Chair (EC1) 152
Smelling Flowers (HW25R) 52
Smoking in the Doorway (SF2) 153
Snow Scene (58) 154
Snowball Fight (HW141R) 151
Soldier Marching (HW18R) 155
Soldiers Marching to the Music (HW18) 155
Space Rocket Launch (SF132) 156
Splashing at Sink (CT33) 171
Spring Cleaning (LF14) 156
Standing by Pram (CT6) 72
Storytime (SF110) 158
Swinging (HW20) 159
Swinging Boats (31) 66

T

Taking Cake from Oven (8) 23
Teacher Scolding (26) 145
Television Time (SF112) 160
Tennis 160
Ticket Office (50) 164
Ticket Queue (SF109) 161
To Celebrate Australia's Bicentenary 1788-1988 189
To Celebrate the Birth of the First Child of T.R.H. the Prince and Princess of Wales 187
To Celebrate the Marriage of the Prince Andrew with Miss Sarah Ferguson 189
To T.R.H. The Prince and Princess of Wales A Second Child 1984 in Joyful Celebration 187
To the Station (HW17R) 65
Toast for Tea Today (SF23) 161
Top Hat (HW14R) 162
Toppling the Fruit Cart (SF134) 162
Toy Shop (SF114) 163
Trimming the Tree (CT80) 165
Trumpeter (EC5) 166
Trying on Hat (12) 74
Trying on Hats (HW28R) 91
Trying on Knitting (HW119R) 167
Tug of War (LF1) 166

U

Unravelling the Knitting (HW119) 167

V	Page No.
Vegetable Stall (2)	150
Visiting the Cottage	
First Version (SF6a)	168
Second Version (SF6b)	168

W	
Waiting for Train (49)	164
Washing Day (HW8R)	169
Washing in the Open Air (HW10R)	170
Washing the Fire Engine (10)	74
Washing Up	
First Variation (CT15)	171
Second Variation (CT32)	171

W (cont.)	Page No.
Watering the Flowers (SF15)	172
Wedding (LFd)	173
Wheelbarrow Race	
Style One (HW22)	174
Style Two (CT1)	175
Windy Day (HW27)	176
Winning Post (LF106)	177
Writing Letters (HW19R)	130

X	
Xmas Menu (LF8)	177

NUMERICAL INDEX TO BUNNYKINS TABLEWARE

Design No.	Name	Page No.
1	Shopping	150
2	Vegetable Stall	150
3	Eating Apples	150
4	Fishing at the Pond	75
5	Rest by Pond	75
6	Carrying Net	75
7	Baking Cakes with Mother	23
8	Taking Cake from Oven	23
9	Decorating the Cake	23
10	Washing the Fire Engine	74
11	Pumping Water	74
12	Trying on Hat	74
13	Bedtime in Bunks	30
14	Pillow Fight	30
15	Playing and Reading	30
16	Picnic, Style Two	121
17	Playing Badminton	121
18	Resting, Style One	121
19	Dusting	157
20	Beating Carpet	157
21	Resting, Style Two	157
22	Bathtime, Style Three	28
23	Blowing and Bursting Bubbles	28
24	Blowing Bubbles and Sailing Boat	28
25	Maths Lesson	145
26	Teacher Scolding	145
27	Bunny with Bag	145
28	Posting Letters	129
29	Letter Box	129
30	Carrying Letter	129
31	Swinging Boats	66
32	Coconut Shy	66
33	Playing with Balloons	66
34	Camping	41
35	Campfire	41
36	Asleep in a Sleeping Bag	41
37	Petrol in the Sports Car	81
38	Pumping Tyre	81
39	Sitting on Oil Drum	81
40	Showing Baby at Window	115
41	Pushing Pram	115
42	Playing with Ball	115
43	Preparing Dinner	55
44	Serving Dinner	55
45	Carrying Plates	55
46	Cycle Ride	51
47	Resting, Style Three	51
48	Cleaning Bike	51
49	Waiting for Train	164
50	Ticket Office	164
51	Sitting on Suitcase	164
52	See-saw, Style Two	127
53	Pushing Swing	127
54	Bunny on Swing	127
55	Gardening, Style Two	84
56	Playing in Tree House	84
57	Resting in Wheelbarrow	84
58	Snow Scene	154
59	Building Snowman	154
60	Sledging, Style Two	154
CT1	Wheelbarrow Race, Style Two	175
CT2	Picnic and Cake Stall	120
CT3	Pushing the Wheelbarrow	175
CT4	Picking Daisies	120
CT5	Ice Cream Seller, First Variation	98
CT6	Standing by Pram	72
CT7	Queen of the May, First Variation	135
CT8	Counting Motif	135
CT9	Jack and Jill	101
CT10	Jack and Jill Nursery Rhyme	101
CT11	Ice Cream Seller, Second Variation	98
CT12	Cake Stall	120
CT13	Queen of the May, Second Variation	135
CT14	Family with Pram, Style Two	72

Design No.	Name	Page No.
CT15	Washing Up, First Variation	171
CT16	Classroom Scene, Style Two, Second Version	46
CT17	School Dinner, First Variation	146
CT18	Home from Fishing, First Variation	96
CT19	Nursery, First Version	116
CT20	School Gates, First Variation	147
CT21	Bathtime, Style Two, First Variation	26
CT22	School Gates, Second Variation	147
CT23	Bunny on Trike	147
CT24	Bathtime, Style Two, Second Variation	26
CT25	Bunnies in the Bath, First Version	26
CT26	Home from Fishing, Second Variation	97
CT27	Father Bunnykins with Fishing Rod	97
CT28	Nursery, Second Version	116
CT29	Bunny on Rocking Horse	116
CT30	School Dinner, Second Variation	146
CT31	Cook and Bunny	146
CT32	Washing Up, Second Variation	171
CT33	Splashing at Sink	171
CT34	Bunnies in the Bath, Second Version	27
CT35	Bunny with Mirror	117
CT36	Classroom Scene, Style Two, First Version	39, 46
CT37	Happy Birthday from Bunnykins, Style Two, First Version	89
CT38	Bunnykins Celebrate your Christening, Style Two, First Variation	36
CT39	Merry Christmas from Bunnykins, Style Two, First Variation	109
CT40	Happy Easter from Bunnykins, First Version	90
CT41	Bunnykins Celebrate you Christening, Style Two, Second Variation	36
CT42	Christening Inscription	36
CT43	Merry Christmas from Bunnykins, Style Two, Second Variation	109
CT44	Christmas Inscription	109
CT45	In the Park	Not Issued
CT46	In the Park	Not Issued
CT47	Boating	Not Issued
CT48	Boating	Not Issued
CT49	Model Yachting	Not Issued
CT50	Model Yachting	Not Issued
CT51	Train	Not Issued
CT52	In the Park	Not Issued
CT53	Model Yachting	Not Issued
CT54	Boating	Not Issued
CT55	Decorating the Tree	Not Issued
CT56	Sorting the Decorations	Not Issued
CT57	Showing the Baby the Tree	Not Issued
CT58	Santa Claus	Not Issued
CT59	Christmas Tree Ornament	Not Issued
CT60	Happy Birthday from Bunnykins Style Two, Second Version	89
CT61	Birthday Inscription	89
CT62	Happy Easter from Bunnykins Second Version	90
CT63	Happy Easter Inscription	90
CT64	Birthday Inscription	89
CT65	Bunnykins Celebrate your Christening Rhyme	36
CT66	Merry Christmas Inscription	109
CT67	Happy Easter Inscription	90
CT68	Santa Bunnykins (Christmas ornament)	143
CT69	Christmas 1991	143
CT70	Carol Singer Bunnykins (Christmas ornament)	42
CT71	Christmas 1992	42
CT72	Family Christmas Scene, First Version	110
CT73	Christmas Inscription	110
CT74	Family Christmas Scene, Second Version	110
CT75	Merry Christmas from Bunnykins Inscription	110

Design No.	Name	Page No.
CT76	Bunnykins Celebrate your Christening Baby in Crib with Father Looking On	37
CT77	Bunnykins Celebrate Your Christening Inscription	37
CT78	Baby in Crib	37
CT79	Christening Inscription	37
CT80	Trimming the Tree (Christmas ornament)	165
CT81	Christmas 1994	165
CT84	Picnic with Kangaroo and Koala First Variation	20
CT85	Commemorate Leaf Border	20
CT86	Picnic with Kangaroo and Koala Second Variation	20
CT87	Picnic Scene	21
CT88	Bunny with Cake Plate	21
CT89	Picnic Scene with Hamper	21
CT90	Father Asleep Second Version, First Variation	21
CT91	Dancing in the Moonlight	190
CT92	Dancing in the Moonlight Second Version, Second Variation	53
CT93	Bunnykins 60th Anniversary Inscription	190
CT94	ABCDEF Scene	13
CT95	ABC Scene	13
CT96	A Scene	13
CT97	Family Group with Father Standing	114
CT98	Family Group with Father Kneeling	114
CT99	New Arrival Inscription	114
EC1	Sleeping in a Rocking Chair	152
EC2	Drummer	61
EC3	Sheltering Under and Umbrella	149
EC4	Holding Hat and Coat	95
EC5	Trumpeter	166
EC6	Playing with Cup and Spoon	124
EC7	Raising Hat, Style Two	138
EC121	Hobby Horse, Style Two	94
EC122	Reading	138
EC123	Playing with Doll and Pram	125
EC124	Hikers	93
EC125	Bedtime with Dollies	31
EC126	Drummer and Bugler	61
HW1	Artist	18
HW1R	Dunce	63
HW2	Pulling on Trousers	133
HW2R	Reading the Times	139
HW3	Fixing Braces	77
HW3R	Fishing in the Goldfish Bowl	76
HW4	Cuddling Under a Mushroom	49
HW4R	Golfer	87
HW5	Embracing at a Window	64
HW6	Netting a Cricket	113
HW7	Greetings	87
HW8	Family Going out on Washing Day	69
HW8R	Washing Day	169
HW9	Gardening, Style One	83
HW9R	Gardener with Wheelbarrow	82
HW10	Asleep in the Open Air	19
HW10R	Washing in the Open Air	170
HW11	Proposal	132
HW11R	Kissing Under the Mistletoe	102
HW12	Family at Breakfast	67
HW12R	Leapfrog	105
HW13	Feeding the Baby	73
HW13R	Footballer	78
HW14	Pressing Trousers	131
HW14R	Top Hat	162
HW15	Family with Pram. Style One	71
HW15R	Cycling	50
HW16	Lambeth Walk	103, 104
HW16R	Raising Hat, Style One	137
HW17	Engine Pulling a Carriage	65
HW17R	To the Station	65

Design No.	Name	Page No.
HW18	Soldiers Marching to the Music	155
HW18R	Soldier Marching	155
HW19	Postman Delivering Letters	130
HW19R	Writing Letters	130
HW20	Swinging	159
HW20R	Skipping	159
HW21	Row Boat	142
HW21R	Nipped by a Crab	142
HW22	Wheelbarrow Race, Style One	174
HW22R	Cricketer	174
HW23	Ice Cream Vendor	99
HW23R	Hiker Resting with Ice Cream	99
HW24	Rocking Horse	140
HW24R	Hobby Horse, Style One	140
HW25	Daisy Chains	52
HW25R	Smelling Flowers	52
HW26	Dress Making	59
HW26R	Bugler with Toy Donkey	59
HW27	Windy Day	176
HW27R	Broken Umbrella	176
HW28	Hat Shop	91
HW28R	Trying on Hats	91
HW29	Haymaking	92
HW29R	Lunch Break	92
HW115	Playing with Dolls and Prams	126
HW115R	Dancing with Doll	126
HW116	Afternoon Tea	15
HW116R	Serving Tea	15
HW117	Lasso Games	105
HW117R	Lassoing	105
HW118	Disturbing Sleeping Father	56
HW118R	Pea Shooter	56
HW119	Unravelling the Knitting	167
HW119R	Trying on Knitting	167
HW120	The Doll's House	58
HW120R	Playing with Doll and Teddy	58
HW136	Punch and Judy Show	134
HW136R	Ice Cream on the Beach	134
HW137	Roller Skating Race	141
HW137R	Roller Skating Arm in Arm	141
HW138	Building Sand Castles	33
HW138R	Sailing Boats	33
HW139	Dancing Round the Barrel Organ	54
HW139R	Skipping Game	54
HW140	Cowboys and Indians	48
HW140R	Cowboy on Rocking Horse	48
HW141	Sledging, Style One	151
HW141R	Snowball Fight	151
HW142	Bunnykins Celebrate Your Christening Style One, Second Version	35
HW142R	Christening Inscription	35
LFa	Airmail Delivery	16
LFb	Dancing in the Moonlight, First Version	53
LFc	Carving the Chicken	42
LFd	Wedding	173
LFe	Dog Carriage	57
LF1	Tug of War	166
LF2	Getting Dressed	85
LF3	Fishing on the Pier	76
LF4	Dodgem Cars	57
LF5	Conducting the Orchestra	47
LF6	Mrs. Moppet's Tea Room	112
LF7	Bath Night	24
LF8	Xmas Menu	177
LF9	Christmas Party	44
LF10	Picnic, Style One, Second Version	119
LF11	Family Cycling	68
LF12	Cricket Game	49
LF13	The Duet	62
LF14	Spring Cleaning	156
LF15	Family Photograph	70
LF16	Christmas Tree	45
LF17	Geography Lesson	85
LF106	Winning Post	177
LF107	Art Class	17
LF108	Beware of the Bull	31
LF127	Juggling	101
LF128	Bonfire	32
LF129	Hoopla	97
PN175	Bunnykins Help Santa	38
PN198	Bunnykins Build a Snowman	34
SF1	Medicine Time	107
SF2	Smoking in the Doorway	153
SF3	Bedtime in Bunks, Style One	29
SF4	Frightening Spider	79
SF5	Convalescing	47
SF6a	Visiting the Cottage, First Version	168
SF6b	Visiting the Cottage, Second Version	168
SF7	Pillow Fight, Style One	122
SF8	Chicken Pulling a Cart	43
SF9	Santa Claus	144
SF10	Going Shopping	86
SF11	Game of Golf	80
SF12	Orange Vendor	118
SF13	Letterbox	106
SF14	Mr. Piggly's Stores	111
SF15	Watering the Flowers	172
SF16	Playing on the River	123
SF17	See-saw, Style One	148
SF18	Bathtime, Style One	25, 38
SF19	Baking	22
SF20	Portrait Painter	128
SF21	Ring-a-Ring o'Roses	139
SF22	Dressing Up, First Version	60
SF23	Toast for Tea Today	161
SF24	Ice Skating	100
SF25	Apple Picking	17
SF109	Ticket Queue	161
SF110	Storytime	158
SF111	Raft	136
SF112	Television Time	38, 160
SF113	Camp Site	38, 40
SF114	Toy Shop	163
SF130	Bedtime Story	29, 38
SF131	Home Decorating	38, 96
SF132	Space Rocket Launch	38, 156
SF133	Flying Kites	38, 77
SF134	Toppling the Fruit Cart	38, 162
SF135	Family in the Garden	38, 70
SF136	Happy Birthday from Bunnykins, Style One	88
SF137	Merry Christmas from Bunnykins, Style One	108
SF138	Classroom Scene, Style One	39
SF139	Bunnykins Celebrate your Christening, Style One, First Version	35
SF140	Bunnykins Celebrate Their Golden Jubilee, Birthday Cake	188
SF141	Bunnykins Celebrate their Golden Jubilee, Chicken Pulling a Cart	188

ALPHABETICAL INDEX

A

A Big Noise For A Little Piglet, WP64 465
A Cheerful Blaze, DBH60 359
A Clean Bear is a Happy Bear, WP49 461
A Clean Little Roo is Best, WP54 462
A Flower and his Heart, FAN5 428
(Shostakovich's Piano Concerto No. 2)
A Helping Hand, TW10 384
A Little Sponge for a Little Piglet, WP51 461
A Little Tree Trimming is in Order, WP41 458
A Present for Me? How Grand!, WP40 458
A Sleepy Day in the Hundred Acre Wood, WP53 462
Ace Bunnykins, DB42 220
Aerobic Bunnykins, DB40 219
Ah, Ah, Aachoo, SW29 443
Air Controller Bunnykins, DB382 328
Airman Bunnykins, DB199 269
Alice
Style One 338
Style Two, AW1 415
All Fueled Up, DB362 321
All the Flowers are Waking Up (Spring), WP37 457
American Firefighter Bunnykins, DB268 292
Angel Bunnykins, DB196 268
Ankhesenamun Bunnykins, DB295 301
Anne Bolelyn, DB307 305
Anne of Cleves, DB309 306
Any Hunny Left for Me?, WP48 460
Arabian Nights Bunnykins, DB315 308
Ariel
Style One, HN3831 412
Style Two, LM1 420
Style Three, DP4 413
Arthurian Legends Collection Camelot Base 329
Artist Bunnykins, DB13 209
As Good as New!, WW7 400
Astro Bunnykins Rocket Man, DB20 211
Music Box, DB35 217
Aurora, HN3833 412
Aussie Explorer Bunnykins Teapot, D7027 181
Aussie Surfer Bunnykins, DB133 248
Australian Bunnykins, DB58 225
Aw Shucks, SW23 441

B

Baby Elephant, JB2 417
Badger's Winter Store, WW8 400
Bagheera, JB4 418
Ballerina Bunnykins, DB176 261
Balloon Man Bunnykins, DB366 322
Baloo, JB3 418
Bambi, FC1 429
Banging on his Drum, RB17 380
Banjo Player Bunnykins, DB182 263
Barrister Bunnykins, DB374 325
Bashful, SW8 / SW16 439
Bashful's Melody, SW18 440
Basil
Style One, DBH14 345
Style Two, DBH38 352
Basketball Bunnykins
Style One, DB208 272
Style Two, DB262 290
Bass Drummer Snowman, DS9 389
Bath Night Bunnykins, DB241 283
Bathtime Bunnykins, DB148 252
Batsman Bunnykins, DB144 251
Be Prepared Bunnykins, DB56 224
Bedtime Bunnykins
First Variation, DB55 224
Second Variation, DB63 226
Third Variation, DB79 232
Fourth Variation, DB103 240
Beefeater Bunnykins, DB163 257
Belle
Style One, HN3830 411
Style Two, DP3 413
Betsy Ross Bunnykins, DB313 307
Bibendun the Michelin Man, MCL9 478
Big Chief Pooh (Winnie the Pooh), WP88 472
Big Chief Toucan, MCL3 477
Big Ears, 3676 368
Billie & Buntie Bunnykins Sleigh Ride
First Variation, DB4 206
Second Variation, DB81 233
Billie Bunnykins Cooling Off, DB3 205
Billy Bunnykin, D6001 203
Bingo's Huge Firework, RB10 378
Birth of Norbert (The), HP17 366
Birthday Boy, DBR17 336
Birthday Girl, DBR16 336
Birthday Girl Bunnykins, DB290 299
Bisto Kids, MCL4 477
Boatswain, DB323 310
Bob Badger, TW4 382
Body Brush, NT7 398
Bogey Bunnykins, DB32 216
Bouncy Bouncy Boo-To-You!, WP52 462
Bowler Bunnykins, DB145 251
Boy Skater Bunnykins
First Variation. DB152 253
Second Variation, DB187 265
Brain of Pooh (The), WP31 455
Bramwell Brown Has a Good Idea, OB4603 370
Briar Rose Singing of Loves Dreams, SB1 434
Bride and Groom, The DBH44 354
Bride Bunnykins, DB101 239
Bridesmaid Bunnykins, DB173 260
Britannia Bunnykins, B219 276
Brownie Bunnykins, DB61 226
Buckets of Mischief, FAN1 427
Building the Snowman, DS23 393
Bunnybank
First Version, D6615A 186
Second Version, D6615B 186
Third Version, D6615C 186
Bunnykins Camping, DB364 322
Buntie Bunnykins Helping Mother, DB2 205
Businessman Bunnykins, DB203 270
Busy Needles Bunnykins, DB10 208

C

Cabin Boy, DB324 311
Caddie Bunnykins, DB271 293
Captain, DB319 309
Captain Cook Bunnykins, DB251 286
Captain Hook, PAN4 423
Captain's Wife, DB320 309
Carol Singer Bunnykins, DB104 240
Music Box, DB53 223
Cat and the Fiddle (The), DNR4 369
Catherine of Aragon, DB306 305
Catherine Parr, DB311 306
Catkin, DBH12 344
Cavalier Bunnykins, DB179 262

Cellist Snowman, DS17 391
Centurion Bunnykins, DB294 301
Cheerleader Bunnykins
First Variation, DB142 250
Second Variation, DB143 250
Chef Bunnykins, DB379 327
Cheshire Cat
Style One 338
Style Two, AW 5 416
Chocs Away Bunnykins, DB267 292
Choir Singer Bunnykins, DB223 277
Choosing Good Feet, NT4 397
Christening Day Boy, DB328 312
Christening Day Girl. DB327 312
Christmas Angel, DB345 316
Christmas Busker, DB349 317
Christmas Carol Singer, DB348 317
Christmas Cracker, DB347 316
Christmas Elf, DB342 315
Christmas Eve, DB346 316
Christmas Morning Bunnykins, DB285 298
Christmas Piglet, WP76 469
Christmas Surprise Bunnykins, DB146 251
Christmas Toucan, MCL6 477
Christopher Dresses the Tree, WP57 463
Christopher Reads to Pooh, WP32 455
Christopher Robin, WP9 447
Christopher Robin and Pooh, WP10 448
Christopher Robin Strums a Melody, WP79 470
Christopher to the Rescue, WP92 474
Cinderella
Style One, HN3677 411
Style Two, DP1 413
Cinderella Bunnykins, DB231 280
Cinderella, The Dress of Dreams, CN1 408
Clarence the Clown, DB332 313
Clarinet Player Bunnykins, DB184 264
Clarrisa the Clown, DB331 313
Clover, DBH16 345
Clown Bunnykins
First Variation, DB128 247
Second Variation, DB129 247
Coca-Cola Bathing Belle, MCL14 478
Collector Bunnykins, DB54 223
Congratulations Bunnykins, DB291 300
Conker, DBH21 347
Cook Bunnykins, DB85 234
Cookie Jar (Bunnykins Tea Set) 182
Country Manor Butler Cream Jug, DBD5 183
Country Manor Chef Candy Box, DBD7 183
Country Manor Maid Covered Sugar, DBD6 183
Cowboy Bunnykins, DB201 270
Cowboy Snowman, DS7 388
Cream Jug, D6057 (Bunnykins Breakfast Set) 180
Creamer (Bunnykins Tea Set) 182
Cruella De Vil
Style One, DM1 404
Style Two, HN3839 425
Cymbal Player Snowman, DS14 390
Cymbals Bunnykins
First Variation, DB25 213
Second Variation, DB88 235
Third Variation, DB107 241

D

Daisie Bunnykins Spring Time, DB7 207
Daisy Duck, MM4/MM10 433
Dancing in the Snow 394
Daniel Duck, TW7 383
Day Trip Bunnykins, DB260 289
Dear Old Doc, SW25 442
Deborah Dormouse, TW11 384
Deep Sea Diver Bunnykins, DB273 294
Delight of Spring (The), WW1 399
Deputy Eeyore, WP91 473
Detecting Ailments, NT8 398
Detective Bunnykins, DB193 267
Digger Bunnykins, DB248 285
Dobby, HP23 367
Doc, SW2 / SW10 437
Doc with Lantern, SW19 440
Doctor Bunnykins
Style One, DB181 263
Style Two, DB381 327
Dodgem Bunnykins, DB249 286
Dodo 338
Dollie Bunnykins Playtime
First Variation, DB8 207
Second Variation, DB80 232
Donald Duck, MM3/MM9 432
Don't Forget Old Bear, OB4611 371
Don't Worry Rabbit, OB4604 370
Dopey, SW5 / SW13 438
Dopey by Candlelight, SW17 439
Dopey's First Kiss, SW21 441
Dorothy, 3732 402
Double Bass Player Bunnykins, DB185 264
Downhill Bunnykins, DB31 216
Dr. Christopher, WP71 467
Dressing the Snowman 396
Drum-major Bunnykins
First Variation, DB27 214
Second Variation, DB90 236
Third Variation, DB109 242
Drummer Bunnykins, Style One
First Variation, DB26A 213
Second Variation, DB26B 213
Third Variation, DB89 235
Fourth Variation, DB108 242
Drummer Bunnykins, Style Two, DB250 286
Drummer Snowman, DS15 391
Duck, OB4619 372
Duel (The), PAN3 423
Dumbo, FC3 430
Dunlop Caddie, MCL2 477
Dursley Family, HP 24 367
Dusty and Baby, DBH26 349
Dusty Dogwood
Style One, DBH6 341
Style Two, DBH37 351
Dusty's Buns, DBH51 356
Dutch Bunnykins, DB274 294

E

Easter Greetings Bunnykins, DB149 252
Easter Parade Bunnykins, DB292 300
Easter Surprise Bunnykins, DB225 278
Easter Treat Bunnykins, DB289 299
Eeyore Loses a Tail, WP15 449
Eeyore Made a Wintery Wish (Winter), WP44 459
Eeyore Nose to the Ground, WP25 453
Eeyore on Percussion, WP80 470
Eeyore's Birthday, WP14 449
Eeyore's Tail, WP7 447
Egg Cup, Style One, D6034 (Bunnykins Breakfast Set) 179
Egyptian Bunnykins, DB314 307
Emperor Bunnykins, DB312 307
England Athlete Bunnykins
First Variation, DB216A 275
Second Variation, DB216B 275
Eskimo Bunnykins, DB275 294
Evacuees Bunnykins, DB373 325

Every Hole Possessed a Face, WW9 401
Excessive Praise, NT5 398
Exhausted, NT3 397

F

Family Photograph Bunnykins
First Variation, DB1 205
Second Variation, DB67 228
Farmer Bunnykin, D6003 203
Father Bunnykins
Style One, DB154 254
Style Two, DB227 279
Father Bunnykins and Harry Decorating the Tree, DBR 12 334
Father Bunnykins Home From Work, DBR8 333
Father Christmas, DB343 315
Father Christmas Bunnykins, DB237 282
Father, Mother & Victoria Bunnykins, DB68 228
Father William, AC2 476
Fauna, Thoughtful Fairy, SB3 435
Federation Bunnykins, DB224 278
Finishing Arrows and Stringing his Bow (Rupert), RB7 378
Fireman Bunnykins
Style One, First Variation, DB75 231
Style One, Second Variation, DB183 264
Style Two, DB376 326
First Aid Friends, WP72 468
Fisherman Bunnykins
Style One, DB84 234
Style Two, DB170 259
Flamenco Bunnykins, DB256 288
Flautist Snowman, DS10 389
Flax Weaver
Style One, DBH20 347
Style Two, DBH55 357
Floating Along, JB6 419
Flora, Nurturing Fairy, SB2 434
Flounder, LM2 420
Follow Me, FAN2 427
Footballer Bunnykins
First Variation, DB117 243
Second Variation, DB119 244
Third Variation, DB121 244
Fortune Teller Bunnykins, DB218 276
Fortune Teller Bunnykins Toby Jug, D7157 184
Fox's Polar Bear, AC4 476
Franchesca Fawn, TW13 385
Fred Fox, TW3 382
Freddie Bunnykin, D6024 204
Freefall Bunnykins, DB41 219
Friends, TW9 384
Friendship Begins (The), HP8 365
Friar Tuck Bunnykins
First Variation, DB246 285
Second Variation, DB354 319
Frosty Family Tree, The , FF7 363

G

Gardener Bunnykins, DB156 255
Geisha Girl Bunnykins Teapot, D7126 181
George Washington, DB367 323
Girl Skater Bunnykins, DB153 254
Gladiator, DB326 311
Goalkeeper Bunnykins
First Variation, DB116 243
Second Variation, DB118 243
Third Variation, DB120 244
Fourth Variation, DB122 245
Going Out Late, RB18 380
Going Sledging, WP34 456
Golfer Bunnykins, DB255 288
Golly, AC1 476
Goodnight Bunnykins, DB157 255
Goofy, MM5/MM11 433
Graduation Day Bunnykins, DB286 298
Graduation Time, DB329 312
Grandpa's Story Bunnykins, DB14 209
Groom Bunnykins, DB102 240
Grumpy, SW3 / SW11 437
Grumpy's Bathtime, SW20 440
Guardsman Bunnykins, DB127 246
Guinness Toucan, AC8 476
Gus, CN6 410
Gymnast Bunnykins, DB207 272

H

Halloween Bunnykins, DB132 248
Happy, SW4 / SW12 438
Happy Birthday Bunnykins, DB21 211
Music Box, DB36 218
Happy Birthday Wilfred, DBH45 354
Happy Christmas from the Bunnykins Family, DBR14 335
Happy Christmas Tigger, WP87 472
Happy Millennium Bunnykins Tableau, DB200 269
Happy, That's Me, SW27 443
Harry Bunnykins, DB73 230
Harry Bunnykins A Little Bunny at Play, DBR1 331
Harry Bunnykins Playtime, DBR2 331
Harry Casts a Magical Spell, HP2 364
Harry Hedgehog, TW2 381
Harry Potter Playing Quidditch, HP 22 367
Harry the Herald
First Variation, DB49 222
Second Variation, DB95 237
Third Variation, DB115 242
Harry's 11th Birthday, HP9 365
Heading For Skull Rock, PAN7 424
Heading Home, DBH48 355
Headmaster Albus Dumbledore, HP6 365
Heart on a String (Pomp and Circumstance), FAN4 428
Hedwig, HP16 366
Heigh Ho, SW31 444
He'll Find You, NT12 398
Henry VIII, DB305 304
Henry Hedgehog, TW1 381
Hermione Learns to Levitate, HP13 366
Hermione Studies for Potions Class, HP3 364
Highland Snowman, DS7 388
His Master's Voice 478
HMMPH!, SW26 442
Hold on Tight, OB4612 371
Home for Supper, DBH69 362
Home Run Bunnykins, DB43 220
Homeguard Bunnykins, DB371 324
Honey and Tea is a Very Grand Thing, WP75 469
Hornpiper Bunnykins, DB261 290
Hot Buttered Toast for Breakfast, DBH68 362
How Sweet to be a Cloud (Clock), WP24 452
Howdy Sheriff (Piglet), WP89 473
Humpty Dumpty, DNR1 369

I

I Love You So Much Bear, WP46 460
Ice Ball, The DBH30 349
Ice Cream Bunnykins, DB82 233
Ice Cream Treat, NT9 398
Ice Hockey Bunnykins, DB282 297
Ideal Pony for a Nervous Child, NT10 398
Imp of Spring (The), RB15 379
In the Brambles, DBH65 361
In the Woods, DBH64 360

Indian Bunnykins, DB202 270
Irishman Bunnykins, DB178 262
Irresistibly Loveable, SW24 442
Isn't it Funny How a Bear Likes Honey, WP60 464
It's a Perfect Fit, CN7 410
It's Honey all the Way Down, WP61 464
I've Found Somebody Just Like Me, WP22 452

J

Jack and Jill Bunnykins, DB222 277
James
    Style One, DS1 386
    Style Two 394
    Style Three 395
Jane Seymour, DB308 305
Jaq, CN2 408
Jasmine
    Style One, HN3832 412
    Style Two, DP6 414
Jester Bunnykins, DB161 256
Jiminy Cricket, FC5 430
Jockey Bunnykins, DB169 259
Jogging Bunnykins, DB22 212
    Music Box, DB37 218
John Bull Bunnykins, DB134 249
John Ginger, AC6 476
Joker Bunnykins, DB171 260
Journey Ends (The) 396
Journey to Hogwarts (The), HP19 366
Judge Bunnykins, DB188 265
Judy Bunnykins, DB235 281
Juggler Bunnykins, DB164 257
Juliet Bunnykins, DB283 297
Just Like New, DB361 321

K

Kanga and Roo, WP8 447
Kathryn Howard, DB310 306
King Arthur, DB304 304
King John
    First Variation, DB45 220
    Second Variation, DB91 236
King Louie, JB7 419
King Richard Bunnykins
    First Variation, DB258 289
    Second Variation, DB351 318
Knockout Bunnykins, DB30 215

L

Lady, FC7 431
Lady of the Manor Teapot, DBD2 183
Lady Ratley Her Ladyship Explains, DBR6 332
Lady Snowman, DS8 388
Lady Woodmouse
    Style One, DBH5 341
    Style Two, DBH32 350
Land Girl Bunnykins, DB372 324
Lawyer Bunnykins, DB214 274
Leading the Way (Ping Pong), RB3 377
Let's Make a Snowmouse, DBH67 361
Liberty Bell Bunnykins, DB257 288
Lily Weaver
    Style One, DBH19 346
    Style Two, DBH54 357
Lily Weaver Spinning, DBH58 358
Lion, 3731 402
Little Bo Peep Bunnykins, DB220 276
Little Boy Blue Bunnykins, DB239 282
Little Indians (Kanga and Roo), WP93 474
Little Jack Horner Bunnykins, DB221 277
Little John Bunnykins
    First Variation, DB243 284
    Second Variation, DB355 319
Little Miss Muffet, DNR2 369
Little Miss Muffet Bunnykins, DB240 283
Little Red Riding Hood Bunnykins, DB230 280
Lollipopman Bunnykins, DB65 227
London City Gent Bunnykins Teapot, D6966 181
Long Red Scarf (The), OB4605 371
Looking for a Sailor, OB4614 372
Looking Like Robin Hood (Algy Pug), RB6 378
Lord of the Manor Coffee Pot, DBD1 183
Lord Woodmouse
    Style One, DBH4 341
    Style Two, DBH31 349
Losing Hurts, NT1 397
Love Heart Bunnykins, DB288 299
Love Makes All Your Bothers Disappear, WP39 457
Loves First Kiss, SB7 436
Lucifer, CN3 409
Lucky, DM8 406
Lucky and Freckles on Ice, DM10 407

M

Mad Hatter
    Style One 339
    Style Two, AW2 415
Madame Hooch, HP20 366
Magician Bunnykins
    First Variation, DB126 246
    Second Variation, DB159 256
Maid Marion Bunnykins
    First Variation, DB245 284
    Second Variation, DB356 319
Maleficent, HN3840 425
Maleficent, Stand Back You Fools, SB5 435
Mandarin Bunnykins, DB252 287
Many Happy Returns of the Day, WP83 471
March Hare, AW3 416
Mary Bunnykin, D6002 203
Mary Mary Quite Contrary Bunnykins, DB247 285
Master of the Manor Cup and Saucer, DBD3 183
Master Potter Bunnykins, DB131 248
Matador Bunnykins, DB281 296
Merlin, DB303 304
Mermaid Bunnykins, DB263 290
Merry Christmas Bunnykins Tableau, DB194 267
Merryweather, Feisty Fairy, SB4 435
Mexican Bunnykins, DB316 308
Mickey Mouse, MM1/MM7 432
Milkman Bunnykins, DB125 246
Milky Bar Kid (The), AC7 476
Miner Toucan, MCL10 478
Minnie Mouse, MM2/MM8 432
Minstrel Bunnykins, DB211 273
Mirror Holds the Answer (The), HP18 366
Miss of the Manor Cup and Saucer, DBD4 183
Monty Mole, TW12 385
Morris Dancer Bunnykins, DB204 271
Mother and Baby Bunnykins
    Style One, DB167 258
    Style Two , DB226 278
Mother Bunnykin, D6004 204
Mother Bunnykins, DB189 266
Mother Christmas, DB344 315
Mother's Day Bunnykins, DB155 254
Mountie Bunnykins, DB135 249

Mowgli, JB1 417
Mr. Apple
Style One, DBH2 340
Style Two, DBH53 357
Mr. Bunnybeat Strumming, DB16 210
Music Box, DB38. 218
Mr. Bunnykins at the Easter Parade
First Variation, DB18 210
Second Variation, DB51 222
Mr. Bunnykins Autumn Days, DB5 206
Mr. Frosty's Special Gift, FF1 363
Mr. Plod, 3679 368
Mr. Punch Bunnykins, DB234 281
Mr. Saltapple
Style One, DBH24 348
Style Two, DBH39 352
Mr. Toadflax,
Style One, First Version, DBH10A 343
Style One, Second Version, DBH10B 343
Style One, Third Version, DBH10C 343
Style Two, DBH46 354
Mrs. Apple
Style One, DBH3 340
Style Two, DBH47 355
Mrs. Bunnykins a Busy Morning Shopping, DBR7 333
Mrs. Bunnykins and William The Birthday Cake, DBR13 335
Mrs. Bunnykins at the Easter Parade
First Variation, DB19 211
Second Variation, DB52 223
Music Box, DB39 219
Mrs. Bunnykins Clean Sweep, DB6 206
Mrs. Collector Bunnykins, DB335 314
Mrs. Crustybread, DBH15 345
Mrs. Frosty's Finishing Touch, FF2 363
Mrs. Saltapple
Style One, DBH25 348
Style Two, DBH40 352
Mrs. Toadflax, DBH11 344
Mrs. Toadflax Decorates Cake, DBH52 356
Mystic Bunnykins, DB197 268

N

Nelson Bunnykins, DB365 322
Nest of Socks, OB4616 372
New Baby, DBR18 336
New Baby Bunnykins, DB158 255
Newsvendor Namestand, MCL11 478
No Amount of Shaking, WW3 399
Noah's Helper, FAN3 428
Noddy, 3678 368
Noddy and Big Ears 368
Nurse Bunnykins
Style One, First Variation, DB74A 230
Style One, Second Variation, DB74B 230
Style Two, DB375 325
Nurse Tigger, WP73 468

O

Occasions Collection Scenic Base 329
Off to Pick Mushrooms, DBH66 361
Off to the Ball, CN8 410
Oh Dear! Bathtime's Here, WP59 464
Old Balloon Seller Bunnykins, DB217 275
Old Bear, OB4601 370
Old King Cole, DNR5 369
Old Mother Hubbard, DNR3 369
Old Mrs. Eyebright
Style One, DBH9 342
Style Two, DBH62 360
Old Vole, DBH13 344
Oliver Owl, TW8 383
Olympic Bunnykins
First Variation, DB28A 214
Second Variation, DB28B 214
On Line Bunnykins, DB238 282
On the Edge, DBH57 358
Open Road, The Dusty Highway, (The) WW2 399
Out For a Duck Bunnykins, DB160 256
Out for the Day, RB14 379

P

P..P..P..Pick Up A...Penguin, MCL5 477
Paddington at Christmas Time, PB9 375
Paddington at the Station (Style One), PB1 373
Paddington Bakes a Cake, PB2 373
Paddington Bathtime, PB6 374
Paddington Decorating, PB3 373
Paddington Gardening, PB5 374
Paddington Going to Bed, PB11 376
Paddington Marmalade Sandwich, PB10 376
Paddington Surfing, PB4 374
Paddington the Fisherman, PB12 376
Paddington the Golfer, PB7 375
Paddington the Musician, PB8 375
Paperboy Bunnykins, DB77 231
Parisian Bunnykins, DB317 308
Partners in Collecting, DB151 253
Party Time Bunnykins Toby Jug, D7160 184
Patch in Basket, DM9 407
Patch, Rolly and Freckles, DM5 405
Patient Bear, WP74 468
Pebble, DBH41 353
Perfect Hat for Gardening (The), WP70 467
Penfold Golfer, MCL1 477
Penny, DM2 404
Penny and Freckles, DM3 405
Perdita, DM7 406
Persuading Ratty, WW4 400
Peter Pan, PAN1 422
Pianist Snowman, DS12 390
Picnic Time with the Bunnykins Family, DBR15 335
Piglet and the Balloon, WP5 446
Piglet and the Honey Pot, WP29 454
Piglet Picking the Violets, WP13 449
Piglet Planting a Haycorn, WP26 453
Piglet's Tea Time, WP78 470
Pilgrim Bunnykins, DB212 273
Pilot Bunnykins, DB369 323
Pinocchio, FC4 430
Piper Bunnykins, DB191 266
Pirate, DB321 310
Player's 'Hero' Sailor, AC5 476
Plumber Bunnykins, DB378 326
Pluto, MM6/MM12 433
Podgy Lands with a Bump, RB9 378
Policeman Bunnykins, DB64 227
Polly Bunnykins, DB71 229
Pongo, DM6 406
Pooh and Piglet – The Windy Day, WP2 445
Pooh and the Party Hat, WP33 455
Pooh Began to Eat, WP28 454
Pooh Counting the Honeypots, WP12 448
Pooh Lights the Candle, WP11 448
Pooh Sticks, WP84 472
Pooh's Blue Balloon (Money Box), WP16 450
Poppy Eyebright
Style One, DBH1 340
Style Two, DBH36 351
Postman Bunnykins
Style One, DB76 231
Style Two, DB377 326

Powerful Hindquarters are a Distinct Advantage, NT2 397
Preparations for Carrot Honey Pie, WP69 467
Presents and Parties, WP50 461
Pretending to be an Outlaw (Edward Trunk), RB2 377
Primrose Entertains, DBH22 347
Primrose Picking Berries, DBH33 350
Primrose Woodmouse, DBH8 342
Prince Frederick
First Variation, DB48 221
Second Variation, DB94 237
Prince John Bunnykins
First Variation, DB266 291
Second Variation, DB350 317
Princess Beatrice
First Variation, DB47 221
Second Variation, DB93 237
Professor McGonagall, HP14 366
Professor Quirrell, HP15 366
Professor Severus Snape, HP5 365
Professor Sprout, HP21 367
Pups in the Chair, DM11 407
Push...Pull! Come on Pooh (Bookends), WP55/56 463

Q

Quality Street Figure, MCL13 478
Queen (The), HN3847 426
Queen Guinevere, DB302 303
Queen of Hearts 339
Queen Sophie
First Variation, DB46 221
Second Variation, DB92 236

R

Rabbit Reads the Plan, WP23 452
Rabbit's Harvest?, WP67 466
Rainy Day Bunnykins, DB147 252
Randolph the Ringmaster, DB330 313
Ratty! Is that Really You?, WW10 401
Ready to Ride, DB363 321
Reggie and Rex, RB12 379
Reggie Bunnykin, D6025 204
Reginald Ratley Up to No Good, DBR3 331
Remembrall Recovery (The), HP1 364
Rescue in the Forbidden Forest, HP26 367
Resting with Cat, OB4613 372
Ringmaster Bunnykins, DB165 258
Rise and Shine Bunnykins, DB11 208
Robin Hood Bunnykins
First Variation, DB244 284
Second Variation, DB357 320
Robin Hood Collection Base 329
Rock and Roll Bunnykins, DB124 245
Rocking Horse, DBR19 336
Rolly, DM4 405
Romeo Bunnykins, DB284 297
Ron and Scabbers, HP12 365
Ron Follows the Weasley Family Tradition, HP4 364
Rosie Rabbit, TW5 382
Ruff's Prize, OB4609 371
Rugby Player Bunnykins, DB318 309
Rum-Tum-Tum Winnie on his Drum, WP63 465
Runner Bunnykins, DB205 271
Rupert and the King, RB21 380
Rupert, Bill and the Mysterious Car, RB11 379
Rupert Rides Home, RB4 378
Rupert Takes a Flying Lesson, RB26 380
Rupert Takes a Ski-ing Lesson, RB20 380
Rupert's Silver Trumpet, RB8 378
Rupert's Toy Railway, RB1 377

S

Sailor Bunnykins
Style One, DB166 258
Style Two, DB370 324
Salt and Pepper Set (Bunnykins Tea Set) 182
Samurai Bunnykins, DB280 296
Sandcastle Money Box, DB228 279
Sands of Time Bunnykins, DB229 279
Santa Bunnykins Happy Christmas, DB17 210
Christmas Tree Ornament, DB62 226
Music Box, DB34 217
Santa's Helper Bunnykins, DB192 267
Sarah Squirrel, TW6 383
Saxophone Player Bunnykins, DB186 265
Scarecrow, 3709 402
Scarecrow Bunnykins, DB359 320
Schoolboy Bunnykins, DB66 227
Schooldays Bunnykins, DB57 224
Schoolmaster Bunnykins, DB60 225
Scotsman Bunnykins, DB180 263
Scuttle, LM5 421
Seaman, DB322 310
Seaside Bunnykins, DB177 262
Seaside Toucan, MCL7 477
Sebastian, LM3 421
Sergeant Mountie Bunnykins, DB136 249
Shearer Bunnykins, DB368 323
Shell, DBH42 353
Shere Khan, JB5 418
Sheriff of Nottingham Bunnykins
First Variation, DB265 291
Second Variation, DB353 318
Ship Ahoy Bunnykins, DB279 296
Shipmates Collection Tall Ship Base 330
Ship's Cook, DB325 311
Shooting the Rapids, DBH61 359
Shopper Bunnykins, DB233 280
Short Winter Days, WW11 401
Shrimp, DBH43 353
Sightseer Bunnykins, DB215 274
Sir Galahad, DB299 302
Sir Gawain, DB300 302
Sir Kreemy Knut, AC3 476
Sir Lancelot, DB301 303
Sister Mary Barbara Bunnykins, DB334 314
60th Anniversary Bunnykins, DB137 250
Sleeping Beauty, DP2 413
Sleepy, SW7 / SW15 439
Sleepytime Bunnykins, DB15 209
Slushy Builds a Snowman, FF4 363
Slytherin or Gryffindor, HP11 365
Sneezy, SW6 / SW14 438
Snow Decorations, OB4617 372
Snow White
Style One, HN3678 411
Style Two, SW1 / SW9 437
Style Three, DP5 414
Snow White Fairest of them All, SW22 441
Snowdrift Leads the Way, FF6 363
Snowdrift's Christmas Surprise, FF5 363
Snowflake Biscuits (The), OB4607 371
Snowflake on Ice, FF3 363
Snowman (The)
Style One, DS2 386
Style Two 394
Style Three 395
Snowman and James, The Adventure Begins 395
Snowman Magic Music Box, DS5 387
Snowman Money Box, DS19 392
Snowman Musical Box, DS18 392

Snowman Skiing (The) DS21 393
Snowman Snowballing (The) DS22 393
Snowman Tobogganing (The) DS20 392
Snowman's Piano, DS13 390
So Treat Him Like a Friend, NT11 398
Soccer Bunnykins, DB209 272
Soccer Player Bunnykins, DB123 245
Something to Draw, RB13 379
Sometimes Autumn Tickles your Nose (Autumn), WP43 459
Sousaphone Bunnykins
    First Variation, DB23 212
    Second Variation, DB86 234
    Third Variation, DB105 241
Sprawling by the Riverbank, WW5 400
Statue of Liberty Bunnykins, DB198 269
Stop Watch Bunnykins, DB253 287
Store Stump Money Box, DBH18 346
Storytime, OB4618 372
Storytime Bunnykins
    First Variation, DB9 207
    Second Variation, DB59 225
Strawberries Bunnykins, DB277 295
Struggling Through Potions Class, HP10 365
Stylish Snowman, DS3 387
Sugar Bowl, D6056 (Bunnykins Breakfast Set) 180
Sugar Dish (Bunnykins Tea Set) 182
Sugar Sifter, D6040 (Bunnykins Breakfast Set) 179
Summer is Full of Fluttery Surprises (Summer), WP38 457
Summer Lapland, DB298 302
Summer's Day Picnic, WP21 451
Sundial Bunnykins, DB213 274
Suppling Exercises, NT6 398
Susan and Harry Bunnykins Minding Baby Brother, DBR11 334
Susan Bunnykins, DB70 229
Susan Bunnykins as Queen of the May, DB83 233
Susan Bunnykins the Helper, DBR4 332
Susan Bunnykins Wildlife Spotting, DBR10 334
Sweet Dreams Baby Bunny, DB276 295
Sweetheart Bunnykins
    First Variation, DB130 247
    Second Variation, DB174 261
Swimmer Bunnykins, DB206 271
Sydney Bunnykins, DB195 268

T

Take the Apple, Dearie, SW30 444
Tally Ho! Bunnykins
    First Variation, DB12 208
    Second Variation, DB78 232
    Music Box
        First Variation, DB33A 216
        Second Variation, DB33B 217
Tea at Hornbeam Tree, DBH59 359
Tea for Two, WP77 469
Teacher Bunnykins, DB380 327
Tea Pot, D6010 (Bunnykins Breakfast Set) 179
Teapot (Bunnykins Tea Set) 182
Teasel, DBH17 346
Tempted to Trespass, RB5 378
Tennis Bunnykins, DB278 295
Tessie Bear, 3770 368
Test Century Bunnykins, DB272 293
Thank You Snowman, DS4 387
The More it Snows, Tiddely Pom, WP20 451
The Most Perfect Tree in all the Wood, WP42 458
They Can't Stop Me From Dreaming, CN5 409
Thumper, FC2 429
Tic Toc Crocodile, PAN6 424
Tigger Loves Tigger Lilies, WP27 453
Tigger Plays Ball, WP30 454
Tigger Signs the Rissoluton, WP6 446
Tigger's Birthday Surprise, WP65 466
Tigger's Bouncy Beat, WP81 471
Tigger's Loveheart, WP82 471
Tigger's Splash Time, WP58 463
Time for a Cuddle, Hug Me Tight, OB4610 371
Time for Bed, OB4602 370
Timothy Mouse, FC6 431
Tinker Bell, PAN2 422
Tinman, 3738 402
Tino the Trixstar, DB333 314
Tom Bunnykins, DB72 229
Tony the Tiger, MCL8 477
Too Much Food, OB4615 372
Toot Toot Went the Whistle, WP47 460
Touchdown Bunnykins
    First Variation, DB29A 215
    Second Variation (Boston), DB29B 215
    Third Variation (Ohio), DB96 238
    Fourth Variation (Michigan), DB97 238
    Fifth Variation (Cincinnati), DB98 238
    Sixth Variation (Notre Dame), DB99 239
    Seventh Variation (Indiana), DB100 239
Tourist Bunnykins, DB190 266
Town Crier Bunnykins, DB259 289
Toy Soldier Bunnykins Toby Jug, D7185 184
Tramp, FC8 431
Trick or Treat Bunnykins, DB162 257
Trumpet Player Bunnykins, DB210 273
Trumpeter Bunnykins
    First Variation, DB24 212
    Second Variation, DB87 235
    Third Variation, DB106 241
Trumpeter Snowman, DS16 391
Tudor Collection Scenic Base 330
Tutankhamun Bunnykins, DB296 301
Tyrolean Dancer Bunnykins, DB242 283

U

Umpire Bunnykins, DB360 320
Uncle Sam Bunnykins
    First Variation, DB50 222
    Second Variation, DB175 261
Under the Name 'Mr. Sanders', WP36 456
Up, Up and Away, OB4620 372
Ursula, LM4 421
U.S.A. President Bunnykins Teapot, D6996 181

V

Vicar Bunnykins, DB254 287
Violinist Snowman, DS11 389

W

Waiting for Snow, OB4606 371
Walking in the Air (Wall Plaque) 396
Waltzing Matilda Bunnykins, DB236 281
We Meant to Put Them Back!, RB16 379
Wedding Day Bunnykins, DB287 298
Wee Willie Winkle Bunnykins, DB270 293
Welcome Home, Old Bear, OB4608 371
Welshlady Bunnykins, DB172 260
Wendy, PAN5 423
Where are Basil's Trousers?, DBH50 356
Where Does The Wind Come From?, WP62 465
Whiskas Cat, MCL15 478
White Rabbit
    Style One 339
    Style Two, AW4 416
Who is it This Time?, WW6 400
Whomping Willow, HP 25 367

Who's Cake? Pooh's Cake, WP45 459
Wicketkeeper Bunnykins, DB150 253
Wilfed and the Toy Chest (Money Box) DBH35 351
Wilfred Carries the Picnic, DBH34 350
Wilfred Entertains, DBH23 348
Wilfred Toadflax
Style One, DBH7 342
Style Two, DBH56 358
Wildfred's Birthday Cake, DBH49 355
Will Scarlet Bunnykins
First Variation, DB264 291
Second Variation, DB352 318
William Bunnykins, DB69 228
William Bunnykins A Bunny in a Hurry, DBR9 333
William Bunnykins Asleep in the Sun, DBR5 332
Winnie the Pooh and the Fair-Sized Basket, WP19 451
Winnie the Pooh and the Honeypot, WP1 445
Winnie the Pooh and the Paw Marks, WP3 445
Winnie the Pooh and the Present, WP18 450
Winnie the Pooh in the Armchair, WP4 446
Winter Lapland, BD297 302
Witch (The), HN3848 426
Witches Cauldron Bunnykins, DB293 300
Witching Time Bunnykins Toby Jug, D7166 184
With a Wave of her Magic Wand, CN4 409
With Love, WP66 466
With Love Bunnykins, DB269 292
Wizard Bunnykins, DB168 259
Wizard-in-Training, HP7 365
Wol and the Honeypot, WP35 456
Wol Signs the Rissolution, WP17 450
Woodland Waltz, SB6 436

Y

Yee Hah! (Tigger), WP90 473
You're Safe, DBH63 360

Z

ZZZZZZ, SW28 443

LOUIS TAYLOR

LT

EST 1877

FINE ART AUCTIONEERS & VALUERS

SPECIALIST AUCTIONS OF DOULTON AND BESWICK INCLUDING STORYBOOK FIGURINES

Bunnykins, Beatrix Potter, Brambly Hedge, Snowman, Alice in Wonderland, Disney Characters, etc.

SPECIALIST SALES HELD QUARTERLY • March • June • September • December •

CATALOGUES AVAILABLE ON REQUEST
£7 Including Postage & Packing UK
£14 Including Postage & Packing Overseas

For further information contact Clive Hillier, MRICS, or Sheila Doolan on 01782 214111 or Fax 01782 215283

Clown Bunnykins DB128 Limited Edition of 750

Trick or Treat Bunnykins DB162

Britannia House,

10 Town Road, Hanley, Stoke-on Trent, Staffs

Tel: 01782 214111

Fax: 01782 215283

Collecting Doulton & Beswick Collectors Club

The independent magazine for collectors of Royal Doulton and Beswick

Published six times a year, Collecting Doulton contains articles by leading experts on the wide range of Doulton and Beswick ceramics, including:

- Latest auction results
- Your questions answered
- Collectors' profiles
- Free wants and for sale small ads
- Histories of artists, designers and wares
- Events diary
- News from around the world
- Book reviews

Amongst the subjects regularly covered are Lambeth wares, seriesware, figurines, character jugs, Bunnykins, Burslem wares, Doulton and Beswick animals, commemorative wares, advertising wares, new discoveries, rarities, Beatrix Potter etc etc... *Subscribe today*

Website: www.collectingdoulton.com • Email: barryjhill@hotmail.com